INTRODUCTION TO
YUGOSLAV LITERATURE

Introduction to YUGOSLAV LITERATURE

An Anthology of
Fiction and Poetry

edited by

BRANKO MIKASINOVICH
DRAGAN MILIVOJEVIĆ
and
VASA D. MIHAILOVICH

TWAYNE PUBLISHERS, INC.   NEW YORK

891.8

M636i

Contents

Contents vii

Contents

Preface

Introduction to Yugoslav Literature is the first comprehensive anthology of Yugoslav literature published in English representing the most important authors of the 19th and 20th centuries. The choice of the authors was based on their generally accepted reputation, and their number represented in Serbian, Croatian, Slovenian, and Macedonian sections was determined, by and large, on the basis of a numerical proportion of the respective nationalities. Their order in the anthology follows the order of their appearance as writers.

The editors regret that it was not possible to obtain copyrights from some important contemporary authors.

Although many translations appear here for the first time, some are of older vintage. Due to copyright considerations, these and other previously existing translations were not substantially changed.

Introduction to Yugoslav Literature is the result of the collective work of the editors. Professor Vasa D. Mihailovich is responsible for the Serbian section, Professor Branko Mikasinovich for the Croatian section, and Professor Dragan Milivojević for the Slovenian and Macedonian sections. They are also responsible for respective introductions.

The editors would like to express their appreciation to Mrs. Merrill K. Lindsay for her editorial assistance. Professor Mikasinovich would like to express his gratitude to Dr. Carl Feinstein for assistance in connection with most of his translations.

The publication of the works in this anthology in English has not been indicated. For a complete list of translations consult *A Bibliography of Yugoslav Literature in English Translation*, Vasa D. Mihailovich and Mateja Matejić, eds. (New York: Ungar, 1973).

Acknowledgments

The editors wish to thank the Yugoslav Authors Agency (Jugoslovenska autorska agencija) for permission to reprint the majority of selections in this volume. Acknowledgment is also made to *The Literary Review* of Fairleigh Dickinson University for use of translations of Miodrag Pavlović, Vladan Desnica, Jure Kaštelan, Slavko Mihalić, Ciril Zlobec, Pavle Zidar, Dane Zajc, Slavko Janevski, Aco Šopov, and Živko Čingo. Acknowledgment is further made to The Vanguard Press for selections of Vladan Desnica, Ivan Dončević, Ranko Marinković, and Prežihov Voranc in *Death of a Simple Giant and Other Modern Yugoslav Stories*, copyright © 1965; to the University of California Press for the selection of Dositej Obradović; and to *Poet Lore* for the play of Ivo Vojnović.

The editors also express their gratitude to New American Library for permission to reprint excerpts from *The Bridge on the Drina* by Ivo Andrić, copyright © 1959; to Alfred A. Knopf for the excerpts from *Bosnian Chronicle*, copyright © 1963; to Bernard Geis Associates for excerpts from *The Red Cock Flies to Heaven* by Miodrag Bulatović, copyright © 1962; and to Oxford University Press for the stories by Vjekoslav Kaleb and Ciril Kosmač in *Yugoslav Short Stories*, copyright © 1966.

A number of shorter pieces and excerpts has been reprinted from the older publications of *Slavonic and East European Review*, E. P. Dutton, D.C. Health, Allen-Unwin, The Mosher Press, Jonathan Cape, Duffield & Co., Basil Blackwell, and John Calder. The editors wish to express to these publishers their sincere gratitude. A diligent search was made to trace other copyrights.

To the Reader

Note on the Spelling and Pronunciation of Serbo-Croatian, Slovenian, and Macedonian Words and Names

$$s = s \text{ as in sink}$$
$$š = sh \text{ as in shift}$$
$$c = ts \text{ as in mats}$$
$$č = ch \text{ as in charge}$$
$$ć = \text{similar to, but lighter than, č—as in arch}$$
$$ž = j \text{ as in French } jour$$
$$z = z \text{ as in zodiac}$$
$$j = y \text{ as in yell}$$
$$nj = ni \text{ as in minion}$$
$$g = g \text{ as in go}$$
$$g = \text{soft 'g' as in geese}$$
$$k = \text{soft 'k' as in key}$$
$$s = dz$$
$$dž = g \text{ as in George}$$
$$dj = \text{soft 'g' 'j' as in jive}$$
$$lj = li \text{ as in million}$$

Introduction

Serbian Literature from 1800 to the Present

Serbian literature is a branch of the large tree that grew on the rocky and often bloody Balkan Peninsula during the last millennium. Its initial impulse came from the introduction of Christianity in the 9th century among the pagan Slavic tribes, which had descended from the common Slavic lands in Eastern Europe. The first written document, the beautifully ornamented *Miroslav's Gospel*, is from the twelfth century. Not surprisingly, the first written literature was not only closely connected with the church but was practically inspired, created, and developed by the ecclesiastics—the only intellectuals at the time. As the fledgling Serbian state grew and eventually became the Balkan's mightiest empire during Tsar Dušan's reign in the first half of the fourteenth century, so did Serbian literature grow, although at a slower pace. From the twelfth to the fourteenth century it blossomed, suddenly but genuinely, in the form of the now famous old Serbian biographies of the state and church rulers. Until modern times, this brilliance was equaled only by the literature of the medieval republic of Dubrovnik. Then came the Turkish invasion, and a night, four centuries long, descended upon Serbia and every aspect of its life. The literary activity in the entire area during those dark ages was either driven underground or interrupted altogether. The only possible form of literature was oral literature. Consisting of epic poems, lyric songs, folk tales, proverbs, conundrums, etc., it murmured like an underground current for centuries until it was brought to light at the beginning of the nineteenth century. In retrospect, it is a miracle that anything, let alone the ability to bounce back into life when the opportunity arose, survived this long, sterile, cold night.

Modern Serbian literature has its crude beginnings approximately in the last two decades of the eighteenth century. The revival of the literary life is closely connected with the stirrings of national aspirations on the entire Balkan Peninsula against Ottoman rule. During the Turkish occupation, the Serbian Orthodox Church was the only force that kept alive the national spirit and the hope for a better future. In the process, the Church emerged as the strongest factor when the nation was preparing for the final battle with the declining empire. As a consequence, the Church was able not only to influence the thinking of the few Serbian intellectuals but even to impose upon them a written language, the so-called Slavic-Serbian—an odd mixture of the Old Church Slavic, Serbian, and Russian. It was created under the influence of the Russian Church to promote church affairs. In its early form it was distinctly removed from the everyday spoken language. The only literature in the people's language at this time was still folk poetry, which was quite different from the officially fostered literature.

Because they lived in the Austrian Empire, only the Serbs in the northern province of Vojvodina—in contrast to other Serbs still suppressed by the Turks—were permitted to carry on literary activity, even if this was under the auspices of the Austrian authorities and in the official, church-sponsored language. In addition to the Russian influence, they were exposed to the liberal and rationalistic thinking of Western Europe. Long periods of Rationalism and Pseudo-Classicism ensued at the end of the eighteenth century and in the first four decades of the nineteenth. It was mainly the work of one man, Dositej Obradović, that initiated the process of liberation from Slavic-Serbian in Serbian letters. Thus he launched the revival of Serbian literature, that led to its phoenixlike rise around the middle of the nineteenth century. A former monk, Dositej renounced the shackling atmosphere of his early education and, instinctively drawn to the learned world yet unknown to him, set off on wide travels throughout Europe, learning everything within his grasp. Eventually, he became one of the best educated Serbs of his time. He never forgot his national allegiance, however. On the contrary, the more he learned the more he realized the backwardness of his foreigndominated people and the need for a pioneering work among them. He spent the rest of his life enlightening his countrymen and establishing various educational institutions, the most important of which were a university and a national museum.

Dositej's literary merits rest largely on his autobiography, *The Life and Adventures of Dimitrije Obradović*, and on his pedagogical, utilitarian writings. More important, however, is his use of a language that, although not yet a replica of the everyday speech of the people, freed literature from the unnatural bond with the church-fostered linguistic invention. Thus he made the first hopeful steps towards full use of the people's language in literature a few decades later.

To be sure, the victory of the reformists did not come overnight. For a number of years the official language was still Slavic-Serbian. Even those writers, like the playwright Jovan Sterija Popović, who decided to write in a language accessible to the broad masses could not avoid altogether that super-imposed hybrid language. It was not until another self-made Serbian writer, Vuk Karadzić, declared an all-out war against Slavic-Serbian that the battle was fully engaged. He was fortunate to attract to his ideas several talented writers and scholars, who applied in their works his concepts about the purity of the written language. But Vuk went even farther than just liberating literature from the parasitic burden of an artificial language. With his peasant genius he created an entirely new alphabet by following his own slogan "write as you speak," allocating to each sound in the Serbian speech only one character. The consequence of his ingenious work was an almost completely phonetic alphabet that is still used in Serbian and Croatian literature (the latter uses the Latin script) and, much later, provided the foundation for the Macedonian alphabet.

Karadžić's other accomplishments include the translation of the Bible into language comprehensible to all Serbs, the first grammar of modern Serbian, the first encyclopedic dictionary of Serbian, and the first large and systematic collection of epic poems, folk tales, and other forms of folk literature. Through him the outside world, by way of the Brothers Grimm, Goethe, Lamartine and others, learned of the priceless treasure that had hitherto been hidden among the "primitive," "uncultured" Serbs and Croats.

If Dositej ushered in a new era in Serbian literature, Vuk gave it substance, meaning, and direction. It is not surprising, therefore, that in a very brief span Serbian literature witnessed a flourishing of young writers and, under the circumstances, remarkable works in both poetry and prose. After Vuk's spade work, it remained for the poets to dot the i. A young Serb from Vojvodina, Branko Radičević, proved with his highly lyrical, emotional, and rhythmical poems that good poetry could be written in the people's speech. The Montenegrin Prince and Bishop, Petar Petrović Njegoš, wrote several enduring works, patterned after the epic poetry not only in form but in spirit as well. His most significant work is a verse play, *The Mountain Wreath*, which depicts an important moment in the history of the Montenegrin heroic struggle against the Turks. His philosophical epic, *The Ray Of Microcosm*, resembling Milton's *Paradise Lost* in more ways than one, showed that even the most profound thought could be expressed in the language of the people. For these two works alone Njegoš would enjoy immortal fame in Serbian letters; but he wrote many other works of lasting value. Today he is still considered one of the greatest Serbian poets, if not the greatest.

With Njegoš and Branko, the Romantic movement in Serbian literature began in the 1840's. It lasted about three decades following, somewhat belatedly, the other European Romantic movements. The poets dominated the scene. Their flights of emotion and fantasy easily match those in other literatures. Jovan Jovanović Zmaj, with his highly sensitive love lyrics, Djura Jakšić, with his exuberance and fiery patriotic verses, and Laza Kostić, with important though at times awkward prosodic innovations, were the other most important Romanticists.

Romanticism in Serbian literature faded slowly and reluctantly. By the 1870's, a new movement, Realism, made its appearance. A similar change was taking place throughout European literature, on a smaller scale and, by now, at a somewhat accelerated pace. The acknowledged catalyst of the new trend was Svetozar Marković, although his influence was only an indirect one; he was primarily a social and political thinker and publicist. Practically all the new writers—Milovan Glišić, Laza Lazarević, Janko Veselinović, Simo Matavulj, to name only the best—reflected in their works the newly attained awareness of existing social problems and matters other than individual concerns. A corollary to the increased social awareness was the emergence of the village as the main, and at times the only milieu and subject matter. Glisić, an author with his ear to the ground and somewhat more optimistic than the others, was, in addition, highly critical of the cities' intrusion into the secluded peasant life, which threatened to destroy the simple but durable fabric of the Serbian village, the principal factor in the survival of the national spirit after centuries of foreign occupation. Laza Lazarević, who mastered the craft of a finely woven psychological short story, was far more pessimistic about the ability of the village to withstand the onslaught, and about the fact that the cities themselves were beginning to show the symptoms of corruption. Veselinović's presentation of idyllic village life revealed not only his lack of sophistication but also his desire to delay the inevitable by saturating his stories with hope, inherent in the peasant philosophy of life. In addition, Matavulj (*Bakonja Fra-Brne*) reflected in his stories and novels the life of the Serbs and Croats along the South Adriatic shore, penetrating the complex make-up of these two peoples.

Other Realists followed more or less in the same vein until the turn of the century. Stevan Sremac divided his allegiance between Vojvodina in the North and the southern provinces, which were newly liberated from the Turks. His was a crafty idiom of people's daily life, sprinkled with a hefty dose of ribald humor. Svetolik Ranković, having studied in Russia, was heavily influenced by the great Russian writers of the nineteenth century. His three novels displayed a fine insight into the psychology of an outlaw, a monk, and a village teacher. Radoje Domanović is the best satirist in all Serbian literature. A gifted writer interested in politics, he wielded his implacable pen against the injustices of a democracy in the making.

All these writers, as can be clearly seen, were closely attached to their home town or their narrow region, yet they did not completely shut themselves off from the rest of the world; indeed, they were trying to speak to all mankind by presenting the seemingly inconsequential destinies of peasants, artisans, small merchants, and incipient proletarians. Some works of the Realists crossed the boundaries of narrow regionalism, but by and large they remained locally bound, folkloristic, conventional, and artistically frugal. Thus they struck a note that was to last for decades, a note of practical and somewhat limited concern with the here and now, devoid of a loftier and universal scope.

One of the few lyric poets at the turn of the century, but a good one at that, was Vojislav Ilić. He was able to combine the Realists' concern for the concrete with the genuine emotion and sensitivity of a lyrically tinged landscape painter. In the drama, towards the end of this period, the playwright Branislav Nušić began his long and fruitful career. When he died half a century later, he left behind scores of plays, mostly hearty comedies, with which he was able to make people laugh while at the same time throwing sharp barbs at the causes of the social ills. He enriched a genre notoriously weak in all of Serbian literature.

The first two decades of this century saw new trends in Serbian literature, usually referred to as the Moderna. Undoubtedly, the Moderna came as a result of the sharply increased but still indirect and somewhat vague influence of the leading literary movements in Europe, notably that of Symbolism. This influence was more pronounced in Croatian and Slovenian literatures. In the Serbian, it was more an influence of mood and esthetic attitude than of literary craftsmanship. It was manifested most keenly in two poets, Jovan Dučić and Milan Rakić. Dučić was a poet of refined taste, worldly culture, and preference for things past. His melancholic and almost fatalistic dispostion reflected the decadent *fin de siecle* mood of the French Symbolists, whom he admired. An avowed esthete, he wrote some of the most beautiful and sonorous poetry in Serbian literature. Rakić, though similar to Dučić in the basic poetic attitude, was different in many respects. He wrote a small amount of contemplative, analytical poetry, permeated with pessimism and awareness of man's inability to change his fate. His love lyrics show a keen understanding of love relationships. He also wrote several topical but unconventional patriotic poems. The third leading poet of this time was Aleksa Šantić. His was a much simpler poetry, but what he lacked in sophistication and the philosophical approach he made up with sincerity and pathos. He wrote poems with personal, romantic, patriotic, and social overtones.

There were other young poets who struck independent paths and showed great advancement not only in their world view but also in the craft of poetry: Vladislav Petković Dis, Milutin Bojić, Sima Pandurović, Veljko Petrović. They all showed a surprising savoirfaire, sophistication, and maturity in poetic matters. Most of them were pessimistic in their outlook, while at the same time warmly patriotic in supporting their country's cause on the eve of the fateful events culminating in World War I.

In prose, a new generation of writers also made its presence felt. Perhaps the strongest was Borisav Stanković, a writer of boundless talent but limited skill. His best work, *The Tainted Blood*, is considered one of the best Serbian novels despite its serious technical shortcomings. His was the world of the quaint, tradition-laden town of Vranje, close to the border between Serbia and Macedonia. This world of merchants and landowners was on its way out together with the retreat of the Turkish empire from the area. Similarly, Svetozar Ćorović depicted his native Herzegovina, where the changes brought about by the shift of the Moslem population were most severely felt. Ivo Ćipiko, like Matavulj, gave us a picture of the South Adriatic which was not always sunny and blue. He frequently injected into his lyrical writings a sense of alarm concerning the deterioration of social conditions (*The Spiders*). Another regional writer, Petar Kočić, described in a highly lyrical prose the Bosnian Serbs and their struggle for independence from the Austro-Hungarian Empire and for unification with Serbia. In his most enduring work, a play *The Badger Before the Court*, he ridiculed with devastating satire the right of the Austro-Hungarians to rule over the Slavic people. The Bosnian peasant, by nature sly, suspicious, and witty, is shown here as morally superior to his foreign oppressors.

The efforts of the writers of this time were aided by several capable critics educated in the West, especially by Jovan Skerlić and Bogdan Popović. Skerlić, with his sweeping historical survey, and Popović, with his refined, Western-schooled estheticism, not only weighed the writers' achievements but also pointed out the directions of modern world literature to them.

By a quirk of fate, several writers from this period (Dis, Bojić, Uskoković, to name only the best known) made the ultimate sacrifice during World War I, adding to the enormous toll the small Serbian nation had to pay on its way to victory.

The First World War represents a natural watershed in the development of Serbian literature. Although the majority of prewar writers reappeared on the scene after the war, it was mainly the new generation that brought a new and different spirit into literature. Six groups of authors can be distinguished, according to their orientation. In the first, two poets, Miloš Crnjanski and Rastko Petrović, especially embodied and exploited the postwar mood in their works. On the one hand, they were revolutionary in demanding vigorously a new approach to life's problems; on the other hand, they showed signs of revulsion and tiredness after the colossal slaughter of humans they had just witnessed. But it was in the form of their work that they, together with many other authors, struck a very modern note, seeking a new, more forceful expression in poetry, and in literature in general. The entire first decade of the postwar development was permeated with the spirit of innovations, marked by heated polemics with the opponents of Modernism as well as among the modernists themselves.

The counterpart to the modernists was provided by a number of prewar and new writers who followed the traditional realistic line and who, while enriching their language with new possibilities, generally shied away from the extravagant experimentation of the modernists. Ivo Andrić grew during this period into a mature short story writer and his skill, poise, and wider historical scope made him one of the most significant interwar storytellers. Some prewar writers continued their well-trodden paths—Dučić, Rakić and Šantić in poetry, Stanko-vić, Ćipiko, V. Petrović in prose, Nušić in drama—but most of them left the scene, one by one, realizing that their era had ended with the war.

Early in this period, a small but vocal third group of young writers declared their allegiance to the French surrealist movement, trying to transplant it onto Serbian literary soil, with greater or lesser success. The Serbian surrealist episode was very important for the enlivening of the literary atmosphere.

A similar characterization can be made of the writers with a pro-nounced or exclusive socialist orientation. Few of them amounted to much by way of literary production, yet they represented both the symptoms and the causes of the social ills that beset the country prior to World War II.

A fifth group can be called, for lack of a better term, the "folk-lorists." These writers—there were quite a few of them, mostly young ones—were very close to the so-called traditionalists: they too were realistic and conservative in their outlook and the treatment of the subject matter. But they clung to their narrow region and were uniquely untouched by outside literary currents. They limited themselves to the description of people, customs, and problems of their home pro-vinces, renewing the tradition of the second half of the nineteenth century in Serbian prose. Like their predecessors, however, they too tried to focus on the universally human pathos by presenting their little man, usually a peasant, in his microcosm. Some stories and novels by these writers have survived the erosion of time and winds.

Finally, a few highly individualistic writers worked secluded in their private worlds, the "loners" who either cared not to, or could not, find rapport with their fellow writers. The best example of this isolated attitude is Momčilo Nastasijević, a darkly strange and powerful creator, whose mystifying poems and stories have yet to be fully fathomed, mostly because of their obscure language.

The interwar period, despite an evident hustle and bustle, left relatively few great works: poems by R. Petrović, Crnjanski, S. Vinaver, D. Maksimović, and Nastasijević; short stories by Andrić, V. Petrović, D. Vasić and B. Ćopić; novels by Crnjanski (*Migrations*), B. Ćosić (*The Mowed Field*); and a few plays by Nušić. This period of less than great literary productions is not to be underestimated, however; for some writers it was a time of maturation. For, when another world cataclysm was over, it was these writers who gave Serbian literature a new breath of life, notably Andrić with his three great novels, *The Bridge on the Drina*, *The Chronicle of Travnik* and *Miss*. The socialistically oriented prewar writers and the former surrealists attempted to adopt the norms of Soviet style Socialist Realism in the immediate postwar period. Political developments, however, aborted this movement.

Between 1948 and 1955, approximately, two groups fought each other for supremacy. They can be called the "realists," who advocated adherence to straightforward, utilitarian literature, and the "modernists," who demanded greater freedom, especially in matters of form. The struggle ended in the mid-fifties with the victory of the "modernists." Since then, Serbian literature has followed its own meandering path of accommodation to, and acceptance of, reality. As a result, several new writers have attained prominence, and a number of enduring works has been produced, particularly novels. All Serbian literature has been steadily gaining in stature, the rise culminating in the Nobel Prize for Ivo Andrić in 1961, the first of its kind in the entire Southeastern part of Europe.

In addition to Andrić's achievements, there are those by Branko Ćopić, Mihailo Lalić, Oskar Davičo, Miodrag Bulatović in prose; and in poetry by Desanka Maksimović, Davićo, Vasko Popa, Miodrag Pavlović, and Stevan Raičković, among others. Lalić is considered the best living Serbian writer next to Andrić. Although basically a one-theme writer—the last war and man's predicament in it—he explores the darkest corners of man's soul at moments when he is stripped of the last vestiges of civilization, as in his greatest novel so far, *The Wailing Mountain*. Bulatović is perhaps the most popular Serbian writer outside his country, ironically more popular abroad than at home. His popularity undoubtedly stems from his fashionable approach to reality depicting a nightmarish, demented, perverted world which knows neither the causes and consequences of its plight nor the remedy.

The present-day situation is one of fluid activity and great expectations. An entirely new generation has entered the literary scene, young writers who have brought with them their own ideas and problems, and who are surprisingly deft and knowledgeable about literary matters. They are benefiting from the international exchange of ideas, of which they freely partake. Indeed, the most important aspect of contemporary Serbian literature is that in the last two decades it has, together with other Yugoslav literatures, broken the centuries-old indifference toward it on the part of the outside world. Although only time will judge the true merits of the works written now in Yugoslavia, it can be said that Yugoslav literature as a whole has found its proper place among others, and that it is willing to listen and eager to be heard.

In sum, through these six periods (Transition, Romanticism, Realism, Moderna, Interwar, and Contemporary) Serbian literature has made its tortuous way from low existence and obscurity to respectable membership in world literature. Following in the main the developments in other European literatures while at the same time adhering to the peculiarities of its own nature, trying to satisfy both the quest for esthetic fulfillment and the need for a spokesman of historical, social, and patriotic causes, and creating traditions where there were none while often destroying those that might still serve well, Serbian literature has asserted itself against mighty odds. Aware of the difficulty a small nation, with an unfamiliar language, has in being heard in the outside world, but also conscious of their own shortcomings and limitations (due above all to historical developments—four wars on their soil in the last half century, to cite one example), Serbian writers have seldom sought excuses or demanded undeserved laurels. Instead, they have worked patiently and hard to justify their membership in the family of world literature, to which they have made a modest but genuine and heartfelt contribution.

Dositej Obradović

(1742–1811)

Obradović is one of the most deserving men in Serbian literature. Born in Čakovo, Vojvodina, and orphaned early, he entered the monastery of Hopovo as a monk. He spent all his time reading. His inquisitive mind and wanderlust made him leave the monastery. He traveled through the Balkans, Austria, Russia, Germany, France, and England, tutoring children for financial support, learning foreign languages, and studying philosophy, especially the 18th century English Rationalists. He became perhaps the most learned man among the Serbs of his time.

After returning to his homeland, he was invited to Belgrade, which had just been liberated from the Turks. Appointed Minister of Education, he put to good use his knowledge and experience by opening schools and by founding a higher school (which eventually became the University of Belgrade), the National Museum, and many other cultural institutions. He died in Belgrade having seen his efforts toward enlightening his countrymen begin to bear fruit.

Dositej began writing short didactic pieces to combat illiteracy among his people. This lead to larger works: the autobiography, *Život i priključenija Dimitrija Obradoviča, narečenoga u kaludjerstvu Dositej* (The life and Adventures of Dimitrije Obradovič, Who as a Monk Was Given the Name Dositej, 1783–1788); *Sovjeti zdravago razuma* (Counsels of Common Sense, 1784); *Basne* (Fables, 1788); and *Sobranie* (Collection). As the titles imply, these works are not true literature but rather practical didactic writings, having the teaching and enlightenment of a young nation as a primary goal. They are mostly translations from other literatures, but they also reveal Dositej's common sense, keen observation, and patriotism. His style was also reformatory. Although unable to break off completely from the church-fostered style and language based on Old Church Slavic, he nevertheless wrote in a language closer to that of the people and introduced many innovations, which later facilitated the language reform. Thus, he is justifiedly called the founder of modern Serbian literature.

THE LIFE AND ADVENTURES OF DIMITRIJE OBRADOVIĆ

(Excerpt)

A thirst for learning was the main reason why I lost all desire to remain longer in that Srem paradise, Hopovo monastery in Fruška Gora. When I read Chrysostom's sermons on the Acts and on the epistles of St. Paul, strange feelings were awakened within me and took form in my young heart. "Had not Chrysostom studied," I thought to myself, "even though he had read the Acts and St. Paul's epistles for a thousand years he would have been unable to discourse upon them so beautifully and so sweetly. What countless other men had read the same compositions and knew them by heart, but were totally unfit to speak of them so copiously and so finely! That was reserved for scholars who had studied in Athens or in Alexandria." Thenceforth, not only when I was awake, but in my dreams, my mind and heart were full of naught else than great libraries, academies, and schools, where teachers gave instruction in various sciences and where industrious pupils, like bees, gathered the honey of wisdom.

But all this burning desire was restrained and to a certain extent crushed by my heartfelt, almost filial love for that pure and virtuous soul, my benefactor Todor Milutinović. Often when he observed my zeal for learning he would tell me with a sigh that he regretted that I was wasting my youthful days in his monastery. But I was terrified at even letting the thought occur to me that I might desert so good and kind a man and never see him again! After his decease, however, nothing remained in Hopovo that could detain me and keep me there any longer.

At this time it happened that one of the monastery novices, named Atanasije, had made plans for returning to his family in Croatia. But since he knew that his uncle Dionisije, who had brought him to Hopovo in order to make a monk of him, would on no consideration release him, he intended to take French leave and go home. And since he and I were on excellent terms he informed me of his purpose. Bursting with impatience, I could hardly wait to tell him in the same confidential fashion that I also was anxious to quit the monastery and to settle in any place I could find where young men were pursuing their studies; but, not knowing which way to turn, I begged that he would take me with him as far as Croatia, whence I should proceed wherever God might prompt. "Why not," he replied: "It is much pleasanter to travel with a comrade than alone."

I gave him some money and he went to Irig, where he bought me a blue dolman, Turkish trousers, and red haiduk sandals; and the next morning, without least delay, we set out together across Mount Rakovac. We descended into Rakovac, but by a roundabout way, since I was known in that region, and proceeded between Fruška Gora and the Danube toward Zelengrad. We touched at Osek and passed into Slavonia; and while we were going on toward Pakrac, in one village we had an adventure such as we had never expected.

From a yard there came to our ears songs and the conversation of a whole throng of people. "I tell you what," Atanasije said to me; "I'm thirsty anyhow; let's go into the yard to ask for water and see what's going on." We went in and came upon a marriage and a merrymaking. When we asked for water the bridegroom's mother said to us: "My dear travelers, today we are not drinking water here, but wine; come indoors if you wish." We did so. And when we had told the bridal party that we had come from a distance, the groomsman called out: "Well, well, it's good luck when guests come from far away to a jolly party like this." He told us to sit down, eat, drink, and be merry. They asked us about the grain crop in Srem, about the vineyards, and so on. So we had a fine, friendly talk while we listened to the music and watched the gay young people dance.

Then a big student suddenly made his appearance and sat down directly opposite me. After listening to our conversation for a few moments he addressed me, saying: "From your pronunciation I judge that you are a Schismatic." "I am no Schismatic," I replied without hesitation, "but an Orthodox Christian"; and I added that I was a better Christian than he, if he was interested in the matter. Then according to custom we immediately began to discuss the supremacy of the Pope and the question of seniority between the Greek and the Roman Church. I had read a book on those topics in the Rumanian language by a certain Maxim Peloponesiotski and I knew it almost by heart, so that I could argue the questions till the earth shook beneath me. Hence the student got into great difficulties with me and began to mix into his talk Latin words and phrases, while at that time I was as innocent of the Latin language as were the rest of the wedding party. After every word he would shout, *"Probo majorem"* or *"probo minorem."*

The groomsman, the senior wooer, and the rest of the company, though they were all sons of the Roman Church, nevertheless with one voice began to compliment me, explaining that they could understand whatever I had to say; but they jeered at their own student, since he called on majors and minors to help him, though the subject had nothing to do with majors or captains, but with Christ, St. Peter, the Pope and the patriarchs. This so vexed the fellow that he threatened he would have me tied and set to Požega. Hardly had he said this than they all descended on him, the women worse than the men for everybody had stopped dancing and making music in order to listen to our discussion; they all called him all kinds of names. "When you get married," they told him, "go ahead and tie up travelers and guests at your own wedding party, but let them alone in our house and at our party!" And so they turned him out of house and yard and bade me not be in the least alarmed; then we started to chat peaceably and agreeably once more, as we had been doing previously. Night was coming on and those good people would not let us leave. So we spent the night there and the next day they gave us breakfast and said farewell to us in the most friendly fashion, kissing and embracing us as if we had been kinsfolk.

We were just as cordially received, not only at a wedding party and not merely in one place, but everywhere on our way through Slavonia and Croatia. Everywhere those good people are glad to see someone from a distance who speaks the same language as they. Whoever has enough bread in his house is glad to have somebody come for dinner or supper. Love of strangers is one of their inborn traits, and nothing divides and estranges them from one another so much as the Greek and Latin churches. The church, which ought to bring them nearer together, uniting them in kindness and in love! Would it not, then, be an extremely useful thing to open the eyes of good people on this subject, and to tell them, that, no matter which church they belong to, they may nevertheless serve as godfathers and godmothers for one another, may be friends, may honor and love one another?

From Slavonia we passed into Croatia and not far from Garevica reached the house of my friend's brothers, where all his kindred, his brothers and their wives and his sisters, welcomed him as joyously as if he had escaped from slavery. It was autumn. At that time the Seven Years' War was in progress between the House of Austria, Prussia, and Russia. Atanasije's brothers, when they heard that I was anxious to visit Russian and study there, advised me to go to Germany with the chaplain of some regiment; telling me that there, since a large number of Serbian officers were then in the Russian service, some one of them would very likely befriend me and send me wherever I wished. For the moment, in order to find such a chaplain, they thought I had best go to Zagreb and wait there, for the Croatian regiments kept passing in that direction. These kind people kept me for twelve days, not allowing me to depart. Only with great difficulty could I escape from them; it was as if we had purposed to live together for all eternity.

My friend Atanasije set out to accompany me only to Petrinja, but went with me all the way to Zagreb, where I took a room for a month with a merchant in the suburbs. That evening, on hearing of my plans, my landlord told me that in the city there was a college maintained by the Vlach bishop; and that, while I was waiting for a chance to join the army, I could there begin my Latin studies. This suggestion appealed to me, and the next day Atanasije and I went to see what sort of college our bishop had there—for they gave us the name of Vlachs.

We arrived at the college. They conducted us to the principal, who received us courteously. When he heard that I wished to study there he told me that he would write to the bishop that very day in my behalf and that he was confident of obtaining for me the privilege of board and lodging with them. I kissed his hand and thanked him for his promise.

"But I must forewarn you, my son," he added, "that though you may study here for several years if you desire, and may have all needful sustenance, it is on condition that you become a Uniate, just as we are ourselves."

"What, are you Uniates?" I asked him in alarm.

"We are," he replied; "and if we were not, not only could we have no college here, but they would not even let us live here."

"If that's the case," I told him, "don't write anything about me to your bishop, for I won't become a Uniate, not even if I be absolutely certain that I shall never learn a single thing more."

He saw that I was terrified and so he said to us gently: "Don't be afraid, my lads, we will not make you Uniates by force. Just stay and dine with us, and then good-bye: go wherever you please."

We took leave of him and left his room. He said something in Latin to the other boys, who followed us out and in a kindly fashion asked us to stay and eat with them. "It is time for dinner," they said; "don't go away hungry!" But I was in no mood for dinner, since my knees were trembling beneath me. I do not remember how we excused ourselves; I know only that we went out and fled from the city.

Even now, when I think of that occurrence, I am horrified at what an awful thing prejudice may become. Those same lads, boys of my own age, whom a bit earlier I had gazed on with ineffable joy, just as if they were my dear brothers and kinsfolk, now, when I had heard that they were Uniates, appeared to me in a different light; they had become terrible enemies, who desired and sought my destruction. O gracious and eternal God, why and wherefore does this happen among men, that thy sweet and eternal love, which should serve them as a bond of most holy kinship, of most faithful friendship, and most sweet and heartfelt love—that this same love, when men misinterpret it and abuse it, serves to divide them and to make them bitterly hate one another!

(Part Two, Letter I)

COUNSELS OF SOUND REASON

(Excerpt)

I recall that when I was in Montenegro Prince-Bishop Vasilije had brought in from Russia a large number of little books; it seems to me that they were called Monthly Publications. In one of these I read an article on the rainbow; and on a summer day, when a gentle rain was falling, I was in the upper room, telling old Prince-Bishop Sava what I had been reading about the rainbow, and at the same time we were gazing at a magnificent rainbow in front of us. And then there came riding up on an ass a certain abbot, a huge personage with an enormous beard. Prince-Bishop Vasilije, who had joined us while we were talking, caught sight of the abbot and said to me:

"Deacon, I beg you, just ask that abbot what a rainbow is and why it has many colors."

I had not yet learned of Bishop Vasilije's crafty habit of continually striving to stir up a dispute between other people, just to have something to laugh at. I was overjoyed at the suggestion. My mischievous heart started to leap for joy at the thought of dumbfounding the big abbot. The door opened and in walked the abbot. I barely gave him time to bow to the bishops and sit down. Then I rushed in like a game-cock and blurted out:

"Father Abbot, tell me, please, what a rainbow is and why it has many colors."

I had already begun to feel amusement, anticipating that he would be disconcerted and would not know what to reply, but I could hardly keep from exploding with laughter. But if he had been disconcerted he would not have been a real Montenegrin. He seized his great bushy beard with one huge hand, looked at the rainbow for a moment, and then turned on me his large, terrible, black eyes: they would have scared Newton himself. And instead of answering he inquired:

"Do you see that jackass of mine?"

"I see it," I replied, "but I was not talking about it. What has a jackass to do with a rainbow?"

"I understand your question," retorted the abbot; "but just let me tell you that jackass of mine has a lot more sense than you have."

"I should like to know how you measure my sense and that of the jackass," I asked him.

"Listen to me and I swear you'll find out!" said the abbot. "That jackass recognizes the chaff that's in front of him. If you don't believe it, look at him chewing. But despite all the years you've lived you don't yet know what a rainbow is! A rainbow's a rainbow, and not a hoop for a tub! But you ask why it has many colors. Why, confound you, how can it be a rainbow without having many colors?

Did you ever see a black rainbow anywhere?"

The bishops thought they'd die of laughing, and I felt the walls of the room whirl around me, and I was so ashamed that the rainbow grew black before my eyes owing to the charming comparison that the man had made of me to my face. If he had at least likened me to a horse or an ox I should not have minded, but he said I was worse than a jackass. And he was mighty well satisfied with himself, and he kept twirling first one mustache and then the other with as much exultation as if he were parading Cleopatra in triumph.

My experience with this man was just like that of certain Catholic theologians in Zadar. They once heard that there had come to town a certain priest, Father Muzdalo, famous throughout all Dalmatia for his skill in disputations. They wasted no time, but came and surrounded him in the middle of the town; and in order to make fun of him they asked him who begat Melchizedek.

"Tell me first who begat me," he replied.

"Who the deuce wants to know who begat you!" the theologians answered. "That's not written in any book!"

"Bah, shame on you!" shouted Father Muzdalo. "The women in my village have more sense than you do; they all know who begat me! And now you want me to tell you who begat Melchizedek!"

"Bravo, bravo, Father Muzdalo!" exclaimed all the bystanders.

And the theologians returned whence they came. They had found out by experience that it is not safe to start an argument with people of another sphere in life than yourself.

But when my abbot noticed that I was holding in my hands a little book printed in civil letters, he told me frankly and plainly, like a Delphic priestess speaking from her tripod, that if I did not forswear such books I should lose even the little sense that I had.

"Don't you see," he told me, "that half the letters in it are Latin, and that every book is accursed that contains even a single little Latin letter?"

He told me that from the time when such books came into the world people had begun to eat snails.

"Ho, confound you!" he shouted, "the world might have lasted another hundred years if you had not corrupted it with such books!"

G. R. Noyes

Vuk Stefanovic Karadzic

(1784–1864)

Karadžić was born in the village Tršić, Western Serbia, in 1787. He was one of Serbia's first students of higher education. He participated in the first Serbian uprising against the Turks and, after its failure, had to emigrate. He went to Vienna, where he met Jan Kopitar, the censor for Slavic publications in the Austro-Hungarian Empire. Under his encouragement, Karadžić began to write down folk poems and songs he knew by heart and to collect new ones later among the Serbian people. This led to the first small edition of folk songs, *Mala prostonarodna slaveno-serbska pjesmarica* (A Short Popular Slavic-Serbian Songbook, 1814). More and extended volumes were published later. He also collected folk tales, proverbs, and riddles. The sudden appearance of these epic folk poems made a great impression on European scholars and writers and prompted some, Goethe and Mérimée among others, to translate them.

Karadžić was also interested in the language problems. Like Dositej Obradović, he was dissatisfied with the hybrid Slavic-Serbian language, used exclusively by writers at that time. He began to work on reforming it and eventually devised a new alphabet consisting of thirty characters, one for each sound, following the slogan "Write as You Speak." In 1814 he published a small grammar of Serbian language spoken by common people, with which the "war" for the reform of the language began. This was followed by an extensive *Srpski rječnik* (Serbian Dictionary, 1818), for which Kopitar provided the German and Latin definitions. Karadžić's efforts toward linguistic reform met with strong opposition on the part of the church and the church-led intelligentsia, who were afraid that the abandonment of some letters borrowed from the Russian and introduction of others from Latin would weaken the ties with Russia and affect the dominant position of the Church. Their most vocal argument was that the language of the peasants could not serve loftier purposes, such as the Bible and poetry. But Karadžić's cause was espoused by many young linguists and writers. Toward the middle of the century, two important works, *Gorski vijenac* (The Mountain Wreath) by Petar Petrović Njegoš and *Pesme* (Poems) by Branko Radičević, were published in the language spoken by common people. The Bible also was translated into the vernacular (1847). In 1850, the leading Serbian and Croatian writers, at a meeting in Vienna agreed to one grammar and spelling. This signaled the total victory of the principles advocated by Karadžić, although the struggle was to last a few more years.

Karadžić spent his last years enlarging his collection of folk poetry and other folk literature, writing historical pieces, and encouraging younger writers to write in the people's language. After his death in 1864, his reform was officially adopted in Serbia in 1868. He was soon recognized as the father of the modern Serbian language—a self-made man of peasant origin who accomplished one of the most striking feats in the annals of linguistics.

A MEETING WITH GOETHE

I was in Weimar eight days and can say that those were the most glorious days of my life up until now. I had a letter for Goethe from Grimm, in which he sent him a translation in German of the epic poem *The Partition of Jakšić*. I cannot . . . say how much Grimm praised our epic poetry in that letter.

"From what I know of this genre," he said, "nothing can compare with Serbian poems: and the more a person tries to translate them faithfully, the more he realizes and feels the inadequacies and imperfections of our [German] language compared to this [Serbian]."

I gave the letter to Goethe's chamberlain in the evening, just as Goethe was getting ready to go out somewhere by coach. After the chamberlain had presented the letter to him, he said to me that His Excellency had told him that he would be especially pleased if I would call on him at two tomorrow.

When I came the following day, Goethe welcomed me from the middle of the room, and when after many compliments, we had sat down on the sofa on which lay unfolded Grimm's letter and the translation of *The Partition of Jakšić*, together with an unwrapped bundle of newspapers, Goethe, putting his hand on the bundle of newspapers said:

"You can see that you are not in my room for the first time today. You have been here with me for a long time."

When I glanced at the newspapers, I saw a review of my first Serbian grammar. . . . What a triumph it was for me! Then we talked a long time about our poems. He read me *The Partition of Jakšić*, asked me about some verses in the original, said that he would have it printed, and he begged me to translate for him, word for word, several other poems and send them to him.

From a letter to J. Kopitar,
11/23 October, 1823

TO THE SERBIAN COUNCIL

I am being persecuted and harassed both secretly and in public, and I am forbidden to justify and defend myself.

When thousands of leaflets were printed and distributed among the people, saying that I had written or done something for Luther and the Catholic Church against our Orthodox Church and that I was an enemy of our laws and our nation, it was no more important to me than if someone had printed and sent around an allegation that you had stolen something or squandered people's money. Just think how everyone would feel if he were not permitted to answer and justify himself from such attacks.

And yet, let us look who attacks me so unjustly in my own country. I am being harassed by the newcomers who have come there at the sound of a taler, like grasshoppers that hop about the earth after the grass and leaves. And why do they persecute me? They do it because I was born in Serbia and, for one thing, they are sorry and ashamed that the learned world, on the basis of my works, thinks that I, who was born and raised in Serbia and did not attend school as long as they, know something better than all of them, especially as far as our people are concerned. For another thing, they are afraid that the people and government in Serbia would know and appreciate me as much as learned people abroad do, and thus place me ahead of my persecutors. That is why they slander me in various ways in order to conceal my literary achievements, or at least belittle them.

Judging by the deeds of my pursuers and enemies, it can be seen that they have neither common sense nor conscience, nor do they know what shame or sin, literature, criticism, or censorship are.

These enemies of mine are the reason that I live outside Serbia.

When a friend, in 1841, wrote me from Belgrade that I ought to move to Serbia, I answered him that I do not live in Vienna because Vienna is dearer to me than Serbia, but only because I would be able to be of more use to our country here. And if I live to see Serbia in such a state that I could go about my own business there as peacefully as here, so that I could be of some use to our country—if no more, then at least as much as from here—then I will immediately, and with great joy, move to Serbia without invitation. That is what I wrote seven years ago, and it is exactly what I say today.

Just as there is a big storm raised now against me, my language, and orthography because of the translation of the New Testament, so Jovan Hadžić raised the storm in 1839 on account of my Serbian history, so that some reviled me to my face, saying that I, describing popular customs, have said that girls in Serbia were being abducted, and by that in their opinion, I have disgraced the nation. And for the collecting of our folk poetry, there were poeple who called me a mockery to my face and asked me how long I would carry on this ridicule. All this clearly shows that I would not be able to do any of my literary work as I see fit, but that I would have to work as some-one else wished and in the wrong way, or not work at all. When, the year before last, two councilmen there said that I should move to Serbia, that my pension would be raised, it was on the tip of my tongue to tell them all this, but I again restrained myself, mostly so people would not say that I slandered the Austrian Serbs in Serbia.

And such people so far have not allowed me to stay in Serbia and do my work, and now they want to forbid me even to come there. This spring I meant to go there, for one reason, to travel along the southern and northeastern borders of present-day Serbia, to study our language, customs, and the more recent history, and for another reason, to tend to some of my private affairs: now seeing how my enemies can freely do me these injustices, I do not dare go there until the Honorable Council convinces me that they did that without the knowledge of the Honorable Government, and that the Honorable Government, learning of that and recognizing that the injustice was done to me, takes me under its protection. Who could be surprised or even laugh when he hears that I say I do not dare to enter my own country, for whose benefit and glory I have worked all my life? But when one thinks and examines what is being done to me, then he will admit that I am right in thinking that he who is not ashamed and not fearful of God to distribute among the people such lies and injustices against me, he will not be ashamed and afraid to do any other evil; and when they are allowed to do that, everybody might think that everything else will be allowed to them, for whoever accuses me also sits in judgment on me.

I am very sorry that I must speak so against the Austrian Serbs in Serbia, because among them I have friends whom I love and honor with all my heart, and who, I am certain, also love and honor me. I hope that they, and all other sensible men, will not take this as being evil on my part; and even less, that they will say or think that I accuse all Austrian Serbs in Serbia, and that I believe that they should not be accepted in service. I complain about and accuse only those who to the Government's shame and the people's detriment unjustly persecute and hinder me, not only in private, but also in literary, or more precisely, in national affairs. . . .

As no human work can in any way be without error, so I do not think that there are no errors in my works, and at all times I have said, and I say now, that I will be pleased when somebody points them out to me, because through criticism, that is, when more people reveal their thoughts about certain matters, the truth is found. But whoever says that something is this or that way and forbids others to say something against his thoughts, shows that he fears the truth and that he would try to hide it from the people. And when, instead of pointing to mistakes in a book, someone attacks the author by slander and abuse, that is not criticism, but a shameless swearing.

Consequently I do not wish that the Honorable Council forbid the writing against me by others and the criticism of my works, but rather I ask that I be permitted to defend and justify myself freely, with just as much right as my enemies write against me.

From a letter to the Council,
March 17, 1848.

Donald Davenport

Jovan Sterija Popović

(1806–1856)

Sterija, as he is usually called, was born in Vršac, Vojvodina, into a merchant family of a Greek father and a Serbian mother. After finishing law school, he became a high school teacher and a lawyer in his hometown. At the same time he began to write historical dramas but soon switched to comedy. In 1840 he went to Serbia, where he was very active as a college professor, school administrator, and a theater organizer. He was instrumental in founding the Serbian Academy of Sciences, Science Museum, and National Library. He continued to write dramas, and he also organized, staged, and directed them. His own plays constituted the main repertory of the young Serbian theater. In 1848 he returned to Vršac. His increasing disagreement with the leading political figures and deteriorating health forced him to withdraw from public life in a strongly pessimistic mood. He died in Vršac in 1856.

Although Sterija wrote poetry, numerous historical plays, and novels, it is in comedy that he achieved his greatest successes. His *Laža i paralaža* (Liar and Super-Liar, 1830), *Kir-Janja* (Miser, 1837), *Zla žena* (An Evil Woman, 1838), *Pokondirena tikva* (Upstart, 1838), *Ženidba i udadba* (The Wedding, 1841), *Beograd nekad i sad* (Belgrade Then and Now, 1853), and posthumous *Rodoljupci* (Patriots, 1903), are considered among the best in Serbian drama and are still staged. In his geniunely humorous plays Sterija depicts realistically the life of the middle class, championing the little man but also lampooning his foibles and idiosyncrasies, such as greed, falsehood, and pseudopatriotism. Some of his themes and types are admittedly borrowed from other writers (Shakespeare, Moliere, Kotzebue) but they are given local coloring and implications. *Kir-Janja*, modeled after Moliere's *Tartuffe*, is a fitting illustration of this.

KIR-JANJA

(Excerpt)

Act II, Scene 3

KIR-JANJA *(enters, does not look at anybody, only paces the room):*
Hu, hu, hu!

MIŠIĆ: What is it, kir-Janja?

JANJA: Hu! I'm going to have a stroke.

KATICA: Dear me, let's call a doctor!

JANJA: To take a few more *kreutžers* out of my pocket, you puppy?

KATICA: I did not want you to suffer, for God's sake!

JANJA: Let me perish! Let the wind rise, lift me by the hair and carry me into the air! Oh, my pretty Miško, my pretty Galin! Now I should take a cane and go begging in my old age.

MIŠIĆ: Not like that, kir-Janja. You are only endangering your health with an attitude like that.

JANJA: What are you talking about, Mr. Notary? My stall has fallen, cost me more than five thousand forints; my horses have been killed: two thousand forints. Show me the man who can lose so much money these days! Show me, do please! Poor Janja, your luck has run out. Take a stick, go in front of the church, sit down and beg for kreutzers in your misfortune.

MIŠIĆ: And who will take care of what remains at home?

JANJA: What is there at home? Empty walls, three pieces of firewood, two chairs . . .

MIŠIĆ: And those nine hundred gallons of wine and one sealed trunk.

JANJA: (Damned Eve!) It's easy for you to make fun of an old man. Eh, Mr. Notary, what a terrible loss!

MIŠIĆ: The loss is great, especially such good horses. In the whole town you could not find two more like them.

JANJA: And now they lie dead. If I could only cure their meat with salt; this way dogs will eat it for nothing. Oh, poor Janja, what will become of you?

KATICA: Sweet papa!

JANJA: Don't sweet papa me! Say "bitter papa," "unfortunate papa," "papa who will contract the fever, who will go down like a big galley on the wide sea."

MIŠIĆ: Why do you torture yourself when you can find help?

JANJA: Find help? To build another stall? To buy new horses? What am I and my children going to eat afterwards?

MIŠIĆ: Wait until I tell you what I have read in the newspapers. Somebody in Berlin has discovered a new method of constructing a balloon exclusively with horse fat. Therefore it was announced that he who has such fat can earn a thousand forints in silver for a hundred pounds of fat. Since your horses were stout, you will get three hundred pounds for them, so that you will not only recoup the loss, you will profit.

JANJA: Er . . . is that true, Mr. Notary?

MIŠIĆ: Come to my house whenever you wish and I will give you the same newspapers to see for yourself.

JANJA: He, he, he! Mr. Notary, that's a good speculation! Perhaps I should buy more horses, fatten them and then slaughter them. What a nice profit!

MIŠIĆ: (This one is crazy!) The reason the price of this fat is so high is because the imperial authorities have very strictly forbidden the killing of horses on account of their great usefulness to man. But since this has happened to you by accident, you are a lucky man.

JANJA: He, he, he! The Greek wisdom is right: "Where there is misfortune—there is fortune, too." You know what, Mr. Notary? I too would like to make a balloon and go to America. I've read in an old, wise Greek book that there is as much gold there as there's dry beans in Europe.

MIŠIĆ: Yes, there are some birds there that lay pearls.

JANJA: Oh, oh, oh! What a sweet word! And so, I too will see the world in my old age.

KATICA: For heaven's sake, papa, what are you up to?

JANJA: Quiet, puppy! I will bring you a pearl and a golden earring, you know. My poor Miško and Galin! Since they could not carry me to America when they were alive, let them carry me when they are dead. Mr. Notary, you're a wise man for telling me about this nice speculation. You must be Greek.

MIŠIĆ: (Smiling) That could easily be.

JANJA: What did I tell you, eh! A true Greek, real Greek mind! When I go through Athens, I will enter a note about you in the library. And when I return from America I'll bring you a pipe, a pretty Turkish pipe. And for my Juca—a hat.

JUCA: I don't know what will happen when you return. I want my hat now.

JANJA: (His eyes bulging) There's no end to this! Do you have brains in your head?

JUCA: That is a good question.

JANJA: You don't have brains in your head but garbage. Don't you see the big damage in the house, huh? What do you want, to cover yourself with jewels? Take off the stockings and shoes, wretch, and make mud to patch up the stall.

JUCA: (Looking at Mišić) If Juca were a fool.

JANJA: A fool? He who works is a fool? And he who is all spruced up is wise? Oh, accursed, indifferent world, you must go under! Poverty and misfortune will trample on you, as they did on me, like a wild horse upon the green grass.

Vasa D. Mihailovich

Petar Petrović Njegoš

(1813–1851)

Njegoš was born in the Montenegrin village of Njeguš in 1813. Because of the unsettled conditions in Montenegro, he could not receive a regular education; instead, he was privately tutored, mostly by a gifted but eccentric poet named Sima Milutinović Sarajlija, who cultivated the young Njegoš's imagination and instilled in him a love for folk poetry. When his uncle, Bishop Petar I, died Njegoš ascended the throne and was ordained a Bishop of Montenegro in Petrograd in 1833. Njegoš tried to be a good ruler, but the isolated position of his country, the backwardness of his countrymen, and the incessant pressure on the part of the Turks made the attainment of this goal very difficult. Concerned for his people and trying to find help, he traveled abroad extensively. He contracted tuberculosis and died in his thirty-eighth year in Cetinje. His tomb on the highest peak of Mount Lovćen has become a national shrine.

Njegoš is generally considered the greatest Serbian poet. He began to write early. His first collection of poems, *Pustinjak cetinjski* (The Hermit of Cetinje, 1834), is characterized by contemplative lyricism and imitation of folk poetry. In his next books of poetry, *Lijek jarosti turske* (The Cure for Turkish Madness, 1834) and *Svobodijada* (To Liberty, 1854), he dealt with the foremost topic of the day—the struggle against the Turks.

His more ambitious writings produced three works of lasting value: *Luča mikrokozma* (The Light of Microcosm, 1845), *Gorski Vijenac* (The Mountain Wreath, 1847) and *Lažni car Šćepan Mali* (Tsar Šćepan the Small, the Impostor, 1851). *Luča mikrokozma* is a philosophical-religious epic, resembling Milton's *Paradise Lost*. Njegoš treats the problem of the meaning of human existence as a repentance resulting from man's rebellion, together with Satan, against God. However, while the body suffers, the soul preserves the link with God and immortality. Deep thought and sporadic poetic beauty made this work a significant contribution to the young Serbian literature, despite its flaws.

Njegoš brought his poetic expression to perfection in *Gorski vijenac*. The epic drama describes a historic event that took place at the beginning of the 18th century. At a meeting of Montenegrin clan leaders to decide what to do with those Montenegrins who had become Moslems, it was concluded that their extermination was the best method of combatting the Turkish menace. The action takes place in long dialogues, during which the leaders expound their views and philosophy. In the meditative Bishop Danilo, Njegoš portrayed his own dilemma in which, as a bishop and Christian ruler, he had to support the policies of war and death. Thus the local historical event offers the poet an opportunity to muse about the universal struggle between God and Satan, good and evil. The third large work, *Lažni car Šćepan Mali*, is considered the weakest of the three. It describes in dramatic form a visit to Montenegro in the 18th century by an adventurer who pretended to be Czar Peter of Russia.

Aside from purely literary merits, Njegoš's works were also of great significance at the time of their appearance—during the struggle of Karadžić for the reform of the language. His imitation of folk poetry, the use of the spoken language by way of proverbs and sayings, and his great poetic talent showed that even the highly contemplative and artistic forms of literature can be written in a language accessible to all people.

THE MOUNTAIN WREATH

(Excerpts)

The Montenegrins are gathered together on the mountain Lovćen on the eve of the Whitsuntide, amidst the growing menace posed by the Turks, greedy for power, and by those Serbs who have turned Moslem. At night, while everybody seems asleep, Prince-Bishop Danilo contemplates, in a despairing, Hamlet-like fashion, about the plight of his people torn asunder by disunity and threatened to be engulfed by the Turkish tide.

VLADIKA DANILO (*in contemplation*)

I see my people sleep a deadly sleep,
No parent's hand to wipe away my tears;
God's Heaven is shut above my head,
Giving no answer to my cries and prayers.
This world is now become a hell,
And men but demons in disguise.
Oh, dark, dark Day! oh, outlook ever black!
My fearing folk held ever underfoot!
Sure I have seen thy woe and all thine ill,
Yet 'gainst the worst I now must set my will!

When deadly wound is given in the head,
The quivering frame doth painfully expire.
    Plague of mankind! May God make end of thee!
Is half a world so small, to thee so small—
A half-world filled with horror of thy deeds—
That pois'nous stenches from thy demon soul
Thou now must bring to spue upon our Rock?
    Is it small offering—of Serbia the whole,
From Danube river to the deep blue sea?
Thy seat thou hast, all wickedly to ride;
Thy blood-stained sceptre is thy boast and pride,
From sacred altar thou insultest God,
And where was outrag'd Cross dost rear a Mosque!—

Later, while Prince Danilo still vacillates, the assembly of people,
dancing and chanting like a Greek chorus, deplores the very same
plight that has descended upon all Serbian people since the Battle
of Kosovo (1389). In their chant, the people urge the leaders to unite,
fight the Turks and thus avenge the loss of Serbian kingdom to the
Turks. The same sentiment is echoed by Vuk Mićunović, one of the
younger leaders.

THE PEOPLE (*as they dance the Kolo, sing*)

Our God hath poured His wrath upon the Serbs,
Our deadly sins withdrawn His favor from us:
Our Rulers trampled underfoot all law,
With bloody hatred fought each other down,
Tore from fraternal brows the living eyes;
Authority and Law they cast aside,
Instead chose folly as their rule and guide!
And those who served our kings became untrue,
Crimson they bathed themselves in kingly blood!
Our noblemen—God's curse be on their souls—
Did tear and rend the Kingdom into pieces,
And wasted wantonly our people's power.
The Serbian magnates—may their name rot out!—
They scatter'd broadcast Discord's evil seed,

And poisoned thus the life-springs of our race.
Our Serbian chiefs, most miserable cowards,
The Serbian stock did heartlessly betray.

Oh, let our losses all be light,
If the hard mountains of our land
Become the grave of Moslem might!
Lo! What the cause, that long time now,
Our homeland hills have silent grown,
No longer echoing to heroic shout?
Our idling armour is consum'd by rust,
And without chieftains is our country left,
Our hillsides reek with tramp of Moslem feet.—
In the same fold behold both wolves and sheep!
United now the Turk with Montenegrin,
The hodja calls upon Cetinje's plain;
The artful Turk hath run the lion to cage;
The Montenegrin Name is underground,
The cross with fingers three is no more found!

Vuk Mićunović:

Apart from Suffering never can be Song;
Apart from sweat of brow no sword is forged;
Heroic spirit conquers all life's ills;
Deeds nobly done are sweet unto the soul,
And wine most rich for those who follow on.
Thrice happy he whose name rings down the years,
For he had reason in this world to come;
A flaming torch is he when times are dark;
A touch ne'er burning low, ne're 'minished to a spark!

After Prince Danilo had received a sly but humiliating letter from
Selim-Pasha, in which he is invited to visit him and pay due homage
to the great Ottoman Empire, Danilo finally decides to act. Thus
the fight against, and the eventual defeat of, the "Turks" of Serbian
descent is joined.

VLADIKA DANILO (*writing the answer*):

"From the Prince-Bishop and from all his nobles,
To Selim-Pasha: Greeting responsive to the letter!
This hard nut is fruit that giveth wonder:
Thou crack'st it not, except thou crack thy teeth;
The price of wine is not what once it was;
Nor is the world as ye have thought it!
Europe to give as present to the Prophet—
A sin 'twould be to think of it:
That luscious fruit sticks half-way down his throat.
The blood of men is monstrous nourishment,
Already to the nose it choketh up;
O'erfull the measure of your sins!
Mahomet's mare hath snapp'd her saddle-girth!
Duke Charles the Valiant of Lorraine;
John Sobieski; Prince Eugene the Noble,—
They broke the Turkish demon's horns!
    The scroll of fate reveals not lot the same
For two brothers having name the same!
Mohammed's horse did stumble at Vienna,
And down the hill his chariot roll'd.
What good is empire to inhuman men,
Except to spread them shame thro' all the world!
A mind all wild with virulent desire
Becometh well wild hog, but not a man!
Along his path who maketh Might his Right—
Rise stenches of inhuman cruelty.
I have divin'd what thou wouldst wish to say!
Footprints are many to the cave:
For guests well hated is no feast prepar'd.
I know full well ye have no other thought
Than greedy tooth to sharpen on your neighbors,
And only your own flocks to guard from wolves!
Narrow the way of entrance to the hives;
For use against the bear is forged an axe;
Of sheep and fair domain ye have enough,
    Yet still ye would both man and beast despoil!

Where e'er ye come, rise groans on every side;
Bad men oppress'd by worse; good men by bad!
I have essayed descent upon your rope!
And, truth to tell, I was most like to choke;
Friends at a distance since are we;
Into my head some wisdom have put ye!"

* * *

This lament, sung by a young girl mourning her fallen brother
in a fight against the Turks, is one of the most beautiful scenes in the
epic drama. It is different from the rest both in tone and prosody.

THE SISTER OF BATRIĆ:

Whither hast thou flown from me,
  O falcon mine!
From all thy noble company,
  O brother mine!
Didst thou not know the faithless Turk,—
  May God him curse!
Could never faithful be?
  Most lovely head!
My world is gone now thou art gone,
  My sun! My brother!
Never can my wounds be sooth'd,
  My smarting wounds!
My very eyes are pluck'd from me,
  Light of mine eyes!
To whom shall now go all they brothers!
  O thou their pride!
And Pera grey, thy stricken sire?—
  Thy stricken sire!
Young sisters three bereft of thee,—
  Each mourning thee!
Bereft thy seven brothers' wives!
  O darken'd lives!
Why throw thy handsome head away,
  Thou princely spirit!

O'er thy head now gloats the foe!
    Our boast and pride!
'Gainst honor's word they hew'd thee down!
    Most treach'rous brood!
Too well they garnish'd Travnik town!
    God make them pay!
They deck'd it with thy lovely head!
    My heart lies dead!
Round whom now will heroes gather?
    Thou of men the leader!
Who now defend the far-flung wing?
    Protecting wing!
Who now keep count of Turkish heads?
    Keen sword wast thou!
Hadst thou been slain in combat sharp
    Thou warrior soul!
Where hot young heroes headlong ride
    To glory's goal!
To take their toll of arms and men,
    Thy death were priced!
Faith o'ermuch thou gav'st the faithless!
    Thou loyal mind!
Madness now creeps over me—
    O'erwhelm'd in night!
Oh, might I everything forget!
    My broken heart!
Thou was ever wise in counsel,
    My fair brother!
And couldst an Emperor well have serv'd!
    With clearest mind!
Full well a Vizier hadst thou been!
    My broken pride!
Or hadst thou served before a king,
    O ruler mine!
Thou wouldst have marshall'd bravest troops,
    Thou Rose of Mine!
Oh, might we once more talk together,
    Heart of mine!

Might I caress thy head so still!—
    No solace mine!
Again to glance in thy dark eyes!
    Thou wert mine eyes!
Thy now cold head to kiss again,—
    As 'twere still part of thee!
Again to tend thy wavy locks!
    It ne'er can be!
Thy hero's turban could I wind!
    O day most blind!
All-blood hands round thee to find!
    But God requite!
Thy lovely head is all despoil'd!—
    Arch-enemy!
Many a brother shalt thou greet!
    We hapless ones behind!
Thou shalt find most knightly souls;
    But wretched me!
Hoist upon the walls of Travnik!
    Deed accurst!
Comrades' heads thou may'st not know!
    Oh, empty world!
Insults heap'd upon us sorely!
    Oh, the Moslem foe!
Whither will thy heart's young love?
    Tears 'stead of sleep!
And her two hapless children weak,
    Orphan'd they and lone?
And grandsire Baiko, now grown old,
    In Batritch clan?
Thy grandsire he did train thee well!
    He'll mourn thee well!
Forgiveness o'er thy deadly wounds,
    Batritch belov'd!
The whelming woes of our whole race—
    Not pardon'd these!
Our land falls under Islam's yoke!
    Oh, judgment-stroke!

Our chiefs have now all heart of stone,—
Let death come to their home!

(She kills herself.)

James W. Wiles

Branko Radičević

(1824-1853)

Radičević was born in Brod na Savi, in 1824. He finished high school in Sremski Karlovci, the setting of his best poems. He studied in Vienna. In 1847 his first book of poetry appeared, announcing a new era in Serbian poetry. He went to Serbia but soon returned to Vienna to study medicine. His second collection of poetry was weaker than the first. His awareness of his impending death from tuberculosis, in his twenty-ninth year, is manifested in *Kad mlidijah umreti* (When I Thought of Dying).

In his poetry Branko gave expression to simple emotions such as joy on a sunny morning or in a fishing boat, pleasure derived from flowers, the exuberance of school youth, patriotic fervor, and love's joys and sorrows. His youthful zeal is also expressed in unabashed eroticism and in the exultation of wine, women, and song. More importantly, he was the first to write poetry in the simple language of the common people. He attempted to recreate the rhythm of the folk song, thus supporting the belief of Karadžić that even poetry can be written in the language of peasants and shepherds.

Among his best poems are: *Djački rastanak* (The Parting of Schoolfriends), *Put* (A Journey), *Tuga i opomena* (Sadness and Warning), and *Kad mlidijah umreti.*

AS I THOUGHT OF DYING

Already on the trees the leaves are yellowing,
Already yellowed, sink.
I do not think
That I shall see them green another spring.
My head droops low, my face is ashen gray,
From slow disease my eyes are hollowing,
My knees, their strength departed, cave,
My hand is frail, my body wastes away,
The time is come to go to my grave.

39

Farewell then, life, all beauty's dreamy spell,
Farewell then, dawn, oh light of day unfurled,
You earth that was my paradise, farewell,
I must be gone now to another world.
Ah, if I only did not love you so!
I would yet see your sun's bright slivers,
Hark tempests, mark the thunder's hail,
And marvel at your nightingale,
Your springs, your rivers—
Alas, the whirltide of my life is ebbing.

Oh songs of mine, poor orphans that I mourn,
Dear children of my younger years, good-bye,
I meant to snatch the rainbow from the sky
To clothe you with its varied lusters,
I meant to spangle you with starry clusters,
With rays of sunlight rim you and adorn.
The rainbow spans its hour and dies,
The constellations glitter and burn out,
And the dear sun, too, sags
And tumbles from the skies.
All I intended for you is in rout:
Your father leaves you in rags.

Vasa D. Mihailovich

Djura Jakšić

(1832-1878)

Jakšić was born in Srpska Crnja, Vojvodina. A son of a priest, he studied painting, but the revolution of 1848 interrupted his schooling, which he was never able to finish. After moving to Serbia, he served as a schoolteacher and in various other capacities, although he was often unemployed. A political liberal, he was persecuted by authorities. He died in despair and ravaged by illness in 1878, after he had taken part in the uprising against the Turks in Bosnia and Herzegovina.

Jakšić wrote poems, short stories, and plays. His best works are his poems and the short stories are the weakest. In all his works he was a typical representative of Serbian Romanticism. Among his few poems are several that belong to the best in the Serbian poetry of the nineteenth century: *Na Liparu* (On the Lipar), *Put u Gornjak* (The Road to Gornjak), *Mila, Otadžbina* (Fatherland), *Veče* (Evening), *Ponoć* (Midnight). Through them he expressed his pessimism and bitterness about the harsh blows life and people had dealt him. Jakšić was both the beneficiary and the victim of the romantic spirit, in his works as well as in life.

His stories and plays are, for the most part, attempts to revive the glorious Serbian past. Jakšić was also an accomplished painter.

THE BIRTHLAND

This rocky pile of Serbian earth which thrusts
Up through the cloud, and menaces the sun,
By the dark wrinkles of its sullen brow
Tells of time infinitely far away
And shows us, as in silent mimicry,
The deep-sunk furrows on its face engraven.
Ages of darkness—here behold their print
In those black wrinkles, in those pits of gloom;
This pile of stone is like some pyramid
That springs out of the dust toward high heaven:
—A heap, no more, of craggy skeletons

Which, in their mortal combat with the foe,
Thy fathers of their own free choice had raised,
Cementing with the blood of patriot hearts
Their shattered bones and sinews—to prepare
For their sons' sons a place of ambuscade
Whence *they*, with scornful valor, should thereafter
Await the foe, with all his ravening bands.

Thus far, no farther, to this pile of stone,
This mighty rampart,
Thy unclean foot may chance to penetrate!
Wilt thou dare farther? . . . Thou shall hear the thunders
Breaking the quiet of this land of freemen
With horrible clamor; thou shalt understand
Then, in thy coward soul, their dauntless voice;
And then, upon that hard and rocky wall
Shalt break the bald crown of thy shaven pate
In wild distraction and dismay; and yet
Through the dread crash and rattle of that warfare
Shalt hear one single utterance, one thought:
"Behold the Serbians' birthland, now their own!"

Oliver Elton

PATHS

Two paths are before me
One with flowers, the other with thorns
My legs are of iron
I shall return to the thorns

I cede the path of flowers
to those whose legs are soft
Let women tread on the grass
The thorns are made for men

Branko Mikasinovich

Jovan Jovanović Zmaj

(1833-1904)

Zmaj was born into a distinguished middle-class family in Novi Sad. He studied law and medicine in Budapest, Prague, and Vienna. Upon completion of his education, he practiced medicine in various cities. He also served as an administrator, theater director, and journal editor. (One of his satirical journals was entitled "Zmaj"—a name that later became a part of his own name). He expressed his happiness in married life in the collection of poems *Djulići* (Rosebuds, 1864); however, his happiness turned into tragedy when his wife and all their children died. He dwelt on this shattering experience in another collection, *Djulići uveoci* (Rosebuds Withered, 1888). After he had lost his own children, Zmaj turned increasingly toward writing juvenile literature; today, he is considered perhaps the foremost Serbian author of children's literature. He spent his last years practicing medicine, editing journals, participating in political affairs, and writing copiously. He died in Sremska Kamenica in 1904, as a celebrated author and public servant.

Zmaj's opus is considerable. He was most prolific in poetry and in literature for children, but he also wrote short stories, plays, and journalistic essays. In addition, he translated widely from German, Russian and Hungarian literatures. His best poems are on the themes of love and patriotism. Here he combined sincerity and purity of heart with a gentle humor. His poetic idiom is direct and highly emotional. Beloved by children of all generations, he tried to teach them through understanding, unobtrusive but firm adherence to morality, and, at times, hilarious humor.

SHE MUST NOT DIE!

I begin to pace, falter, go on, stop,
Hold the pendulum of the rushing clock,
I dash, run, and with a desperate sigh
Utter senseless words, words that stupefy:
  "She must not die!"

To God I cry: She is still a young sprout!
She's still full of hope! to Justice I shout.
To the angels: Her virtuous heart you know!
To the earth: She is not ready to go!
No response from anywhere, to be sure.
I cry to myself: Don't you know a cure?
I pace, stop, and with a desperate sigh
Again speak senseless words that stupefy:
        "She must not die!"

I pace, halt, my head droops, a tear tumbles
Into the cradle where our child slumbers,
The cherub wakes up, looks without a peep;
We gaze at each other and start to weep;
To him, also, with a desperate sigh
I whisper senseless words that stupefy:
        "She must not die!"

                                Vasa D. Mihailovich

THE GYPSY AND HIS HORSE

At my horse you're looking. . . . What, Sir!
Old Land-Owner!
Is it beast or is it bird . . . speak?
Perhaps it is a swift-winged swallow?
Down with your eye-glass.
You can't see through glass the best way. . . .
Buy him! That is better.

You dare ask me if "Halaulich's"
A good horse?
Why, why, no man. . . .
If he were not, be sure
That a gypsy would not ride him.
Such an one the emperor owns not. . . .

Dare not call his. . . .
Only I, the gypsy, I
Have no words with which to praise him.

If you'd forge a statue of him
Out of pure gold
A gold coin would e'en
Be cheaper.

If you've hay there he will eat it,
Aye . . . and oats, too!
But if nothing, he will not care,
He'll grow stronger.

Don't stand there and count his teeth, Sir,
His mane measure!
I myself, I have not seen them
Since the desert steed years touch not.
He grows younger, always younger.
Let him beware
Who would tame him.

What? You dare ask? The insult!
Can he leap a ditch!
Ditch . . . ditch . . . pray what ditch?
Begone, Sir! They're not worthy!
He would clear them like a hound, Sir . . .
Not their width . . . no, no, their length, Sir!
I ride him without a saddle.
Do not ask about his paces . . . .
You would wound him.

Of his eyesight do not ask him!
You could not insult him worse, Sir.
He sees backward,
He sees forward,
In the nighttime, in the daytime.
What! You ask what his faults are?

I'm astonished!
Now I'll sell him! Now I'll sell him!
He has no faults. . . .
Not one, Sir!
Such a rare horse I'm not rich enough to own . . .
I, Gypsy.

Is he swift?
How bitter! Bitter!
Swift as lightning, Good Land-Holder.
Let me tell you
Truthfully:
Once I'd return home and swiftly,
And although the storm raced with us
He would yield not.
Then the rain came . . . nearer . . . nearer. . . .
But my horse was ever swifter.
Then the rain grew angry . . . angry . . .
Tried to catch him.
But my wise horse he divined it . . .
He outran it.
When we reached my tent and entered
Only just his tail was wet.

E. W. Underwood

Laza Kostić

(1841-1910)

Kostić, another leading Serbian writer from Vojvodina, was born in Kovilj in 1841. After finishing law school, he occupied several positions and was very active in cultural and political life in Novi Sad, Belgrade, and Montenegro. He was among the leaders of *Ujedinjena omladina srpska* (United Serbian Youth) and was elected a Serbian representative to the Hungarian parliament. Because of his liberal and nationalistic views he had to leave Hungary, but after several years in Serbia and Montenegro he returned home. He died in Vienna in 1910.

Kostić remained a Romanticist poet and playwright all his life. An erudite and connoisseur of European languages and literatures, he brought into Serbian poetry elements of wider horizons, boldness, and originality. In his lyric poetry he often touched upon universal human concerns, especially the relationship between man and God, society, and fellow man. Perhaps his most important contributions are stylistic and linguistic innovations; he experimented freely, often at the expense of clarity. Closer to European Romanticism than any other Serbian poet of his time, Kostić attempted unsuccessfully in numerous, unfortunately incomplete theoretical essays to combine the elements of the native folk song with those of European Romanticism. The lack of success can be attributed to the advanced nature of his poetry and the ideas of his time and to his eccentricity. Indeed, his exuberance prevented him from becoming a truly great poet. However, today he is beginning to be reevaluated and appreciated.

Of his plays, *Maksim Crnojević* (1863) represents the first attempt to dramatize an epic poem, and *Pera Segedinac* (1875) deals with the struggle of the Serbs for their rights in the Austro-Hungarian Empire.

BETWEEN REALITY AND DREAM

My heart, my self-sufficient heart,
    who enticed you to my stream?
you tireless, masterly knitter,
of dainty knittings a deft fitter
    'tween reality and dream.

My heart, my mad, ravenous heart,
      of your knitting what's the scheme?
the day's knitting should the night unstitch,
as does that olden knitter-witch?
      'tween reality and dream

My heart, oh my vengeful heart,
      may the thunder blast your scheme!
for not giving me an inkling
of the secrets of your knitting
      'tween reality and dream.

Vasa D. Mihailovich

Milovan Glišić

(1847-1908)

Glišić was born into a poor peasant family in Gradac, near Valjevo. He had to begin work at a very early age to support himself and the family, but he managed to have some education in Belgrade. He worked as a journalist, librarian, and translator. As a liberal he often attacked the establishment, but as he rose on the social ladder he became less critical. However, he never forgot his rural background. He died in Dubrovnik in 1908.

Glišić wrote short stories and two comedies, *Dva cvancika* (Two Zwanzigers, 1883) and *Podvala* (Fraud, 1885). As the oldest of Serbian realists, influenced by Russian writers, he started a long tradition of realistic stories about the Serbian village. On the one hand, he idealized the Serbian peasant, his moral conduct and strength; on the other, he criticized sharply the external forces that oppress the peasant and prevent his emancipation. Thus, straight realism, the borrowing from folklore, idealization, satire, and humor distinguish his style. His best stories are: *Glava šećera* (A Lump of Sugar), *Redak zver* (A Rare Animal), and *Prva brazda* (The First Furrow).

He was also a prolific translator from Russian and French literatures, thus enabling writers in these languages, especially the Russian, to exert a considerable influence on Serbian writers.

THE FIRST FURROW

I

Further up from the upper end of the village Velika Vrbnica, near the mountain of Vratarna, a modest peasant's cottage could be seen with two or three other small buildings huddled around.

This is the home of the widow Miona. Her late husband, Sibin Džamić, was killed near Janko's Cliff in the Second War. Tales are still told of Sibin's courage, and whenever anyone mentions him at Vrbnica, they always say: "May God forgive his sins." His Miona was left alone to feed herself and three children, two small sons and a daughter. They were close to each other in size and age. Ognjan, the eldest, was only seven.

Nothing can be worse for a peasant family than to be left without a male head. The same misfortune had struck many other homes in the countryside. Many a widow had mourned for her husband, and had been consoled. Some had remarried after a year or two; others had gone to new families, taking their children to a stepfather.

Sibin's Miona would not follow the example of her friends in sorrow. An alert and industrious woman, she took on even the heavy farm work.

It seemed all the time to Miona that Sibin would come back. If he were to come, how could she face him if he were to find his house deserted and ruined?

The late Sibin had had many brothers and relatives, but they had not lived with him. They were all hard working people, intelligent and kind, and a day never passed without one of them coming to Miona's house to help her a little with her work.

Sibin's younger brother, Jelenko, helped her the most. Often he said to his sister-in-law:

"Why won't you listen to me, sister? Why won't you move to our house? Can't you see, poor thing, that with these three children you can never make ends meet! How are you going to do it all? You couldn't do everything even if you had a hundred arms. Why not come and live with us, at least until the children become big and strong?"

"I can't, brother," Miona answered, sighing.

"But why not? Everything would be easier and more comfortable for you in our house."

"But brother, how can I let the fire die on the hearth, where these orphans were first warmed? What could I say to my children later when they ask me, 'Mother, whose house is that, smothered by bushes and weeds, which none ever dares enter even in daylight?' If I did that, every bit of food I shared with Sibin would turn to poison. God save me from that! Never, brother, never."

Jelenko could do nothing but shrug his shoulders and hire a plough and a pair of oxen to plough up as much land as Miona needed for the crop.

These good people always helped her with the harder field work that was too heavy for a weak woman's hands. They ploughed up part of her fallow land, harrowed and sowed it as carefully as if the fields were their own. Miona did everything else herself. She hoed, weeded, and harvested. She never complained about the hard work. When they wanted to help her even here, she almost was annoyed. She used to thank them by saying, "You helped me with the hardest part. I can do this alone."

II

The years passed, one after another, and Miona became so used to her loneliness and hard work that she felt that this could not be otherwise. Her children were growing up. Ognjan was almost fifteen and he was going to school. He was a good pupil. Dušanka completed her thirteenth year and relieved her mother of many household duties. If Miona went to the field early in the morning to bundle up some sheaves or to the meadow to stack up what Jelenko had mowed the day before, she would not miss her dinner when she returned home at noon. Dušanka was taking care of it like an old matron. She even knew how to bake unleavened bread well. The youngest, Senadin, was nine. He still made guns out of alder-shoots, but he could take care of the lambs, and could lead the sheep to pasture, making himself a little bit useful too.

Thank God Miona's children were healthy, happy, intelligent, and industrious. They were dressed as if they came from the best home. Her heart overflowed with happiness when she looked at them.

"My lovely little birds," she used to sigh, "may God Almighty keep me in health and strength until their wings become stronger."

God is good. He answered the fervent prayer of the lonely widow. The men of the village respected Miona for her determination. They praised her everywhere and used her as an example to their wives when scolding them for their idleness. Only one thing surprised them: Why should she, being self-supporting, send Ognjan to school, and support him there? This they resented, and Jelenko himself reproached her for it once. It was when he and his old uncle, Jezdimir, were at her house and after they had discussed many things, he said to his sister-in-law:

"To be honest, everyone is surprised at the burden you are struggling under. You are industrious, and sensible, and yet you did something foolish."

"But what, brother?" she asked, a little startled.

"Why didn't you keep that child home to help you with at least some work? Many people who are richer and more prosperous than you are not able to do without their children. You are poor and you suffer, and yet . . ."

"I won't ever let my children be the worst educated in the village, brother," answered Miona, flushing a little. "My late Sibin—may God forgive him—often used to say that if nothing were to happen to him, he would send Ognjan to school. I am fulfilling his wish. I have suffered for it many years. It won't do me any harm to suffer a little longer."

"That is true, sister-in-law," said old Jezdimir, "that is fine and good. But, on the other hand, you are alone in the house and any aid, no matter how small, is of value to you."

"Ognjan will finish his school in July on St. Peter's Day and after that he will stay with me. With God's help, I will send Senadin to school next autumn. I don't want my children to be blind when they have eyes." She spoke with conviction, and so abruptly that Jelenko could say nothing. They talked a while of other things and then they went away.

"That isn't a woman, that is a man," said old Jezdimir slowly as they left Miona's house.

III

Lent had started and winter was almost over. The harsh east wind and the icy north wind no longer blew. The wind from the south now stirred the bare branches of the giant beech trees, coming from Župa and going even as far north as Zeljin, Neradja and Kopaonik. The snow almost everywhere melted. Only that snow on the Suvo Rudište did not care about the south wind; it would not melt until later, under the June sun.

The industrious farmers swarmed everywhere. They were ploughing the fallow land singing as they worked, hoping for a good year.

It was noon one day when Miona got back from town, where she had gone at dawn to see Senadin.

She had kept her word. Ognjan had completed the fourth grade on the feast of St. Peter, and shortly after the Transfiguration Senadin had entered the first grade.

Miona was climbing up through the orchard to the house, when Dušanka suddenly came out of the house. She had something rolled up in a little mottled bag and was in a hurry.

"Where are you going, Dušanka?"

"Oh, it's you. Back so soon?" Dušanka answered, a little confused. "That's good because the house will not be left empty. I am going to meet brother."

"Yes? Where is he?"

"In the field, down beyond the clearing. He told me to bring him his lunch."

"Isn't he coming back to the house to eat?"

"No."

"Why not?"

"He went with the oxen and the plough."

"Oh," Miona almost shouted, "why didn't you tell me at once. Give me the little bag, I will take it to him myself."

"No, let me, mother, you are tired and besides . . ."

"Besides what, my child?"

"My brother begged me not to tell you right away. He said, 'I want to make my mother happy.' "

"May God make him happy. I am not tired, child. I have not even noticed that I came back so quickly. Is wasn't very nice of you not to tell me immediately. Look what he is up to. Give me this little bag. See how late it is—already past noon. Has he been out long?"

"He probably just reached the field."

Miona snatched Dušanka's bag, looked into it to see what she had prepared, and hurried away. Dušanka, remained in front of the house, wondering and watching her mother go.

IV

This field, beyond the clearing, needed not more than one day's ploughing. The ground was not very rich and even in good years the harvest never produced more than two or three stacks of spring wheat.

Ognjan had just ploughed up the first furrow and was about to start the second when his mother suddenly appeared.

"Ah, just look at my old boy working!" cried Miona happily. Running up to Ognjan, she began to hug and kiss him. The boy was a little surprised.

"May your labor bring a good harvest, my landlord! What a superb little furrow and how deep it is! Oh, I'm silly, I am talking nonsense but you are tired, my toiler! Here, take this. Your little sister prepared your lunch for you."

Miona quickly emptied everything from the cloth bag, spread the bag out, and sorted out on it some salt, onions, a few cooked potatoes, a thin loaf of bread, a bowl of pea soup, and a small gourd of wine, saying:

"Ah, see what a girl Dušanka is! She even thought of wine. My matron! She already knows what a tired man needs. Stop ploughing, my son. You have worked enough."

And she burst into tears.

"What's the matter, mother?" asked Ognjan, sitting down. "You are crying."

"It's nothing, my son, nothing. See, I am laughing. Eat! I know that you are hungry. The truth is that I was delayed a little in town. You can't imagine how pleased the teacher is with our Senadin!"

"You sit down, too, mother, so we can eat together," said Ognjan breaking off a piece of the loaf for her.

"No, son, I will eat at home. Dušanka is waiting for me," answered Miona, still standing almost as if waiting on him. "You think that I am also tired, Ognjan, but I am not. I can be on my feet all day, my son. Take it easy, you have plenty of time, you do not have to plough up everything today. Look at him. He ploughs like a grown-up! Dušanka told me, but I thought she was joking—the little rascal!"

Again her eyes filled with tears. She was wiping them away with her sleeve while laughing.

Ognjan became confused. He blushed and felt like saying something, but he didn't know how.

Miona told him to eat again.

She began chatting with him as if he were a child, still standing in front of him. She said that she would save the wheat from that field to use only on feast days. She would use it to make the cake for the Patron's Day. The best flour is made from old grain, she added.

"If only the seed will sprout!" said Ognjan. "You know well, mother, that this field is one of our worst ones. The grain from here is almost always rotten."

"Oh, it will sprout, son, it must sprout! There is no better ground, even in Morava. There has never been anything bad from this field. You will see what good wheat will sprout here!"

Ognjan finished eating, stood up, took up the plough again, striking the oxen with his whip.

Miona stood looking at her son jumping from side to side like a rooster tugging at the handle, and directing the plough left and right. It was hard work and the boy's arms were still weak.

Several times Miona wanted to run up and help him, but for some reason she did not dare, she herself did not know why!

She straightened the little bag again and slowly went back home.

She turned around to look back at Ognjan time and again. She could still see him as he was ploughing up even the third furrow.

A strange new joy seized her. She felt like crying and laughing. She didn't know why. From time to time, she would whisper: "Is not God giving me my turn to rejoice. Am I not happy? Who could deny it! Oh, how happy I am! Look here, I have a son. I have a man in the house, haven't I! Other hands won't work for me any more. Nobody has such a youngster. There he is plowing! Even Jelenko could not do better. He is already a man. In one or two years, God willing, I shall have him married. My house will sing again."

Dušanka had never remembered seeing her mother so cheerful as then, when she returned from the field beyond the clearing.

The mother came home, humming a gay little song.

Branko Mikasinovich

Laza Lazarević

(1851–1890)

Lazarević was born in Šabac in 1851. A graduate of the University of Berlin Medical School, he practiced medicine in Serbian towns until his untimely death in 1890. In his student years he was attracted to progressive liberal ideas and movements, but later became a conservative, believing that only the patriarchal way of family life could form the basis for a political system. He saw the greatest danger for Serbian society in the attacks on this patriarchal way of life, as manifested in *Prvi put s ocem na jutrenje* (The First Matins with Father).

Lazarević wrote relatively little: only nine completed and several incomplete stories. A founder of psychological realism in Serbian prose, he was above all interested in the inner world of his characters. They are for the most part representative of the traditional morality under attack from the outside forces, new ideas, and wilful individualism—all these rebelling against the centuries-old cooperative family setup (*zadruga*). Lazarević was interested in village and small-town life. He also depicted the young Serbian intelligentsia exposed to, and influenced by, the outside world. While defending the patriarchal way of life, however, he was not oblivious to its shortcomings.

Just as important is Lazarević's style. He is a careful fabulist who excels in fine detail, compact structure, and dramatic quality. He is considered one of the best prose writers of the 19th century. His main stories are: *Školska ikona* (The School Icon), *Švabica* (The German Girl), *Sve će to narod pozlatiti* (People Will Reward), *Verter*, *Na bunaru* (At the Well), and undoubtedly his best, *Prvi put s ocem na jutrenje*.

THE FIRST MATINS WITH MY FATHER

I was only nine years old at the time. I don't remember the exact details of what happened, so I can only tell you what I recall. My sister who is older than I am remembers too, but my younger brother, on the contrary, knows nothing about it. I was never fool enough to tell him.

When I was grown up, I questioned my mother, who told me many things about the affair. My father, naturally, never breathed a word.

He, my father, was, of course, always dressed as a Turk. I can still see him putting on his clothes. He wore a short under vest of red velvet edged with several rows of gold braid, and over that a green cloth jacket. Behind his belt, which was stamped in gold, he stuck a thin walking stick with an ivory top and a dagger with silver scabbard and ivory handle. A fringed sash, tied on the left side, covered the belt. His trousers were ornamented with silk braid and embroidery, huge flaps hung half way down his legs, and he wore white stockings and flat shoes. A Tunisian fez, worn a little over the left ear, served as headgear. He carried in his hand an ebony pipe with an amber mouthpiece, and stuck in his sash on the right side was a tobacco pouch embroidered in gold and false pearls. He was a real dandy.

His disposition was peculiar, and though it is true that he was my father, since I have started to tell the story, there is no use in lying about it. He was extremely severe, he always commanded, and if his orders, given once for all, were not immediately executed, there was nothing left for you to do but to escape as fast as possible. Passionate and forcible, he required that everything should be done in his way; in short, no one dared to have the audacity to contradict him. When he was really angry, he would blaspheme the *Alleluia*. He never gave but one blow, but my dear fellow, you were on the ground as soon as you were hit! He was easily offended; when he scowled, bit his lower lip, and twisted his moustache, turning up the ends, his eyebrows joined across his forehead, and his black eyes gleamed. Woe, if at that moment someone came to tell him that I did not know my lesson. I don't know why I was so afraid. He might have boxed my ears once. But his eyes made me shiver, and when he turned them on you like a bullet from a sling, you would begin to tremble like an apple twig, without rhyme or reason.

He never laughed, at least never like other people. I remember one day, when he was holding my little brother on his knee. He had given the child his watch to play with, and Djokica insisted on jamming the watch into his mouth and yelling like one possessed because he couldn't open it. My sister and I almost died of laughing, and the thing seemed amusing even to my father, for he several times partly opened his mouth on the left side and his face wrinkled at the corner of his left eye. This was an extraordinary event, and was his way of laughing at a thing which would have made anyone else roar so that they could be heard at the Inn of Tetreb.

I remember the day that my uncle died, Papa's brother and partner, whom he cared for deeply. My aunt, my mother, my cousins, all of us children sobbed and groaned, with tears and lamentations, all, all, crying aloud. But Papa never faltered, he did not shed a tear, or even say an "Oh" of pain. Only as he went out of the house his lower lip trembled nervously and he shivered. He was white as linen and supported himself against the doorway, but he did not open his lips.

Even at the risk of his head, he would never go back on what he had said, though the thing might be required by his conscience. I remember the day that he dismissed his clerk, Proka. I saw clearly that he hated doing it, and that he was sorry for the man, but he did not give in. He liked Proka better than any of the other clerks. I remember that he had never struck him but once when, after drawing some brandy, Proka had closed the spigot so badly that almost the value of a keg had flowed away. Except that one time he had never laid a finger on him. He trusted him in everything, even sending him to the village to collect the money for things that had been sold on credit, and things like that. And why do you suppose he sent Proka away? For no reason at all! Just because he had seen him gambling for pennies!

But wait, you will soon be still more astonished!

It was near the feast of St. George. Proka came into the shop to have his agreement renewed. Papa took ninety groschen out of his pocket and said, "Here is your money. I have no more need of you. Go and find a place where you can gamble for pennies." Proka, holding his fez before his eyes, and shedding a veritable rain of tears, began to plead for pardon. I could see that my father was touched, but do you think he yielded?

God forbid that it should be said that he was like some men who beat their wives, and do other things of that kind, but he was cold and churlish with my mother—worse than a stranger, he really was. Whereas my mother, good as any saint, brooded over him with her eyes as an ostrich does over her eggs. When he spoke harshly, and her tears choked her, she always hid them, not only from us but from

him. He never went out with her, and she did not dare open her mouth
to ask him to take her anywhere.

He would not tolerate any suggestions from her about the shop or
about his business.

One day she said to him:

"Mitar, why don't you give any brandy to Stanoje? There will soon
be plenty of the new, and where will you put it?"

He only answered this by shouting:

"Are you hungry, or do you need anything? The money is in your
hands, if it gives out you have only to say so. But don't meddle with
my affairs."

My mother bowed her head and was silent.

He talked very little with anyone. His group of friends met at the
cafe, and it was only with them that he said a few words. He had a
great respect for his partner, Ilija, the only man who ever spoke frankly
to him, and of whom my father was in a certain way, a little afraid.

It could be seen that he loved us, his children, and my mother, but
he held us under very severe control. I do not remember ever having
received any mark of affection from him. It is true that at night, he
tucked us in again when we were uncovered, and he would not let us
lean over the well or climb the mulberry trees, but what did that mean
to me? Other fathers did as much, and also brought their children
candy and gold paper and balls that bounced as high as the poplar
trees.

He went to church only on the feast of St. George, but he went to
the cafe every night. We had supper, and immediately after it he put
his chibouk under his left arm, his tobacco pouch in his belt, and behold
he was gone! In summer he came back at nine o'clock and in winter
even earlier, though sometimes midnight had struck before he was at
home.

This troubled my poor mother and sister, but I at that time knew
nothing of what such revelry meant. They never went to sleep before
my father's return even if he did not get back until dawn. Sitting up
in their beds they dared not even light a candle. He went into a rage
at once, you see, if he found one burning. One day when he had come
in I heard him growl.

"What is the meaning of that candle burning at such an hour?"

"It is so that you can see to undress, Mitar," said my mother.

"Do you think that I don't know how to light a candle, or that I am too drunk to find one?"

"But no, Mitar," said my mother, soothingly, "I only thought—"

"You thought what? You wanted the neighbors to think that there was a corpse in the house!"

A corpse! Do you imagine for a moment that he meant that? He who cared so little about the neighbors? He merely did not want my mother to pay any attention to his goings and comings, and in his anger he did not know what to accuse her of. He would have preferred finding my mother asleep, or if she must lie awake, that he should at least be able to go on a spree without having any fuss made about it. That evidently irritated him.

He drank very little, and then only wine. When he had to taste the brandy that he bought, he always spit it out at once, making a grimace.

He cared no more, and God knows how little that was, for coffee. You ask me "What did he do all night in the cafe?"

It was a bad thing, that was what it was. It seems to me that if he had drunk hard it would have done only half as much harm. But you will see.

It shortened my mother's life by half. Sometimes she cried and choked, but she never complained to anyone.

One day he came home very late. Nothing happened. Again the next day, nothing. Do you suppose, my dear fellow, that my mother did not know that he no longer had a watch! At last the poor woman asked him, "Where is your watch, Mitar?"

He frowned, and turning away his eyes, answered.

"I have sent it to Belgrade to be repaired."

"But it worked quite well, Mitar."

"I suppose that I am neither one-eyed nor an idiot, and that it is probable that I know whether a watch works well or not."

What could my mother do? She was silent, but later she said to my sister with tears, "This is very hard on me, he will throw away everything that we possess, and in my old age I shall have to live by washing other people's shirts."

Another time it was barely ten o'clock, when he suddenly returned from the cafe.

An astrachan cap was cocked over one ear, a chain as thick as your finger hung across his breast, and a pistol encrusted with gold and precious stones was stuck in his belt. He came in, and from the look of the few wrinkles around his left eye, he seemed to be in a good enough humor.

As soon as he was in the house, he pulled out his watch, as if to see what time it was.

"You have come back?" said my mother, walking with a start. "And is your watch repaired?"

"It is repaired."

"And what is that chain?"

"It is a chain, like any other chain," he answered in a quiet voice without shouting.

"I know that," said my mother, "but where did you get it?"

"I bought it."

"And that cap? Only Mića the treasurer has one like it."

"I bought that also."

"He sold it to you?"

"He sold it."

"And what . . . ?"

But here my father looked at my mother in a certain manner, and she was silent.

He began to undress. I risked an eye outside of my quilt.

He took out of his pocket a package as big as my fist, and tossed it onto the table, where it rang; nothing less than ducats, my dear fellow.

"Here, keep this," he said, and went into the kitchen.

My mother took up the paper between two fingers—as you might say—the way that she would have lifted dirty linen.

"What shall I do with this money?" she asked my sister. "It is accursed. It is from the devil, and the devil will take it back in the same way that he has given it."

As you see there was neither life nor happiness in this thing. My mother was unhappy, and we were unhappy with her.

My mother has told us that he was formerly quite a different sort of man, and I remember myself, as if in a dream, that when I was tiny he held me on his knee, and that he made me a whistle out of a reed, and took me with him in the cart out into the fields. "But," said my mother, "after he began to go with the treasurer Mića, Krsta who lives in Makevina Street, Albert the druggist, and a few others, every thing was upside down, and went crookedly."

He grew cross, and would allow no questions, always saying, "Mind your own affairs," or "Have you nothing else to worry about?"

He was good at nothing, and as I have told you he realized that what he was doing was wrong, but that which had taken possession of him, and from which God preserve us, would not let him go.

And yet, though it seems absurd to say it, he was really a fine man. Yes, by the Lord he was! But . . .

One day when he came home he was not alone! My mother was surprised. He passed by the door with someone and they were whispering together. They went into the courtyard. Then we heard the neighing and stamping of a horse. I did not know what it meant.

When he came in later I began to snore and my sister pretended to be asleep. He said good evening, and nothing more. Both he and my mother were silent, and as for me, I waited. At last my mother said in a choked voice.

"He has taken the black horse!"

"He has taken him."

Again they were silent, but my mother blew her nose several times, and I thought she was crying.

"Mitar, for the love of God, and in the name of our children here, stop this traffic with the devil. The man who leagues himself with him is damned in this world and the next. Look what happened to Jovan who gambled with cards, think of him! A man of his position, who has sunk until today he must pick up nutgalls for other people, and buy skins in the villages for the Jews. For the love of God, have you no pity for me, who when I grow old will have to seek my crust of bread in the houses of others, or these children of ours who will have to serve strangers?" And she began to sob.

"What's the matter with you that you should call on me in the name of the children and you mourn me before I am dead? What makes you howl about a wretched nag? It was not she that owned me, but I that bought her! Tomorrow, if you want them, I will buy ten."

My mother only cried harder.

"I know, dear Mitar," she said patiently, "but your enemies will take everything from you. O my beloved, leave those wretched cards alone. Remember that it was by the strength of our backs and the sweat of our blood that we were able to raise this roof above our heads. Is it possible that some miserable moneylender will turn me out of my own house?"

"But who is turning you out?"

"No one is turning me out, my dear, but I shall be turned out if you go on as you are doing. It is a trade accursed of God."

"Haven't I told you a hundred times not to preach to me, or to whimper without cause. There is no reason to think that some crow has picked out my brain so that I need my wife for a guardian."

She said no more, that brave soul. Her throat contracted and she shed no more tears. They ran down her breast and fell on her heart. and turned to stone there.

The days followed each other, and he kept on in just the same way. Sometimes he brought home rolls of money, which he lost again as he had won it. He often came back without his rings or watch or gold embroidered belt.

Again he would have two or three watches and several rings. One day it would be a pair of high boots, a cloak, a saddle, or a dozen silver spoons; once it was even a barrel full of liquorice, and all sorts of other trifles. One evening he brought a black horse, the same one that had belonged to us before.

The next day he bought a new harness; the false martingale hung below the knees of the beast, and the fringes beat against his jaws. My father harnessed him to the carriage, shut the door of the shop with a chair, and drove through the town! The pebbles flew from under the horse's hoofs.

We were prepared for anything. My mother cried and was anxious. How could she be anything but unhappy? The shop was deserted. He sent away the clerks one after another. Everything went wrong in that unlucky house, and the money ran away like rain.

His companions, heaven help us, began to come to us. They shut themselves up in the big room and lighted several candles; ducats rang and cards slid on the table, pipes smoked, and our servant Stojan never stopped making them coffee (the next morning he showed us some ducats that had been given to him for fees). My mother stayed with us in the other room. Her eyes were red, her face pale, her hands dry, and she repeated over and over again, "O God, be with us!"

He became, at last, completely detached from household life. He never spoke. He never looked my mother in the face. He never caressed us, his children, and while not using really abusive words to us, he was very far from ever saying a kind one. Everybody kept away from the house. He did give us whatever we needed. If I asked for money to buy a slate pencil, he gave me enough to pay for a whole package. My clothes were the finest in the whole school, and for food he bought the very best to be found in the city. But all the same, something that I did not understand made me suffer whenever I looked at my mother and sister. They had become older, and grown pale and grave and sad. They went nowhere, hardly even to see a few neighbors at the Slava, and very few women came to us. Only the men came, and most of these were dissipated "good for nothings" as my mother called them. There was hardly any work done in the shop. "Do you expect me," said my father, "to amuse myself by selling twenty cents worth of indigo to a boor? That is good enough for the Jews."

My mother was no longer able to protest. She told me that he had said to her one day, "If you will listen, listen, and understand what I am telling you; if ever again you say one word of that kind to me, I will find another house and move into it, and then you can preach here to whoever you choose. Keep that clearly in you mind!"

She was as silent, poor soul, as if she had been ducked. Her heart was rent, she grew whiter day by day, and never stopped imploring God for help. "My God," she prayed, "do not abandon me."

And then . . . you can probably imagine what the end of all this was!

One night they all came. A certain Pero Zelenbać was with them, a pig merchant, who as he expressed it, "worked with Pest." His moustache was waxed and his hair, which was separated by a part in the back, was allowed to fall in curls over his cheeks. He was fat faced and corpulent and wore a curious little hat over one ear. He wore a gold chain on his waistcoat like the one papa had formerly owned, and on his hand was a ring that sparkled, really, my dear fellow, it sparkled so that you couldn't look at it. He waddled in his walk, and spoke in a hoarse bass voice, and you were confused before his little yellow-green eyes, which inspired a sort of dread, such as one feels when looking at an owl.

They arrived , as I said. Stojan was in his place at the stove making their coffee.

Four candles were lighted. The tobacco smoke rose as if from a chimney. They drank coffee in silence like Turks, but the cards fell, and you could hear the ducats ring.

It was a terrible night!

We were shut up in the other room with my mother. She no longer cried. Neither did my sister. With faces set and sunken eyes, they gazed straight in front of them in deadly fear. What happened at my uncle's death was nothing compared to this.

My father came into our room several times. He was covered with sweat. He had unbuttoned his vest and unhooked his shirt, so that one could see the coarse hair on his chest. He was scowling like a Turk.

"Give me more," he said to my mother.

Her heart shrank. Silent, as if made of stone, she opened the chest and gave him handfulls of money which he tied in a handkerchief. He glanced nervously from side to side, and stamped his feet where he stood, as I do when the boys are waiting for me outside and I want my sister to cut me a piece of bread. He took the money, turned away his head, and muttered as he went out, "More than that."

After that you might have said that he ran away from the place.

But still saying, "More than that, more than that," he came, I think, five more times into our room, and this went on until it was almost three o'clock in the morning.

"Give," he said to my mother, and his face was livid.

My mother went to the chest, her legs trembled and she staggered.

Hidden under my quilt, I could still see how my father's tall figure was shaking and how he supported himself against the stove.

"Be quicker!" he said to my mother, losing all patience and with impatient gestures of his arms.

My mother handed him the money.

"Give me all of it," he said.

"These are the last ten ducats," she answered. It was no longer a voice or a whisper that we heard, but something like a death rattle.

He gathered up the money and rushed out of the room.

My mother sank beside the chest, and fainted. My sister screamed. I sprang out of bed. Djokica did the same. We sat down on the floor around her, and began to kiss her hand, crying, "Mamma, Mamma."

She put her hand on my head and murmured something. Then she rose and lit a small taper and the votive lamp before St. George.

"Come children, pray to God, that he may deliver us from misfortune," she said. Her voice rang like a bell, and her eyes shone like the star of the shepherds, radiant in the sky.

We ran after her to the icon, and all knelt down; while Djokica, kneeling in front of mother, turned his face toward her, crossed himself, and repeated, poor little chap, the half of the pater which he had already learned. Then he crossed himself again, kissed mother's hand, and gave himself up to gazing at her. Two rivers of tears poured from her eyes. Her look was upturned to the saint and to God. There, on high, was something that she could see, her God, whom she adored and who looked down again upon her. At that moment there came over her face an expression of rapture, a sort of radiance, and it seemed to me that God caressed her with his hand, and that the Saint smiled, and that the dragon died beneath his spear. Then my eyes were dazzled, and I fell forward on the edge of my mother's dress and against her left arm which supported me, and I prayed for the hundredth time, "Oh God, you see my mother! My God, I beseech you for my father!" Then I added, I don't know why, "O God, kill that Zelenbać!"

We prayed like this for a long time.

At last my mother rose and climbing on a chair, kissed the image of St. George, my sister did the same, and lifted up Djokica and me so that we could kiss it also. Then my mother took the spray of dried basil which was kept behind the icon and the vial of water that had been blessed at the Epiphany from where it hung below the image. She dipped the basil in the water and murmuring something, with the spray she made a sign of the cross in the room. After that, opening the door very softly, she tiptoed down to the big room, on the door of which she made another cross with her spray of basil.

Ah, how light I felt then, and how happy, as if I had just come from taking a bath. Why is it that I never have that sort of feeling now?

My mother had hardly made her sign of the cross on the door of the big room, when a tumult began inside. It was impossible to distinguish anything, except that once we heard Zelenbać shout with all his might.

"Who can force me to go on with the game? Who is the man who will try that?"

Then there was more confused noise and violent disputing. We heard the door open, then a murmur, and steps. . . .

But papa did not come back to our room. We waited in vain. The dawn began to break, we fell asleep, Djokica and I, but still he did not come.

When I awoke the sun was already high. I felt horribly tired, but couldn't close my eyes again, so I got up.

Everything seemed in some strange way solemn, but sad. Out of doors, the air was calm, a clear shaft of sunshine fell through the open window, and in front of the icon, a little flame still trembled in the lamp.

My mother and sister were as white as linen, their eyes were soft with tears and their faces seemed made of wax. Without letting even their fingers crack, they moved about on tiptoe, and in silence, except for a few whispered words of prayer. They did not give us any breakfast or ask if we were hungry, and my mother did not send me to school.

"What does it mean," I asked myself, "is there a death in the house, or has my uncle come back, and shall we have to bury him over again?"

Then I felt frozen with fear, remembering what had happened during the night, and I murmured mechanically, "Oh God, you know I prayed to you for papa," and again, "My God, kill that Zelenbać."

Without thinking I dressed, went out of my room, and turned naturally toward the big room, but recoiled at once as I felt my mother seize my arm. I turned to her, but she told me nothing, only putting her fingers to her lips; and then led me to the house door and left me there. She went back to her room, and I, following her with my eyes, did not know what to think. I slipped back on my toes to the big room, and put my eye to the keyhole.

I noticed carefully what I saw. The table was in the middle of the room, the chairs were scattered about and two or three were overturned. Strewn over the floor were thousands of cards, cigars, some whole and some trodden on, a broken coffee cup, and lying on a card gleamed one gold ducat. The tablecloth was pulled half off. On the table were scattered playing cards, overturned cups full of stubs and cigar ashes and some empty saucers into one of which someone had cleaned out his pipe. Besides this there were four empty candlesticks, in one of which the coarse paper which had been around the candle still burned with a line of black smoke that rose and broke against the ceiling.

On a chair by the table, with his back to the door, my father was sitting. His elbows were on the table, his head in his hands, he did not move.

I watched a long time but he remained motionless. I was frightened, and imagined some mysterious trouble. It seemed to me, I don't know why, that my father was dead, and I was surprised that a corpse could breathe. Then I thought that his strong arms were made of cardboard, and he could never use them to strike again, and other fancies of the same kind came into my mind.

God knows how long I would have stayed there watching if my mother's hand had not touched me again. She said nothing, but with her eyes she showed me the way to the house door.

And I, I don't know why, took off my hat, kissed her hand, and left the house.

That day was a Saturday.

When I went out into the street, all the world were following their ordinary lives and attending to their business. Sturdy peasants were bringing all sorts of things to the market place, merchants were examining the bags of vegetables and feeling of the lambs. Novak, the guard, shouted, and directed where each man should put his cart. The children stole cherries. Sreten, the towncryer, went through the streets, calling out that it was forbidden to let pigs run free in the streets. Trivko showed quarters of lamb, crying, "Come and buy roasts," and Jova the drunkard dabbled his feet in a puddle.

"What is the matter, is your shop closed?" Ignace the furrier who was passing at the moment asked me.

"Yes," I said.

"Mitar isn't ill?"

"No," I answered.

"He has gone away somewhere?"

"To the village," I replied, and escaped from the courtyard.

And now there arrived two "witnesses" or "boys of honor" as they were called, that is to say two of my schoolmates who had been sent by the teacher to see why I had not come to school.

I never remembered until that moment that I should have gone. I caught up my books and a piece of bread, and looked at my mother and the witnesses.

"Say to the master, children, that Miša could not come earlier, that he was detained."

That dear hand! Could I ever kiss it enough—when she was asleep —when she could not see me.

I do not know what happened at home while I was at school, but I know that when I returned everything was just as I had left it. My mother and sister were sitting with their hands on their knees, the dinner was not cooked, and they tiptoed by the big room and sighed as they had done when my uncle died. Djokica, out in the court, had tied a coffeepot to the cat's tail and was watching it run. The clerks were sewing on blouses in their room, while Stojan had buried himself in the hay and was snoring as if it was midnight.

My father was sitting in the same place. He had not stirred. His furlined coat, fastened around his broad shoulders, gaped open at the waist from his heavy breathing.

Vespers had rung long ago.

The day was drawing to its close, and in our hearts reigned the same despair, to which no one could see any end, but only clouds that gathered thicker and thicker. Everything grew more intolerable, more terrible and more desperate.

"Return again, O my God, and have mercy."

I sat on the doorstep, in front of the house. I held some schoolbook in my hand, but I did not read it. I saw in the window my mother's white face, resting on her little feverish hand. My ears rang, and I could not think at all.

Suddenly a key grated in the lock. My mother disappeared from the window. I simply could not think.

The door of the big room was open. He stood on the threshold— he—my father!

His fez, pushed back a little, showed the hair which fell over his wide brow. His moustache drooped, and his face had grown sombre and much older. But his eyes, those eyes! They had not the least resemblance to what his eyes had been. They had simply vanished, sunk into his head; half covered by the lids, they moved slowly and looked out with no interest or expression. They looked for nothing and they noticed nothing. There was about them a sort of emptiness, like spectacles with the glass broken out. On his lips was a sad gentle smile, such as had never been seen there before. It was the same expression that my uncle had had, when, just before his death, he asked for the sacrament.

He went slowly down the hall, opened the door of our room, looked in, and then passed through without a word. Having closed the door behind him, he went out into the street, and walked slowly toward the house of his partner Ilija.

Toma, the latter's son, told me later that his father and mine were shut up together in a room, that they talked a long time about something in a low voice, that they had had paper brought in, and ink, and that they had written something and put seals on it. What this was he did not know, and no one ever found out.

At about half-past nine, we were all in bed except my mother who sat with folded hands, gazing at the candle. At that moment the gate of the courtyard creaked. My mother blew out the candle and slipped into bed.

My heart beat under my blanket as if someone was hitting my chest with a hammer.

The door opened and my father came in. He moved once or twice across the room, and undressed without lighting the candle and went to bed. For a long time I heard him turning in his bed, and then I fell asleep.

I don't know how long I had slept, when I felt something damp on my forehead. I opened my eyes and watched. The full moon looked directly into our room and its rays fell on my mother's face, like spiderwebs.

Her eyes were closed, she had the look of a person who is very ill, and her breath came quick and short.

Above her stood my father, motionless, with his eyes riveted on her face.

After a little while he came to our bed, but merely looked at us and at my sister. Then he placed himself once more in the middle of the room, encircled it again with his eyes and muttered, "They are asleep."

But he shuddered at the sound of his own voice, and seemed to turn to stone. There, in the center of the room, he stood a long time without any change except that I saw his eyes soften from time to time as he looked, first at us and then at my mother.

We never made a sign!

Then, moving quietly and without ever taking his eyes off us he carefully unhooked his silver pistol from the cloakstand where it hung, thrust it into his coat, pulled his fez over his eyes, and walking with quick long strides, went out of the house.

The door had hardly closed after him when my mother rose up in her bed. My sister did the same. You might have thought them spirits!

My mother got up quickly, but with caution, and went to the door. My sister followed her.

"Stay with the children," whispered my mother, and went out.

I sprang up and started for the door. My sister caught me by the arm, but I slipped out of her grasp, and said:

"Stay with the children."

As soon as I was out of the house I ran to the hedgerow and slipping along it, hiding under the cherry trees, I got to the well, behind which I hid myself.

The night was divinely beautiful. The sky was clear, the moon brilliant, the air full of freshness, and nothing was moving anywhere. I saw my father look into the window of the clerk's room, and then go on. At last he stopped under the shed roof, and drew out his pistol. But, just at this moment, my mother, coming from I don't know where, appeared beside him.

The poor man was frozen with terror. He gazed at her with open mouth.

"Mitar, my dear, my Lord and Master, what do you mean to do?"

My father trembled. Stuck there like a candle, he looked at my mother with empty eyes, and said in a voice like a cracked bell:

"Go away, Marica, leave me, I am lost."

"What! Lost, my Lord? May God help you, why do you say that?"

"I have thrown away everything!"

"But, my dear, it was you who first earned it!"

My father started back, and stood abashed before my mother.

"Yes, but all," he said, "all, all."

"And even if that is so?" said my mother.

"The horse too," he replied.

"An old nag," she answered.

"And the field!"

"Just dirt."

He came close to my mother, and looked into the whites of her eyes, as if he would scorch her, but she stood like a saint of the good God.

"The house too," he said, opening his eyes very wide.

"And what of that," said my mother, "so long as you, yourself, are here strong and well?"

"Marica!"

"Mitar!"

"What do you mean, Marica?"

"I mean, may God grant you long life, and to our children. It is not the house nor the field that takes care of us, but you, our provider. We will never suffer from hunger while you are with us."

My father seemed moved. Putting his hand on my mother's shoulder, he began—

"Marica! Do you . . ." His voice choked. He covered his eyes with his sleeve and was silent.

My mother took his hand.

"When we were married," she said, "we had nothing but one blanket, just one, and only two or three tubs and barrels. While now, thank God, the house is full."

I saw a drop fall, which shone in the moonlight, as it traced its path down my father's sleeve.

"And have you forgotten that the garret is full of gall nuts?"

"Yes, it is full of them," said my father, in a voice as soft as silk. He took his sleeve away from his eyes, and let his arms fall.

"What is that wretched ducat doing there? What is that money lying on the ground? Take it for your business!"

"We will put it into wheat!"

"Are we too old to begin again? By the grace of God we are well and our children are in good health. Let us pray to the good God and go to work."

"Like the honest people we are!"

"You are not stupid like some men. I would not give your arms for all the money of Paranos and others like him."

"And then we will buy another house."

"We will bring up our children in the right path," said my mother.

"So that they may not curse me when I am dead. How long it is since I have seen them!"

"Come and see them," said my mother, and she led him like a child, by the hand.

In three bounds I was back in my room. I whispered to my sister, "get into bed," and then pulled the blanket over my own head.

Those two crossed the threshold, just as the church bells rang for the early mass. They reverberate through the night and the Christian soul trembles. Like a bed of dry branches, their sound softens grief and pain, and breaks the chains of vanity, so that the contrite soul can speak with heaven.

"Rise my son, and let us go to church!"

When I was in Belgrade, last year, buying some merchandise I saw Pero Zelenbać, at Topčider, in the dress of a convict. He was breaking stones.

Pavle Popović

THE GERMAN GIRL

(Excerpt)

TENTH LETTER

In N——187—

Dear bosom friend,

"Call me but love, and I'll be new baptiz'd
....
My name is hateful to myself
Because it is an enemy to thee;
Had I it written, I would tear the word."[1]

Surely you didn't expect to receive my letter so quickly; you couldn't have. You can imagine my position: I stand in the sea, alone, on a board, in an awful thunderstorm, and I am shaking.

---

[1]William Shakespeare, *Romeo and Juliet*, act II, scene II.

What am I to do? What lie shall I tell you? I love her. You knew it yourself. Surely, you did not take me for a playboy, who runs around with girls, deceiving them.

I have thought of nothing else during the first weeks since I kissed her. I have suppressed any voice of conscience, for the thought of home and her together with me in the house. Even if I had wanted to think of a way out—I couldn't. I was too happy for even a slightly more somber thought to arise to coat this whole sweet dream with bitter reality.

I have been with her all the time. She comes to my room, as soon as the old woman goes to market or to town. She straightens my books, she lifts my exercise weights and marvels at my strength; and after that she caresses me and is very sweet—I sit on the sofa looking at her and melting.

Everyday I become more and more deeply involved. When I speak of myself, I always say "we." She looks at me, kisses me—lives happily. Since that first time, whenever we wanted to take a walk, we went to the forest. We both hated the world. We were undisturbed in the forest.

One evening while we were walking again together, speaking French, two Prussian soldiers passed by.

When they were several steps away from us, one turned and said mockingly:

"Eine grosse nation."[2]

I turned to look at him. She took me by the arm and pulled me orward.

"You are quickly angered," she said soothingly.

I nodded my head in an indifferent fashion.

"Mišo," she said carefully, "you don't like Germans."

That confused me a bit.

"How can I answer you? . . . No, I don't like them. You yourself told me that your grandfather was a Pole."

"My father, mother, brothers and sisters, are all German," she said sorrowfully.

"You are mine," I said, "whatever you are."

She moved closer to me.

---

[2] A great nation.

We walked further. I felt unusually pleasant. It was the end of March and the first time I had gone out in my spring overcoat. The air was mild and the forest had started to blossom.

We arrived at a small lake and sat on a bench. The frogs were croaking. A swan was swimming in the middle of the lake, leaving a wake behind it. All was quiet.

There was a ringing in my ears. I put my head in her lap and looked at the sky, listening to the croaking of the frogs.

I felt unusually calm. She kissed my forehead many times.

I took out my tobacco pouch and asked her in Serbian:

"Make me a cigarette."

She sensed that it meant, "drehe mir eine zigarette."[3] Somehow she rolled a cigarette and gave it to me.

"You see, I understood," she said happily.

"Anna, do you want me to teach you Serbian?"

Her face brightened. Some sort of ceaseless happiness showed in her eyes and lips. Instead of an answer, she started to kiss me again.

While we were returning, I gave her the first lesson in Serbian. I explained to her the imperfective and perfective verbs. I taught her several words and sentences, after which I tested her; she seemed happy as a child. When we came home it was time for supper.

After supper I went to my room, feeling pleasantly fatigued. I don't know why they hadn't brought me a lamp, but I lit a candle and put it on the table. Then I opened the window and pure, clean air came into my room. I unbuttoned my vest and shirt and lay on the sofa. In my thoughts, she was constantly beside me, happy as a dove.

I started to think of all that, but could not concentrate. Images were flying before my eyes without order; I couldn't capture any of them. I repeated several times the word "marriage" but could attach no meaning to it.

In this state, I fell asleep, although it was barely nine o'clock.

I slept dreamlessly. Something seemed to be pressing against my chest and choking me.

When I opened my eyes again it was late at night. My candle had completely burned out and the paper, with which the candle was

---

[3]Make me a cigarette.

wrapped at the bottom had caught fire. A thick smoke was rising in the hazy light, reaching the ceiling, for it was so tranquil that nothing disturbed its journey towards the sky. It was the smoke that awakened me. I, sleepy as I was, grabbed a glass of water and poured it on the candle holder. Then I got up and opened a second window so that the smoke could escape, and stood for a while at the window, which had a view of the garden.

I was drowsy. It was quiet in the garden. A train could be heard far away.

Suddenly I was overtaken by sorrow, not understandable, unclear. I could not seem to console myself with anything, although I had no knowledge of the source of my oppression. It seemed o me that there was something, and I tried to recall it. Suddenly her picture came to me. I trembled and felt the air cooling my chest.

I was afraid, I don't know why, to continue to think of her. I wanted to light a candle, to undress and lie in bed. I started looking for matches on the table. The matches were soaked by the water that I had poured on the candle holder, and none of them would light. Then I remembered that I had some matches in my new coat. I found them quickly and, lighting one after the other, I started looking for a new candle. The red-hot candle holder had cracked when I poured water over it. I set the new candle on the wet table.

My room seemed indescribably sad to me. I was used to the illumination of the lamp; and the candle was giving such poor light that it seemed to me that I didn't recognize anything in the room. The table was completely wet and water was dripping off the edges onto the floor, along with crumbs of tobacco and cigarette ashes, which I had dropped on the candle holder. I picked up the wet books whose covers had swollen and suddenly noticed a letter on the table.

I recognized it as a letter from my sister. I opened it. You know how sisters write. The whole letter was about me. She wrote to me about how they constantly speak of me, how the children constantly ask when I will return, how eager everybody is to see me, and how it seems to them that they can't wait for the happy hour when I will graduate and come home, never again to leave them.

My throat tightened even more. I closed the windows and started to walk about the room. Then I reread the letter and walked some more.

It seemed to me that I was preparing myself for a battle, and that I needed courage for it. I started to collect my thoughts. I crossed my arms, looked at the candle, and, as if challenging someone, I asked myself: "Well, what it is then?"

It seemed to me that my breast was completely empty, and that I listened to the voice of my conscience which asked me: What are you doing to yourself?

"Poor Anna!" I grabbed my chest with my hand, wanting to tear myself apart.

My sister's letter had brought me to a point from where Anna could not be seen.

I began to despair—What should I do?

She renounces her name, nationality, language! All this because of me. She firmly believes that I will marry her. And I?

Everything seemed more and more unclear to me; I had left her and had again looked for her, and had embraced her, and had been ready never to leave her until my death. Then, suddenly, I saw my mother's and my sister's letters from their completely different—completely different life.

I wanted to scream: What shall I do?

Having no idea, I took out a handkerchief and started to clean up the wet table. Then I sat at it and brooded.

"An idea!?" I told myself, joyfully. Write to my sisters and brothers to prepare them, and to see what they will say.

I wrote the letter, whose contents I no longer fully remember, although I know it started with a dream and that, in that dream I painted how I had fallen in love with a German girl, who was not beautiful, who was poor, and who was already 24 years old. I asked them, half-jestingly, what they would do if I married her; what would our mother say to all this, etc. The letter, as I say, was written half in jest, half in earnest; or, rather, in such a way that I could retreat at any time and tell them that all this was a joke and that I wanted to scare them a bit.

Then I put it in an envelope, sealed it, and went to bed; but I could not fall asleep. I tossed about and tortured myself. I strained to reach a decision. Suddenly, I said, "Well, all right, I am going to tell her that I cannot marry her. The thing is ended. Let's get some sleep."

And then another thought quietly entered the cage in which this thought was "firmly" enclosed: "If they would give me some definite answer! . . . Ach, I should not be even thinking about it."

It was all in vain; I could not sleep. I became annoyed, thinking that I had to end it once and for all.

It was no use, I could not fall asleep with the thought of leaving her, and yet had no basis to spin out more pleasant dreams. After long torture, I jumped from the bed and picked up the letter.

"Who knows. . . ." I thought. I got dressed and went to town. Everything was quiet. I walked to the first mailbox and posted the letter. "Who knows?"

"God, why is it so sweet to deceive oneself?"

When I had put the letter in the mailbox I returned home. Two drunk men passed by me, one made faces at me and jostled me. I did not attack him; I did not ask for my "satisfaction," as I would do at some other time (although all of you call me hot-tempered). I kept quiet and walked further. It did not even occur to me that somebody had pushed me deliberately with his elbow. I was preoccupied with the unclear thought: I sent the letter—who knows?

When I again lay down, I felt far more at ease; I don't know why myself. I was not afraid of her picture any more. I was thinking of my walks with her. It occurred to me that she would be abandoning her name, her language, and her religion; that she would do everything I wished. To everything she would answer: "As you say!"

Sleep overtook me; I began to dream. The images were mixed. I saw my sister and the letter. It was 4 o'clock. I started to sink into the deep; everything became more and more unclear to me. "Who knows?"

Since that time I have become very restless. On the one hand, I feel badly that I sent the letter, "for what reason," I asked myself. I know very well what kind of a reply to expect. On the other hand, it seems to me that everything will turn out for the best.

Such has been my attitude towards her these days. At one moment, I avoid her and run away; at another, I look for her, chat with her, walk with her and kiss her, as a gipsy kisses her child.

Why do I tell you this? You can imagine yourself what two people in love can do. At one moment, we start to fight, at another we are reconciled and, again kiss, etc.

But, this must be boring you.

It would be better if I continued.

It happened one evening, approximately two weeks after I sent the letter. Nobody was at home except the two of us.

I sat all afternoon at home and read. In the evening, I got up, opened the window, and looked at the garden, where the wind was reshaping the black ground, which was emanating that humid spring smell. The wind was making paths in the garden. The weather was mild.

I thought of you, needless to say, about myself, and about her. I wondered why I had received no letter, yet I somehow feared I could not allow myself to give an account about my present relationship with her.

I felt someone leaning on my shoulder, I was startled, turned, and saw her.

"Oh, you!" I said happily.

"There is nobody in the house, and I am afraid."

"Well, then sit with me."

I took her by the hand. I led her to the sofa. I sat down first and then ordered her to sit beside me, leaving her so little space that she had to sit half on the sofa and half on my lap. She hesitated at first and then sat down. She tried to get up several times, but I didn't let her. She turned her head away from me:

"Mišo, what are we doing?"

"Nothing bad, my child."

"Mišo," she said bashfully—"What would your mother . . ."

That touched me.

"Keep quiet," I told her.

It must have appeared too serious. She arose slowly and went out on some pretext. I got up to take a walk.

Everything is clear to me now, I said to myself. "I shouldn't lie to her a minute longer. And the letter; it will probably come . . ."

ELEVENTH LETTER

Bosom friend,

I received letters from home and from you. They are similar, except that the one from home is twisted and confused, and the one from you is clear and understandable. And you, also! Well, all right. I won't commit suicide. I am either a coward, or you are too clever.

I agree. I find everything in your letter reasonable and clever. You are an attorney and I a doctor. What do we care if a heart is broken? Let reason live! We are modern people, decent people. We don't sit by the road, expecting rich travelers. We return what we take, as a loan. We are honest! Why do we need virtue. Duty is enough. It's true, what obliges me? People get engaged and then separate in peace, without killing each other. After all, I cannot tell you what I feel. Even great people complain about this, and I don't want to be a great man. I want peace, I want liberty, to spend it without consideration and without enjoyment, as a gambler who today gambles away half his estate without thinking that tomorrow he will be a beggar. I have been wasting my feelings and soon will have none for myself, for you, or for my home. I have firmly decided to break with her. I have to do it, as you have said, for my sake, for your sake, for the sake of home. . . . Well, all right then. Don't think that I don't have courage for that—My God! That will be a good deed! Oh, if my mother could know that I am preparing myself for such a deed, she would pray to God to give me strength. Really, what has poor Anna done? Then, what have I done to Anna, how have I wronged her, and what will I do to her that I should be afraid? I see, and you see, that I will not be happy with her, and it is a clear account.Why delay, eating one's heart out? All the reasons are "for" and one carefree part of the heart is "against." Down with the heart!

But, please, think a bit: What binds me to her? Is there any young man in the world who has not "let love" (had a love affair) from which comes only onion and water? Again, I am only a simple man, and have tasted of that sweetness to which the immortal poets sing odes. Could I be the one to run this awful circle of foolish marriage? Well, I am going to her right now, I will tell her. . . . . I already know what I am going to tell her.

Yours,

TWELFTH LETTER

Leipzig

You can see that I have left my lodgings by the postmark. Well, how shall I tell you. . . . I left the place of my suffering. Everything is ended. I am free. I am free as a bird whose nest was burned and whose young have been strangled. My chains have been undone, but even so my hands are paralyzed.

I don't remember everything in order, or how it all happened. I only know that I was as cold as a diplomat, that I started with "Fraulein," that I mentioned several times "deeper reasons," and that "I should not think only about myself; I should not make her unhappy; I, unstable nature; obligations of my family. My heart knows how I feel, but . . .," etc.

She looked at me, she was as pale as the collar of her shirt. Her eyes were open wide and there was a dry fire in them. When I had ended, after I pathetically recited for the tenth time: "Anna, think it over! Not I, not mine, but your happiness, your tranquility. Say it, after all, if you think that in spite of all this our marriage would ever perhaps have some consequence . . . how can I say it. . . . Think it over—I am nevertheless ready for everything!" She jumped up and leaned on the tips of her fingers on the piano. Her voice was so changed that I shivered.

"Mišo," she said, "all this is so unexpected, that I don't know what to tell you. I don't want pity. You are . . . you are free!"

Then she slumped down on the chair, striking the piano with her elbow and leaning her head on her arm. The strings echoed confusedly without any order, exactly as it was in my head. The lampshade colored the room with a greenish light. The corners were dark. In the next room one could hear deep breathing.

I stood like a convict. "Take it, you criminal," I said to myself, "you deserve much worse."

After about five minutes, she lifted her head, looked at me—so miserable, without dignity, without strength, without masculine pride. Her eyes were wet, cold like a first winter rain, which, unnoticeably becomes ice. And there, behind the eyes, there was something unlimitedly empty, where it was certain, I did not exist any more. I saw that our relationship has been cut off as if by a knife, that I could not now retreat.

I came up to her, knelt before her and took her cold hand, and pressed it to my lips; I was again mumbling something constantly. As I recall, I said, "God is my witness, I never loved anybody as much as I love you, neither will I ever. But think it over. Perhaps all my reasons are invalid and I am a nature to be despised, who is not worth the flame with which you lit me. Can you forgive me?"

She did not pull her hand away. . . .

THIRTEENTH LETTER

Today, exactly two years have passed since Anna died. What hasn't changed since that time! I have become completely different.

My friend, let me cry out a final time.

I am left alone. Ideals and ideas, wide chest and tight shoes, patriotism, work—I would like to laugh at all of that. A year ago I bought a hat, which is now so dirty that it is not unlike the collar of my coat. My books are still in the same trunk in which I brought them when I came. I took only the book with prescriptions and I carry it constantly in my pocket. Chemicals are lying about unused, and only my little nephew toys with them sometimes. Joka found my Azot acid and designed eggs with it for Christmas. Grandmother Maga boiled my knives and now she peels tomatoes and cuts fish with them. Children play with my microscope—they observe flies. They threw away all the strongest lenses; they said they don't see anything with them. Trifun found my surgical gown in the attic and now he puts it on when he curries horses. From my uncut medical journals, which I once received, children make kites and general's hats.

I look at all this. I go regularly three times a day to Cijuk's tavern for a beer and play cards with Jovo—the attorney and with Nikola —the lieutenant. . . .

The children of my sister still love me; they do not leave my room. And my sister—ah, bosom friend.

You tell me: change, man. Shake off the dust, raise your proud head once again . . . I have tried.

My sister took me to a tailor, chose a suit for me, fixed my room, cleaned the microscope and threatened the children that she would spank them if they touched anything of their uncle's.

So, I tried again. I took out several books and placed them on the table. To my patients I gave certain times of the day when I was home, etc., ... The following day it was the same as it was before. I opened the album and looked at her picture, and everything was wrapped in darkness.

The other day, I looked for her picture and couldn't find it any-where. I went to sister's room.

"Sister, did you take her picture?"

She shook her head, bit her lower lip and looked at me to see if I was angry with her.

"And what do you need it for, my sister?"

"Give it to me as a gift," she said.

"Sister, I will give you anything you want, even her picture, if you insist. But what do you need it for? Give it to me, please."

She took the picture from her bosom and gave it to me and burst into tears, putting her head on my chest: "My brother! My brother."

"Don't weep sister," I told her. I took the picture and went out. . . .

Branko Mikasinovich

Janko Veselinović

(1862–1905)

A son of a village priest, Veselinović was born in Crnobarski Salaš, in Mačva. After graduating from a teacher-training school, he returned to his village to teach. Living close to his villagers, he began to write stories about their life and soon published his first collection of short stories, *Slike iz seoskog života* (Pictures of Village Life, 1886). More were to follow; by the end of his relatively short life he had written many stories about life in a Serbian village. He moved to Belgrade, tried to write about the life in capital, but failed. Moreover, the stay in the capital ruined his health. He returned to his village and died in Glogovac in 1905.

Veselinović is best known for his description of the idyllic peasant life. Even though a realist, he idealized his peasants, frequently adding poetic touches to his realistic descriptions. He also drew heavily from the native folklore. Even though he depicted the seamy side of rural life as well, he seemed to prefer its idyllic aspect, as if wishing to arrest the advance of civilization.

His novels are much weaker than his stories. Only *Seljanka* (A Peasant Woman, 1893), a bleak picture of the life of a peasant woman, and *Hajduk Stanko* (The Rebel Stanko, 1896), a semihistorical novel about the first uprising against the Turks at the beginning of the 19th century, have literary merit.

THE KUM'S CURSE*

Villagers, like townspeople, beguile the long winter nights. Some of them either establish themselves around the still which they jokingly call the priest, and there they "make confessions"; or they collect at someone's house and there they drink, sing to the gusle,** talk, and tell stories.

---

*The "Kum" is the godfather at the christening and also the chief witness at the wedding. In Serbia the kum is an object of particular veneration.
**Gusle—a one-string instrument used to accompany recitation of folk poetry.

I once was in such a little village. There was a large company. We had drunk, sung, and talked to satiety. One of the company begged an old man, Ranko Draganović, to tell us something. He twisted his moustaches, drank a glass of wine, drew some thick clouds of smoke from his long pipe, and began to tell this story.

I

In the whole of our village there is not an older man than myself. Whichever one of us is here—I know when he was born. I remember much! I remember when our church was not here and when there was an old one there in the graveyard. I remember when Ravnje was invaded; I was eight years old then. I remember when Lord Miloš was chosen prince, when he was driven out, and when he came again. I remember a great deal. I know when the Turks came over there, when the monks went from village to village and heard confessions and beat the women in order that the women might not deprive them of any cuts of roast meat—and I hated them worse than the Turks.

And today I recollect when the captains began to judge, as they do now, in districts; and when they began to appoint the mayors. Before that there was not a captain; but the village, that is the villagers, proclaimed a man mayor, gave him a staff, and he was mayor after that as long as he was willing to carry on the work honestly. As soon as he began to deal falsely we turned him out and chose another. That is how it was done before, in the old world.

In our village my neighbor Stanojlo Puretić was mayor. He was indeed rich and surrounded with a family, that man! There is nothing of that kind today. He was master, then there were his four brothers, then two of his nephews, then two more and a son unmarried, three marriageable girls, then wives, children; a full house and belongings for half a village. Fields, meadows, pastures and woods. On the fields were stubble or fruitful maize and on the pastures fed whole herds of horses, oxen, sheep, and pigs.

Stanojlo was a tall man, straight as a candle, stout and powerful. One had only to glance at those powerful hands of his to bow before him. He must have been about fifty years old, because he was getting grey. He was extraordinarily strong in character. What he said he did not unsay, even though it might mean the loss of his head. He paid attention to no one; but did everything upon his own judgment.

In his house no one dared to go against his orders. In the community it was the same, because he would get angry then and beat everything he got hold of. He generally carried a whip in his hand and would beat whomever he could reach when he was angry.

There was no master like him in the world. The people and the children were like him, and all like angels. He just got up in the morning— and he got up early—and called:"Milisav!"

The eldest brother came, and he then allotted the work, and each one went off to his task. No one dared to make confusion! Then he washed himself, crossed himself several times, and went to the loft, climbed up into it and gathered maize into a sack. Then he sat down and shelled it, then he went out and fed the little pigs (this was his favorite work). When he came back he called the daughter-in-law who was serving him—she was generally the youngest of the wives. She came and poured water for him, and when she had washed his hands she brought his breakfast. Whether he feasted on dry meat or bacon, or fasted on bean soup, feast or fast, there was always on a little plate a cake white as snow and so supple that it twisted under the knife like a strap. He took his cake, crossed himself, called upon God's name and His Holy Archangels, and bent his head. Afterwards he breakfasted. When he had eaten, his daughter-in-law took away his plate and served him wine. He took out his long pipe, put out his hand for his tobacco pouch that he had made out of a bladder, and filled his precious pipe. His daughter-in-law brought him a live coal and then he smoked.

When you come to his house you are received like a bishop, God forgive me! Just glance at what is done among those people. Stanojlo generally is silent and smokes; but when he wants anything he has only to cough and the daughters-in-law fly as though they had wings! They seek round with their eyes to see what is wanted, for Stanojlo says nothing.

And you, you have only just to mention what you want, and it is before you that instant.

For instance, you would drink boiled brandy. Just say so—and one is free to ask for things in Stanojlo's house—"Bring boiled brandy, my child."

And immediately it is before you, as though the woman had been holding it in her lap like an apple. There, that is how Stanojlo was in his own house.

And in the village? In the village he was as fierce as in his house. Formerly there was no court of justice such as there is today; but the court then was under any leafy tree, either in front of the mayor's house or in the middle of the village. It was there generally that the mayor gave judgment between litigants who came to him with disputes. In our village, just by the cross, there was such a tree. There is none there now.

Stanojlo went out to the cross.* The men who had anything to dispute or complain about, came to him, called upon God and greeted him, then they brought their complaint before him. Stanojlo listened to each one attentively and then said: "Let such and such a thing be done in such and such a way." And so it was.

When it was necessary for us to be collected together either for a conference or for a corvee Stanojlo immediately, the day before the assembly, sent an order to the crier, one-eyed Veljko, and he made it known to the people. He had to call upon the desert places and to be heard throughout the village. And then—just don't come, and see what happens!

Perhaps you would defend yourself by saying that you had not heard. Stanojlo would just look at you and then burst out: "Twenty-five strokes. Veljko told him! He says that he did not hear!"

Beseech, implore, call him your brother, bring down the sky upon the earth, it is no good. What Stanojlo had said must be, even if by reason of his decision he were to go to war with God. Veljko hisses like a serpent and thereafter you scratch yourself well and hear each time when Veljko calls.

When he collected a tax, he marked it all on a tally-stick—and then he knew everyone by name—who had given and how much he had given. And in this also he was violent. He simply said:

"A week from today I wish the tax to be in my hands."

And then he mounted his white horse, seized that cursed whip, and the man who did not give would be whipped as his nobody. Sometimes this meant the man's being sold up to pay the tax. The older men loved this and praised Stanojlo whenever it happened.

---

*Crossroads where a great cross is generally erected.

"This is worth while! That is how to be mayor! He will not let a man be a trouble for long. Be like this or like that. Beat him and let him steam. Afterwards there is no escape. What Stanojlo says must be—like bread if you wish to be satisfied. Assuredly other villages have not mayors like that."

The younger generation did not exactly love Stanojlo. He did not please them because he was too self-willed whether he had or had not the right, but they did not dare to go against the will of the elder ones.

And Stanojlo, he was mayor as he had been proclaimed. No one could have any conception that anyone could be found to oppose him, and yet such a man was found.

II

It was his kum Srećko Soković.

Small, grey, red-faced, with some front teeth missing, but a brisk-walking little old man was Srećko, or as we called him in the village, Uncle-Srećko. God rest his soul. He was a happy little old man. He could never have a discussion with a man without turning around like a weatherglass and beating the ground with his stick. When he, saw that you were attending and were coming around to his opinion he simply did not know what to do for joy. It was as much pleasure to him as though he had obtained God knew what.

Uncle-Srećko was of great importance in the village. When it was necessary to increase anyone's barley, they would immediately call Uncle-Srećko and he then, happy because no wise man was willing to do anything without his advice, would come at once and would speak much on every point and advise that such and such a thing should be done.

He would never actually say in words, however, that he enjoyed this; rather he would be angry, wriggle and throw himself about, and say to each one that he had to leave his work to go there and mix himself up in the affairs of the mayoralty, but in the end he did it for love of the community. We saw, however, how much he enjoyed it, how he thought that with his remonstrance he was concealing his pleasure from us, and we only laughed when he turned his back upon us.

On one occasion, I do not know why, he had a disagreement with his godson, Mayor Stanojlo. Stanojlo advised something and Uncle-Srećko did not approve; but began to prove that Stanojlo's advice was not at all sound. Stanojlo, accustomed to having his advice accepted, could hardly bear this in front of people; and from that moment he hated his kum Srećko and was on the lookout for a suitable opportunity for gratifying his desire to pay him back for his affront.

Uncle-Srećko, again, began gradually to insinuate against Stanojlo, calling him "the self-willed." Whereever people were gathered together talk about Stanojlo began immediately. The younger generation was exceedingly anxious that there should be a discussion with Uncle-Srećko.

Stanojlo heard of this. He went almost mad when they told him of it.

"Why should he alone defy me? Why are the others silent and he alone curses me? He shall pay me for that at once."

So Stanojlo thought, and hardly had he taken this decision when he held back, thinking:

"What shall I do to him? The man is old; and also . . . also he is my kum. Who would dare to do this?"

Day after day he delayed. The men went on with their business. It seemed that Uncle-Srećko was pacified; but again little by little there grew up a murmur against Stanojlo, and Stanojlo again waited for an opportunity to pay his kum Srećko for all this—and that opportunity was given him.

It was exactly on Ognjena Marija (17th July). It was a general custom for the men not to work on that day, but to collect beside the cross and to talk there. Both Stanojlo and Srećko were there with other honest householders. They sat down and talked.

"Who is that?" said Uncle-Jova.

"Mirko," said Uncle-Srećko putting his hand over his eyes.

"Which Mirko? Is it Stojić?"

"Yes, he."

"What is he hurrying like that for?"

"I do not know, God be with me!" said Uncle-Srećko.

And at that instant Mirko was among them.

"God help you!"

"God hear you!"

"What are you doing?"

"Why, we are sitting."

"Why are you so covered with sweat?" Uncle Srećko asked him.

"Well, I was looking for you."

"Me?"

"Yes. Those boys of yours who look after the hedges have let the oxen into my maize and it is all broken down."

"It cannot be!"

"Come and see."

"But how could it be allowed?"

"How indeed. I told you that your palings up to my meadow had been overturned and that you would have to put them up. You know —thanks to God—that that black ox of yours is a thief."

"Yes, yes, and I told the children to look after him, and now they have let him go. There is much damage, you say?"

"Very much, indeed."

Stanojlo's eyes flashed.

"Veljko!" he called.

One-eyed Veljko came up.

"Have you given notice that the people should guard their own stock so that their beasts should not go out and do damage?"

"Yes, truly," said Veljko.

"Did you say that I would punish anyone who should let his stock go to someone else's feed?"

"I did."

"Well, Kum Srećko?" said Stanojlo, hardly concealing his joy at having Srećko so completely under his feet.

"I, godson, I also told my people and, you see, they have let them out."

"And what kind of a head of a family are you if your young people do not obey you?"

"They obey me, godson, but you see, children, they played. See? I will pay what damage there is. I will not repudiate it."

"I know you will pay! You will have to pay. But why should it have happened?"

"But it will not any more."

"You will not dare to let it happen any more! Now, did you hear what Veljko gave out—that everyone who lets his beasts do damage would be punished?"

"I heard it."

"And you did not pay attention, eh?"

"But the children—"

"Veljko. Prepare!"

"What, godson. What?" cried Uncle-Srećko, springing up as though he had been scalded.

"What? Five and twenty, that is what!"

Stanojlo was dreadful. His great eyebrows came down over his eyes, and his eyes shone like two stars. Uncle-Srećko looked at him, looked, and his shirt hardly trembled.

"Five and twenty for whom?"

"For you," Stanojlo hardly answered.

"For me!"

"For you!"

"For this grey hair?" said Uncle-Srećko taking off his cap and holding up a mass of grey hair.

"Yes!"

"For the kum who held you in his arms?"

"For my kum and for my father and for God, and for everyone who does not obey me. Down!"

"I will pay," said Uncle-Srećko.

"Down!" said Stanojlo.

"Down?"

"Down!"

"I will not."

His small eyes blazed and he drew his sword. He looked around him and cried:

"Whoever comes to me is a dead man. Godson Stanojlo, see, I will pay you a ducat for every blow. You see this grey hair. Look! I have become white and have never yet received one blow, and you—you wish to strike me five and twenty times!"

"Yes, I do wish it. Veljko hold him!"

Veljko ran up, struck Uncle Srećko's-hand with his staff and the knife fell down. Veljko bound him by the arms. Men sprang forward.

"What do you want, Stanojlo?" cried Uncle-Jova.

Stanojlo seized his staff, sprang upon Jova and cried out:

"Back! All of you! Veljko, take him to the whipping bench."

The throng drew back. No one dared so much as to look at Stanojlo, or make it his duty to prevent him from doing what he intended! Everything was silenced. It seemed as though you could hear hearts beating. Stanojlo simply shook with joy.

"Not upon your kum and Saint John!" cried Uncle-Srećko when they had brought him to that ill-omened plank known as the whipping bench.

"No, not upon my kum," said Stanojlo in a quasi-peaceful voice, and he took off his cap and put it upon the ground far from himself.

"See. There is our kumship in the cap."

"Godson, let me pay."

"You are going to pay now."

The people turned their heads and looked into the copse. Veljko took Uncle-Srećko, who besought him up to the last moment, and threw him down onto the bench. Then, with special chains, he bound his body to the plank by the arms, legs, and shoulders. He drew back to choose a rod. Uncle-Srećko again pleaded; but Stanojlo lifted his eyebrows, and only said every now and then:

"See, the kumship is in the cap."

III

One-eyed Veljko threw the broken rod away and unbound the old man from the whipping bench. Uncle-Srećko was silent, lying as though there were no life in him. Veljko pushed him from the plank to the ground. The old man sprang up, with bloodshot, weeping eyes; he looked at the assembled people, cast a glance at Stanojlo who avoided his eyes, and at Veljko who stood beside Stanojlo quietly scratching his head, then he cast his eyes down. He was silent for some moments, with his head bent down in that way; his breast heaved with his breathing, and he let his hands fall by his side. All of a sudden tears came to him, and he began to weep. He put both hands before his eyes, came up to the cross and bowed before it. Then he raised his head, looked over the assembled people and spat out:

"Shame upon you! Why did you allow such a thing to happen before your eyes? Truly, you are not men!"

He tore the cap from his head, crossed himself, kissed the cross and cried:

"Almighty God! Hear the voice of thy serf and listen to his prayer!"

Then he looked at Stanojlo. Stanojlo trembled.

"God grant, godson, that sorrow await you for your life. May your happiness be turned to mourning. May your seed be blotted out. And you, hero, may you not die until you fall before me on your knees to seek pardon. You say your kumship is in the cap—and see, you have denied it, and I deny it too. Now we are no longer kums."

Having said this he cast the cap which he held in his hands under his feet and trampled it. Then he passed through the people and went on his way to his house. A breeze played among his hair, white as snow, and the people followed him with their eyes filled with horror.

IV

A dead silence prevailed for some moments. No one uttered a single word. The people just eyed each other as though they were talking with their eyes. Suddenly there began a noise which grew steadily greater and greater. The voice of Uncle-Jova could already be distinguished:

"Men, brothers, can this be?"

"Misfortune!" cried some.

"Scandal!" cried others.

"Shame!" cried a third group.

"How could he—in that way?"

"And God did not see fit to kill him!"

"Nor thunder to consume him!"

"To beat an old man like that!"

"And the kum who had held him in his arms!"

"If he does not pay respect to his kum God will not pay it to him!"

"And is he our mayor?" said Uncle-Jova.

"He must be deposed," groaned the people. "Give his staff here!"

"Give it to Uncle-Jova!" cried the old men.

Stanojlo was standing as though petrified. He did not hear the shouts of the people, but was looking with a long glance after Uncle-Srećko. He did not move his eyelids at all and his eyes were dull and glazed like those of a corpse.

"Stanojlo!"

"Well?"

"The people do not wish you any longer as mayor. Will you give your staff here?"

He looked at Uncle-Jova in such a way that Jova drew back several paces.

"The people do not wish you as mayor!" said Uncle-Jova almost choking.

"They do not wish me?"

"They do not wish you. We do not want you! Give your staff here. You are no longer mayor!" shouted the people.

Stanojlo was silent. Then Ivko Čulobrk went out from the people—a stout and powerful giant. He seized the staff from Stanojlo's hand and cried:

"People, brothers! Here is the staff. To whom do you say we shall give it?"

"To Jova. Uncle-Jova," cried the people.

Ivko held out the staff to Jovan. Jovan took it. Stanojlo was silent with hands drooping beside him.

"You make me mayor, brothers?" asked Uncle-Jova.

"Yes, Jova. Yes Uncle-Jova."

"But, brothers, I am a fierce man."

"But you are not heartless."

"No. That I am not."

"You pay attention both to God and to your soul."

"Well, you know me."

"Yes, we know you."

"But, brothers, I seek to be obeyed."

"We will obey."

"And I shall work again with a conference."

"So. So."

And so they changed the mayor in a moment.

One-eyed Veljko immediately went up to Uncle-Jova.

"What do you want?" Jova asked him.

"But you are the mayor!"

"And Stanojlo?"

"He is not any more."

"But how can you be crier under me? Would you give Stanojlo five and twenty?"

"If you were to order me!" said Veljko.

Stanojlo simply was silent. It was as though he had not heard what was said there, as though this whole discussion did not concern him at all. Bowed at the cross, with limp hands and wrinkled forehead, he meditated upon all that this short moment had brought forth. It seemed as if his crime had bitten into him. Thick sweat flowed from his face and not once did he move his hand or his sleeve to wipe it off. Surely things had not come to such a pass for him. Finally he cast a glance around him. All standing around looked at him with black glances. He understood the position in which he found himself. Surrounded by such a throng he was alone, quite alone. There was not one heart for him there, and that this was hard for him could be seen from his labored breathing. Powerless to command because they would not obey him. Powerless to reconcile them because he himself had not been merciful. Having no power to bear these glances full of hate as well as grief in his heart, he was compelled to move away.

He moved away from the cross. The earth seemed to give way under his feet, he began to stumble. Those same people who a short moment before had trembled before his shadow now looked confidently at him. Already the one-eyed had denounced him, and twos and threes had coughed ironically.

Stumbling he came to the crossroads and stopped. He would have stayed there, but something within himself impelled him to go further. He did not look where he was going—only to go, to flee from this throng, from these people.

He passed along the whole street. Two or three dogs barked at him several times. He went out into the fields and rushed like the wind among the piled-up sheaves and stooks, not going by the path but through the straw.

"What have I done, great sinner that I am! Cursed be my brain. Cursed by my nature, and my morning's morning, and my day's day. What can happen to me—to have beaten my kum who christened me? The kum is greater than the father. He cursed me. What was that he said? 'May your rejoicing be turned to mourning. May your seed be blotted out!' "

"And a kum can curse. God accepts his curse sooner than that of a father or of a mother. What a kum has cursed can never prosper. And I have an only son. I have my Radoje who is as the apple of my eye! He is my happiness and my joy and my fortune—everything. 'May your seed be blotted out!' "

He trembled. Something cold passed over his whole body from head to foot. His knees gave way and he fell like a stone.

"Oh God my Savior, I beseech Thee, preserve, Lord, my only son, my only joy, my house, my fortune, my Radoje! Kill me, me! I am guilty. Oh earth, why do you not open. Strike me with thunder, Lord, strike the ill-omened one who has raised his hand against his kum. But my Radoje, my child, he is still young, green. I beseech you— he—he is—he must still be. I implore Thee, Father of Heaven, pre- serve—!"

There weeping suffocated him. He fell on his knees on the gound and buried his head in his hands. A river of tears rushed to his eyes. These were his first tears since his childhood.

Blessed is the man whose eyes can weep tears. What plaster is to a wound tears are to a sick heart. They carry pain away as wind carries chaff.

He rose. He was rather more quiet; but horror seized him again. He rolled in his walk, thinking:

"What shall I do? I must make my peace with my kum, but how? Who will broach the subject to him? I—I cannot. How shall I come before his eyes? How dare I look at him? Shall I ask the people to make peace between us? No one will! The whole world hates me and God hates me. And I myself hate myself. But I must carry it through before the curse falls upon me. But see, there is no one who could help me! And I myself, if I were to set about it could not finish anything. I am not afraid for myself, if death were to come upon me it would be very welcome. But Radoje—if it were to come upon him!"

Once more despair seized him. He longed to turn his back by force upon these thoughts. He began to think of something else; but came back to his former thoughts. The thought "May your rejoicing be turned to sorrow. May your seed be blotted out" could not be driven out of his head.

The sun had set when he returned to the village. An evening breeze was cooling the fever of the day, the women were standing talking at their doors, children were playing in the road, collecting the dust into little piles.

The affair had already been heard of throughout the whole village and whoever had a mouth was talking of Stanojlo and Uncle-Srećko, in particular the women, for until they had sifted out the whole matter, they could do nothing.

"Have you heard what happened by the cross to our poor friend Srećko?" one was saying.

"Yes, indeed. I heard it at the very moment!"

"May thunder burn him! How could he dare to do it, and actually to his kum!"

"And why did you expect better of him? He is a fiend. I said so to my husband before, when they made him mayor."

"They say that he cursed him."

"He cursed him, yes, what do you expect! It would not help him, thank Heaven, even if he were to go into a monastery and if a hundred monks were to read to him!"

"They say, also, that he violated the kumship, that he denied it!"

"And what do you expect! Why should he not deny his enemy?"

"Quiet, silly one. Here he is!"

Stanojlo walked with bent head, stooping. He went straight by the path.

"Run away, there is the mayor!" said a child.

The children turned around. One, the eldest of them, said:

"The mayor? He is not the mayor now. My father says he is nothing."

Saying nothing to them, he passed through them and went to his house.

V

If thunder had struck the household of Stanojlo Puretić it would not have aroused such consternation as that aroused by the news that Stanojlo had beaten Uncle-Srećko. The men wandered hither and thither and uttered only a hollow sound. The women collected their children around them as brooding hens do their chickens and then caressed and kissed them. Each one looked at her own children with tearful eyes for they knew that it was upon the children that the curse would fall first of all. The brothers of Stanojlo were discussing how the one way of salvation from the curse was to split up the household.

"And we will not, truly, eat any more from the same dish with him, even if he were to die," said Milisav.

"Better to die, brothers, than to see the young ones dying," said Petar.

"I told him not to accept that cursed mayoralty; but he railed at me then and told me to mind my own business," said Kuzman.

"What he has done, let him suffer for himself also," said Djuradj.

"Well, have we decided to split up?" asked Milisav.

"We have decided."

"Who is willing to tell him so?" asked Petar.

"I," said Milisav.

"Why did he bring this upon himself and upon us?" said Kuzman.

"I said from the very first that he was not the man for mayor," said Milisav.

"You said so, and what happened to you? The same as to me," said Kuzman.

"Why isn't he here?" asked Petar.

"I don't know."

"Did he stay by the cross?"

"No. They say that he went out to the woods."

"And he is no longer mayor?"

"No. It is Uncle-Jova now."

"It is dark already. Why is he not here?"

At that moment the gate clicked. They looked up. Stanojlo came in stooping. He passed through them with no greeting and went into the house. All were silent as though cast in a mound. They waited for him to come out; but he did not come.

No one slept that night. The women only sighed and the men were silent, smoking their pipes. The night passed, day had almost dawned. Milisav expected that Stanojlo would call him as usual, and give him orders about the work. He waited, waited, but the summons did not come. Finally he went himself into Stanojlo's room. Stanojlo was sitting on a bench, he had buried his head in his hands, and was silent. His wife Stepanija was standing beside the stove. He did not raise his head when Milisav opened the door. Milisav coughed. Still he did not raise his head.

"Stanojlo!" Milisav called to him.

"Well?" he said, raising his head.

Milisav looked at him. His eyes were bloodshot, his face somewhat more lined, and his hair whiter.

"Come here."

"What shall I do for you?"

"We have something to discuss with you."

"But what?" said Stanojlo transfixing him with his glance.

It was as though someone had caught Milisav by the throat—his voice was so constrained.

"Let me call the others too."

"Call them, then," said Stanojlo.

Milisav went out. Very soon all four came in. Stanojlo rose and told Stepanija to go outside. When they were left alone he asked them in a harsh voice:

"What do you want?"

"We want to split up!" said Milisav.

"To split off from me?"

"Yes, to split off," cried all three.

"I want to say something to you myself."

"What?" they asked.

"That you should go to my kum."

"He is no longer your kum. People say that he renounced the kum-ship. Is that true?"

"Yes, but he—beseech him—"

"And you?"

"I dare not."

"Then why should we?"

"Go, beg him. He will forgive you."

"What do you say, Milisav?"

"I dare not."

"Nor dare we!" said the three. "It would be better to cut ourselves off from you."

"But, I implore you."

"We dare not!"

"We want a division of property," said Djuradj.

"You may have everything!"

"No. Only our shares."

"I need nothing."

"You may not need it but what about Radoje?" said Kuzman.

Stanojlo bowed his head. Then he said:

"Leave him whatever you will!"

"We must think it out well."

"Yes, that is right. Go and discuss it. Here is Radoje."

Stepanija flew into the room as though maddened, shrieking.

"What is it?" they asked her.

"Kum Srećko is dead!"

If a bomb had fallen amongst them they would have been equally overwhelmed. Stanojlo was the first to come to himself.

"Dead? But when?" he asked.

"At dawn," was the answer.

Nothing more was even mentioned of the further preservation of the household. This house was under a curse and they must leave it. The property was quickly divided—no one wished to have the house.

VI

Stepanija had been ill before, and the news of Uncle-Srećko's death struck her down to her bed. She became fearfully ill. Everyone who saw her said she would never leave her bed. Stanojlo was quite struck dumb. The world paid no attention to him, every living person fled from him, and he himself never went among people. From the time when Stepanija fell ill, one of the daughters-in-law in turn came from Milisav's house to keep things in order.

Stepanija grew worse and worse. One evening she closed her eyes forever.

That event to a certain extent reconciled the neighbors to Stanojlo. Amongst us, as you know, there is a custom of inviting guests both on occasions of rejoicing and of mourning, so the neighbors came to accompanying Stepanija to her last home.

The very appearance of Stanojlo astonished them. It was as though he felt that the fulfillment of the kum's curse was beginning. He was convinced that in the course of the year yet another would leave the house for the grave, because the eyes of the dead body were open, and that was a sign that someone else would die. His heart was, as it were, a boiler at the boil. An internal fire consumed him, and what boils inside a man is always visible on his face.

Seeing what condition Stanojlo was in, the neighbors began to pity him, and, the world is the world. It easily forgets today what happened yesterday. What it praised yesterday it will condemn today, and what it blamed yesterday it will praise today. As it is said, "Another day, another custom."

"Why, man, I could never have imagined that a man could change so!" said one.

"And I, brother. But you never know," said a second.

"I know now. Why, here is Stanojlo."

"And he has got thin," said a third.

"And pale," added the first.

"Then, you see, men, that he was not exactly a bad man," said the second.

"Only fierce."

"That is what he is paying for now."

"But, it seems to me that the dead Stepanija's eyes were open."

"Not really?"

"Yes, trully."

"Then another from the house."

"That will be Stanojlo. See how he is already smelling of the funeral cake."

Old Uncle-Ćira shook his head in sign of disagreement.

"What is it, Uncle?"

"I am afraid for the child."

"But the child is as healthy as a dogberry tree."

"There is the curse, my sons. The dead Srećko said, it seems to me, 'May your seed be blotted out!' "

"Yes."

"Well!" said Uncle-Ćira, once more shaking his head.

"Here is Stanojlo."

He came among them and asked them whether they had brandy in their flasks.

They buried Stepanija. Stanojlo gave her everything in order, the funeral feast, the feast on the third day, the feast on the fortieth, the feast at the half year, and the feast at the year. When it was all finished he gave his mind to marrying Radoje. And it was indeed time. The house had been without women for a year, and a house without women—we know what that is!

And that Radoje of his was a fine young man, in the perfection of health and strength. The down on his upper lip was getting black and when a little began to appear on his chin, the falcon shaved it. A good dancer, a good flute player, a good singer, a happy temperament, you could get what you wished from him. The girls forgot the curse that was on him when they saw him.

When he looked at Radoje, Stanojlo began to forget his troubles. He began to go among people again; he even was reconciled with the sons of Srećko.

Stanojlo began to give his attention to girls, and he found one in Selići. The girl was exactly suitable to the man, and in form they were as alike as box trees.

Stanojlo had already invited his wedding guests. There was a flask decorated with a chain of old Austrian coins. He invited also Jovan, the son of Uncle-Srećko, to be kum; but he said his father on his deathbed had made him swear that he would not be kum. He promised, however, to come as a wedding guest.

Stanojlo made Uncle-Jova the mayor, kum. The heart of Stanojlo rejoiced. The feet of the old man became younger. He made preparations, bought furniture and ran around, which did not seem like him.

"O God, thanks be to Thee! Give me still enough life to see and to know that the smoke is twisting from his chimney, and that there will be someone to celebrate my burial. And then, then let me die, for I shall have no more joy to wait for!"

So Stanojlo prayed to God; but, in the midst of that prayer, there darted through his head like a red-hot rod, the kum's curse, and the old man trembled, his nerves died, and he only repeated without any kind of conviction, almost unconsciously, the words: "God is good, He will hear my prayer!"

His first idea again prevailed and as though in opposition to it, he repeated the bitter words. He wished by so doing to beat out from his head the idea that was assailing him.

The actual day came. Stanojlo rose early, and happy and yet sorrowful, wandered through the court. It was one of those beautiful autumn days. The wedding guests were beginning to assemble. The kum came, the best man came, the dever (Radoje's best friend—son of a certain Krsman Petrović, whose name was Sima) and the other gaily-dressed wedding guests. The best man led in the musicians. There was a violin, cymbals, a tambourine and a great drum; but there was no sound. The best man came to Stanojlo after the wedding guests had dined and said:

"Let us start."

"Go ahead. Where are you going, Radoje?"

"I am going to fetch pistols for my best friend."

"Very well, go."

They turned away. There was singing, rejoicing. You should have seen those forty horsemen—all picked men!

Pistols fired, the wedding guests sang, everything resounded, Stanojlo wept for joy. Then, brushing away his tears with his broad sleeve, he said:

"What is the matter with me, that I begin to weep?"

"Why," said the kum, "it is for joy."

"Yes, it is for joy."

"May you not know tears of a different kind!"

"God grant that!"

At that moment there flashed through his head again the kum's curse, and as though to strangle that idea, he sang:

> "The mother sent Mara under the mountains,
> The mother sent her; but Mara did not wish it!
> While I am alive, mother, I will not go under the mountains,
> Under the mountains the Turks often go."

"What can that be, kum?" said Uncle-Jova.

The riders had sprung down from their horses. They rushed to the spot—and there was something to see! Radoje lay dead. In his hand was a pistol.

"How did it happen? What is this?"

The affair became clear immediately.

Radoje had told his best friend Sima to fire the pistol because they were near the girl's house. He obeyed, but the pistol misfired. Radoje told him that the pistol had already been loaded, but that he must pack up the powder beside the flint. He did so; packed it, pulled the trigger, it ignited, and only the gunpowder flared up to the flint. Radoje took the pistol to see whether it was loaded and just as he put the barrel to his mouth, the pistol fired, and he fell dead. The pistol had been filled already, but it was not clean, and the fire kept first of all in the touch hole, and afterwards the gunpowder caught—as was the custom with flintlocks.

Great and small wept. Stanojlo alone had no tears. He stood like a rock—dumb. He put his hands under his belt and looked at his only son as he lay with shattered head, all bathed in blood. Who knows what thoughts turned in his brain! That only he can know who has suffered as Stanojlo had, and, be it said, I would not wish that on anyone.

Stanojlo suddenly turned, drew a second pistol from the belt of the dever, cocked it, put it against his forehead and before they could seize him, fired it. It scattered his brain over those who stood around, and instead of one there now lie two corpses—father and son.

The wedding guests, with open eyes, watched the whole of this scene and when it was over, Uncle-Jova spoke.

"In vain, my children. What must be, must be—and a kum can curse like a mother when she withdraws her breast."

There. That is "The Kum's Curse."

Pavle Popović

Simo Matavulj

(1852–1908)

Matavulj was born in Šibenik, Dalmatia, in 1852. He spent some time in a monastery, later finished a school of education. As a teacher, he served in various villages and towns in Dalmatia, Serbia, and Montenegro. He knew Italian and French well and in his later literary development showed influences of Italian verism and French naturalism. He spent the last years of his life in Belgrade, where he died in 1908.

Like many writers of his time, Matavulj was a strict realist, whose guiding principle was absolute truth and objectivity. In his stories and novels he described both peasants and city dwellers, depicting with cold objectivity the difficult, stifling life of sea fishermen and the middle-class malversations in Dalmatia; the heroic but backward people of Montenegro; and the machinations of the builders and makers in the bustling metropolis of Belgrade. His main collections of short stories are: *Iz Crne Gore i Primorja* (From Montenegro and the Seacoast, 1888, 1889), *Iz beogradskog života* (From Belgrade Life, 1891), and *Iz raznijeh krajeva* (From Various Parts, 1893). His best work, the novel *Bakonja Fra Brne* (1892) depicts in a humorous and satirical fashion the life in a Catholic cloister. His other novel, *Uskok* (Rebel, 1892), describes the heroic struggle of the Montenegrins against the Turks.

Of interest is also Matavulj's autobiographical work *Bilješke jednog pisca* (Notes of a Writer, 1903), in which he recorded his own thoughts and views on life, literature, and art.

POVARETA

Between the town and the island, the calm sea was as smooth as glass in the reflection of the hot sun, which was already sinking in the west. A boat was approaching the island, with two men in it, one rowing, the other sitting at the rudder. And although it was early in April, the sun was burning right in their eyes, and they turned their heads towards the hills, of which the more distant were still capped with snow. The boat was heavy. The rower, a man of middle age, looked more like a porter than a boatman, while the man at the rudder was young, tanned and stalwart, dressed in naval uniform. As they were drawing away from the town, the old man plied him with questions, asking who he was, where he came from, whom did he know, how long had he been in the service, but receiving no answer, at length relapsed into silence. For the young islander, Juraj Lukešić from Krapan, was, like his fellow-islanders, taciturn, and disinclined to be conversational. He simply sat quietly and smoked, looking at the great world around him, and the sea and the sky.

Little by little the outlines of the island became discernible. First they distinguished a wood, and a high bell-tower; that is at one end of the island, while the village is at the other. An age-old pine forest with a monastery distinguish the island of Krapan from all the others.

The ruddy glow behind Krapan suddenly became more brilliant. The gulls began to dip into the surface of the water more frequently, and shoals of dolphins to shoot past the boat. That roused the young man from his reverie.

"In God's name!" he muttered, and took the starboard oar from the old man.

Soon the boat's keel grated on the sands of the landing place and at the same moment the bells of the monastery began to boom out their evening call to service. Juraj sprang ashore and stood for a moment bareheaded, in prayer. And the old man, before pushing off again, raised his cap in respect to the "Lord of Angels."

With quick steps the sailor walked to the street which might be called the main one, as there are two others, but they are side streets and much shorter. The houses are of stone, dark with age, in one or more colors, with medium-sized windows and green shutters. Scarcely one was without a little courtyard for the donkeys and the store of dried old vine-stumps, dug up for firewood. If the young man had been a stranger who had chanced to come to the little island, he would certainly have been startled to find the village deserted, with not a living soul in sight, nor the sound of a human voice, as though a plague had carried off all the inhabitants, and the smoke was rising from deserted hearths. But Juraj never noticed this, for he knew that almost all his folk were in their gardens, which are across the water in the villages of Razina and Jadrtovac.

His home was at the end of the main street. He came to the back and walked quietly around, when he found a little girl of seven or eight standing on a high pile of vine-boughs over by the wall of the yard. When he came towards her, just as though he had fallen from heaven, the child wanted to scream, but the sailor whispered, "Joji!" and put his finger to his lips, and opened his arms, saying:

"Come, jump now, one! two! three!"

The little girl jumped into his arms. Interrupting her kisses, Juraj asked her:

"What were you doing on the wood-pile? And where is Mummy?"

"Mummy is in the kitchen," answered Joji, holding his hand and dancing for joy. "And so you have come home! I jumped down because Miš said I would not dare."

Juraj took her into the yard, saying:

"You should not jump from so high, that is not good for little girls. And Miš is a young rascal to dare you. Come along now, quietly, and let's give Mummy a surprise."

"Let us jump at her," whispered Joji.

Juraj stood at the door behind the ground floor room, which occupied the whole length of the house. The two windows opposite were wide open and that gave light enough. His eyes took in everything; all was in its own place, just as he had left it, almost the same as his ancestors had left it: the shelves with the pots and pans, two big walnut chests, and a long oak table, with a large crucifix above it, a bench and some three-legged chairs. His glance rested on the outline of a woman who, near the hearth, had turned her face towards the fire. Juraj gave a little cough, the woman turned round, stood still a moment, and they met between the windows.

They exclaimed at once:

"In God's Name, Juraj!"

"Mother! Dear mother!"

After a first embrace, they gazed into each other's eyes, those small, clear, blue eyes which each generation in our islands hands down faithfully to the next, just as they transmit the short head and rounded face, joy of life, sturdy faith, lack of imagination and restricted vocabulary. Juraj's mother, Luca, looked more like his elder sister, hardly ten years older, certainly not more. They both had the slightly blunt nose, short rounded chin, rosy and white cheeks. In fact, almost the only difference between them lay in the earrings, which the mother wore in both ears, but the lad only in the right one.

Then they began a whole series of questions and answers, all beginning with "Why," as the islanders do when they are moved.

"Why, how are you, mother?"

"Why, I am well enough, Juraj, and how are you?"

"Why, I am fit and well. And how is dad?"

"Why, dad is quite well too."

"Why, how is Miš?"

"Why, Miš is well too, and quite grown up."

The mother was silent a moment, and took the biggest three-legged chair, which for centuries had been the special one of the head of the family, and dragged it near the fire. The lad sat down, and began to roll a cigarette. His mother began to scrape some fish in a bowl.

Luca stooped low over her work and when she spoke again, her voice was shaky, as though very tired.

"But you wrote that you would not come for another ten days."

"Yes. I took you in . . . to give you a little surprise."

"And have you been right round the world?"

"Not quite round, but a very long way, right away to America."

"And have you seen all sorts of countries?"

"All sorts."

"And black men?"

"Yes, and yellow too . . . And has the harvest been a good one?"

"No, hail spoiled the grapes and we had only thirty barrels of wine and six of oil."

After another pause, Juraj said:

"Why, what news is there?"

As his mother did not reply at once, he added:

"And what news of Marica? Well, mother?"

"Not good news, my son," muttered his mother in reply.

Juraj sprang up and cried:

"Lord of Angels! What is it?"

"It is not good news, no—no—," repeated the woman, shaking her head, with a deep sigh.

"By Christ's Passion! mother, what is the matter? Why don't you speak? Is she ill?"

"She has been. . . ."

"What—dead?"

"Yes. . . ."

Juraj sank upon his chair. Livid, he stared aghast at his mother for a moment, and could scarcely utter: "Is it really true?"

"Yes," affirmed his mother, wiping a tear from her eyes. For a long time the lad sat and sobbed, exclaiming:

"Oh, mother! Oh, mother!"

At length he asked:

"By Jesus' Wounds! What was the matter?"

"A tumor formed under the right arm. Old Matija took her to the town to the doctor, but he at once said, 'It is not well.' Then Matija took her to the wise women, old Grmina, and she said, 'It is not well.' Then Matija performed a vow and walked barefoot to the Lord of Angels. But nothing availed. It is now eight days since her sweet young body lies rotting in the blessed earth."

"Her—Oh, mother! Have you been to the poor girl's grave?"

"God help you, my poor boy! Except myself, no one knows that you had chosen her; nor did she herself, poor child, know."

"Povareta! Povareta!" cried Juraj, burying his face in his hands. "My poor little girl! And she never knew that I had vowed my soul to her, that I was ever thinking of her, on the sea, in America, and even when on duty. Look, yesterday in the town I bought a ring for her."

He stood up and out of his breeches he took a box with a golden ring, which he handed to his mother. And again he sat down and wept.

"Mother, mother, I will die too."

"God help you, crazy child!" cried Luca, putting the ring into the deep pocket of her skirt. "And are you a Christian or have you turned Jew? Are you going to work against God's will? Come, here come our men. It would be a shame if you did not go to meet them. And it would be a greater shame if men knew why you are mourning, for you never claimed her hand, nor is it known that you intended to when you came home. Say your prayers for her soul, and go to meet the boats."

She brought a basin of water, and he washed his hands and bathed his eyes, and rather abashed, taking his little sister, went out by the same way he had come.

The little landing place was already full of craft and resounded with men's cries and donkeys' braying, for every "gayeta" of Krapan (that is a boat of over a ton, with the bows decked over), carried a donkey laden with firewood. It was Saturday, so the men were returning rather late.

His heart froze when among the first he saw Matija wearing a black cap, and his two daughters with black veils. He felt it keenly when one of them recognized him and called out:

"See, that sailor, why, it is Aunt Luca's Juraj!"

That was Pava Tanfara, Marica's sister, and very much like her.

As all were busy collecting their tools and getting their donkeys ashore, hardly anybody noticed him, but he quickly scanned them all, the Grms, Lukešićes, Jarans, Tanfaras, Prebundas, Jugars, with all their families and young men, and then he felt he must cry out: "And where are you, Loveliest Flower of Krapan, Marica Tanfara? Where are you, coming from your garden, that I may hear your little silver voice, and gaze upon your slender figure, that white face and those dear black eyes?"

Marko Lukešić had made his boat fast when his son came up to him from behind. The "old man," lean and tough, about forty-five years old, was dragging his donkey Rižan by the halter, while Miš was pushing his hindquarters. It was vain for Joji to keep calling out: "Juraj has come home! Here he is!" Neither of them turned their head until Rižan had jumped ashore with his load. Then Miš, a lively lad of sixteen, embraced his brother and refused to be separated from him. But Marko simply shook hands with Juraj, holding out a grimy fist, saying:

"Hullo! A little surprise, eh? And how are you?"

"I am well enough, dad," answered Juraj, shaking his father's hand. "How Miš has grown!"

"Like a weed," said the man, and he held a burning match to Juraj's face before lighting his pipe. After a puff or two, he put his hand on Juraj's shoulder and said:

"Well, what is all the trouble about?"

"Why, dad?"

"Because your face is white and pale, and your eyes all red. Why, young Jurega, who came home from the navy six weeks ago, told us that you were as red as a rose."

"I have not been quite myself since yesterday."

The villagers began to pass them, and even in the dark his uniform attracted attention. Voices could be heard saying: "Is that young Juraj?" "Why, yes, it is Juraj," and "Hullo, Juraj, how are you?"

As a matter of fact, Marko never hurried, even old Rižan the donkey knew this and when the crowd had passed by, he went on alone. Joji and Miš took their brother by the arm, while the father, crunching the gravel as he walked, began to tell his son all about the past summer, about their work, what they had spent, and all the little details of their daily life, which had occurred during the five and twenty months of the lad's absence.

Luca was waiting for them in front of the house. On the bench there was a big earthen basin of water and towels. The children took Rižan to unload him and bed him down, but Marko quickly stripped off his jacket, waistcoat and shirt, bent his swarthy frame over the basin, showing all his ribs and spine. He washed his hands first, and then his face with clean water, and then his neck again with fresh water. When his wife had scrubbed and dried his back, he ran indoors and put on clean clothes. Miš did the same, only Joji rubbed his shoulders.

On the supper table there were a bowl of greens, a dish of fried fish, crumbs of barley bread, and a jug of "bevanda" or wine mixed with water.

Luca took from the foot of the crucifix two chaplets, giving one to her husband. All five of them turned to the sacred emblem, while the father said aloud: "In the Name of the Father, and of the Son, and of the Holy Ghost, Amen." Then they all repeated together the Lord's Prayer, the Hail Mary, and the other prayers that make up the rosary. This lasted about a quarter of an hour.

Supper lasted about twice as long. Nobody spoke. Luca nudged Juraj, who tried hard to swallow a few mouthfuls. Marko solemnly chewed each mouthful, resting his tired head on his palm. Only when they first poured out the wine, he looked quickly at Juraj, then at his wife, then took a drink, and finally said:

"Why, in God's Name, what a fine fellow this boy of ours is! What a grand young gentleman! Just wait a bit until we put a hoe in his hand."

All drank from the same jug, and then at a sign from the mother, the young folk went upstairs to bed. Luca brought a smaller jug and a glass, and when she poured it out it was obviously pure wine, black and thick. Marko drank to his son, "Welcome home!" and emptied his glass. Luca herself then drank half a glass to his welcome home, and stood the jug and glass before her son. At the same time his father put a pipe in front of him, filled it, and said:

"You spent the night in Zadar on the spree, I can see that; and today you had a good drink in town. Anybody can see that, eh?"

"Why?" asked the lad, forcing a smile.

"And what the devil did you see in America?"

"How do I know, dad? An order comes, and then it is forward! In front of us was a cruiser, the *Maria Teresa*, bound for Australia, a full six months' trip."

"And he has seen black and yellow men," added his mother, drumming on the table with her fingers.

"And do you really believe all the sailors tell you?" asked Marko, turning his head towards the ceiling with a yawn. "They are full of lies. But tell me, how much have you saved?"

"Fifteen thalers, father," answered Juraj.

"That's not much. Roko Tanfara brought back twenty. Give me another, and then to bed, and tomorrow after prayers, go and pay a visit to your uncle Josa and aunt Marija."

"Naturally," put in the mother.

As soon as his father had drunk his glass of wine, he stood up and lazily went out. Luca lit a little oil lamp and followed her husband. Juraj rested his head on his elbows, and remained in that position. From the room above there began to penetrate the deep and rhythmic snoring of his parents, which completed the picture of daily domestic life. Juraj, his head entirely occupied with one dreadful sentiment, began to listen attentively to the snoring. That everyday occurrence seemed to him something mysterious that marked the passage of the night, of everything that passes away forever, and he began to count the snores. He counted a hundred, two hundred, when a loud noise and a hoarse voice startled him from his reverie. Their cock was the first to decide to break the stillness of the village, and then the rest joined in rivalry.

As soon as all was quiet again, a terror gripped Juraj, and he remembered all the tales of his childhood, how the white graves around the Lord of Angels opened and the dead came out, especially the newly buried who had not yet grown accustomed to the solitude. There was the poor girl, Marica, who never knew of his love, who had only learnt that very evening, and was now hurrying to him to receive the ring. A flame played upon the table, something crackled among the sparks, and Juraj, in terror, sprang to his feet. But that lasted only a second, for his real character, his farming and seafaring strength, overcame his momentary weakness, and with bowed head he began to recite prayers for her soul. Then he sat down again, put his weary head on his folded arms, and fell asleep.

Luca, as usual, was the first astir, and found her son thus. She lit the fire, brewed coffee, put it before him, and gently pushed him. The lad stood up, and looked sleepily, half-unconsciously at his mother. At last he took out his handsome new metal tobacco box, put some tobacco in a paper, rolled a cigarette, and began to puff. His mother sat opposite, with lowered eyes, tapping with her fingers on the table.

"Mother, I will not go out today."

"Not even to church?" she asked, without raising her eyes.

"Nowhere. I will lie down in the little room, and you can tell people that I am ill."

"That would be a sin. I had a dream last night, just before waking, at the dawn, when God sends dreams."

Luca really wanted Juraj to ask what her dream was, but as she did not hear his voice, she continued in a low monotonous tone, her eyes downcast:

"I dreamt of the poor maid, of the Povareta. She came to me to the house when I was alone, at dusk. She came, poor child, pale and weeping, with her poor arm in bandages. She led me to the window, and with her whole arm pointed out to the sea, and to a great ship upon it, and you were on the ship. And she, poor girl, said sobbing, 'There he is! He is coming! But I cannot . . . this poor arm drags me down, down to the very depths. Let him take Pava!' "

Luca ceased, wiping her eyes upon her sleeve.

Long they were silent; then the mother raised her eyes, and looked at his face, on which there was gradually returning the joy of living.

At length he asked in a broken voice:

"Is that true, mother?"

"Yes, my son, and my witness is the blessed Lord of Angels."

"Well, mother, let God's will be done . . . Povareta . . . Poor child . . . Poor little girl . . ."

Pavle Popović

Stevan Sremac

(1855–1906)

Although Sremac was born in the Vojvodina city of Senta, he spent most of his life in Serbia proper. After graduating from the University of Belgrade, he served as a high school teacher in Niš and Belgrade. He died accidentally of blood poisoning in Sokobanja in 1906.

Sremac was a prolific writer of short stories and novels. A conservative by conviction, he attempted to revive the old historical legends in many of his early stories. His best works, however, deal with contemporary life in Niš, Belgrade, and Vojvodina. His best novels of provincial life, *Ivkova slava* (Ivko's House Patron Day, 1895), *Limunacija na selu* (Fireworks in the Village, 1896), *Pop Ćira i pop Spira* (Father Ćira and Father Spira, 1898), *Vukadin* (1903), and *Zona Zamfirova* (1907), are characterized by conventional realism, humor, and satire. Because of their high dramatic quality, many of these were later dramatized. Sremac's characters are usually small merchants, clerks, priests, artisans, and just simple people in small Serbian towns. A realist and a sharp observer, he was able to point out the changes sweeping Serbian society into a new era. Some of his stories dealing with the vanishing way of life that had persisted for centuries have an unforgettable nostalgic flavor. But it is his humor for which Sremac is best remembered. He is considered one of the best truly humorous Serbian writers.

IVKO'S SLAVA[1]

(Excerpt)

The carousing guests again remained alone. In the yard they made a regular tent out of a rug and moved into it. By now they had officially

---

Slava is a traditional Serbian family holiday honoring one of the saints. On this day the doors are open and everybody can come in and partake of the feast. On Ivko's *slava*, St. George's Day, several guests, among them an unknown person, refused to leave after two days of feasting. When Ivko protested, they moved into the yard.

usurped all the unfortunate Ivko's authority and rights, thus terminating his function as a host. The kitchen, the cellar, the food storage —everything was in their hands. Kalča took out his gun and cartridges and was killing chickens, while Kurjak, with the help of a drafted apprentice from the neighborhood, was plucking them, putting them on a spit, and roasting them. Everybody was busy. Kalča left for a short while (and then only with their permission), to run home quickly. Remembering, as a good family man, his dog Čapa, he went to fetch him. Čapa would be busy in the yard for three days.

"May I run home for a minute to get Čapa?" he begged. "It's three days since we've seen each other, and you haven't seen him either, so let me bring him. May I?"

On the way he would invite some other people to the *slava* and would send Gypsies over, should he run into some.

When he came back with Čapa, everybody rejoiced at the sight of the dog and greeted him; he, too, greeted them in his fashion, that is, wagging his tail. Immediately thereafter, he went to the corner where many leftovers had been thrown, quickly became lost in "business," and did not bother to come over here any more.

In the afternoon of the third day, Ivko started for his home to make a last try, firmly resolved to send the "guests" away and get them off his chest, either with cajoling words or, if necessary, with force. And it was time! For, there had been no such carousal since Homer's time—then, in Ithaca, and now, in Ivko's home on April 23, 24, and 25. The pals took over in Ivko's house in the same way Penelope's suitors did in Ulysses' home. But, to Ivko's shame, Penelope's suitors treated themselves at least while Ulysses was away, whereas these here were doing it while Ivko was alive and present—and that was disgraceful indeed!

Upon arriving he entered his home slowly and cautiously.

"Oho, hi *pobratim*,"* yelled those in front of the tent.

"It's my *slava* and you're nowhere to be found. Sit down, *pobratim*. Make yourself at home," shouted Smuk, who only now had thoroughly begun to feel the effects of drinking.

Ivko stopped and looked at them.

---

*Pobratim is the best friend, almost like a brother. However, it can be used jocularly sometimes, as it is done here.

"People, have you ever seen that—my wife isn't here. Where are you coming from, *pobratim*?" Smuk asked him.

"I came from the market," Ivko muttered.

"Since you are coming from there, for God's sake, have you seen my wife somewhere?"

"She is sitting at home like a good wife should and not like her husband, like you."

"But where is she if she is at home?" Smuk insisted.

"At her own home, where else?"

"But whose house is this, nitwit?" Smuk asked grinding his teeth because it seemed to him that Ivko wanted to take away "his" house from him.

"Why, it's mine, mine! What d'you think! Mine only. Not even this much"—and he pointed at the black under his fingernails—"is mortgaged anywhere."

"What, this is your house?" Smuk wondered aloud. "People, did you hear the crazy man say this is his house? And where's mine?"

"Well, your house is on your street."

"Man, three days I haven't stepped out of my house here, and he is teaching me which is mine! My Ivko, my poor *pobratim*," Smuk felt sorry for him. "You better go and take a nap. Why d'you drink if it doesn't agree with you! And whose is this street?"

"It's my street!" Ivko said.

"Yes, yes, brother, yours the house, the street, the town, all Serbia is yours, too. Everything is yours, but we have nothing. Neither I nor Kurjak, nor Kalča, nobody has anything—only Ivko, the quilt-maker, is rich. And we're homeless gipsies. Thanks, thanks, *pobratim* Ivko, for what we have received from you."

Ivko let out a groan and fell silent. He began to pace for a while in his yard, and suddenly returned as if a clever thought had occurred to him.

"Well, I was only joking."

"It was no joke. I don't allow any one to make fun of my home. That's not for jokes."

"Well, I admit it's your house, yours alone, there."

"It is!" Smuk affirmed resolutely. "Mine, and how! With this here gun I'll kill every one who dares to take it away from me. Your house!

Are you my wife's brother that I should share it with you?" Smuk finished and put the gun across his knees.

"It's yours, brother, yours," Ivko condescended. "I only came to take you to my house a little. C'mon, company! C'mon, drop in on me for drinks and eating!"

"Where to?" some asked him.

"To my house, didn't I say?"

"Well, let's go!" said Kalča and the Unknown.

"No, no," Smuk refused. "I'm not like Ivko. He chases away his guests, but I don't let them go. I'm a different man. To die together, if need be!"

"To die all together!" Kalča chimed in.

"Whoever moves one step from here will be shot down with this gun," Smuk was grinding his teeth. "Everybody stay here! Let Ivko go; he never was for company anyway," he added contemptuously.

"Please, *pobratim*, just one word," Ivko begged.

"Don't 'please' me for nothing. I'm not chasing you away as you're doing to us, but don't try to snatch away my quests, if you still like to live," Smuk told him. "And what I've gotten from you after so many years of friendship I regret very much. . . . That I won't forgive you 'til I'm dead! Pour, Kalča! You are serving a gentleman, not a freeloader."

"Ho, ho, *pobratim*-Ivko," Kalča laughed at him, "you won't find a rabbit in that bush."

Ivko realized that he had gotten the short end again and that that gunpowder did not catch fire, so to speak. He left them alone and again began to walk around in the yard looking in a daze at its disarray. Without thinking he reached down and lifted a velvet collar, a cuff and a piece of somebody's cane. He turned around, looked at everybody and saw that no one was missing a collar. Who, in God's name, has forgotten this collar and broken his cane! Ivko asked himself. Did he drop his collar when he was being held back or thrown out? And who broke the cane and on what? It was no use asking them; who knows what they'll answer him? And devils know whether they've seen it at all or whether they still remember it. We might never find out, Ivko thought walking perplexed, with his head lowered. He was looking at the velvet collar and he became ashamed on account of his nasty neighbor Jordan, who even today was busying himself around the fence, sowing the morning-glory.

"*Pobratim*," somebody called, "come here for a glass of wine. We have washed the glasses to drink better."

"You leave me alone!"

"Well, go, go if you want to!" they all yelled back at him.

Ivko started to beseech anew: "Please, brothers and friends, I beg you! Are you Christians and Serbs, or are you Turks or Tartars or something? Of what faith are you? Leave my house, that's all I'm asking of you."

"Well, well, listen to him talking!" Smuk sneered firing his gun in the air. "And since when is this house yours?"

"Since the day before yesterday it's no longer mine, I can see that," Ivko said. "Brothers, it's too much."

"Too much is only when one is beating you," the Unknown answered and emptied his glass.

"You keep quiet, you bald devil!" Ivko shot back, but then calmed himself, took up a modest pose and continued: "Go away, haven't you had enough?!" He began to count on his fingers: "You came, sat down, drank, ate, and drank again; you ate supper, breakfast and drank again; you slept, fired you guns, killed my chickens, beat my servants, upset the neighborhood, turned the house upside down, put me to shame. . . . What else do you reckon to do? Are you Christians? Do you have a soul? I am not a rich man to afford such levy."

"No, no," everybody shouted, "you just go away!"

"Who is to go away?" Ivko flared up again. "Me? Well, you'll leave here, and singing! You'll jump like young brides when I summon the neighborhood . . . and my boys and servants. Then I'll see what you'll do."

"To summon whom? Whom, man, speak!" Kalča roared at him. "Blood will flow like in olden times at Ćele-kula, if that's what you want. I'll kill you off like a rabbit with this gun. Your feathers will fly all over the yard and neighborhood, like from a partridge, when I take aim with this here gun."

"Well . . . you don't want to leave?"

"We won't!"

"Then I'll go and report you to the police."

"Have a nice trip!" Kalča laughed at him. "You are frightening

a bear with a mouse. Ha, ha, ha . . . You won't catch a rabbit in
that bush."

"O dear, what am I to do?" Ivko moaned walking off. "To complain—nobody'll believe me. I am ruined, through and through."

He went straight for the gate and began to pace to and fro in front
of the house thinking hard and mumbling to himself: "To whom
am I to tell of my disgrace! Is there in the whole world a complaint
for something like this?" Then he returned. "Will you leave my house
so that there'll be no scandal, neither about you nor about me?"

"We won't! We'll stay here," Kalča said.

"I beg you like this," Ivko pleaded taking off his cap and placing
it before his feet on the ground. "Go home!"

"What are you talking about?" Kalča yelped. "Don't even mention
it, Ivko. Stand behind that corner over there and don't come into
the yard with those words 'cause you'll be killed . . . you'll be as good
as dead!" Kalča added loudly and took the gun from Smuk.

"God, am I to get killed on my *slava*?" Ivko lamented at the top
of his voice, involuntarily stepping back behind the corner as if behind some demarcation line. "Why should I die? Go away!"

Kalča shouted even louder: "The books will be written and read
about us: how *pobratim* killed *pobratim* and how a host was killed
on his *slava*, see?"

"Killed!" Ivko shuddered peering from behind the corner. "and
why killed?"

"Who killed him? the people will ask later.—Kalča, his *pobratim*,
killed him because he was ashamed of their company and did not
uphold his own *slava*.—Good that he killed him, they'll say, may
his hand be consecrated. It was not Kalča that killed him, it was his
own *slava*. Didn't our ancestors, they'll say, respect and preserve
slava for five hundred years, even in those violent times, so that we,
Serbs, can be distinguished from the Greeks, Armenians, even Bulgarians? . . . And he to fritter it away in these free times! He had it
coming to him, he deserved it, people will say. Kalča is not a heathen.
Kalča did not kill a *pobratim*, he killed a mutt," he finished in the
highest voice, rolling his bloodshot eyes and grinding his teeth.

"O St. George!" exclaimed Ivko, who was listening to all this
behind the corner, beating his chest, "you caused all this. And now
you keep mum instead of saving me. What tough luck I have! There

is none other like me in the whole wide world. What should I do, to whom should I complain?" he wailed and started to go but immediately returned and stuck his head from behind the corner.

"I am asking you for the last time . . ."

"Not even a step this way!" Kalča shouted and aimed his gun, "otherwise you're dead this very minute."

"How long are you going to quarrel like gipsies?" a voice of he Jordan, the neighbor, was heard. "What is this, fellows? Were two days not enough for you? Are we in a gipsy camp—so much shouting, arguing and scolding. I am a regular taxpayer . . ."

Ivko grunted. "Well, now I know it. It's to die, isn't it?"

"Why should I waste gunpowder for nothing. I'll sick Čapa on you," Kalča said and put the gun aside. "These shoes are killing me," he added taking off his shoes and putting on Ivko's slippers. "Your troubles are only beginning cause I need to loosen up a little."

"Ah, you stubborn oafs!" Ivko threatened again starting off and buttoning his coat angrily when he saw how Kalča was making himself comfortable. "If you don't understand plain language, I'll see what you'll do when the cops come. If you want force, I know how to use it well, too."

"U-a-a-a-a! Sick on him!" it resounded from the yard. Kalča fired his gun after Ivko, who ran straight for the police hall.

"Did you see how ashamed he is of our company, the good-for-nothing mongrel!" Kalča swore.

"U-a-a-a-a! After him!" Ivko heard the howling behind him even though he was already quite far from his house.

Vasa D. Mihailovich

Vojislav Ilić

(1862–1894)

Ilić, the son of a well-known poet, was born in Belgrade. He failed to finish school and was forced to take various small clerical positions. Living for the most part in poverty, he wrote poetry extensively and soon became the leading Serbian poet in the last decades of the nineteenth century. As so many Serbian artists of his time, he died young, of tuberculosis, in 1894.

His poetry represents a welcome change in the romantic poetry prevalent before him. He enlarged the thematic scope of Serbian poetry, and introduced formal innovations. He was especially successful in achieving harmony between idea and form. His poems can be classified into several distinct groups: elegiac poems; highly realistic descriptive poems, at times resembling prose descriptions; poems with love themes; patriotic poetry; social and satirical poems; and poems with classical motifs, in which Ilić tried to imitate the classical hexameter. The main characteristics of his poetry are intimacy and directness, depiction of nature as inspirational force, strong employment of sensory perceptions, and a firm control of form.

Ilić has influenced many poets immediately following him, thus paving the way for higher achievements in Serbian poetry in the first two decades of the twentieth century.

IN LATE AUTUMN

Hear how the wind through these our desolate pastures is howling,
  Rolls thick layers of mist down to the watery dale . . .
Hark to the croak of the raven who rises and circles above me;
  Dark is the sky, like a veil.

Hurrying, the colt, all drenched, snorts loud as he enters the village;
  Ancient and wretched indeed is the dwelling he now has spied.

There on the threshold the dame stands calling the rain-sodden poultry;
  Monstrous and shaggy of tail paces the hound at her side.

Saddly the wind through the gloomy and desolate pastures is whistling,
  Rolls thick layers of mist down to the watery dale;
Hark to the croak of the raven who rises and circles above me;
  Dark is the sky, like a veil.

Oliver Elton

Radoje Domanović

(1873–1908)

Born in the village of Ovsište, Serbia, Domanović graduated from the University of Belgrade and spent his life teaching high school. Because of his liberal and critical views and his opposition to the prevailing political system, he was persecuted by the authorities. Only in the last years of his short life did he enjoy peace. He died mentally ill in his thirty-fifth year.

Domanović is the best Serbian satirist. Interested in politics but also a talented short story writer, he lashed mercilessly at the wrongdoings and excesses in the political and social life of a society trying to find itself. In his allegories he castigated the ruthlessness of the authority and obsequiousness of its subjects (*Stradija*—The Suffering; *Danga*—The Stigma), incompetent leadership (*Vodja*—The Leader), and false promises for a better future (*Kraljević Marko po drugi put medju Srbima*—Kraljević Marko for the Second Time Among the Serbs). Thus Domanović satirizes not only the political conditions of the day but also some universal human weaknesses—a quality that has made his prevalently topical political satire retain its appeal to this day.

THE LEADER

"Brothers and friends, I have listened to all your speeches, so I ask you now to listen to me. All our deliberations and conversations aren't worth anything as long as we remain in this barren region. In this sandy soil and on these rocks nothing has been able to grow, even when there were rainy years, let alone in this drought the likes of which none of us has ever seen before.

"How long will we get together like this and talk in vain? The cattle are dying without food, and pretty soon we and our children will starve too. We must find another solution that's better and more sensible. I think it would be best to leave this arid land and set out into the world to find better and more fertile soil because we simply can't live like this any longer."

Thus an inhabitant of some infertile province spoke once in a tired voice at some meeting. Where and when that was does not concern you or me, I think. It is important to believe me that it happened somewhere in some land long ago, and that is enough. To be honest, at one time I thought I had somehow invented this whole story, but little by little I freed myself from this nasty delusion. Now I firmly believe that all I am going to relate really happened and must have happened somewhere and sometime and that I could never by any means have made it up.

The listeners, with pale, haggard faces and blank, gloomy, almost uncomprehending gazes, with their hands under their belts, seemed to come alive at these wise words. Each was already imagining that he was in some kind of magic, paradisaical land where the reward of backbreaking work would be a rich harvest.

"He's right! He is right!" whispered the exhausted voices on all sides.

"Is this place nea . . . r . . . by?" a drawn-out murmur was heard from a corner.

"Brothers!" another began with a somewhat stronger voice. "We must follow this advice immediately because we can't go on like this any longer. We have toiled and strained ourselves, but all has been in vain. We have sown seed that could have been used for food, but the floods came and washed the seed and soil away from the slopes so that only bare rock was left. Should we stay here forever and labor from morning to night only to remain hungry and thirsty, naked and barefooted? We've got to set out and look for better and more fertile soil where hard work will yield plentiful crops."

"Let's go! Let's go immediately because this place is not fit to be lived in anymore!" Whispering arose, and each began walking away, not thinking where he was going.

"Wait, brothers! Where are you going?" the first speaker started again. "Sure we must go, but not like this. We've got to know where we're going. Otherwise we might end up in a worse situation instead of saving ourselves. I suggest that we choose a leader whom we'll all have to obey and who'll show us the best and most direct way."

"Let's choose! Let's choose somebody right away," was heard all around.

Only now did the arguing arise, a real chaos. Everybody was talking and no one was either listening or able to hear. They began splitting up in groups, each person mumbling to himself, and then even the groups broke up. In twos, they began taking each other by the arm, talking, trying to prove something, pulling each other by the sleeve and motioning silence with their hands. Then they all assembled again, still talking.

"Brothers!" suddenly resounded a stronger voice which drowned out all the other hoarse, dull voices. "We can't reach any kind of agreement like this. Everybody is talking and nobody is listening. Let's pick a leader! Whom among us can we choose? Who among us has traveled enough to know the roads? We all know each other well, and yet I for one wouldn't put myself and my children under the leadership of a single person here. Rather, tell me who knows that traveler over there who's been sitting in the shade on the edge of the road since this morning?"

Silence fell. All turned toward the stranger and sized him up from head to toe.

The traveler, middle-aged, with a somber face which was scarcely visible on account of his beard and long hair, sat and remained silent as before, absorbed in thought, and tapped his big cane on the ground from time to time.

"Yesterday I saw that same man with a young boy. They were holding each other by the hand and going down the street. And last night the boy left the village but the stranger stayed here."

"Brothers, let's forget these silly trifles so we won't lose any time. Whoever he is, he's come from far away since none of us knows him and he most certainly knows the shortest and best way to lead us. It's my judgment he's a very wise man because he's sitting there silently and thinking. Anyone else would have already pried into our affairs ten times or more by now or would have begun a conversation with one of us, but he has been sitting there the whole time quite alone and saying nothing."

"Of course, the man's sitting quietly because he's thinking about something. It can't be otherwise except that he's very smart," concurred the others and began to examine the stranger again. Each had discovered a brilliant trait in him, a proof of his extraordinary intelligence.

Not much more time was spent talking, so finally all agreed that it would be best to ask this traveler—whom, it seemed to them, God had sent—to lead them out into the world to look for a better territory and more fertile soil. He should be their leader, and they would listen to him and obey him without question.

They chose ten men from among themselves who were to go to the stranger to explain their decision to him. This delegation was to show him the miserable state of affairs and ask him to be their leader.

So the ten went over and bowed humbly. One of them began talking about the unproductive soil of their area, about the dry years and the misery in which they all found themselves. He finished in the following manner:

"These conditions force us to leave our homes and our land and to move out into the world to find a better homeland. Just at this moment when we finally reached agreement, it appears that God has shown mercy on us, that he has sent you to us—you, a wise and worthy stranger—and that you'll lead us and free us from our misery. In the name of all the inhabitants here, we ask you to be our leader. Wherever you might go, we'll follow. You know the roads and you were certainly born in a happier and better homeland. We'll listen to you and obey each of your commands. Will you, wise stranger, agree to save so many souls from ruin? Will you be our leader?"

All during this imploring speech, the wise stranger never lifted his head. The whole time he remained in the same position in which they had found him. His head was lowered, he was frowning and he said nothing. He only tapped his cane on the ground from time to time and—thought. When the speech was over, he muttered curtly and slowly without changing his position, "I will!"

"Can we go with you then and look for a better place?"

"You can!" he continued without lifting his head.

Enthusiasm and expressions of appreciation arose now, but the stranger did not say a word to any of it.

The ten informed the gathering of their success, adding that only now did they see what great wisdom this man possessed.

"He didn't even move from the spot or lift his head at least to see who was talking to him. He only sat quietly and meditated. To all our talk and appreciation he uttered only four words."

"A real sage! Rare intelligence!" they happily shouted from all sides, claiming that God himself had sent him as an angel from heaven to save them. All were firmly convinced of success under such a leader whom nothing in the world could disconcert.

And so it was decided to set out the next day at daybreak.

On the next day everyone who had the courage to go on a long journey assembled. More than two hundred families came to the appointed place. Only a few remained at home to look after the old homesite.

It was indeed sad to look at this mass of miserable people whom bitter misfortune had forced to forsake the land in which they were born and in which lay the graves of their ancestors. Their faces were haggard, worn-out and sunburned. The suffering of many long, laborious years showed its effect on them and conveyed a picture of misery and bitter despair. But in this very instant there was seen the first glimmer of hope—mixed with homesickness to be sure. A tear flowed down the wrinkled face of many an old man who sighed desperately and shook his head with an air of evil foreboding. He would rather remain for some time so that he too could die among these rocks instead of looking for a better homeland. Many of the women lamented loudly and bade farewell to their dead loved ones whose graves they were leaving.

The men were trying to put up a brave front and were shouting, "Well, do you want to keep on starving in this damned land and living in these shacks?" Actually they would have liked best of all to take the whole cursed region and their run-down houses with them if it had been possible.

There was the usual noise and shouting as in every mass of people. Both men and women were restless. The children were shrieking in cradles on their mother's backs. Even the livestock were a bit uneasy. There were not too many cattle, a calf here and there and then a lean, shaggy hack with a large head and fat legs on which they were loading old rugs, bags and even two sacks over the pack saddle, so that the poor animal swayed under the weight. Yet it managed to stay up and neigh from time to time. Others were loading donkeys; the children were pulling at dogs on leashes. Talking, shouting, cursing, wailing, crying, barking, neighing—all abounded. Even a jackass brayed a few times. But the leader did not utter a word, as if the whole affair were none of his business. A real wise man!

He just sat pensively and silently, with his head down. Now and then he spat; that was all. But on account of his strange behavior, his popularity grew so much that all would have gone through fire and water, as they say, for him. The following conversations could be heard:

"We should be happy to have found such a man. Had we gone ahead without him, God forbid! We would have perished. He has real intelligence, I tell you! Hé's silent. He hasn't said a word yet!" said one while looking at the leader with respect and pride.

"What should he say? Whoever talks a lot doesn't think very much. A smart man, that's for sure! He only ponders and says nothing," added another, and he too looked at the leader with awe.

"It's not easy to lead so many people! He has to collect his thoughts because he's got a big job on his hands," said the first again.

The time came to get started. They waited awhile, however, to see if anyone else would change his mind and come with them, but since no one came, they could not linger any longer.

"Shouldn't we get going?" they asked the leader.

He got up without saying a word.

The most courageous men immediately grouped around him to be at hand in case of danger or an emergency.

The leader, frowning, his head down, took a few steps, swinging his cane in front of himself in a dignified fashion. The gathering moved along behind him and shouted several times, "Long live our leader!" He took a few more steps and bumped into the fence in front of the village hall. There, naturally, he stopped; so the group stopped too. The leader then stepped back a bit and rapped his cane on the fence several times.

"What do you want us to do?" they asked.

He said nothing.

"What should we do? Tear the fence down! That's what we're to do. Don't you see that he's shown us with his cane what to do?" shouted those who stood around the leader.

"There is the gate! There is the gate!" screamed the children and pointed at the gate which stood opposite them.

"Hush, quiet, children!"

"God help us, what's going on?" A few women crossed themselves.

"Not a word! He knows what to do. Tear the fence down!"

In an instant the fence was down as if it had never been there.

They went past the fence.

Scarcely had they gone a hundred steps when the leader ran into a large thorn bush and stopped. With great difficulty he managed to pull himself out and then began tapping his cane in all directions. No one budged.

"And what's the matter now?" shouted those in the rear.

"Cut the thorn bush down!" cried the ones standing around the leader.

"There's the road, behind the thorn bushes! There it is!" screamed the children and even many people in the back.

"There's the road! There's the road!" jeered those around the leader, mimicking angrily. "And how can we blind men know where he's leading us? Everyone can't give orders. The leader knows the best and most direct route. Cut down the thorn bush!"

They plunged in to clear the way.

"Ouch," cried someone who was stuck in the hand by a thorn and someone else whose face was struck by a blackberry branch.

"Brothers, you don't get something for nothing. You have to strain yourselves a bit to succeed," answered the bravest in the group.

They broke through the bush after much effort and moved forward.

After wandering along a little farther, they came upon a bunch of logs. These, too, were thrown to the side. Then they continued.

Very little ground was covered on this first day because they had to overcome several, similar obstacles. And all this on little food because some had brought only dried bread and a little cheese while others had only some bread to satisfy their hunger. Some had nothing at all. Fortunately it was summertime so that they found a fruit tree here and there.

Thus, although on the first day only a small stretch lay behind them, they felt very tired. No great dangers turned up and there were no accidents either. Naturally in such a large undertaking the following events must be considered trifles: a thorn struck one woman's left eye, which she covered with a damp cloth; one child bawled and limped after he bumped into a log; an old man tripped over a blackberry bush, fell down and sprained his ankle; after ground onion was put on it, the man bravely endured the pain and, leaning on his cane, limped forward valiantly behind the leader. (To be sure, several said that the old man was lying about the ankle, that he was only pretending because he was eager to go back.) Soon, there were only a few who did not have a thorn in their arm or a scratched face. The men endured it all heroically while the women cursed the very hour they departed and the children cried, naturally, because they did not understand that all this toil and pain would be richly rewarded.

Much to everyone's happiness and joy, nothing at all happened to the leader. Frankly, if we are to tell the truth, he was very much protected, but still, the man was simply lucky. At the first night's campsite everyone prayed and thanked God that the day's journey was successful and that nothing, not even the slightest misfortune, had befallen the leader. Then one of the bravest men began to speak. His face had been scratched by a blackberry bush, but he simply paid no attention to it.

"Brothers," he began. "One day's journey lies successfully behind us, thank God. The road is not easy, but we've got to stick it out because we all know that this difficult road will lead us to happiness. May almighty God protect our leader from any harm so that he may continue to lead us so successfully."

"Tomorrow I'll lose my other eye if things go like today!" one of the women muttered angrily.

"Ouch, my leg!" the old man cried out, encouraged by the woman's remark.

The children kept on whining and crying, and the mothers had a hard time silencing them so that the spokesman could be heard.

"Yes, you'll lose your other eye," he burst out in anger, "and may you lose both! It's no big misfortune for one woman to lose her eyes for such a great cause. For shame! Don't you ever think about the well-being of your children? Let half of us perish in this endeavor! What difference does it make? What's one eye? Of what use are your eyes when there's someone who's looking for us and leading us to happiness? Should we abandon our undertaking merely on account of your eye and the old man's leg?"

"He's lying! The old man's lying! He's only pretending so he can go back," resounded voices from all sides.

"Brothers, whoever doesn't want to go any farther," said the spokesman again, "let him go back instead of complaining and stirring up the rest of us. As far as I'm concerned, I'm going to follow this wise leader as long as there's anything left in me!"

"We'll all follow! We'll all follow him as long as we live!"

The leader was silent.

Everyone began looking at him and whispering:

"He's absorbed in his thoughts!"

"A wise man!"

"Look at his forehead!"

"And always frowning!"

"Serious!"

"He's brave! That's seen in everything about him."

"You can say that again! Fence, logs, briars—he plows through it all. He somberly taps his cane, saying nothing, and you must guess what he has in mind."

Thus the first day passed, and there followed more days with the same success. Nothing of very great importance happened, only trivial occurrences: they tumbled headfirst into a ditch, then into a ravine; they brushed against hedges and blackberry bushes; they stepped on bottles; several broke arms and legs; some suffered blows on the head. But all this torment was endured. A few old men were left lying dead on the road. "They would have died even if they had stayed at home, not to mention on the road!" the spokesman said, encouraging the others to continue. A few smaller children, one to two years old, also perished. The parents stoically suppressed their heartaches because it was God's will. And the smaller the child, the less the grief. "When they are younger, the sorrow is less. God grant that the parents never lose their children when they have reached the marrying age. If the children are so destined, it's better that they die early. Then the sorrow is not so great!" the spokesman consoled them again. Many limped and staggered. Some wrapped cloths around their heads and put cold compresses on their bruises. Others carried their arms in slings. All were ragged and cut up. Their clothes hung in shreds, but they nevertheless pushed happily forward. All this would have been easier to bear if they had not been racked with hunger many times over. But they had to keep going.

One day, something more significant happened.

The leader was walking in front, surrounded by the bravest men in the group. (Two of them were missing, and no one knew where they were. It was the general opinion that they had betrayed their cause and fled. On one occasion the spokesman said something about their shameful treason. Only a few believed the two had died on the way, but they did not voice their opinion in order not to arouse the others.) The rest of the group was in line behind them. Suddenly there appeared an exceedingly large and deep, rocky gorge—a real abyss. The slope was so steep that they did not dare take a step forward. Even the bravest ones stopped short and looked at the leader. Frowning, absorbed in thoughts with his head down, he boldly stepped forward, tapping his cane in front, first to the right, then to the left in his characteristic way. Many said it all made him seem still more dignified. He neither looked at anyone nor said anything. On his face there was no change of expression or trace of fear as he got nearer and nearer to the precipice. Even the very boldest men became pale as death but no one dared warn the valiant, wise leader. Two more steps and he was at the edge. In morbid fear and with wide open eyes, they all trembled. The bravest men were just on the point of holding the leader back, even if it meant a breach of discipline, when he stepped once, twice, and plunged into the ravine. There arose bewilderment, wailing, screaming; fear got the upperhand. Some began to flee.

"Hold it, brothers! What's the hurry? Is this the way you keep your word? We must follow this wise man because he knows what he's doing. He would be insane to ruin himself. Forward, after him! This is the biggest and perhaps the last hazard, the last hurdle. Who knows? Maybe on the other side of this ravine we'll find a magnificent, fertile land which God meant for us. Forward! Without sacrifice, we'll get nowhere!" Such were the spokesman's words of advice and he too took two steps forward, disappearing into the ravine. The bravest followed and then everyone else plunged in.

There was wailing, groaning, tumbling, moaning on the steep slope of this vast gorge. One would have sworn that no one would ever get out alive, much less unhurt and in one piece. But human life is tenacious. The leader was unusually lucky. He hung onto bushes as he fell so that he was not hurt. He managed to pull himself together and climb out. While wailing, moaning and weeping resounded below, he sat motionless, pensively silent. A few who were battered and angry began to curse him but he paid no heed. Those who luckily were able to grab hold of a bush or a tree while falling began trying strenuously to climb out. Some had cracked heads so that blood was gushing out of their faces. There was nobody in one piece except the leader. They all sullenly frowned at him and groaned in agony but he did not even lift his head. He was silent and assumed the reflective pose of a real sage!

Some time passed. The number of travelers was becoming smaller and smaller. Each day took its toll. Some left the group and turned back.

Of the large number that started, only about twenty remained. Their haggard, exhausted faces mirrored signs of despair, doubt, fatigue and hunger, but no one said as much as a word. They were as silent as their leader and kept plodding along. Even the spirited spokesman shook his head desperately. The road was difficult indeed.

Their numbers diminished daily until there were only ten. With despondent faces, they only groaned and complained instead of conversing.

They looked more like cripples than men. Some were on crutches. Some held their arms in slings fastened around their necks. On their heads were numerous bandages and compresses. Even if they had wanted to make new sacrifices, they could not because there was almost no room on their bodies for any new wounds.

Even the strongest and bravest among them had already lost faith and hope but they still struggled farther; that is, they somehow hobbled along with great effort, complaining, racked with pain. What else could they do if they could not go back? So many sacrifices and now to abandon the journey?

Twilight descended. Limping along on crutches, they suddenly saw that the leader was not in front of them anymore. Another step and they all plunged into another ravine.

"Oh, my leg! Oh, my hand!" resounded the wailing and groaning. One weak voice even cursed the worthy leader but then became silent.

When the sun came up, there sat the leader, the same as on that day when he was chosen. There was not the least change in his appearance.

The spokesman climbed out of the ravine, followed by two others. Disfigured and bloody, they turned around to see how many were left, but they were the only ones. Deathly fear and hopelessness filled their hearts. The region was unknown, hilly, rocky—no paths anywhere. Two days before they had come upon a road but left it behind. The leader led them that way.

They thought about all the many friends and relatives who had died on this fantastic trip. A sadness stronger than the pain in their crippled limbs overcame them. They had witnessed their own destruction with their own eyes.

The spokesman went up to the leader and began speaking with a tired, trembling voice full of pain, despair and bitterness.

"Where are we going now?"

The leader was silent.

"Where are you taking us and where have you brought us? We placed ourselves and our families in your hands and we followed you, leaving behind our homes and our ancestors' graves in hopes that we could save ourselves from ruin in that barren land. But you have ruined us in a worse way. There were two hundred families behind you and now look how many there are!"

"You mean everyone is not here?" mumbled the leader without lifting his head.

"How can you ask such a question? Look up and see! Count how many of us are left on this unfortunate journey! Look at the shape we're in! It would be better to have died than to be crippled like this."

"I can't look at you!"

"Why not?"

"I'm blind."

A dead silence.

"Did you lose your sight during the journey!?"

"I was born blind!"

The three hung their heads in despair.

The autumn wind blew sinisterly through the mountains and brought down the withered leaves. A fog hovered over the hills, and through the cold, misty air fluttered ravens' wings. An ill-omened cawing resounded. The sun was concealed behind the clouds, which were rolling and hurrying along farther and farther.

The three looked at each other in utter horror.

"Where can we go now?" mumbled one gravely.

"We don't know!"

W. Murray Linker

Aleksa Šantić

(1868–1924)

A native of Mostar in Herzegovina, Šantić was born in 1868 into a wealthy middle-class family. After attending trade schools in Trieste and Ljubljana, he returned to his native city, where he spent the rest of his life participating in the cultural life of the city, editing literary journals, and writing poetry.

His first poems were imitative of the older Serbian poets: Njegoš, Zmaj, Jakšić, and Ilić. The Belgrade critic Bogdan Popović was instrumental in pointing out his shortcomings and setting him on a more original course. Šantić wrote love, elegiac, patriotic, and social poetry. His love poems are written in a low-key, depicting the sincere, earthy emotions of an average man for his chosen woman. As a patriotic bard, he remained close to his soil and uncluttered by foreign influences, giving expression to a fervent desire for the unity of all Serbs. However, in his poems with predominantly social themes he showed that he was very close to his people, not unaware of the serious problems facing them. Not a poet of wide scope and keen perception, Šantić compensated for it by writing pure and highly emotional lyrics, some of which were set to music and are still very popular.

Šantić also wrote plays in verse, two of which are still performed: *Pod maglom* (In the Fog) and *Hasanaginica* (The Lady of Hasan-aga). He also translated successfully from German.

WE KNOW OUR FATE

We know our fate; what waits for us we can
now watch with hearts devoid of fears that scare.
Not humans-oxen like the yoke to bear:
God has created liberty for man.

Our mountain rivers lend us force and breadth.
There's no obstruction we would not defy:
the people of this land are wont to die—
to consecrate, if need be, life through death.

We know our way, the way of God and man.
Hence powerfully like a rolling stream
we'll crush all rocks, however hard they seem.

Thus on we go up to Golgotha hill,
and if you shed the blood of all our clan,
our very graves will scorn and fight you still.

A. Lenarčič and J. Lavrin

EVENING ON THE ISLES

The purple deep
is asleep,
      chilly darkness falls

The last ray
dies away
      across black cliffs and walls.

There sounds the knell
of a bell,
the cliffs with it are loud

With sigh and moan
monotone
      prays the humble crowd.

Their heads low bent,
penitent,
      before their God they kneel.

But he is mute,
absolute,
      deaf to their appeal.

Nearer creep,
dreams of sleep,
    chilly darkness falls.

The last ray
dies away
    across black cliffs and walls.

A. Lenarčič

Jovan Dučić

(1874—1943)

Born in Trebinje, Herzegovina, Dučić, together with Šantić and Ćorović, brought this province into the mainstream of Serbian literary life at the beginning of this century. After studying at the teacher-training school, he taught for a while in Mostar, afterwards studied in Geneva and Paris for several years. In Paris he became thoroughly acquainted with the poetry of the French Symbolists and fell under their influence. He spent the rest of his life in the diplomatic service in various European capitals. In 1941 he emigrated to the United States, and died in Gary, Indiana in 1943.

Dučić is considered one of the finest craftsmen in Serbian poetry at the beginning of this century. An erudite and esthete, with a refined taste and aristocratic selectivity of subject matter, he wrote poetry in the manner of the French decadent poets, secluded in his isolated poetic world. He was often criticized for his inclination toward art for art's sake. Nevertheless, he was recognized for his lyric poetry on pseudo-philosophical themes, for the poetry evoking the beauty of the Adriatic (*Jadranski soneti*—Adriatic Sonnets, 1898-1906) and the Serbian glorious past (*Carski soneti*—Imperial Sonnets, 1930), and for his unique poems in prose (*Plave Legende*—Blue Legends, 1902). He enriched poetic expression in Serbian language, lending it the brilliance of a sensitive man with richly felt experience.

Dučić also wrote a sophisticated travelogue, *Gradovi i himere* (Cities and Chimeraes, 1930) and a book of essays of popular philosophy, *Blago cara Radovana* (The Treasure of Tzar Radovan, 1932).

SUNSET

The sky, like copper in the furnace, shines;
   The river crimsons in the evening glow;
And now, from that dark wood of ancient pines
   Does not a stealthy flame begin to show?
And listen—somewhere in the distance, turns

The waterwheel, with droning hoarse and deep;
But while the heaven above the valley burns,
    The mayfly on the water lies asleep.

Another evening! . . . in my mind I see
    Beyond three oceans, in some land afar,
In the first hush of sunset, mournfully
Sitting, where shadowy emerald mountains are,
Pale as Desire, a woman I do not know,
    Thinking of me, and crowned, and shining bright;
Heavy, perpetual, boundless is her woe,
    There, on the verge of stillness, gloom, and night.

Before the gardens lies the sea outspread;
    The dark-blue gulls fly off, a scattered throng,
And in the rosebush, withered now and dead,
    Once more the wind is murmuring its sad song;
And two huge sphinxes face the golden sky
    And keep their mute and voiceless watch, while she
Weeps, and the tired sun slowly from on high
    Sinks down behind the vast and spacious sea.

To me her name, her features, are unknown;
    Yet, standing here, I fill her every thought;
For those pale lips declare true faith alone,
    Faith mighty as death, as love that hopes for nought.
—Ah, never tell me 'tis not so, nor say
    That my poor heart on lies itself hath fed;
For I should weep, for ever and a day;
    —No, never again should I be comforted!

Oliver Elton

THE SEA WILLOW

A lonely willow stands above the sea.
She plaits the tresses of her long green hair
like to a nymph that's doomed to be a tree.

At dawn she hears the singing mountain-side,
at evening time the melancholy ocean;
and motionless she stands where all is motion:
the clouds, the winds, the weather and the tide.

Midst these she stands and to the gale would part .
with many a leaf, with branches to the billow,
and like a pulsing sorrow-ridden heart
sad life she echoes. Lonely stands the willow.

A. Lenarčič and J. Lavrin

LETTER FROM FRANCE

(Excerpt)

Paris, Spring 19—

Something has suddenly changed today in my old, miserable, anonymous street. Until now it was as narrow as a prison corridor. The black rains have showered on it for months and it's darkened already at noon. The mornings could not be recognized by the lightened windows but by our despair because of the eternal twilight. But today a stream of light unexpectedly flowed in from somewhere and the young sun kindled on the ceiling whole pantomimes of dragons and large flaming forests. On the wet, black roofs the fiery pigeons flew around and the bulky cloud lit itself in the height. And when abruptly the bells started to toll from some church, the sounds crossed over the sky like big, silver sails, thousands of peals, one after another.

Spring cannot be hidden even in the biggest city above whose streets hang only the narrow linens of the sky. Here spring is not as much of the things as it is in the eyes of men and in the movements of women. It is spring because yesterday's happiness is not that any more; because love and betrayal are in the air and in the water; because the women are prettier today than ever before; and because we wake up with a verse in our mind and with a new woman's name on our lips; and, finally, because today we cross the old Latin quarter like the old Greek God through the golden rain.

The tepid Paris spring is felt in the odor of the first dust and in the mildness of the wind that now crawls on the ground. In the Seine the sunny flags flutter; the black roofs make their orgies on the red-hot sky. It is heard how somewhere, on the other side of all walls, the young woods bud, the rivers full of embers glow, the pagan songs resound, the centaurs run. One big devil and three hundred small ones sing in the heart. On one poor tree, in some dusty Parisian square, the greenish splendor of all Brazilian forests could be imagined. In one meek voice of a bird could be heard all the flocks from the equator. Spring is not on the earth yet, but it is already in the blood and soul; the heart follows the sun, and the mind follows the wind.

Vasa D. Mihailovich

Milan Rakić

(1876–1938)

Rakić was born in Belgrade into a distinguished family. After receiving good education at home, he studied law in Paris where, like Dučić, he came under the influence of French poets. He spent his entire mature life in the diplomatic service, first in the southern Serbian regions still under the Turks, and then in various European capitals. He died relatively young in Zagreb in 1938.

Rakić wrote only about sixty poems, collected in three books. His poetry is mainly on love and philosophical themes. Like Dučić, he shows signs of a decadent spirit acquired in Paris, but he is more profound in his sensitivity and perception of reality. He is also more pessimistic in outlook, resigned to the basically tragic nature of existence as expressed in man's inability to truly enjoy his experiences and to halt the inexorable passage of time. Rakić is also more pensive and subdued than Dučić, finding it difficult to rejoice amidst decay, flight of time, and approaching death. Even his patriotic poems reveal this pessimistic outlook, although he also expresses hope for the revival of Serbian spiritual glory.

Rakić belongs to the best Serbian poets of the twentieth century.

A COMMONPLACE POEM

That love of ours had all too brief a date;
    It lived—what seemed an instant—just one year.
Then, to divide us, some rude sudden fate
    Came—with never a word, or sigh, or tear.

For half our days in wrangling had flown by;
    Half our vexed nights, in making peace, at best;
And so from our abode at last fled I,
    And in the lonely country sought for a rest.

143

All this endured but for a little space,
  And we became as strangers—dull and dazed
Like children cloyed with sweetmeats; so we gazed
  In long unbroken silence, face to face.

All is over, now, and ended—nor may I
  Blaspheme my destiny, or heaven's decree,
Or clench my fists, or plunged in sorrow cry
  Curses on all women and their infamy.

But hadst thou known, if only for an hour,
  The fatal flame in which my soul is caught,
The love that cancels, like some monstrous power,
  All other hopes, all dreams, and every thought;

If once, distracted soul, thou hadst desired
  To speak some tender word, with its caress
Like silk—and by thy burning heart inspired,
  —Long, long, perchance, had been our happiness.

But time now flows at a sluggish pace;
  We have remained as strangers; in a daze,
Like children cloyed with sweetmeats, now we gaze,
  In long unbroken silence, face to face.

Oliver Elton

THE ABANDONED CHURCH

See, Christ upon the Cross, an antique image, lies.
  All down His shattered side a trickle of blood is shed.
Death's self is here; the lips are pale, and dead the eyes;
  A halo, beaten silver, hangs above His head.

A gift from noble folk and godly peasant came;
  For there, about His neck, the strings of ducats shine;

Pure silver filigree is wrought upon the frame.
    That frame a man of Debar cut—some craftsman fine.

Thus lies the Christ, within the empty temple there,
With darkness, shade by shade, descending everywhere,
    Amidst the swarm of night-birds ranging for their prey.

Sole in that empty church, and ringed by phantom bands,
The dreadful Christ, despairing, reaches out His hands,
    And waits forever for His flock—but where are they?

                                        Oliver Elton

Borisav Stanković

(1876–1927)

Born in Vranje, southern Serbia, Stanković became the poet of this quaint and picturesque town at the crossroads of Europe and the Orient. He received some Western education (Paris), but returned unchanged to his native region and subsequently made it immortal in his works. He also finished law school in Belgrade and served as an official in various government institutions in Belgrade, where he died in 1927.

Stanković is one of the raciest writers in Serbian literature. His short stories, novels, and plays have basically the same theme—life in Vranje a few years after liberation from the Turks. This life is depicted through the clash between the centuries-old traditions and the new way of life. The patriarchal spirit, preserved during the long Turkish occupation, grudgingly gave way to the new, Western ideas. Stanković describes this through his simple but emotional characters, who are either slaves to their passion or unable to adjust to the changing world. He has indeed created some unforgettable characters.

His best work, the novel *Nečista krv* (The Tainted Blood, 1911), depicts the plight of a young woman unable to free herself from the old customs and restrictions. The play *Koštana* (1902) is a delightful musical about the sway a beautiful gipsy girl holds over an entire town. In practically all his works Stanković presents unusually strong characters who are at the same time victims of a strange weakness stemming from the realization that their time has irrevocably passed.

His other main works are: short story collections, *Iz starog jevandjelja* (From an Old Gospel, 1899), *Stari dani* (The Old Days, 1902), and *Božji ljudi* (God's Children, 1902); and a play *Tašana* (1910).

IN THE NIGHT

Cveta was sitting in the field and waiting for her husband, Jovan, to bring water for the tobacco they had planted the week before, but which until now had not been able to soak well. She was sitting down, huddled up, with her chin against her bent knees, looking dreamily into the warm dark night. In the field, all around her, could be seen the men working under lanterns on the furrowed, planted fallowed land. The hills and mountain peaks were outlined in the east, standing out against the dark reddish sky where the moon was about to appear. In front of her, along the river and the road, rose tall poplars and dense willows which, in the dark night, with their rustling and swaying, looked like living, human beings. . . . Now and then one could hear the dull metal of a hoe, the hoarse voices of workers calling each other. A warm breeze which blew across the plain from time to time carried the sounds away.

Cveta was dead tired, and she was forcing herself to stay awake. Suddenly she heard the sound of somebody's footsteps approaching and then recognized her husband's voice.

"Here, you have it." He was talking to someone. "Look around brother—the whole year has been dry, not a drop of water. . . . Look how everything has withered. It's a pity even to look at it. . . . If only one out of ten roots survived. . . . It's a disaster, I am telling you. . . ."

". . . That's right, that's right," the other one was answering.

"My God! He's here again?" Cveta started with fright when she heard the second voice, more mellifluous than masculine. She got up quickly, and as if running away, entered the field, picked up the hoe, and started digging. At that moment Jovan came.

"Are you working?" he asked her. Then he took his hoe off his shoulder, rammed it into earth, left his lantern, and sat down on the boundary line. "Come here, Master Stojan." He turned to the man who walked behind him. "Come here, sit down for a while."

"Coming, coming!"

A tall, slender figure appeared also with a lantern and a hoe, straddling the boundary line with uncertain steps.

"Good evening! Are you working?" he asked quietly and somewhat timidly.

Cveta did not answer his greeting at all. As if preoccupied with her work, she pretended not to hear.

"Yes, we're struggling along, master, as all poor people do," answered Jovan, moving a bit so as to make some space.

"Sit down, take a break. How about some tobacco?"

"Yes, thank you!" Looking around, he sat down slowly, crossed his legs, and began to rool up his cigarette and smoke quickly, clumsily.

In the meantime, Jovan started to complain to him about bad years, bad weather, the district council, millers, and about everything that hindered the flow of water to his fields. Stojan was listening to him while smoking, nodding his head in agreement, answering rarely, briefly. And who knows how long this would have lasted had not Jovan suddenly jumped to his feet, leaned down to the earth, and listened. Hearing the creeping, quiet murmur of the water which was coming from far away, he threw away his cigarette in joy, grabbed his hoe again, and without a lantern, ran to meet the water.

"Cveta, prepare these furrows," he said to the woman who kept digging not far from them, "and you, master, wait; I will be back soon. . . . Eh, eh, hey!" He strided out gaily and disappeared into the night.

Stojan quickly stood up and followed him as if frightened by his sudden departure but returned again, sat down, and picked up some dried-up grains, plucking at them and listening to Cveta's hoe hitting the earth. All of a sudden he cupped his mouth with his hand and called quietly.

"Cveta." She did not respond, and the only sound was that of the hoe.

"Cveta," he called louder.

She kept silent again.

"Cveta, do you hear me?" he leaned forward, straining his hearing and his eyes, but saw only that she was bent forward, swinging her hoe with abandon, causing sparks to fly whenever the hoe would hit a stone.

"Cveta, come, or. . . ." and he felt like standing up, but he was startled when she came and bent over him.

"Why did you come?" she asked with a choking voice.

"I?" The words choked in his throat, and he became frightened. "I won't do anything, believe me, I started going to the field, and your husband met me, so we came together! Do you mind?"

"Leave at once!" She turned angrily away from him.

"Are you angry? Don't be!"

"I am not angry," she started swallowing as if in tears. "I am not angry with you, but what are people going to say! Go—if you mean well. What do you want? Don't you see—I am a married woman."

"That's right," he answered softly.

"Well, when you get the chance, why do you come here? Why don't you leave me alone? You have a wife and children."

"Eh," he rejected this with a motion of his hand. "Don't talk about it."

"Yes, you have, and I? What if he comes to know, where am I to go then, where?"

"Don't, Cveta!" he exclaimed, sensing that her voice was breaking into tears. "I am leaving, right now. It is true what you said, but I. . . . You know me. I was just on the way, and I came to see you. And you, well, since you insist on it, I won't any more, . . . good-bye!"

She did not extend her hand to him but moved off and said sharply: "Good-bye, please go!"

"Eh, you are angry!" he repeated in a bewildered way, and casting his hoe over his shoulder, he went away.

When he had disappeared, she quickly, as if by force and as if defending herself from something, turned around, took the hoe and continued digging, whispering to herself:

"He is lying, lying. He will come again. Oh, what does he want?" (Although she knew.) Why does he not leave her alone once and all? She would not dare tell her husband. For the kind of husband she has, even blood would flow. But she has been seeing him; they say he comes to visit her, and her husband still does not know what it is all about. . . . Where are her soul and body going to go in the other world? . . . It is sinful, sinful . . . all this disturbs her even more, fills her with fear and sweet memories. Reason, contrary to will, crossing oneself, and prayers, started to expose intensely everything that has happened in the past. . . .

. . . She was a child when her needy parents gave her to Stojan's family to serve them so that they could marry her off well later on. Stojan's father was a short-tempered and cruel man. By the look of his sullen and hairy face, it seemed that nobody ever heard a gentle tender word from him. He treated his wife and his only son, Stojan, as he did his servants. Everybody was afraid and trembled before him. If it had not been for Stojan's mother, a gentle and compassionate woman, perhaps Cveta would have had the same fate as her girlfriends, maids in rich houses who became mistresses of the servants and sometimes of the masters or else remained stunted from overwork.

Stojan's mother, nevertheless, began to take care of her because Stojan, as a child, preferred to play with her. Because of that, they protected her from the advances of servants, did not give her hard work, so that she developed well and became beautiful. Her stature, beauty, and buxomness enraptured everybody, most of all Stojan, who later, when he grew up, never left Cveta. They were inseparable. In the fields and in the valley they were always next to each other. He never let her feel that she was only a servant in their home. He was always giving her presents—without his father's knowledge—corn, flour, and other things to take to her poor parents. He was more gentle, quiet, shy, and industrious than anybody. Ah, those days!

They went together to the field to prune the tobacco leaves. The plants covered them up to their waists, the dry earth was breaking and crumbling under their bare feet, and around them everywhere the greenness and luxuriance extended as far as their eyes could see. The fresh, clean, and limpid air warmed them, and the blood pulsated in their firm cheeks. They worked, breaking up young shoots. A breeze was coming from the river, and from the reaped fields came the song of the turtledoves. They worked, competing with and teasing each other, and then they would argue, and, as if angry, move away. Both kept quiet, glancing secretly at each other with a trace of a spiteful smile. She was dressed in a tight blouse, her head bound with a kerchief, with a naughty and spiteful smile on her red lips looking at him stealthily. She saw him scratching, fidgeting, looking at her and about to tell her something and then she turned her back on him, pretending not to see him.

"Cveto," he would say finally. "Let us sing."

"I don't want to."

"But why not? I am asking you!" he said more fiercely and came up to her.

"Why are you making me angry?" she said and then, laughing heartily showing her pretended anger, came up to him. "Go ahead. Start!"

And they started. They started singing the most popular song of the time. Their voices were clear, and they were trembling with joy. Their hands went fast to work, and all around the words of the song could be heard.

"The wind is blowing, the wind is blowing, the carnation is
   smelling;
"The dear one writes a small letter to his beloved; the dear one
   writes a letter to his beloved!"

"Cvet-o-o," Stojan shouted and moved away from her in order to
see her better.

"What is the matter with you," she asked him roguishly.

"You, you are . . . mine!"

"Eh," she exclaimed suddenly and unintentionally deep in her chest.
She quickly leaned down to hide her joy and her crimson cheeks.

"Don't Stojan! Let us work."

"No, no," he stammered.

He reached from behind under her armpits, seized her, and pressed
her to him. She struggled, twisted, trying to defend herself but so
clumsily and weakly that she came closer to him.

"Don't. That is enough, enough, my sweet Stojan . . ." She whispered, hiding her face. "Enough, somebody might see us . . . oh!!"

"More, more, let me!" moaned Stojan, pressing her even more and
kissing her wherever he could.

"That's enough. . . . Oh, you are. . . ." Exhausted, numb, and
blissful, she gave herself to him, extending now her left cheek, then
her right cheek to let him kiss them both.

But one evening in the autumn they told her to get dressed in her
best clothes. Then Stojan's father came, took her by the hand, and led
her into the parlor, pointing.

"Kiss their hands!" he told her, at the people who were present.
Her knees faltered; frightened, she looked at him entreatingly and felt
like falling down, but his sharp look and the cruel expression on his
face restored her strength. Hardly walking, she kissed all those people
on their hands. They gave her presents. Even Stojan's father, to the
surprise of everybody, kissed her on the forehead and gave her a big
gold coin.

"May you always be happy and live long. You ate in my home
with a wooden spoon, and may you eat in yours with the silver one
with God's help!"

They took her out. She fell down. She was unconscious all night.
From that time until the wedding, she did not see Stojan at all. She
was married soon afterward. She married Jovan, a widower. He was

not poor but rather a miser and had a horrible temper. Her heart almost broke, but her strong constitution and the never-ending, hard, everyday work won out. . . . It suppressed everything that existed, but now for some time, the same Stojan kept looking at her, trying to find an opportunity to meet her, to see her, and to talk to her. She could not look at him nor listen to his soft, mellifluous voice. He himself was not happy either. They had married him to a rich girl from a well-known family. But he behaved as if he weren't married, since he was not able to stay at home for any length of time. He did not look at his wife at all. Always under the pretext of being engaged in some business, he would visit his peasant's fields where he would stay for several weeks. They did everything possible to endear his wife to him, but nothing helped. They sprayed him with cologne. They fed him with herbs, took him to monasteries and to fortunetellers, but it did not make him more talkative, livelier, or friendlier. He kept always silent and allowed his mother to do with him as she wanted. He did not argue with anyone. His attitude infuriated his father. His poor mother almost died of unhappiness and shame. She begged him, implored him to tell only her, if not his father or anyone else, why he was running away from home and his wife, but in vain. . . . Who knows for how long this would have lasted if it hadn't been for the bride's relatives, who, seeing what was happening, asked that the girl be returned, although married. For, they said, they had not given her to the old man and his house but to Stojan. . . . The father called Stojan to him, not knowing what to do.

"Sit down," he told him grimly, indicating the place beside him on the couch.

Stojan, as always, remained standing in front of him.

"Never mind," he answered. "I can stand."

"Sit beside me, sit as befits a husband and a landlord," and he emphasized the word "landlord." Stojan was obediently silent and did not sit down.

"Sit down and speak!" the old man suddenly burst out in anger and jumped from his seat. "Have you become deaf? Speak up, I want to hear, to know, you understand. Are you able to speak? I want to hear your voice . . . to know if you are still alive?"

"What is there to talk about?" whispered Stojan, and ready for anything, he shrugged his shoulders.

"What, what?" said the old man more quickly, leaning over him angrily, bristling and clenching his overcoat. "And you dare ask? I'll kill you, kill you—good-for-nothing son!" He raised his fist. "Am I to live through this, that they would take back my married daughter-in-law? . . . And that should happen to me, me! . . . Speak up, I say!" He grabbed him angrily by the chest and started to shake him, hurting him. "Speak up . . . I'm going to kill you, I'm going to kill you! . . . so that I won't have to look at you."

"Kill me!"

The old man stepped back.

"Kill you? I will, now, right now!" And he started to turn around in the room as if looking for something with which to kill him. Stojan just kept quiet, bowed his head, and waited. . . . "I will, right away, now!" said the old man and suddenly cried out: "Don't, don't, my son! Don't be like that, please. Here, I, I'm begging you!" And trembling berore Stojan, he took off his hat so that his white hair spread out over his neck and shoulders.

"Here, you kill me . . . you kill me," the old man sobbed, and his hands, his shoulders, his head, his whole body trembled.

Stojan, ready for anything except this—his father's pleading—was startled, frightened.

"No . . . !" and he leaned over to raise him and straighten him up; but when he noticed the large warm tears dropping from the old man's eyes onto his hands, he gave in, frightened, and ran out of the room.

After that day, for several months Stojan became better. He showed affection for his wife and started to live like other married people. He sat at home, supervised the work, and went out sometimes with his wife and his mother to visit relatives or to social gatherings. Everyone was happy about this. But, now, again, with summer approaching—who knows what became of him? He started again to go as before to the fields, to villages, to stay away longer . . . and, what was most important and horrible for Cveta—he started coming to her. It is true that he always came with her husband, but just the same, she knew, she felt, why he was coming. He always tried to arrange to meet her. If she went to the field, he would follow her from afar, going in a roundabout way so it would appear that he was meeting her accidentally. Although, aside from the common greetings, he would never tell her anything, she was somehow afraid. When she saw him, she could not see him approaching, not taking his eyes off her, beaming, and his mouth forming into a painful, petrified smile. Her heart would cramp, her whole body would tremble, and the tears would fill her eyes. She had forgotten her grief a long time ago, but when she saw him as she was, she pitied and mourned for him. But she had to restrain herself, to pretend to be stern and rude to him, for who knows what would have happened if she hadn't? But it was all in vain. It was true that whenever he came to see her he swore that he would not come again, but he came time and again. Ah, for the old days. Only his beautiful, sonorous, soft voice remained. Now he sang so sadly and with such expression that everyone was enthralled. How many times had she seen him alone, at sunrise and in the moonlight, through her window as he was riding home on his horse from the pasture, singing softly, clearly, sadly. He sang, and the voice was coming as if from nowhere while the moonlight shone and quivered. Then she would feel—God forbid—a kind of temptation! She would want, as in the fairy tales, to fly and sit next to him on the horse, to embrace him, and in that moonlight embrace to run away, far away over fields and forests.

"In the moonlight, embracing, far away, far away! . . ." Unconsciously Cveta began to whisper aloud, swaying forward and clasping her breasts. In the moonlight . . . "Oh—!" she screamed, frightened, taking a step backward, frightened when she became aware of herself again and her surroundings, lit up by the moon, which had come out a long time ago and illuminated everything.

"My Lord! . . . My God and the Virgin Mary. . . . My Lord, my Lord. . . . What is this?" she whispered, shivering with fear and hiding her face from the light. "Dear Lord, make me wiser. . . . Oh, how sinful and black I am. . . ." And the thought of sinfulness, the suffering in the other world because of these unclean thoughts, all this came in front of her in black and awful color. . . . To calm somewhat and justify herself, she got up and looked at her illuminated surroundings, following the moon's race across the clear heavens. She started to cross herself, bowing her head, whispering prayers against evil spirits, temptation, and the impure blood. . . . The light illuminated all of her, her slim body, broad shoulders, beautiful flushed face with the hot lips and the black, dim, sunken fiery eyes. . . . She crossed herself, bowed her head, and the moon shone and illuminated it all. And it seemed as if with that light, life itself came. From all sides one could hear noise, shouting, calling, and the song of the people working in the night. The illuminated spacious fields, gentle valleys, rivers and streams with high poplars and dense willows, all had moved as iɪ breathing, and you could smell at once that quiet balsamlike nocturnal perfume. Cveta kept crossing herself, shivering and listening to the river murmuring far away, to the rustling leaves, to the grazing of the fettered horses and the strokes of the hoes. She listened, trembled, and could not work at all. The thought about her sin, that she was thinking about him, Stojan, seized her completely and filled her with indescribable sadness and fear. She stood petrified, leaning on her hoe and not seeing anything, not even the water which came murmuring, rustling, filling dry, thirsty little holes and flowing into the other neighboring fields. . . . Suddenly, in the midst of this glittering radiance in the night, a clear and sad voice rose up, quivered, and spread around.

"Whoo!" she shivered and fell prostrate to the ground.

". . . . Hey, Stojan, listen, Stojan is singing!" As an answer to his song, you could hear from everywhere enthusiastic cries and voices. Indeed, it was Stojan, who from far away, going home, sang that same song:

"The wind is blowing, the wind is blowing, the carnation is
    smelling sweetly;
"The dear one writes a small letter to his beloved; the dear
    one writes a small letter to his beloved!"

"Oh, enough, enough . . ." Cveta whispered unconsciously, as if to herself and to him—prostrate, huddled, pressing her breasts and choking with tears and her burning sensations. Unable to endure any more, she kept fiercely and deliriously kissing the earth and beating her breasts. The plump roundness of her arms pushed her fist into her mouth as if to stop what was gushing out and what was seizing her throughout. . . . But the song lingered on. Stojan was singing so expressively and sadly as never before. His clear voice trembled and resounded, being carried into the illuminated, sparkling heights of this warm and shiny night. . . .

"If you would know, oh girl, if you would know,
"How great it is, oh great, the sorrow of youth!"
one could hear him singing.

"Sorrow!" Cveta breathed out fully. Broken down, defeated, she raised her head, stared in the direction of Stojan, from where his voice was coming, as if she wanted to absorb into herself the last disappearing sound of his voice.

"The water came—and you," her husband's voice startled her. Jovan came down, running all of a sudden, so happy that he was barely able to bring the water. But when he noticed that she neither watched nor opened the furrows so that water could come and soak them, but left everything and allowed water to go aside in the neighboring field, he was dumbfounded. He lifted his hoe threateningly toward her raging with fury and anger.

"What is this—a, a, a, ?" he hissed.

"No, Jovan!" she started stuttering for she became aware just now that she had completely forgotten the water. Feeling quiet, expecting a blow from him, she kept covering her head, trying painfully to stand up. Not knowing what kind of excuse to find, she started begging him: "Don't, I am ill!"

Her illuminated and flushed face, bitten lips, hot eyes, disheveled hair, the unbuttoned blouse, all this struck Jovan with the thought that she might be pregnant and that right now she must be feeling the child in her womb. He put down his hoe and trembled joyfully.

"Well, what is the matter with you?"

"Oh, you don't know!" she burst into a scream and a flood of tears. ". . . You don't know?"

This seemed to Jovan like a reproach: that he, knowing she was pregnant, made her work at night.

"Well, don't cry! Why didn't you say so? I would have left you at home. Wait," he said softly and bent over her, taking her up in his arms. He carried her to the edge of the field, put her down, took off his overcoat, and covered her with it so she wouldn't catch a cold. Then he quickly ran back and returned to the water.

"Look now, that is enough, don't cry. Don't worry. It will be over," he encouraged her, soaking the furrows, listening to her sobbing, crying and rambling.

Dragan Milivojević

THE TAINTED BLOOD

(Excerpts)

But certainly the worst thing of all was that with every advent of spring and passing of summer she noticed, although she never admitted it to herself, a fear like a sly serpent ever more powerful in her waiting to strike, that at last some public gathering, or in the after church parade, there would appear the girl, who by her fresh beauty, would cast her aside forever, Sophka the old maid.

And yet she was sure that could never happen. She did not deny that another might attract attention by the novelty of her first appearance; but none could ever surpass her in beauty; even if her face with the years became treacherous, she knew she could triumph over all. Yet God preserve her from that happening, for she knew that if life thus outwitted her, she would become a savage and desperate creature, and scorn the ways and decencies of her fathers to prove what she knew to be true, and show the blind and crass that even in her withered age no woman was her peer. *That* it would be a terrible thing to do, but she would not be Sophka if she did not do it when the moment came. At other moments, shamed by her thoughts, terrified by them, she would be full of guilt and blame herself and scold herself, for letting such things come into her mind, and for dwelling thus on things that others no doubt never even thought of.

How long were those inward struggles to last? Why could she never be happy, never at ease? When would she be able, like other girls, not to think, but merely to live and be happy thereat? The whole day, from morn to night, she, too, to work and think of naught but how to snatch sweet tidbits without the others seeing; and then with sweet pleasure to eat a gorging meal and after eating it lie down on a soft bed and sink into a bottomless sleep of sweet fatigue and so day after day. To leave everything to fate; blooming in health and strength to wait with delight to be asked for in marriage, and then for the wedding day, when she would possess a husband, and when she would have her house, like her friends already married and be mistress of it and go with her husband visiting his relations and to the household feasts and to the public assemblies—having as good a time as possible.

And whenever thoughts of this nature plagued her she would try by force to be calm; she would take a piece of work, a piece of difficult embroidery, one of the famous old designs, and try to be excited by it and be pleased by it and enter into it, and thus stitch on all day, without raising her head from the work, and her mother with difficulty dragged her from it for meals. She would maintain the effort of this discipline day after day, week after week; and, as the piece of work grew clearer under her fingers and the designs rose up on the linen like living things, she would grow deeper and deeper into it, and gradually be changed by it, sleep more peacefully and in the morning be fresher, no longer with bloodless cheeks. Her food became sweeter to her; the air around her fresher; and she could fall asleep whenever she wanted into a sweet and deep sleep. But yet when such a piece of work was near to its completion it always lost its hold on her, and her industry failed; her mornings ceased to be fresh, every day was heavier with headaches and broken sleep. She imagined then that this came from the strain of too close work, her head heavy, her body racked as from weakness.

Then would begin days of aimless wandering about, of dragging herself about, as if she were ill . . . till, with a sudden onslaught, those thoughts would begin again, her whole torso throbbing and she full of a curious self-delight. A sensation as of melting in sweet feelings, even her mouth dripping with a sweetness, so that every moment she found her tongue feeding on her moist lips, and in her immense desire for something a longing to cry out.

Then she knew quite well that *that* was come on her, felt that she was not one Sophka, but two, one herself, the other that other self outside her, round about her. Then, like a criminal, Sophka waited for nothing but the coming of night, to lie down and, feeling herself alone in her bed, give her body over to that other Sophka. And she would dream of the coming of that other one, with the glory of the August sun, in the dry days, when dust was on the world—the burning globe gently but steadily sinking, drawn to the scented bosom of the billowing hills, sweetly breathing above the town, above the evening haze. And while yet the teeming town wrestled with repose, stirring uneasily in the first dark, night engulfed the drowsy sun; and Sophka slept, dreaming still. And in the morning was idle to wake, but very tired from dreaming.

For a day after *that* she would shrink from her mother and from any other women and sit till night fell in the garden at the back of the house, and there, as if she were mad, would turn to the flowers, and in each flower find one of her lusts and in each twitter of a bird one of her inexplicable unsung yearnings and the voice of a song.

Then she sometimes felt a thing which often happened to her, but which she could never explain. Everything, that is, the garden and the flowers and the trees and the sky above, and on the earth the heights of the hills around her beyond the town and herself, and she herself dressed just like that, sitting like that, in front of that very same flower, and the house even like that, and those voices coming from it and her mother's footsteps and the other footsteps she could hear and the very words they were saying, what they wanted, the tone in which they spoke—everything, exactly like that, had been there before, and moved round her before, like that once before. And with the approach of night the whole of it, and she with it, seemed no more to be earthly, but clearer, more detached, more ecstatic, and stronger; so that when she came into the house from the garden out of all that suffusion of delight and happiness, she would fling her hands in the air and be nigh to singing a song aloud—though afraid to. All her efforts were concentrated on not letting her mother know anything of it; and even though in such moments of bliss she was not hungry she would force herself to eat so that her mother did not notice anything unusual, and then leave the table as soon as she could.

She would not say she was going to bed, but what she wanted was not rest, but to be alone and then, alone in the night beneath her bed coverings, to be like the sun in the strong arms of the hills, lulled by the enchantment of her virginal dreams; and it was most remarkable that, though she was sure she would never marry, all her dreams melted into a vision of married happiness, their bedroom, their furniture, their bed. . . .

And the dream was always the same; a great luxurious room full of intercrossing multicolored rays of light. Around her the other rooms, furnished in the same way, bright with the bridal towels and other gifts she had brought. . . . Down in the courtyard a fountain, the streams from which and the spray from which showed amber yellow as they rustled in the light of her room. Marriage music could be heard. He, her husband, as if winding up the bridal rout, wearily but merrily, was fitfully and delightedly writhing his body in tune to the rhythm of the song the wedding guests, as they left, were singing.

He was lofty-browed, with rather long ebony moustaches, clothed in silk and homespun, and his clothes were aromatic of the bloom of his flesh; and she was there, on the bed, in her bridal shift, in the sea of that light and the murmur of the fountain and the song,—waiting for him. And though he still had not come, she could already feel the form of his body near her and the pain to come, the touch of his hands and his lips and his head on her bosom, and she heard the soft words breathing from his lips. . . . Then he came, they led him in, exactly as she had drawn him, tall and slender like a green poplar, but yet with the glory of the oak in massive shoulders, and conquering jaw, and calm tread.

That was why she was so fond of solitude. Even when she was quite alone in the house, and her mother had gone to the cemetery or on some business, and deep into the night did not return, she even enjoyed suffering the terror of darkness. She would on such occasion retire to the upper rooms and then, the outer gates and the walls enclosing her and making her safe, she would submit to herself. She would unfasten her stiff embroidered *yelek,** parting its harsh walls that imprisoned her gentle flesh, and would free the fast belting that constrained her waist, and thus lounge. For her linen, no longer fiercely held to her, then softly caressed her, and there was a delight in the air that crept over her skin. Her white shirt was then tender to her, and almost with a man's exultation did she gloat on her breasts' ripe forms, rising half hid from the eye, below the satin cream of her neck.

Once she nearly did a foolish thing. It was some time at the end of the summer. It was a Saturday, a market day. Her mother had gone with Magda to the cemetery. Night fell, a warm, stifling night. Still her mother did not come, and she was alone in the way she so often was—walled in by the silent bricks around her,—having nothing to do, being afraid to walk about; was sitting in the upper room, as usual, in deshabille, and even more fiercely than usual that madness of hers

---

*a vest

came upon her; but on this occasion, as never before, she suddenly began to feel an immeasurably deep, disquiet fluttering in the very deeps of her being, clutching her heart,—as to what this would all end in? Would not, indeed, would not the end of it all be death? Then why all this?

And at that moment she heard Vanko the mute coming in from the garden, and singing, probably drunk, as he was every Saturday, on the tips he got running errands in the market, and as he saw nobody downstairs in the kitchen he began to come upstairs, towards her. She started nervously. She covered herself quickly and began to fasten her belt, but suddenly a wild thought came on her, and sweat broke out on her. Why not? He was drunk—he would not know; he was a mute—he could not tell. Why not the one thing she had so often thought and dreamed? Why should she not once know what it feels like to have a man's hand upon you?

And when Vanko had reached the top of the stairs and saw her, delighted at finding a woman, happy and drunk, he mumbled and made signs to tell her how much he had earned that day, and from whom,—all with his "ba, ba, ba!"

But when he saw that there, on the couch, among her cushions, her clothes unfastened, she lay, and did not get up, did not answer him, or smile, he stood petrified in front of her. But she called him, "Give me your hand!" she said.

He reached out his hand without hesitation, the fingers stretched and spread out, and the left hand, which was nearer to her. She took his hand, but not as she usually did, by the fingers; but by the wrist, by his square and bony wrist. Then she saw the spread-out fingers clenching, for he was surprised at the way she had taken his hand, so that when she drew the hand towards her it was black and hard with the veins on it, like an animal's paw. . . .

But she was not the one to hold back once she had made up her mind. . . . quickly she pulled him towards her, and held him to her. She imagined a sense of all-consuming delight, and foolishly thought that her madness would end in repose. But she felt pain, and nothing else. In horror, she quivered, and started up, and pushed the idiot from her.

But now the idiot was excited. Something had served to madden him, and, with distorted features, he clung to her, clutching at her, pulling her towards him as if with giant pincers, uttering spluttering savage cries.

Any other girl in her place would have lost her head, and fainted from terror, at the mercy of the madman, but she in her disgust glared at him, amazed, and then tossed him from her and went quickly from the room.

* * *

What exactly took place between Marko and Stana no one could hear. Yet Sophka was sure, from the tortured, hissing, hollow sounds that came from behind the closed door, that Marko was, in his agony, cross-examining his wife, trying to make her admit she had lain with her father-in-law her first night. And Sophka felt that everything hung on her mother-in-law's admission. He needed that now; that would be his excuse; and if she confessed, in sheer perversity he would go to avenge himself against her with Sophka, and take Sophka. . . .

"Man! man!" she heard Stana, "shhh! the Lord will destroy you! . . . Ohhhhh! You, her father-in-law!"

Then the old woman prayed.

"Open, o earth, for us all to be swallowed up, oh, what have I come to! O! O Lord God, Lord God!"

Then there was Marko's terrible voice:

"*I* am your Lord God!"

and a dull, heavy blow, and a faint moan from old Stana.

Then Arsa's voice crying,

"The master's killed the mistress."

Sophka nearly lost consciousness, for now there seemed no way out, no hope, no saving herself. Blood would flow, he would destroy anything, everything, but she should be his. . . . And then a curious grating noise outside her door brought her quickly to again. It was some animal rolling about, croaking by the threshold. It was Marko. And she knew then that he had not fallen there by stumbling, but by his own fear of himself his legs were refusing to bear him. He had crawled, grovelling, to her door.

And from the great room, where Sophka's mother-in-law lay with a blood-spattered head, came a constant quiet whimper, hopeless and defeated. The old woman in her desolation was whimpering for her long dead mother and her home.

But for him there, at Sophka's very feet, that whimper had no meaning. Nothing had meaning. Everything seemed ended, destroyed: his whole life, his childhood, his father, his mother, all were accursed.

And as in his self-agony Marko groaned on Sophka's threshold, his supple nostrils quivered, as if they were quick to the very scent of her. He seemed to feel her heavy heart beating, her ripe and passionate lips burning. Her hair, spread over the bed, he pictured winding over her body full and rich. . . .

And as in his agony of self-thwarted longing he croaked and rolled on the ground he strove to push open the door and come to her; but he could not, and he fell back. Hands and arms and legs betrayed him. That whimpering of his wife which he had thought he could ignore was like a rope around his neck. Holding him back as on a leash from crossing that threshold to his prey. Yet go back there to his wife into that room he could not—that was all over! The beams and timbers and bricks and tiles of the accursed house seemed to be falling about him and crushing his head; with great difficulty he scrambled to his feet and mastered his legs and staggered away from Sophka's door over the courtyard.

"Arsa!" he called, "my belts!"

His voice was faint and hoarse. He dragged himself to the house, and leaned on one of the timbers of it, and thus held himself up, waiting for Arsa to belt him.

Arsa ran up and, struggling, managed to belt him, though the whole of the lower part of Marko's body, from hips down, trembled and shook. Only by holding his shoulders against the house did he prevent himself from falling, and he could scarcely raise his arms for Arsa to put the belt on him. Then he croaked—"the chestnut!"

Arsa finished winding his cummerbund on him, and went for the horse. Though Marko strained his ears, he could not catch sound from the little room; not even Sophka's sobs. From the great room, though, came Stana's whimpering, and it seemed to Marko that her bloody face must be sunk in the earth of the beaten floor.

The night was dark, the stones in the yard were coldly still. From the corner of the yard used for rubbish came the stench of droppings and decay, and Marko took deeper and deeper breaths of that stink, for it pricked his nostrils and revived him. Arsa led up the chestnut. A shudder shook Marko. He wiped his running brow. His body was limp, and from his emotion a dull deep croaking came from within him, as if he was choking. Arsa guided his heavy feet to the stirrups, and helped him, heaving him up into the saddle. And the feel of the saddle seemed to put life into Marko, and a last flood of fury welled up in him. A knife flashed from out of his cummerbund, and with sudden strength he rose in his stirrups and slashed the chestnut over the flanks with the keen blade. The blood spurted, and the chestnut leapt madly into the night.

Sophka heard Arsa go into the kitchen and tell her mother-in-law.

When Marko had gone they brought Sophka's husband in to her, but she had already fallen into a fevered oblivion. She did not come to herself till morning light. It was shortly after dawn. The great tallow candle in the stick above her head had just burned down and extinguished itself, with a vile smell of tallow. He, her husband, was sleeping at her feet, practically on the bare floor.

He had evidently fallen asleep the moment they brought him in; and he was still sleeping soundly, his arms stretched out and his knees drawn up. Sophka could see that he had been afraid, if he fell asleep, of putting his head on the eiderdown that covered Sophka, and so of dirtying it and harming it; and he had carefully folded the edge away from him.

Through the window the well head showed its black outline, and from the stables came the sound of animals waking and moving about; but no sound came from the house; everything there was dead.

And, so that the cook, when she came to inspect, should find everything as it should be in marriage, Sophka had to get her husband up and undress him. She could not waken him for some time, so deeply was he asleep. She unwound his belt from off him, and undressed him, and drew him into the bed with her, and wrapped him and herself in the great red eiderdown, and waited for full day to come. She felt the hairs of his head pricking her neck and cheeks; for the hair was short cut as on a child. It had been recently washed , and smelled of soap.

Sophka did not get up again that day. A fever came on her, and she was delirious at times, and at night only came to herself again for a space. When she opened her eyes once she saw, beside her, the candle burning in its spattered stick, and a dish of food and drink that her mother-in-law had brought in quietly while she was in fever; because from her shame for all that had happened she dared not yet face Sophka awake. And at the foot of the bed, on a bare rush mat, lay Tomtcha, her husband, half-undressed only, curled up, sound asleep again. Sophka got up, and contrived to make the bed, and then took her husband to her, because she would have none of sparing herself and keeping him at arm's length. She would have none of being spared or pitied; for she had now gone through so much that the thing should be complete.

And so, weeping, she embraced sleeping Tomtcha and kissed him; and then, burning with a new excitement, half-conscious of what she was doing, she got up and went out into the courtyard, in the empty and silent walled-in night. Arsa was there crouching in a corner to protect her, and he came up to her to help her; but not only did she give him no orders—she stared at him as if she did not know him, and her dull and thirsting lascivious eyes made the hair of his scalp stiffen, and shivers course down his backbone.

This happened more than once. She would stride about in the night to tire herself, hair disordered, clinging to her moist temples, a demented sight as she held up her unbelted *shalvari** and her bosom showed beneath her unbuttoned shift. Then she would go back to her room and lie down again, and enfold and kiss her husband, and pray to God for it always to be like that, calm night.

Whole nights passed like that, till, by morning, worn out, she fell into a deep though fevered sleep, which would last on through the following day. And that fever was a good thing for her, since it allowed her to avoid all the customs that follow the bridal night—the inspection of the sheets and the coming of the women visitors, to whom she would have to pretend she was well and happy. . . .

Alec Brown

---

*loose trousers worn by both men and women in India and Southeast Asia.

Petar Kočić

(1877–1916)

Kočić was born in the village of Stričići near Banjaluka, Bosnia, into the family of an Orthodox priest. He came in conflict with the Austrian authorities already in high school in Sarajevo—a plight that plagued him for the rest of his life. He graduated from the University of Vienna and came back to his native region to teach but soon realized that his liberal, nationalistic views were incompatible with the entrenched ғoreign authority. He devoted the rest of his life to politics. He was even less successful in that endeavor even after he had moved to Serbia. He returned to Banjaluka, was persecuted and jailed for his nationalistic stand, and died in a mental hospital in Belgrade during World War I.

Kočić has written three books of short stories: *S planine i ispod planine* (From the Top and Bottom of a Mountain, 1902-1905), *Jauci sa Zmijanja* (Cries from Zmijanje, 1910), and *Sudanija* (Judgment Day, 1912). His best work is the play *Jazavac pred sudom* (The Hedgehog in Court, 1904). In all his works Kočić described realistically and poetically his countrymen from Bosnia, their strength and weaknesses, and their struggle with the Austrian occupation. He treats his peasants with warmth and understanding, although at times he tends to idealize them. This is best evidenced in the satirical *Jazavac pred sudom*, where an uneducated Bosnian peasant berates and outwits the great Austrian Empire.

Though uneven and somewhat limited, Kočić remains one of the most popular Serbian writers.

JABLAN

Dusk had fallen long ago.

In the stubbled field, below the village, on the sheltered side of the hill, Lujo snuggled up under his coat. Only his freckled face, with his large pale gray eyes, and a few little tufts of his yellowish hair, spread across his forehead were visible. Jablan grazed a few steps in front of him.

Every evening since the heat had started, Lujo had grazed Jablan far into the night. He took care of him, as he did of his own eyes. He gave him salt twice a week. He divided even his lunch with him. He loved Jablan—for Jablan was the strongest bull in the whole vicinity. Lujo was proud. He disdained all the other cattle herders and their bulls. He would dare spend a night in the middle of a cemetery if Jablan were with him.

"Only . . . tomorrow," Lujo trembled as if in dream; and, threw off his overcoat, his eyes sparkling with excitement.

He got up, went to the bull, and started patting him, coddling and whispering to him:

"Eat well, Jabo. Eat as much as your soul can stand. Only tomorrow, my dear Jabo, only tomorrow."

Lujo's little hoarse voice trembled softly, tenderly pleading. The bull swung his tail, as he did habitually, switching Lujo a bit on the cheek.

"Me, Jabo," he asked him reproachfully. "Now, I am going to cry."

He moved aside a bit, as if crying. Jablan raised his head.

"I am not, I am not, Jabo. I am kidding. You did not hit me. Well, don't get mad right away for nothing. Let us kiss each other."

They kissed. Lujo put on his overcoat and sat again on the wet grass to dream of tomorrow.

His Jablan was to fight the Imperial bull tomorrow. For a long time he had harbored within him a burning desire for Jablan to fight Rudonja. He had begged the Knez* to grant his wish. The elders too had begged the Knez.

"Well, my people, it is not so easy—it is the Imperial bull. But I will send a request. If the Emperor decrees that they should fight, let it be so. I would not prevent it; if he does not, it is as if nothing happened. Is it not so, brothers?"

"It is so, Knez. Just do it properly and do not fear."

The request had been sent, and the Knez had received the reply: it had been permitted. The following day was Transfiguration Day

---

*Jabo—diminutive of Jablan
**Knez was the regional official of the Austro-Hungarian Empire; he was usually chosen from the local residents.

and also the Emperor's birthday and at the Knez's place Jablan and Rudonja would fight.

Now Lujo began to dream about it. At one moment he saw Jablan falling down, at the next, he saw him gored and expiring; and, then again, he saw him as the winner, standing proudly on the battle field. He heard Jablan roar, so that the hills resounded. He sang:

> My dear little bull is stronger
> than that miserable cow of yours,
> than that big ugly cow.

"Are you cold, my Jabo?" one could hear Lujo say from under his coat.

Jablan grazed silently, and did not answer. Lujo got up, patted him, dragged two bundles of oats out of the hay stack, put them in front of the bull and then lay down next to him. After a time of fitful dreams and restless tossing, sleep overcame him. When Jablan had eaten the grain, he lay down next to his good friend.

The silence was profound. The humid freshness spread through the night. The soft wind sighed about the homes spread in a semi-circular row at the bottom of the mountain. The roofs, covered with moss, could barely be distinquished from the full, green orchards in the moonlight, through which they protruded. The village slept quietly, sweetly, like a sturdy, healthy, gruff mountain boy, whom mother has fed and rocked to sleep. . . .

The sun began to show behind the mountain peaks, still sleeping tiredly in the morning dusk. Soon, the mountain air glistened with light, and the meadow trembled—irridescent. Only there far away at the bottom of the mountains could be seen the remnants of foggy blueness. Everything arose, awakened. Everything steamed as hot blood, breathing with strength and freshness.

"Oh, it is sunrise already!" Lujo stretched, rubbed his eyes, and looked around.

"My Jabo, my brother, why didn't you wake me up?"

Jablan had gotten up early, very early, and had already finished grazing. Lujo was pleased when he saw Jablan's round stomach.

"Well, since you have eaten so well, brother, here is something for dessert," Lujo said cheerfully, and threw several bundles of oats to the bull.

Jablan ate. They started walking towards the Knez's home.

The crows were flying from the surrounding small woods, landing on the corn, which had just started to mature. The watchman chased them off. The scarecrows on the fences around the cornfields were fluttering. The herds were being driven to pasture. The shouting and calling was heard from all sides. Lujo walked thoughtfully behind Jablan. Lost in thought, he did not hear the commotion of that life which was going on around him. He was thinking of Jablan and the fight. Suddenly he started, as he had remembered something. He extended his palm and started to measure a stick.

"My Jabo will win—won't—he will—won't; he will—he won't; he will!" exclaimed Lujo, and his eyes sparkled with excessive joy.

From sheer delight, he began hugging and kissing the bull.

"Is it not so, my Jabo, that you will win? Even though he is the Imperial bull. It does not matter to my dear Jabo. Is it not so? Yes, tell it to your little Lujo."

In this manner, talking to Jablan, Lujo arrived at the Knez's home, where many people had gathered. It was a holiday, and people had gathered to talk a bit, and, as mountaineers, they liked to watch a bullfight.

Lujo's heart contracted when he saw Rudonja. He seemed horrible, huge; far stouter and bigger than Jablan.

"My Jabo, my brother, if you have to pay for this with your head today, do not blame me," Lujo exclaimed and nestled up to the bull, starting again to measure the stick, hiding this from the view of the crowd. Once again it showed that Jablan would win. His face brightened.

"Are you scared, my little one?"

"My son, do not fear anything. Your bull is an old fighter," an old man cheered him.

"I am not frightened at all," said Lujo confidently.

"I bet you will howl, little boy, when Rudonja cuts Jablan's guts," a fieldhand said, frightening him. "To be sure, Jablan has tortured me a lot."

"Well, that remains to be seen," laughed Lujo, with a measure of defiance and sarcasm.

"People, put aside the empty talk. Women and children on the side," ordered the Knez sharply in his most official manner.

"Lead the bulls onto the field, put down the fence."

They were led out. The people circled the bulls from all sides. The bulls started sniffing each other, as if they were getting acquainted.

"Go ahead, Jablan."

"Get him, Rudonja!"

The bulls started roaring, digging the ground with their forelegs, swaying and shoving, until the horns struck powerfully one against another. There was detonation, then breach. The land melted, yielding under them.

Lujo trembled in fear. His every nerve tingled. He stared with his large, pale eyes, not even blinking. He followed each movement; each clash resounded in his trembling heart. He flinched, crouched a little. He would have helped Jablan if he could. His eyes became dazed. He saw only vaguely that something turned around, twisted and yielded before him.

Rudonja attacked with all his might.

"Get him from below," shouted Lujo, as if beside himself.

Jablan, an old cunning fighter, made a move as if stumbling on his right foreleg and caught Rudonja under the neck.

"Don't let him do it, people, he will maim the bull," shouted the Knez, frightened. Under Rudonja's neck blood gushed forth. Lujo sang; Jablan stood proudly on the field and roared, and the mountain tops strongly, powerfully resounded.

Branko Mikasinovich

Veljko Petrović

(1884–1967)

A native of Sombor, Vojvodina, where he graduated from high school, Petrović studied law in Budapest and worked on various Serbian periodicals in Zagreb and Sarajevo. Because of his nationalistic attitude he moved to Belgrade, participated as a reporter in the Balkan Wars and World War I, and wrote poetry. Between the two wars he was active in cultural and educational affairs and continued to be so until his death in Belgrade in 1967.

Petrović first became known for his patriotic poetry, *Rodoljubive pesme* (Patriotic Poems, 1912) and *Na pragu* (On the Treshold, 1914). Afterwards, he turned to the short story and remained in the genre. His patriotic poetry is devoid of bombastic phrases and inflated pathos; it is rather a somber, realistic appraisal of his country and its past and a declaration of sincere, unconspicuous love for it. In his numerous stories he depicts, for the most part the life of the Serbs in Vojvodina, both under Austro-Hungary and later in Yugoslavia. His colorful descriptions of the Vojvodina peasants and small-town inhabitants offer a rich thematic canvas of a teeming life, replete with national, social, and moral problems. He has also written love stories and many stories for children.

His collections of short stories are: *Bunja i drugi iz Ravangrada* (Bunja and Others from Ravangrad, 1921), *Varljivo Proleće* (Changing Spring, 1921), *Pomerene savesti* (Demented Consciences, 1922), *Iskušenja* (Temptations, 1924), *Izdanci iz zapaljena grma* (Shoots from a Burning Stump, 1932), and *Prepelica u ruci* (A Quail in the Hand, 1948).

THE EARTH

In the spring of 1918, from France across Italy to Corfu. That means: in just forty hours from a Parisian spring to a Roman summer, to the excessive heat of Calabria. Such strange trips we're having! No one is capable of describing them any longer. False and scanty

171

indeed are the diaries of those few vain Serbs, because who was not ashamed of making notes of trifling, personal experiences at a time when entire nations were only cogs of one gigantic, roaring, demonic machine? But even those few, when they endeavored to write down everything with Rousseauvian sincerity, did little more than a vain enumeration of stopping places and insignificant personal, daily or general, political occurrences and worries. And that which subterraneously seethed in our souls and eroded them, that which we concealed or drowned out with our superficial intentions, tasks and visible pains, that which has caused us to observe strange lands and strange people in a special way, so that we would not recognize them today at all—all that receded as soon as we would arrive somewhere, at our temporary destinations. Therefore, our people avoided each other during these military, refugee movements even though the Serbs can sense one another in the largest crowds in the square of Milan's cathedral. Or having approached one another, they talked about refugee intrigues rather than about that tragically gloomy mood which lay in their hearts like a leaden sediment.

After the flowers and fruits of Lombardy, which eternally celebrates its Dionysian feast with its grapelike garlands from trunk to trunk, and the sunny Campagna, where even the gloomy Nazarene received the Apollonian toga and Ceasar's diadem instead of a crown of thorns rusted in blood, we entered the blinding-white, glowing South which was shimmering from heat. And those few knarred fig trees, lemon trees and palms were covered with the dust of this almighty, baked white rock. A stunted pony on the road was lost in a white cloud, and the black cassock of a fat priest on a two-wheeled wagon resembled the white garb of a Moslem sheik. Africa—Islamic and Nestorian! If the Christ of the Renaissance should reign in these temples, it would be one of history's many paradoxes. This is a home of either Greco's hysteria or the orthodox, grim Pantokrator.

In the train the passengers, undressed to their shirtsleeves, were sweating, panting and mopping their brows. Two nuns in heavy blue habits, girdled with iron and in hobnailed boots, were reading their prayer books motionlessly. They would not even touch their foreheads with their palms. Sweat was dripping from their noses, but they endured; their lips silently worked faster and faster. Were they repenting now also on account of our sinful, Serbian thoughts?

In Lece everybody ran off for beer, wine and oranges. Only the nuns remained. In that disorder I caught a glimpse of a Serbian back, peculiarly erect and strangely pushing sideways with a slightly raised right shoulder, and of unusually bent neck. His hat was slanted queerly on the back of his head. Luckily we bypassed each other.

But in Gallipoli, at the cry "Serbs, over here!" three of us—a broad-shouldered one, a deputy and myself—rushed right up to a former porter from Belgrade's "Moscow." His officer's cap was smiling and greeting us in a brotherly fashion. The government delegate was especially awaiting the deputy at his home, whereas the porter would take the remaining two of us afterwards to an apartment. He didn't ask us if we wanted to room together. God knows how long we were condemned to common lodging, because the boat, this I knew, did not come regularly.

Mr. Deputy, as soon as he found himself among the three Serbs, obviously became at ease. Without being introduced, he walked with dignity and, taking up the middle, was condescendingly inquiring who we were and why we were going to Corfu. He treated us as his constituents, the voting ballots. That third man was walking separately, a half step behind us, somehow quietly and inconspicuously. I don't know if he answered the deputy's words at all; we heard only his question:

"Well, gentlemen, will there be a boat for Corfu at least by tomorrow?"

The accent of Srem surprised me. Goodness, native sounds of Fruška Gora! While the porter explained that it was never known beforehand and that at times one had to wait here fifteen days, I was looking at my countryman. Since we had stopped for awhile, he took off his hat which stood cocked on top of his head and, wiping it inside with a handkerchief, listened so attentively that his small, deep-seeded, black eyes darted around. He was of medium stature with a round body on disproportionately thin legs; his head was very large, entirely round and fleshy, and all overgrown with plentiful hair that was crudely and evenly trimmed. On account of it, his forehead seemed very low. But what struck one's eye more than anything else was the fairness of the skin on his face, which could not tan even here; a small, waxenlike moustache; equally thin, fine eyebrows; a fleshy nose which seemed to recede into his full cheeks; and a round chin pressed onto a double chin. And his loose, clumsy-looking tie under a button revealed a peasant who was fattened on a rich estate and who maintained his corpulence even in exile, lording over his fields and vineyards at least in his thoughts.

". . . and since submarines have reappeared, as you know . . ."

"That's exactly what I'm asking you about!" The man from Srem impatiently interrupted and stepped up close, examining all three of us with his eyes. "Four days ago at midnight, isn't that right, they torpedoed a boat on which our students were. You know, my son was with them, God forbid. Do you know anything about them? Were they rescued and which ones of them . . . excuse me, but you know. . . ."

All three of us became sombre at once, while the porter hastened stammeringly:

"Yes, yes, unfortunately, we were informed, but we don't know yet if all have been rescued. It could be that they have already landed somewhere, the boats and rafts with them, but there is no news yet. Now we will ask Mr. Deputy."

On the way, the man from Srem explained to us that his son volunteered last year after he and a friend had left with our army when it pulled out of Dobanovac. (That means that he is from the plains of Srem and not from Fruška Gora.) Now he was freed from military duty and was being sent to study in France. His son wrote him that he was coming to Marseilles in a few days, but when the man from Srem read the dispatch in Nice about the torpedoing of our boat with students bound for Corfu, he immediately feared the worst. He sent a telegram to Corfu but, not being able to wait for an answer, set off personally to see and hear what happened to his son. God grant that they pass each other by; there is nothing easier than to return! But considering his misfortune from the very beginning of this war. . . .

The frightened father told us all this slowly and half aloud. He was able to breathe deeply only now and then in the middle of a word, as if he were suppressing a sigh or a cry. We immediately asked him his name, as if that would help us in the search. Sava Nedeljković, said the landowner, but the name of his son was or, God forbid, had been Miloš, a high school graduate of Sremski Karlovci.

The delegate didn't know what else to say either, except that there really were fourteen students on the ship. If there were any still in Corfu who were waiting to depart by another ship or who were perhaps already on their way, he didn't know. But he would send a telegram this very evening to the government asking for exact information, especially about Miloš.

After we saw our room not far from the delegate's apartment, in a narrow little side-street through which sea air was blowing and from which the endless, livid-green sea was seen in the immediate vicinity, as if one were looking from some walled-in stone tower into the clouds and a teeming forest, the man from Srem bid me farewell.

"Just go into town, sir. I somehow don't feel like eating supper or seeing people. I'm going down by the sea a ways to take a walk; then I'll go to bed. You just go ahead. Don't tiptoe if you find me sleeping. I'm a sound sleeper."

After supper, we left in groups for the coast. While some were stopping to cool their feet in the sea, it seemed to me that I saw Nedeljković sitting on a rock and looking out into the water over which the moonlight silently flickered. Afterwards we dropped in for a cup of "espresso" and discussed things of domestic interest. Then each, guessing and feeling in the dark, went to his quarters.

When I lit a candle, I noticed that Nedeljković lay facing the wall but that he was blinking. He pretended that he was asleep, poor man; therefore I undressed quietly. Suddenly he sighed deeply and painfully. I started and turned toward him. He sat up and looked at me with his obviously weeping, bloodshot eyes.

"I've lost him, you'll see! But where, where? . . . Did you see what a huge monster that was, with no end or bottom? . . ."

"Don't despair already, Mr. Nedeljković! Who knows? Wait. Believe in God, in a lucky turn of events. He wouldn't be the first who was rescued. Not long ago I saw one of our majors in Rome who was torpedoed three times, two times on the way from Bizerte, and each time luckily saved himself on a raft."

"God grant, sir! But, you know, it's empty here." He struck himself on the chest. "I keep thinking of the worst—that I will never hear anything more about him. When the sea swallows, it devours all, both man's body and his cross. It probably even holds up the human so until the judgement day. Oh, my great misfortune! What will I tell his mother if she still lives? What will I say to her grave if she is already dead?"

". . . I'm sorry, sir," he continued. "You are certainly tired, and I'm not letting you sleep. Excuse me. As a learned Serb, please listen to me, an unfortunate father and a simple farmer. It is God's dreadful punishment when death overcomes a christened soul on the open sea, without a trace and a sound, without a cross and a suitable grave! If my good child's luck was that the sea should swallow him, at least it should return his dead body to Mother Earth. It should throw him out on land somewhere. As it happens, some good Christians would probably find his remains and bury them . . . so that he could appear to me in a dream and comfort his parent in his great sorrow. But that the Lord should punish us in this way, that the abyss should swallow him, that the fish and the ocean's beasts should devour him. . . ."

"Don't torture yourself with such nonsense, Mr. Nedeljković! Pray that God brings him back to you alive and healthy . . . but, but when one is already dead, it's all the same, so to speak, wherever our dead bodies happen to lie and whatever might be done with them."

"Don't talk like that, sir!" Nedeljković jumped out of his bed and, having seized me by the arm, continued thanking me. "You are young. Wait until you are older, when you have children and bury them! Wait until you return to your people and live with them. You have alienated yourself a little from the people and the soil. Wait until you go back and see how all that is born on earth must return to earth, both the dew and the seed as well as beast and man. Such is the divine law. There is no life on the earth without the dead in the earth. There is neither room nor peace in the heavens for the soul until the body returns to its legitimate owner. I am a simple man and I live on earth and of earth, that's why I know. That is the divine law. We are all indebted to the earth with our body; therefore we must return it when our soul leaves it. If we were not to obey that law, where would prosperity be, where would all the progress be, all the human toil and joy? It cannot be the divine will that my son disappeared in that abyss; rather God has yielded to the devil. But who among us has so sinned that my child should be a reward to the devil? And how much more blood must be shed so that my son's sin can be expiated, so that his soul can find peace? Excuse me, sir. I won't disturb you anymore."

I was completely helpless and, sensing the absurdity of all my words, merely repeated that he must hope, and that peace of mind did not depend on whether a man was buried in the ground or lowered into the sea, as it is done with sailors and on many small islands. I saw that he did not want to understand me.

For some time I did not fall asleep, but Nedeljković in all likelihood didn't even shut his eyes. Pale and haggard, he went to our delegation early to see if news of any kind had come.

Just after I had sat down to breakfast, the "porter" ran in to ask me to come to the delegation. In the market square I met the delegate accompanied by the deputy. Both were very excited and said that it was necessary to hurry to the prefecture before Nedeljković came because we had to arrange in advance how to inform him of the following:

It was reported this hour by the prefect that fishermen from Gallipoli ran upon a raft early this morning with four of our soldiers. As the sun rose out of the water, the fishermen caught sight of them not far from their own boat, and clearly distinguished four people up to their chest in water, who were holding on to the raft by a rope. The fishermen wondered why the soldiers didn't wave or answer to their cries. Only when they approached the raft did they see that all four were dead and stiff. They had to cut the rope in order to separate and load them—quite young soldiers, frozen, with open mouths and eyes as if they were smiling. The bodies were at the prefecture now; the prefect was asking the delegate to forgive the fishermen for having rummaged in their pockets. Identification cards were found on the bodies. The prefect succeeded in reading them. Among them was also Miloš Nedeljković. The delegate and deputy nervously asked me whether I would like to be the one to call Nedeljković to come here. He would most likely be at the beach near his lodging place, if by now somebody hadn't already told him about this morning's event.

This duty was not pleasant, but I had to accept it. The conversation with him last night encouraged me, I admit that.

He was aware that I was bringing with me something painful for him.

"What is it, sir?" But his left eye danced off in fear.

I related to him that he was being called to the prefecture; and, running out in the sun, I told him the whole truth. He ran and breathed as an asthmatic, stumbling and not saying anything.

On the ground floor, before the door of some room, we found them all, about five or six people—Italian officers besides our two countrymen. Nedeljković had enough strength to greet the prefect and to shake his hand.

On two tables, one beside the other, our poor handsome youths lay, their legs spread out a little, their arms drawn together over their heads, painful smiles on their livid faces. From their overcoats, isolated drops were still dripping on the floor. Nedeljković came up immediately, lowered his head for a moment, groaned dejectedly and quietly, and embraced one of the heads kissing it on the forehead.

"My child! . . . my son! . . . that your father should find you so!" He spoke quietly and calmly, crossed himself once more, and, with a tremble that was scarcely noticeable, disappeared behind the others saying:

"Please, gentlemen, you may enter!"

After the formalities were finished, Nedeljković asked that all duties concerning preparations and deathwatch before the funeral in the cemetery chapel be given to him. Because there was not an Eastern Orthodox priest in the town, the Catholic priest sang the requiem. The Serbs who were present only chanted the alleluia. Nedeljković held himself together with a forced composure. Only when the bodies were lowered into the pit carved into the limy rock did he sob. All the people present sensed that it was God's blessing and mitigation for him.

"My son, since God has not granted that I embrace you alive, thanks be to Him that your father has found you dead."

On return; all the Serbs gathered around him as if he were the father of all four drowned youths. But it was not necessary to support or comfort him. Even though he wiped off a few big teardrops every now and then, he spoke to all of us quite calmly.

"Don't these people here have pastures anywhere with yellow earth or at least sand and nitre for their own dead? They hold them above the earth in stone caskets to bake in that heat. That's why that cemetery of theirs smells. Did you notice that, gentlemen? It's a sin even to mention it, but it is suffocating from all sides! Oh, my sweet son, if only your father returns home alive, he'll spend his last penny to take you to your beautiful country, to our flowers and greenery. . . ."

W. Murray Linker

Ivo Andrić

(1892–   )

Andrić was born near Travnik, in Bosnia. He received his education in Zagreb‘ Graz, and Vienna. During World War I he was imprisoned by the Austrians because of his open pro-Yugoslav stand. After the war he served as a diplomat in many European capitals. Following World War II he became the leading living Yugoslav author. In 1961 he received the Nobel Prize, the first and only one in all of Southestern Europe. Today he lives in retirement in Belgrade, working on the third part of his Bosnian trilogy.

His first works, poems in prose *Nemiri* (Unrest, 1918) and *Ex Ponto* (1918), showed early his predilection for musing about the human condition, man's suffering, and his attempts to find rapport with nature, his fellow man, and himself. This has remained his main theme. In many short stories between the wars he consistently chose his native Bosnia at the crossroads of many nations, religions, and creeds, as a microcosm of man's difficult existence. His heroes—Moslems, Christians, and Jews—constantly face violence and alienation, struggling to achieve eluding goals and preserve their dignity. The pronounced local color, taken from Bosnia of the distant and recent past, is used by the author as a stage for dealing with universal problems and concerns.

This method is brought to unusual excellence in his best works, the novels *Na Drini ćuprija* (The Bridge on the Drina, 1945) and *Travnička hronika* (The Chronicle of Travnik, 1945). They form the first two parts of his Bosnian trilogy. In the first, in addition to offering an epic panorama of the life of Bosnian towns during the last several centuries, with all its joys and sorrows, conflicts and suffering, Andrić uses the metaphor of a bridge—his favorite image—to symbolize the need for man to reach agreement with his fellow man of a different persuasion. The alternative has often been death and destruction of man, whereas the bridge endures or rises out of ruins anew. *Travnička hronika* offers a skillful presentation of the historical, philosophical, religious, and cultural atmosphere in one period during the turbulent history of a Bosnian town at the meeting point between the East and the West.

Andrić's penetration into the profound dilemmas facing his native Bosnians, and through them all men, and his ability to distill his artistic expression to perfection have brought him deserved laurels. His crafty style is characterized by keen observation, serenity, the calmness of a sage, and economy of words.

His other important works are: *Gospodjica* (Miss, 1945), *Prokleta avlija* (Accursed Courtyard, 1954), and many short stories of anthological value.

THIRST

Immediately after the Austrian occupation, a gendarme barracks was built in the highland village of Sokolac. The commander of the station brought a pretty blond wife along with him, with large blue eyes which had a glassy look. With her frail beauty, with her European dress and fashion, she looked like a small treasure, which had been lost by travelers journeying over this mountain summit, on the way from one big town to another.

The village had not recovered from its first wonder, nor had the young wife arranged her marriage room, full of small cushions, embroideries and ribbons, when highwaymen appeared in this region. A platoon of gendarmes arrived at the barracks, doubling the staff. The commander spent his days and nights up and down the countryside supervising and arranging patrols. The young wife lived confused and scared, in the company of the village women, just so that she would not be considered to be living alone. Her time passed in waiting. Her sleeping and eating turned into mere expectation with nothing to sustain and strengthen her. The village women begged and urged her to eat and urging, ate and drank everything themselves. At night, they told her stories and personal experiences in order to put her to sleep. Finally, the women, tired of talking, would fall asleep on the red rug, and she would look at them from the bed, wide awake, bothered by the heavy smell of milk and wool, which rose from the sleeping housewives. And when the commander would arrive after many days of waiting, even then she was neither more joyful, nor consoled. The man returned home thoroughly tired from walking, and lack of sleep, bearded, dirty, and wet. Boots that he had not taken off for several days would become tight from moisture and mud; two aids strained to take them off with woolen stockings tearing the skin from the swollen and sore feet. He was worried and distraught because of his lack of success, continually planning in his thoughts a new chase. His worry and zeal made him thin, his lips became chapped, and face darkened from sun, wind and the mountain air. During these short rest periods at home, his wife treated him like a wounded man, and after two or three days, she would send him back again at dawn to the mountain.

Because of this, all her thoughts and prayers had only one aim, that these highwaymen be caught as soon as possible, and that this horrible life be ended.

One day, her greatest desire was realized. The most important and cleverest highwayman, Lazar Zelenović, was caught. After him, according to the talk in the barracks and the village, it would be easier to catch or to chase away the less important, less skillful, and less experienced highwaymen.

Lazar was caught accidentally. A patrol, which was chasing another, younger highwayman, stumbled onto him. Two months earlier, when he came over from Herzegovina, Lazar had been wounded by a bullet in the chest. No one knew this. To cure himself, Lazar, with the help of younger highwaymen, had made a shelter of dry branches, flooded mud, and parts of a fallen tree located near a brook, under a big log. He managed to live in this hole, hidden from view from the paths high above the brook, and was able to reach for water with his hand. He washed the wound on his chest all day long, while the patrols were looking for him everywhere, uphill and downhill. Perhaps he would have recovered had he dared to look for a better hiding place and had it not been for the early hot weather which aggravated the wound. He was defending himself from flies and from mosquitoes as well as he could, but the wound broadened and deepened, where water could not reach it, and the infection spread. His fever rose.

Such was his condition when his younger friend tried to bring some wax and whiskey as medicine. The patrol noticed the young man as he left a shepherd's hut and went to the brook in the mountain. Having noticed the patrol at the last moment, the young man ran away along the brook and disappeared without a trace.

The commander, who had left his horse in the pasture and on foot ran ahead of the gendarmes after the young highwayman, fell up to his waist in mud and sediment and with his leg hit something soft and immovable. Perhaps he would have continued further, were it not difficult to get himself out; and he would not even have noticed Lazar's small and skillfully hidden shelter, had he not smelled the awful stench of the highwayman's wound. After getting his legs out, the commander looked through the gap in the branches and noticed sheepskin. Having sensed that a man was hiding in the hole below him, it did not even occur to him that it might be Lazar himself; he thought that it was the

younger highwayman or one of his friends. In order to deceive the
hidden highwayman, the commander loudly ordered the gendarmes:

"He must have gone along the brook further away. Run after him
and I will follow you slowly, because I hurt my leg on this thorn."

While shouting the order, he gave his men a sign with one hand to
keep quiet and, with the other, to gather around him. When the three
of them had gathered, they threw themselves simultaneously on the
hiding place and caught the highwayman from behind, like a badger.
Since he had only a long rifle and a big knife, he could neither shoot,
nor swing. They chained his hands and tied his feet with rope, and
carried him like a log through the backwoods to the meadow where
the commander's horse was waiting. On the way to the meadow they
smelled the heavy stench, and, when they placed him on the grass,
they saw the big wound in his bear chest. A certain Živan from Goražde,
who worked as a jailor and an informer, recognized Lazar at once.
They were from the same village; both celebrated the same patron's
day, Saint John.

The highwayman rolled his large gray eyes, clear from living in the
open, near water, though inflamed by the fever. The commander asked
Živan to verify once again that it was really Lazar. Everybody leaned
over the highwayman. Živan told him for the second time:

"It is you, Lazar!"

"I see that you know me better than I know you."

"You know me too, Lazar. How would you not know me?"

"Ah, had I never known you, I would have recognized now who
you were and what you did. All the villages, Serbian and Turkish,
would recognize you from here to Goražde. If you were to bring the
stupidest child, who had never seen us, and if the child saw us the way
we are, it would have said: The one who is bound and wounded is
Lazar, and the wicked man who is leaning over him—that is Živan!"

The highwayman had a feverish need to speak, as if in that way
he was prolonging his life, and Živan wanted to show his power and
defend his reputation in front of the others. Who knows for how long
these two would have argued in this way, had they not been interrupted
by the commander? But the highwayman would not answer any other
questions. He did not want to say anything about his friends and
accomplices. He excused himself because of his wound and sickness.
The commander, after consulting with the seargent-major of the gen-

darmes, a husky man from Lika, ordered sharply that the highwayman should not be given even a drop of water, no matter how much he begged for it, but to tell him to address himself to the commander.

While they were preparing what was necessary for the transportation of the wounded highwayman, the young commander sat off to one side to rest and compose himself. He put an elbow on his knee and his head on his wrist looking at the mountain as large as the sea, which only recently had become green. He wanted to think of his success, of the recognition that was awaiting him, of returning to his wife. But his thought could not attach itself to anything. He felt only a leaden tiredness he had to fight, as a man who has to sleep overnight in the snow must resist sleep and freezing. Rising painfully from the ground, he got up and ordered them to move. The other patrol caught up with them. Now there were nine of them. The stretcher which they had made for the highwayman was rough and knotty. One of the gendarmes threw his raincoat over it, turning his face away, while doing it, as if he were throwing it into an abyss.

They were travelling slowly. The sun became hotter. The commander, who had been riding behind the stretcher, had to move up to the front, because the odor from the wounded man wes unbearable. But in the afternoon, when they descended to the plain of Glasinac, they took a wagon and oxen from a peasant. So, they appeared on the plain before Sokolac just before sunset. They looked like a returning hunting party, except that the hunters were thoughtful and the quarry was unusual.

In the meadow in front of the barracks the village women and children gathered. Among them was also the commander's wife. At the beginning she did not even think of the highwayman; she was only waiting for her husband, as always. But as the women talked more and more about the highwayman who was being carried, and as their stories became more fantastic with the approaching column stretched and slow like a funeral, she felt full of apprehension and expectation. Finally they arrived. The people noisily were opening the left wing of the gate, normally opened only when they brought in wood or hay. The column entered directly in front of the barracks' door. Here the commander got off his horse, hitting the ground heavily as a tired man dismounts. The young woman felt his sharp beard of several day's growth on her face, and smelled the sweat, earth and rain which he always brought from his official expeditions.

While the commander was giving orders, his wife cast a glance at the highwayman who was lying tied and still all the time. Only his head was elevated a bit since it rested on a piece of wood against some hay. His eyes looked at no one. A sharp stench was spreading from him as from a wounded animal.

When the commander had ordered what was to be done, he took his wife by the hand and led her into the house, so that she would not see them taking him off the stretcher and untying him. After washing and changing himself, the commander went out once more to see where they had put Lazar and if they had tied him. The highwayman was confined in the basement under the commander's lodging, which was supposed to serve as a temporary prison. The door was weak, with an iron bar in the upper half, and the lock was a common one. Because of this, a guard was posted for the whole night.

The commander ate little but talked to his wife continually. He talked about little things, lively and joyful as a child. He was content. He had caught the most important and the most dangerous highwayman, after five months of wandering and effort and undeserved reproaches from his superiors in Rogatica and the headquarters in Sarajevo. He would learn from Lazar about the highwaymen and their hideouts and the names of their accomplices, and in this way he would be able to rest fully and win recognition.

"And what if he does not want to betray others?" asked his wife fearfully.

"He will do it, he will have to," answered the commander, not talking further about it with his wife.

The commander felt sleepy. Fatigue was overcoming him, and it was even stronger than his joy, hunger, and desire for his wife. The freshness of the bed was intoxicating him. He made himself talk further and tried to show that he was not sleepy, but the words stopped in his mouth, he stuttered and the distance between words became ever longer. He fell asleep in the middle of a sentence, holding his wife's small, white, round shoulder with the fingers of his left hand. His wife was not sleepy. She was pleased and excited, scared and sad. For a long time she looked at the sleeping man, whose right cheek sank in the softness of the featherbedding, with his mouth open a little, as if he were eagerly drinking the pillow. A cold and large distance is always created between a person wide awake and the one asleep, a coldness which grows with every minute and is filled more and more with misunderstanding and with a strange feeling of abandonment and intense loneliness. The woman herself tried to fall asleep. She closed her eyes and breathed evenly. But, the change of the guard in front of the basement door woke her up from her first dream. Her thoughts returned to the highwayman, as if she had not slept and as if she had thought of nothing else.

The same Živan, Lazar's countryman, was on guard. Now, she realized that she was not awakened by the change of the guard, as much as by Lazar's calling. The highwayman asked for water.

"Who is on guard?"

"Silence."

"Is it you Živan?"

"Yes, it is me. Keep quiet!"

"Well, how am I to keep quiet, you traitor, when I am dying of thirst and fever? But, give me some water, Živan for the sake of St. John, our patrons, so that I will not die like this—as an animal."

Živan pretended not to hear anything and did not answer in the hope that the highwayman would get weary of begging. But the highwayman kept calling him with his quiet, hoarse voice.

"If you know what suffering and prison are, do not turn a deaf ear to me, Živan, for the sake of the life of your children!"

"Do not swear by my children. You know that I am obeying orders and that this is my job. Keep quiet. You are going to wake up the commander."

"Let him sleep in misery! He is worse than a Turk, for he tortures me with thirst, in spite of all my evil luck! But, hand me over some water if you are a brother of mine in God."

From their hushed conversation, the wife determined that by the commander's order, they were not giving him water, because they wanted to force him, by thirst, to betray his comrades and accomplices. The highwayman, tortured by unbearable thirst and fever, had apparently found some relief in swearing at God, in a string of harsh words and curses, and in the constant repetition of the word "water." He would keep quiet for several moments, and then he would let out a long, deep, manly sigh, followed by a torrent of words.

"Eh, Živan, Živan, may you get leprosy from my bread and salt for torturing me in a way such as nobody has ever tortured anybody. Give me a jug of water and then kill me at once, and may you be forgiven in this world and the next."

But Živan stopped answering him.

"Živan . . . Živan, I beg you as if you were God . . . I am burning!"

Silence. The last quarter of the scorched moon appeared late.

Živan hid himself in a shadow and now when he spoke his voice was not as clear. The highwayman was calling the commander loudly.

"Oh, commander, please do not torture me any more, for the sake of the Tsar's bread, without need."

After each of his calls, the silence was deeper. In that depth, the highwayman was grunting heavily and growling hoarsely, neither lowering his voice, nor paying attention to what he said.

"Oooh, you filthy bitches, may God let you drink blood all your lives and never quench your thirst. Let your blood gush out through your noses. Where are you, commander; may dogs have your mother!"

He yelled the last words with a choking, feeble voice, which was faltering in the dried-out throat. Again Živan started to hush him up and kept promising that at sunrise he would call the commander and that he would surely give him some water; he only had to confess to them what they asked him, and until that time he should have to endure. But the highwayman, in his fever, forgot about everything after several moments and again whined:

"Živan, for God's sake, I am burning! Water!"

He was repeating this word for the hundredth time the way a child would, changing with his unequal, feverish breath the strength of his voice and pronunciation.

Awake and trembling, the wife listened to all of this—the highwayman's screaming, Živan's whispered orders for silence coming in hisses, and her husband's heavy and deep sleeping beside her—sitting on the edge of the bed and not feeling her body or the room around her, losing herself in the hitherto unknown horror.

During her childhood, in her parent's home, it happened some nights in the autumn or spring that she could not sleep and she would listen to something all night alone, to some oppressive and monotonous noise from outside: the wind turning the tin weather vane, or tapping the little garden gate which they forgot to lock. As a child, she attached particular meaning to this noise, imagining that those noises were living beings, who were fighting, groaning, and sobbing. Life in its wider scope often makes the imaginations and the fears of our child-hood real, and from the little, imaginative fears creates the great and true ones. Would it not be wonderful if the innocent horrors, which sometimes tore her girlish dreams, were real and if this night in the wild village, in her marriage bed, above the horrible highwaymans' conversation and screams, if this were only imagination and a dream.

And during all that time, just as with the tin weather vane or the dry board in the little open garden gate under the wind, the man's heavy, even breathing was coming regularly as did the exhausted human voice, which was passing through a dry wide-open mouth, over the burnt, immovable tongue.

"Water, water! Oooh!"

Živan was replaced on guard-duty by another gendarme, but the highwayman's cry for water did not stop, but became weaker and more tired. The woman was still sitting, stiffly, listening to every murmur from below. She constantly thought about one and the same thing without end and conclusion. How can one comprehend and under-stand this life and these people? She sees only that there are gendarmes and the others, the highwaymen (two faces of one and the same mis-fortune), chasing each other without mercy, and that one has to pine away among them from grief and compassion.

A lot of things had been said long ago about this Lazar in Sokolac. She heard stories of his cruelty. She had heard how he tortured in the most horrible way the peasants who did not submit to him; how he killed gendarmes from ambush, stripping them naked, and leaving them thus on the road. Well, see how here the gendarmes are now paying him back their debt. But, can it go on forever this way? It seemed to her that they were recklessly leaping into an abyss and that all of them would perish in this night without sunrise, in blood, in thirst, and in unknown fears.

From time to time, she thought of waking her husband, to ask him to scatter this horrible dream with one word and one smile. But she did not move from her place, neither did she wake her husband. Instead she sat immovable, as if a dead body were beside her, listening to the voice from the basement, alone, with her fears and her questions. She even thought about the prayers that they taught her in childhood, but these were the prayers of another, forgotten and sunken life, and they could give her neither solace nor help. As with her own death, she was reconciled to the thought that the one who was screaming would beg and howl forever, and this one, beside her, would go on sleeping and breathing like this eternally.

The oppressive night was becoming even thicker and heavier. It was no longer a common night, one of the innumerable ones in a series of days and nights, but the only one, an eternal and endless desert of darkness in which the last living man was howling and begging, asking for a drop of water, without any hope of help. But in all of God's big world, with waters, rains, and dews, there was not even a drop of water, and there was not even one hand out of all living human beings to offer help. The waters have dried up and the people have grieved to death. Only her little flame of awareness lives, as the lone witness of it all.

Nevertheless, the dawn came. The wife looked unbelievingly as the wall became white, in the same place as at previous dawns, and how the dawn, first gray and then rosy, conquered the room and separated and brought to life the things in it.

Straining her hearing, she could still distinguish the highwayman's voice, but as if it came from far away. There was no swearing or cursing, only the hoarse and less frequent:

"Ooooooo, ooooooo, oo!"

Even that she guessed at more than heard.

Although the dawn was conquering, the wife had no strength to move. All stiff, bent with her head in her palms, she sat on the edge of the bed and did not even notice when the commander woke up.

The man opened his rested eyes and looked, and his eyes fell on his wife's bent back and her pale neck. Then, after the first hesitation, an awareness of this joyful reality passed through him like a soft and sweeping wave. He felt like calling his wife, shouting her name, but he changed his mind. Smiling, he raised himself a bit, noiselessly supporting himself on his left elbow, and with his free right hand, silently, suddenly embraced her shoulders, and drew her to him, and pushed her under him.

The wife struggled shortly and in vain. This sudden and irresistible embrace seemed horrible to her. It seemed to her impossible and sacrilegious that she could betray the world of night in which she had lived and suffered until that moment, alone with her suffering, that she could do it so quickly and easily, without a word of explanation. She wanted to resist and to convince him that it would not be, that there are difficult and painful things which she had to tell him, and which cannot be so easily overlooked before the return to everyday life. Bitter words gushed out of her, but she could not utter even one. She only choked and the man did not notice this sign of her resistance; a sound which did not even succeed in becoming a single word. She wanted to push him away, but her movements hardly matched the strength of her bitterness, or the quickness of her thoughts. The very warmth of this rested and alert body oppressed her like a burden. The bones and muscles in her young frame yielded like an obedient machine. Her mouth was sealed by his lips. She felt him on her like a huge stone to which she was bound, falling with it like an arrow without a place to stop.

Losing consciousness, not only of last night but of life itself, she sank into a desolate, gloomy sea of the familiar but always new sweetness. Above her remained the last traces of her nocturnal thoughts, decisions and of all human compassion, which were disappearing one after another, like water bubbles over a drowning man.

The white, decorated room was rapidly becoming full of the living light of the day.

Branko Mikasinovich

THE BRIDGE ON THE DRINA

(Excerpts)

Outside it was growing light. The sun had not yet risen, but the whole horizon was clear. Deep among the hills the clouds lay in long dull purple bands and between them could be seen the clear sky almost green in color. Scattered patches of mist lay over the moist earth out of which peeked the tops of fruit trees with sparse yellowish leaves. Still striking at his boot with his whip, Abidaga gave orders. The criminal should continue to be interrogated, especially about those who had helped him, but he should not be tortured beyond endurance lest he die. Everything must be made ready so that at noon that same day he should be impaled alive on the outermost part of the construction work at its highest point, so that the whole town and all the workers should be able to see him from the banks of the river; Merdžan was to get everything ready and the towncrier to announce the execution through all the quarters of the town, so that at midday all the people might see what happened to those who hindered the building of the bridge, and that the whole male population, both Turks and *rayah*, from children to old men, must gather on one or other of the banks to witness it.

The day which was dawning was a Sunday. On Sunday work went on as on any other day, but this day even the overseers were distrait. As soon as it was broad daylight, the news spread about the capture of the criminal, his torture and his execution which was to take place at midday. The hushed and solemn mood of the stable spread over the whole area about the building works. The men on forced labor worked silently, each one avoided looking his neighbor in the eyes, and each man looked only to the work before him as if that were the beginning and the end of his world.

An hour before noon the people of the town, for the most part Turks, had collected on a level space near the bridge. Children were hoisted on to high blocks of building stone which were lying about. The workmen swarmed around the narrow benches where the meagre rations which kept them alive were usually distributed. Chewing at them, they were silent and looked uneasily about them. A little later Abidaga appeared, accompanied by Tosun Effendi, Mastro Antonio and one or two of the more prominent Turks. All stood on a samll dry hummock between the bridge and the stable where the condemned man was. Abidaga went once more to the stable, where he was told that everything was ready; lying there was an oak stake about eight feet long, pointed as was necessary and tipped with iron, quite thin and sharp, and all well-greased with lard. On the scaffolding were the blocks between which the stake would be embedded and nailed, a wooden mallet for the impalement, ropes and everything else that was needed.

The man from Plevlje was distraught, his face earthen in color and his eyes bloodshot. Even now he was not able to endure Abidaga's flaming glances.

"Listen, you! If everything is not as it should be and if you disgrace me in public, neither you nor your bastard of a gipsy will ever appear before me again, for I will drown you both in the Drina like a pair of blind puppies."

Then, turning to the shivering gipsy, he said more kindly:

"You will get six grosh* for the job, and another six if he stays alive till nightfall. See to it!"

The hodža called out from the main mosque in the marketplace in a clear sharp voice. Uneasiness spread among the assembled people and a few moments later the door of the stable opened. Ten guards were drawn up in two ranks, five on either side. Between them was Radisav, barefooted and bareheaded, alert and stooping as ever, but he no longer "sowed" as he walked but marched strangely with short steps, almost skipping on his mutilated feet with bleeding holes where the nails had been; on his shoulders he carried a long white sharpened stake. Behind him was Merdžan with two other gipsies who were to be his helpers in the execution of the sentence. Suddenly from somewhere or other the man from Plevlje appeared on his bay and took his place at the head of the procession, which only had to go about a hundred paces to reach the first scaffolding.

The people craned their necks and stood on tiptoe to see the man who had hatched the plot and destroyed the building work. They were all astonished at the poor miserable appearance of the man they had imagined to be quite different. Naturally, none of them knew why he hopped in so droll a manner and took abrupt little steps, and none of them could see the burns from the chain which crossed his chest like great belts, for his shirt and cloak hid them. Therefore he seemed to all those there too wretched and too insignificant to have done the deed which now brought him to execution. Only the long white stake gave a sort of gruesome grandeur to the scene and kept everyone's eyes fixed on it.

When they reached the spot on the bank where the excavation work began, the man from Plevlje dismounted and with a sort of solemn and theatrical air gave the reins to a groom, then disappeared with the others in the steep muddy track which led down to the water's edge. A little later the people saw them again as they appeared in the

---

*a copper.

same order on the staging, climbing upwards slowly and carefully. On the narrow passages made of planks and beams the guards closely surrounded Radisav and kept him very near them lest he should leap into the river. They dragged their way along slowly and climbed even higher till they reached the top. There, high above the water, was a boarded space about the size of a small room. On it, as on a raised stage, they took their places, Radisav, the man from Plevlje and the three gipsies, with the rest of the guards posted around them on the platform.

The people watching moved uneasily and shifted about. Only a hundred paces separated them from those planks, so that they could see every man and every movement, but could not hear words or distinguish details. The people and the workmen on the left bank were about three times farther away, and moved around as much as they could and made every effort to try and hear to see better. But they could hear nothing and what they could see seemed at first only too ordinary and uninteresting and at the end so terrible that they turned their heads away and many quickly went home, regretting that they had ever come.

When they ordered Radisav to lie down, he hesitated a moment and then, looking past the gipsies and guards as if they were not there, came close up to the man from Plevlje and said almost confidentially as if speaking to a friend, softly and heavily:

"Listen, by this world and the next, do your best to pierce me well so that I may not suffer like a dog."

The man from Plevlje started and shouted at him, as if defending himself from that too intimate approach:

"March, Vlach! You who are so great a hero as to destroy the Sultan's work now beg for mercy like a woman. It will be as it has been ordered and as you have deserved."

Radisav bent his head still lower and the gipsies came up and began to strip off his cloak and his shirt. On his chest the wounds from the chains stood out, red and swollen. Without another word the peasant lay down as he had been ordered, face downward. The gipsies approached and the first bound his hands behind his back; then they attached a cord to each of his legs, around the ankles. Then they pulled outwards and to the side, stretching his legs wide apart. Meanwhile Merdžan placed the stake on two small wooden chocks so that it pointed between the peasant's legs. Then he took from his belt a short broad knife, knelt beside the stretched-out man and leant over him to cut away the cloth of his trousers and to widen the opening through which the stake would enter his body. This most terrible part of the bloody task was, luckily, invisible to the onlookers. They could only see the bound body shudder at the short and unexpected prick of the knife, then half rise as if it were going to stand up, only to fall back again at once, striking dully against the planks. As soon as he had finished, the gypsy leapt up, took the wooden mallet and with slow measured blows began to strike the lower blunt end of the stake. Between each two blows he would stop for a moment and look first at the body in which the stake was penetrating and then at the two gypsies, reminding them to pull slowly and evenly. The body of the peasant, spread-eagled, writhed convulsively; at each blow of the mallet his spine twisted and bent, but the cords pulled at it and kept it straight. The silence from both banks of the river was such that not only every blow but even its echo from somewhere along the steep bank could be clearly heard. Those nearest could hear how the man beat with his forehead against the planks, and, even more, another and unusual sound, that was neither a scream, nor a wail, nor a groan, nor anything human; that stretched and twisted body emitted a sort of creaking and cracking like a fence that is breaking down or a tree that is being felled. At every second blow the gypsy went over to the stretched-out body and leant over it to see whether the stake was going in the right direction and when he had satisfied himself that it had not touched any of the more important internal organs he returned and went on with his work.

From the banks all this could scarcely be heard and still less seen, but all stood there trembling, their faces blanched and their fingers chilled with cold.

For a moment the hammering ceased. Merdžan now saw that close to the right shoulder muscles the skin was stretched and swollen. He went forward quickly and cut the swollen place with two crossed cuts. Pale blood flowed out, at first slowly then faster and faster. Two or three more blows, light and careful, and the iron-shod point of the stake began to break through at the place where he had cut. He struck a few more times until the point of the stake reached level with the right ear. The man was impaled on the stake as a lamb on the spit, only that the tip did not come through the mouth but in the back and had not seriously damaged the intestines, the heart or the lungs. Then Merdžan threw down the mallet and came nearer. He looked at the unmoving body, avoiding the blood which poured out of the places where the stake had entered and had come out again and was gathering in little pools on the planks. The two gypsies turned the stiffened body on its back and began to bind the legs to the foot of the stake. Meanwhile Merdžan looked to see if the man were still alive and carefully examined the face that had suddenly become swollen, wider and larger. The eyes were wide open and restless, but the eyelids were unmoving, the mouth was wide open but the two lips stiff and contracted and between them the clenched teeth shone white. Since the man could no longer control some of his facial muscles the face looked like a mask. But the heart beat heavily and the lungs worked with short, quickened breath. The two gypsies began to lift him up like a sheep on a spit. Merdžan shouted to them to take care and not shake the body; he himself went to help them. Then they embedded the lower, thicker end of the stake between two beams and fixed it there with huge nails and and then behind, at the same height, buttressed the whole thing with a short strut which was nailed both to the stake and to a beam on the staging.

When that too had been done, the gypsies climbed down and joined the guards, and on that open space, raised a full eight feet upright, stiff and bare to the waist, the man on the stake remained alone. From a distance it could only be guessed that the stake to which his legs had been bound at the ankles passed right through his body. So that the people saw him as a statue, high up in the air on the very edge of the staging, high above the river.

A murmur and a wave of movement passed through the onlookers on the banks. Some lowered their eyes and others went quickly home without turning their heads. But the majority looked dumbly at this human likeness, up there in space, unnaturally stiff and upright. Fear chilled their entrails and their legs threatened to give way beneath them, but they were still unable to move away or take their eyes from the sight. And amid that terrified crowd mad Ilinka threaded her way, looking everyone in the eyes and trying to read their glances to find from them where her sacrificed and buried children were.

Then the man from Plevlje, Merdžan and a pair of guards went up to the impaled man and began to examine him more closely. Only a thin trickle of blood flowed down the stake. He was alive and conscious. His ribs rose and fell, the veins in his neck pulsed and his eyes kept turning slowly but, unceasingly. Through the clenched teeth came a long drawn-out groaning in which a few words could with difficulty be distinguished.

"Turks, Turks, . . ." moaned the man on the stake, "Turks on the bridge . . . may you die like dogs . . . like dogs."

The gypsies picked up their tools and then, with the man from Plevlje, came down from the staging to the bank. The people made way for them and began to disperse. Only the children on the high blocks of stone and the bare trees waited a little longer, not knowing if this were the end or whether there would be more, to see what would happen next with that strange man who hovered over the waters as if suddenly frozen in the midst of a leap.

The man from Plevlje approached Abidaga and reported that everything had been carried out correctly and satisfactorily, that the criminal was still alive and that it seemed that he would go on living since his internal organs had not been damaged. Abidaga did not reply but only gave a sign with his hand to bring his horse and began to say goodbye to Tosun Effendi and Mastro Antonio. Everyone began to disperse. Through the marketplace the town-crier could be heard announcing that the sentence had been carried out and that the same or a worse punishment awaited anyone who would do the like in the future.

The man from Plevlje remained in perplexity on the level space which had now suddenly emptied. His servant held his horse and the guards waited for orders. He felt that he ought to say something but was not able to because of the wave of feeling that only now began to rise within him and choke him. Only now did he become conscious of all that he had forgotten since he had been too busy carrying out the sentence. He remembered Abidaga's threat that it would have been he who would have been placed upon the stake had he not succeeded in catching the criminal. He had escaped that horror, but only by a hair and only at the last moment. But things had turned out otherwise. The sight of that man, who was hanging, bound and still alive, over the river filled him with terror and also with a sort of painful joy that such a fate had not been his and that his body was still undamaged, was free and able to move. At that thought burning pains shot through his chest and spread into his legs and arms and forced him to move about, to smile and to speak, just to prove to himself that he was healthy, that he could move freely, could speak and laugh aloud, could even sing if he so wished, and not merely mutter useless curses from a stake, awaiting death as the only happiness which could still be his. His hands and arms moved of their own volition, his lips opened and from them flowed unwittingly a strangled laugh and a copious flow of words:

"Ha, ha, ha, Radisav, thou mountain vila,* why so stiff? . . . Why not go on and undermine the bridge? . . . Why writhe and groan? Sing vila! Dance, vila!"

Astonished and bewildered, the guards watched their leader dance with outstretched arms, heard him sing and choke with laughter and with strange words, saw the white foam oozing more and more from the corners of his lips. And his bay horse, in fear, cast sidelong glances at him.

*   *   *

In the darkness could be heard the voices of two youths who were walking on the bridge. They were moving slowly and just then halted by the *kapija** behind the angle of the parapet, so that Stiković and Glasinčanin could not see them, or be seen by them, from their seat on the sofa. But they could hear every word and the voices were well known to them. They were two of their younger comrades, Toma Galus and Fehim Bahtijarević. These two kept themselves a little apart from the group which comprised most of the other students which gathered every evening on the *kapija* around Stiković and Herak, for, although younger, Galus was a rival of Stiković both as a poet and as a nationalist speaker. He did not like Stiković nor admire him, while Bahtijarević was exceptionally silent, proud and reserved as befitted a true grandchild of a family of *begs*.

Toma Galus was a tall youth with red cheeks and blue eyes. His father, Alban von Galus, the last descendant of an ancient family of the Burgenland, had come to the town as a civil servant immediately after the occupation. He had been a forestry inspector for twelve

---

*a fairy tale maiden.
*gate.

years and now lived in the town on pension. At the very beginning, he had married the daughter of one of the local landowners, Hadži Toma Stanković, a robust and full-blown young woman of dark skin and strong will. They had had three children, two daughters and one son, all of whom had been christened into the Serbian Orthodox church and had grown up like real townsmen's children and grandchildren of Hadži Toma.

Old Galus, a tall and formerly a very handsome man, with a pleasant smile and masses of thick white hair, had long ago become a real townsman, "Mr. Albo," whom the younger generation could not think of as a foreigner and a newcomer. He had two passions which harmed no one: hunting and his pipe, and had made many old and true friends, both among the Serbs and among the Moslems, throughout the whole district who shared his passion for the chase. He had completely assimilated many of their customs as if he had been born and bred amongst them, especially their habit of cheerful silence and calm conversation, so characteristic of men who are passionate smokers and who love hunting, the forests and life in the open.

Young Galus had matriculated that year at Sarajevo and that autumn was due to go on to Vienna to study. But in the matter of these studies there was a division of opinion in the family. The father wanted his son to study technical sciences or forestry and the son wanted to study philosophy. For Toma Galus only resembled his father in appearance and all his desires led him in a completely opposite direction. He was one of those good scholars, modest and exemplary in everything, who pass all their examinations with ease as if playing at them, but whose real and sincere interests are taken up with satisfying their somewhat confused and disordered spiritual aspirations outside school and outside the official curriculum. These are students of serene and simple heart but of uneasy and inquisitive spirit. Those difficult and dangerous crises of the life of the senses and emotions through which so many other younger men of their age pass, are almost unknown to them; therefore, they find difficulty in stilling their spiritual anxieties and very often remain all their lives dilettantes, interesting eccentrics without stable occupation or definite interests. As every young man must not only fulfill the eternal and natural demands of youth and maturity and also pay tribute to the current spiritual moods and fashions of his time, which for the moment reign amongst youth, Galus too had written verses and was an active member of the revolutionary nationalist student organizations. He had also studied French for five years as an optional subject, taken an interest in literature and, more especially, philosophy. He read passionately and indefatigably. The main body of reading of the young men at school in Sarajevo at that time consisted of works from the well-known and enormous German publishing house Reclams Universal-Bibliotek. These small, cheap booklets with yellow covers and exceptionally small print were the main spiritual food available to the students of that time; from them they could become acquainted not only with German literature, but with all the more important works in world literature in German translation. From them Galus drew his knowledge of modern German philosophers, especially Nietzsche and Stirner, and in his walks in Sarajevo along the banks of the Miljacka held endless discussions about them with a sort of cold passion, in no way linking his reading with his personal life, as so many youths often do. This type of young scholar just through his examinations, ripened too early and overloaded with all kinds of varied, chaotic and uncoordinated knowledge, was not rare among the students of that time. A modest youth and a good student, Galus knew the freedom and the unrestraint of youth only in the daring of his thoughts and the exaggerations of his reading.

Fehim Bahtijarević was a townsman on his mother's side only. His father had been born in Rogatica and was now Kadi (Moslem judge) there, but his mother was from the great local family of Osmanagić. From his earliest childhood he passed a part of the summer vacation in the town with his mother and her relatives. He was a slender youth, graceful and well formed, fine-boned but strong. Everything about him was measured, restrained, controlled. The fine oval of his face was sunburnt, his skin browned with light touches of a dark bluish shade, his movements few and abrupt; his eyes were black with blue shadings in the whites and his glance burning but without sparkle. He had thick eyebrows which met, and a fine black down on his upper lip. Such faces are reminiscent of Persian miniatures.

That summer he too had matriculated and he was now waiting to get a state grant to study oriental languages in Vienna.

The two young men were continuing some conversation begun earlier. The subject was Bahtijarević's choice of studies. Galus was proving to him that he would be making a mistake in taking up oriental studies. In general Galus spoke much more, and more animatedly, than his companion for he was accustomed to be listened to and to lay down the law, while Bahtijarević spoke shortly, like a man who has his own fixed ideas and feels no need to convince anyone else. Like most young men who have read much, Galus spoke with a naive satisfaction in words, picturesque expressions and comparisons, and with a tendency to generalize, whereas Bahtijarević spoke dryly, curtly, almost indifferently.

Hidden in the shadows and reclining on the stone seats, Stiković and Glasinčanin remained silent as if they had tacitly agreed to listen to the conversation of their two comrades on the bridge.

Finishing the conversation about studies, Galus said belligerently:

"In that you Moslems, you begs' sons, often make a mistake. Disconcerted by the new times, you no longer know your exact and rightful place in the world. Your love for everything oriental is only a contemporary expression of your 'will to power'; for you the Eastern way of life and thought is very closely bound up with a social and legal order which was the basis of your centuries of lordship. That is understandable, but it in no way means that you have any sense for orientalism as a study. You are orientals but you are making a mistake when you think that you are thereby called upon to be orientalists. In general you have not got the calling or the true inclination for science."

"Really!"

"No, you haven't. And when I say that, I am not saying anything insulting or offensive. On the contrary. You are the only nobles in this country, or at least you were; for centuries you have enlarged, confirmed and defended your privileges by sword and pen, legally, religiously and by force of arms; that has made of you typical warriors, administrators and landowners, and that class of men nowhere in the world worries about abstract sciences but leaves them to those who have nothing else and can do nothing else. The true studies for you are law and economics, for you are men of practical knowledge. Such are men from the ruling classes, always and everywhere."

"You mean that we should remain uneducated?"

"No, it does not mean that, but it means that you must remain what you are or, if you like, what you have been; you must, for no one can be at the same time what he is and the contrary of what he is."

"But we are no longer a ruling class today. Today we are all equal." Bahtijarević broke in once more with a touch of irony, in which was both bitterness and pride.

"You are not, naturally you are not. The conditions which at one time made you what you were have changed long ago, but that does not mean that you can change with the same speed. This is not the first, nor will it be the last, instance of a social caste losing its reason for existence and yet remaining the same. Conditions of life change but a class remains what it is, for only so can it exist and as such it will die."

The conversation of the two unseen youths broke off for a moment, stifled by Bahtijarević's silence.

In the clear June sky, above the dark mountains on the horizon, the moon appeared. The white plaque with the Turkish inscription suddenly shone in the moonlight, like a dimly lit window in the blue-black darkness.

Bahtijarević then said something, but in so low a voice that only disjointed and incomprehensible words reached Stiković and Glasin-čanin. As so often in young men's discussions, in which changes of subject are rapid and bold, the conversation was now about another matter. From the study of oriental languages, they had now passed on to the content of the inscription on the white plaque before them and to the bridge and he who had built it.

Galus's voice was the louder and more expressive. While agreeing with Bahtijarević's praises of Mehmed Pasha Sokolović and the Turkish administration of his times, which had made possible the building of such a bridge, he now developed his nationalist views on the past and present of the people, their culture and civilization (for in such student discussions each follows his own train of thought).

"You are right," said Galus. "He must have been a man of genius. He was not the first nor the last man of our blood who distinguished himself in the service of a foreign empire. We have given hundreds of such men, statesmen, generals and artists, to Istanbul, Rome and Vienna. The sense of our national unification in a single, great and powerful modern state lies just in that. Our own forces should remain in our own country and develop there and make their contribution to general culture in our name and not from foreign centers."

"Do you really think that those 'centers' arose by chance and that it is possible to create new ones at will whenever and wherever one likes?"

"Chance or not, that is no longer the question; it is not important how they arose, but it is important that today they are disappearing, that they have flowered and decayed, that they must make way for new and different centers, through which young and free nations, appearing for the first time on the stage of history, can express themselves directly."

"Do you think that Mehmed Pasha Sokolović, had he remained a peasant's child up there yonder at Sokolovići, would have become what he became and would, among other things, have built this bridge on which we are now talking?"

"In those times, certainly, he would not. But, when you come to think of it, it was not hard for Istambul to put up such buildings, when it took from us, and from so many other subject peoples, not only property and money, but also our best men and our purest blood. If you stop to think what we are and how much has been stolen from us through the centuries, than all these buildings are merely crumbs. But when we finally achieve our national freedom and our independence, then our money and our blood will be ours alone, and will stay ours. Everything will be solely and uniquely for the improvement of our own national culture, which will bear our mark and our name and which will be mindful of the happiness and prosperity of all our people."

Bahtijarević remained silent, and that silence, like the most lively and eloquent speech, provoked Galus. He raised his voice and continued in a sharper tone. With all his natural vivacity and all the vocabulary then prevalent in nationalist literature, he set out the plans and aims of the revolutionary youth movement. All the living forces of the race must be awakened and set in action. Under their blows Austro-Hungarian monarchy, that prison of the peoples, would disintegrate as the Turkish Empire had disintegrated. All the anti-national and reactionary forces which today hinder, divide and lull to sleep our national forces will be routed and trampled underfoot. All this can be done, for the spirit of the times in which we live is our strongest ally, for all the efforts of all the other small and oppressed nations support us. Modern nationalism will triumph over religious diversities and outmoded prejudice, will liberate our people from foreign influence and exploitation. Then will the national state be born.

Galus then described all the advantages and beauties of the new national state which was to rally all the Southern Slavs around Serbia as a sort of Peidmont on the basis of complete national unity, religious tolerance and civil equality. His speech mixed up bold words of uncertain meaning and expressions that accurately expressed the needs of modern life, the deepest desires of a race, most of which were destined to remain only desires, and the justified and attainable demands of everyday reality. It mingled the great truths which had ripened through the generations but which only youth could perceive in advance and dare to express, with the eternal illusions which are never extinguished but never attain realization, for one generation of youth hands them on to the next like that mythological torch. In the young man's speech there were, naturally, many assertions which could not have stood up to the criticism of reality and many suppositions which could not, perhaps, have borne the proof of experience, but in it too was that freshness, that precious essence which maintains and rejuvenates the tree of humanity.

Bahtijarević remained silent.

"You will see, Fehim," Galus enthusiastically assured his friend as if it were a matter of the same night or the next morning, "you will see. We shall create a state which will make the most precious contribution to the progress of humanity, in which every effort will be blessed, every sacrifice holy, every thought original and expressed in our own words, and every deed marked with the stamp of our name. Then we will carry out work which will be the result of our free labor and the expression of our racial genius, put up buildings in comparison with which all that has been done in the centuries of foreign administration will appear like silly toys. We will bridge greater rivers and deeper abysses. We will build new, greater and better bridges, not to link foreign centres with conquered lands but to link our own lands with the rest of the world. There can no longer be any doubt. We are destined to realize all that the generations before us have aspired to; a state, born in freedom and founded on justice, like a part of God's thought realized here on earth."

Bahtijarević remained silent. Even Galus's voice lowered in tone.

As his ideas became more exalted, his voice became lower and lower, hoarser and hoarser, till it became a strong and passionate whisper and was finally lost in the great silence of the night. At last both young men were silent. But none the less Bahtijarević's silence seemed a thing apart, heavy and obstinate in the night. It seemed like an impassable wall in the darkness which by the very weight of its existence resolutely rejected all that the other had said, and expressed its dumb, clear and unalterable opinion.

"The foundations of the world and the bases of life and human relationships in it have been fixed for centuries. That does not mean that they do not change, but measured by the length of human existence they appear eternal. The relation between their endurance and the length of human existence is the same as the relation between the uneasy, moving and swift surface of a river and its stable and solid bed whose changes are slow and imperceptible. The very idea of the change of these 'centers' is unhealthy and unacceptable. That would be as if someone wished to change the measure and the sources of great rivers or the sites of mountains. The desire for sudden changes and the thought of their realization by force often appear among men like a disease and gain ground mainly in young brains; only these brains do not think as they should, do not amount to anything in the end and the heads that think thus do not remain long on their shoulders. For it is not human desires that dispose and administer the things of the world. Desire is like a wind; it shifts the dust from one place to another, sometimes darkens the whole horizon, but in the end calms down and falls and leaves the old and eternal picture of the world. Lasting deeds are realized on this earth only by God's will, and man is only His blind and humble tool. A deed which is born of desire, human desire, either does not live till realization or is not lasting; in no case is that good. All these tumultuous desires and daring words under the night sky on the *kapija* will not change anything basically; they will pass, beneath the great and permanent realities of the world and will be lost where all desires and winds are stilled. In truth great men and great buildings rise and will rise only where they are appointed to arise in God's thought, in their right place independent of empty transient desires and human vanity."

But Bahtijarević did not utter a single one of these words. Those who, like this Moslem youth of noble family, carry their philosophy in their blood, live and die according to it, do not know how to express it in words, or feel the need to do so. After this long silence Stiković and Glasinčanin only saw one or the other of the pair of unseen comrades throw a cigarette stub over the parapet and watched it fall like a shooting star in a great curve from the bridge into the Drina. At the same time they heard the two friends slowly and softly moving away towards the marketplace. The sound of their footsteps was soon lost.

Lovett F. Edwards

BOSNIAN CHRONICLE

(Excerpts)

In the early morning of that day there was the sound of neighing and stamping horses under his windows. Strapped in his gala official uniform, the Consul awaited the captain of the Vizier's Mameluke Guard, who came accompanied by D'Avenat. Everything went off as arranged and discussed beforehand. There were twelve Mamelukes, from the detachment which the Vizier Mehmed Pasha had brought from Eygpt as his personal bodyguard and of whom he was particularly proud. Their smartly rolled turbans of finely woven silk and gold, their curving scimitars dangling picturesquely from their horses' flanks, their ample cherry-colored greatcoats attracted everyone's attention. The mounts of Daville and his escort were caparisoned from head to tail with choicest cloth; the men were smart and showed good discipline. Daville tried to mount his horse as naturally as possible; the animal was quiet old black, rather broad-crouped. The Consul's dark blue cloak was generously parted at the chest to show the gilded buttons, the silver sash, the medals and service decorations. Sitting straight as a ramrod, his handsome virile head held up high, the Consul cut a fine figure.

Up to the point where they turned into the main street, everything went well and the Consul had reason to be satisfied. But as soon as they reached the first Turkish houses, suspicious calls began to be heard and there was a sudden banging of courtyard gates and a closing of window shutters. Already at the first gate a little girl opened one wing of the door and, muttering something unintelligible, began to spit thinly into the street, as if casting a spell. A moment later other doors flew open and shutters were raised, one after another, revealing faces that were full of hate and fanatical zeal. Veiled women spat and cursed, and small boys shouted abuse, accompanied by obscene gestures and unmistakable threats, as they smacked their bottoms or drew their fingers across their throats in a vicious slitting movement.

As the street was narrow and shut in by jutting balconies on both sides, the procession ran a double gamut of abuse and threats. At first, taken aback, the Consul tightened his reins and slowed down, but D'Avenat spurred his horse nearer and, without turning in the saddle or moving a single facial muscle, began to urge in an agitated whisper: "I beg Your Excellency to ride on quietly and pay no attention. They are wild ignorant people. They hate everything foreign and greet everyone in this way. It is best to ignore them. That's what the Vizier does, ignore them. It's their barbarian way. Please ride on, Your Excellency."

Baffled and outraged, although trying his best to hide it, the Consul rode on, realizing that none of the Vizier's guards did in fact pay any attention to what was happening; but he felt a rush of blood to his head. Confused, rash, and contradictory thoughts raced through his mind. His first thought was whether, as a representative of the great Napoleon, he ought to tolerate this or whether he should return to his house right away and create a scandal. It was a hard decision to make, for as much as he wanted to stand up for the honor of France, he was equally anxious to avoid any impetuous action that would lead to a clash and so ruin his relations with the Vizier and the Turks right on his very first day. Failing to summon up enough resolution to act quickly, he felt humiliated and bitter toward himself; and he was disgusted with the Levantine D'Avenat who kept repeating behind him: "I beg Your Excellency to ride on and pay no attention. These are just loutish Bosnian customs and ways. Let us proceed quietly."

In this irresolute and unhappy frame of mind, Daville was consious of his burning cheeks and his clammy armpits, which were full of sweat in spite of the cold. He hated D'Avenat's persistent whispering, which struck him as boorish and revolting. It was an intimation, it seemed to him, of the kind of life a Westerner might expect if he moved to the Orient and hitched his destiny to it permanently.

Throughout this time, from behind their window grilles, invisible women spat down on the horses and the riders. Once more the Consul halted for a second; once more he went on, yielding to D'Avenat's urgings and carried along by the stolid progress of his escorts. Soon they left the residential quarter behind them and gained the market street, with its single-storied shops, where Turkish storekeepers and their customers sat on little wooden platforms, smoking and bargaining. It was like passing from an overheated room into a cold one. All of a sudden there were no more blazing looks, no gestures indicating how the throats of unbelievers are slashed, no more sputtering by superstitious womenfolk. Instead, on both sides of the street, there were blank inscrutable faces. Daville saw them dimly, as if through a veil that shivered in front of his eyes. Not one of them paused in his work or stopped smoking or lifted his eyes and deigned to acknowledge with a glance the uncommon sight of a solemn procession. Here and there a shopkeeper did turn his head, as if looking for merchandise on the shelves. Only Orientals knew how to hate and feel contempt so intensely, and to show it in this way.

D'Avenat had fallen silent and backed away as required by protocol, but Daville found this incredible mute contempt of the bazaar just as hard to take, just as insufferable as the loud-voiced hatred and abuse of a little while before. At last they veered to the right and saw the high, long walls and the white building of the Vizier's Residency, a large well-proportioned dwelling with a row of glazed windows. He felt a little easier.

The agonizing journey that now lay behind him would long remain etched in Daville's memory; like an unhappy but portentous dream, it would never be entirely erased. In years to come he was to retrace steps along the same road a hundred times, in similar circumstances; for as often as he would have an audience with the Vizier—and they would be frequent, especially in times of unrest—he would have to ride through the same residential quarter and the same market street. He would sit upright and rigid on his horse, looking neither to the left nor to the right, neither too high nor between the horse's ears, appearing neither distracted nor worried, neither smiling nor dour, but quietly and soberly alert, displaying the kind of studied air with which generals in their portraits contemplate a battle in the distance, gazing at a point somewhere between the road and the horizon where promised and well-trimed reinforcements are supposed to appear. For a long time yet Turkish children would spit at his horse's legs, in frantic but childish imitation of spell-casting, which they had learned from their elders. Moslem shopkeepers would turn their backs to him, pretending to look for something on the shelves.

Only a rare Jew here and there would greet him, coming face to face with him unexpectedly, unable to dodge him. Time and again he was to ride by like this, outwardly calm and dignified but inwardly trembling at the hate and the studied indifference closing in on him from all sides, shuddering at the thought of some sudden, unexpected incident, loathing his work and his present life, yet trying to hide by a convulsive effort both the alarm and the revulsion he felt.

And even much later, when in the course of many years and changes the populace had finally accepted the presence of foreigners, and when Daville had met a number of people and got to know them much better, this first ceremonial procession would linger in his consciousness like a black and burning line which continues to hurt and is only gradually salved and healed by oblivion.

With a hollow clatter, the procession crossed a wooden bridge and came up to a large gate. All at once, with a loud scraping of locks and a bustle of attendants, both wings swung wide open.

Jean Daville was about to enter the stage on which, for nearly eight years, he would play the varied scenes of singularly exacting and thankless role.

Time and again he would stand before this yawning, disproportionately wide gate; and always, at the moment when it gaped open, it would seem to him like the hideous mouth of a jinnee, spewing and belching the smell of everything that lived, grew, steamed, was used up or ailing in the huge Residence. He knew that the town and the district, which had to feed the Vizier and his staff, daily stocked the Residency with almost a ton of assorted provisions and that all of it was distributed, stolen, or consumed. He knew that besides the Vizier and his close family there were eleven other dignitaries, thirty-two guards, and as many, and maybe more, parasites, hangers-on, Christian day workers, and petty clerks; over and above that, an indeterminate number of horses, cattle, dogs, cats, birds, and monkeys. The air was heavy with the stomach-turning reek of rancid butter and tallow, which overpowered those who were not inured to it. After every audience this sickly sweet odor would haunt the Consul for the rest of the day and the very thought of it produced in him a feeling of nausea. He had the impression that the entire Residency was permeated with the smell, as a church with incense, and that it clung not only to people and to their clothes but also to the walls and all other inanimate objects.

Now as the unfamilar gate swung open to receive him for the first time, the Mameluke column detached itself and dismounted, while Daville rode into the courtyard with his own escort. This first, outer courtyard was narrow and shadowy, closed over the upper story of the house from one end to the other; but beyond was a regular open courtyard, with a water well, with grass, and flowerbeds along the walls. At the far end, a tall and impenetrable fence shut off the Vizier's private garden.

Still shaken by his experiences during his passage through the town, Daville was now startled by the polite fuss and ceremonious attention extended to him by the entire population of courtiers and officials of the Residency. They all milled and scurried around him with an avid, overwhelming concern that was unknown in the ceremonials of the West.

The first to greet the Consul was the Vizier's Secretary; the Vizier's Deputy, Suleiman Pasha Skopljak, was not in Travnik. Behind him came the Keeper of Arms, the Quartermaster, the Treasurer, the Protocol Officer, and behind them shoved and elbowed a whole crowd of people of unknown and indeterminate rank and occupation. Some murmured a few indistinct words of welcome, bowing their heads, others spread their arms ceremoniously, and the whole throng moved toward the great hall where the divan—or reception—was to be held. Through it all, the towering and swarthy D'Avenat made his way deftly and with practiced indifference, loftily brushing aside those who stood in the way, and issuing orders and instructions rather more loudly and conspicuously than the occasion warranted. Inwardly confused but calm and self-possessed on the outside, Daville couldn't help seeing himself as one of those saints in the Catholic holy pictures, borne to the heavens by a swarm of angels; the throng simply carried him up to the few broad steps that led from the courtyard to the divan.

The divan was a dim but spacious hall on the ground level. There were a few rugs scattered on the floor; all around were couches draped with cherry-red cloth. In an alcove by the window were cushions for the Vizier and his guest. The walls contained a single picture, the imperial coat of arms: the Sultan's initials in gold letters on a green parchment. Underneath, a sword, two pistols, and a scarlet mantle of honor, gifts from Sultan Selim III to his favorite, Husref Mehmed Pasha.

Above this hall, on the upper story, there was another like it, much brighter though more sparsely furnished, in which the Vizier held his divan during the summer months. Two entire walls of this great room were taken up with windows, one half of which overlooked the garden and the other the river Lashva and the bazaar beyond the bridge. These were the "panels of glass" about which songs were sung and tales told, the likes of which were not to be found in all Bosnia; it was from Austria that Mehmed Pasha had imported them at his own expense, hiring a famous master glazier, a German, to cut and install them. Seated on his cushion a guest could look out through the windows and see the open veranda where under the eaves a nest of swallows perched high on a juniper beam, and he could listen to their twitter and watch the shy mother swallow dart in and out amid the trembling stalks of straw.

Sitting beside these windows was always delightful. It was bright there and full of flowers and greenery, and one sat in a soft breeze, lapped by the purling sound of the water and chirruping birds, and it was always peaceful enough to rest in and quiet for reflection or talk. Many a hard and thorny decision was reached or sanctioned there; but all problems, when discussed in this place, seemed somehow easier, clearer, and more human than in the reception hall on the ground floor.

These two rooms of the Residency were the only ones Daville would ever get to know during his stay in Travnik, and they would be the scene of his trials and satisfactions, failures and successes. Here, in the years to come, he would learn to understand not only the Turks and their peculiar strengths and terrible weaknesses, but also himself, his own capacity and limitations, and mankind in general, and the world and human relationships within it.

This first audience, as was customary in the winter, was held in the divan on the ground floor. Judging by the stale and moldy air, the hall had been opened and heated for the first time that winter, especially for the occasion.

As soon as the Consul crossed the threshold, a door opened on the opposite side of the hall and the Vizier appeared in a colorful gala robe, accompanied by courtiers who walked with their heads slightly bowed and arms humbly folded on their chests.

This was the great ceremonial audience which Daville had sought and negotiated for three days through D'Avenat, and which he hoped would lend special color and spice to his initial report to the Minister. The Turks had suggested that the Vizier await the Consul reclining on his couch, as he did all his other visitors, but the Consul demanded that he greet him standing on his feet. The Consul had invoked the might of France and the battle glory of his sovereign, the Turks their ancient traditions and the greatness of their Empire. At length it was agreed that both the Vizier and the Consul should make their entrance at the same moment and meet in the center of the hall, whence the Vizier would lead the Frenchman to the platform by the window where two identical cushions would be set, on which they would lower themselves at the same instant.

This was in fact what happened. The Vizier, who had a limp in his right foot for which the people had nicknamed him the Lame Pasha, walked up briskly and energetically, as lame people often do, and cordially invited the Consul to be seated.

Between them, but a step lower, squatted the interpreter D'Avenat. He sat doubled up, with hands folded in his lap and his eyes downcast, as if anxious to make himself smaller and less conspicuous than he was, obtruding with his presence and his breath only as much as was necessary to enable these two dignitaries to communicate their thoughts and declarations to each other. The rest of the throng melted away quietly. There remained only servants, standing at a respectful distance, awaiting their master's bidding. During the whole conversation, which took up more than an hour's time, everything that ceremonial hospitality required was passed discreetly from one shadowy boy to another and offered to the Vizier and his guest.

First, lighted chibouks were brought in, then coffee, then sherbet. Then one of the boys, approaching on his knees, held out a shallow bowl of strong aromatic essence and passed it under the Vizier's beard and around the Consul's mustache, as if censing them. Then again more coffee and fresh pipes. All of it was served while they were talking, with the utmost efficiency, inconspicuously, swiftly, and yet with a practiced sense of timing.

For an Oriental, the Vizier was unusually lively, cordial, and outspoken. Daville had already been told about these traits of the Vizier and although he knew they were not to be taken at face value, he still found the man's cordiality and friendliness most agreeable, especially after the humiliating experience in the bazaar. The throbbing of blood in his head subsided. The Vizier's talk, the aroma of coffee, and the smell of pipes were pleasant and soothing, even if they could not altogether erase the earlier sickening impressions. The Vizier tactfully alluded to the backwardness of the land and to the coarse and boorish manners of the people. It was a difficult country and the natives were a problem. What could one expect of women and children, creatures on whom God had not lavished much reason, in a country where even the men were irresponsible louts? Nothing these people did or said could have any significance or importance or any effect on the affairs of serious and enlightened persons. The dog barks but the caravan moves on, said the Vizier in conclusion; for he had obviously been informed of everything that had happened during the Consul's ride through the city and was now trying to minimize and smooth over the incident. Then, without further ado, he passed from these unpleasant trivia to a fresh subject, the signal greatness of Napoleon's victories and the enormous importance of close and realistic collaboration between the two empires, the Ottoman and the French.

These words, spoken quietly and sincerely, were like a balm to Daville, intended as they were to be an indirect apology for the insults of a little while before; in his own eyes, at any rate, they lessened the humiliation he had suffered. Feeling reassured and better disposed he now gave the Vizier more of his attention and remembered all that D'Avenat had told him about the man.

Husref Mehmed Pasha, nicknamed "the Lame," was a Georgian. Brought to Istanbul as a slave in his youth, he had entered the service of the great Kutchuk Hussein Pasha. There he was noticed by Selim

III, even before the latter ascended the throne. Brave, shrewd, bright, eloquent, genuinely devoted to his superiors, this Georgian became, at the age of thirty-one, Vizier of Egypt. His tenure was cut short, however, as the great Mameluke rebellion drove him out of the country; even so, he was not disgraced altogether. After a short stay at Salonica he was appointed Vizier of Bosnia. As punishment this was comparatively mild, and he made it appear lighter still by keeping up a shrewd pretense before the world that he did not regard it as a punishment at all. He brought with him from Egypt a detachment of thirty loyal Mamelukes whom he liked to exercise on the drilling field of Travnik. Well fed and lavishly uniformed, the Mamelukes attracted general curiosity and served to bolster his prestige with the people. The Bosnian Moslems eyed them with hatred but also with fear and secret admiration.

Even more than the Mamelukes, the people admired the Vizier's stud, which far surpassed any other yet seen in Bosnia for both the number and quality of its horses.

The Vizier was young and looked still younger than his years. Of less than medium build, he somehow managed, with his whole bearing, and particularly with his habit of smiling, to give an impression of being an inch or two taller than he was. Although he limped with his right foot, the skillful cut of his clothes and his crisp, energetic movements somehow disguised this defect. Whenever obliged to stand on his feet, he invariably struck a pose that concealed his disability; and when he was obliged to move, he did so swiftly, nimbly, and in short spurts. This gave him a characteristic air of freshness and youth. He had none of that monolithic Ottoman dignity of which Daville had read and heard so much. The color and style of his clothes were simple, though it was evident that they were chosen with the utmost care. There are people who can impart a special glitter and elegance to their dress and adornment by the mere act of wearing it. His face was unusually ruddy, like a seafaring man's, with a short dark beard and slanted black, shiny eyes; it was an open and smiling face. He seemed to be one of those men who hide their true mood in a steady smile and their thoughts, or lack of them, in animated talk. In everything he touched upon he seemed to imply a greater knowledge of the subject than the words themselves might have indicated. His every cordiality, attention, and kindness appeared to be only a preamble, a first installment of what one might still expect of him. Regardless of how much one might have been briefed and forewarned, it was impossible to escape the impression that here was an honorable and sensible man who would not only promise but also carry out a good deed, where and whenever he could; at the same time no person, however astute, could really judge or discern the subtle limits of those promises or the actual scope of the good deed.

The Vizier and the Consul turned to those subjects for which each knew the other had a secret weakness, or which happened to be a favorite topic. The Vizier kept referring to the exceptional personality of Napoleon and to his victories, while the Consul, who had learned from D'Avenat about the Vizier's love of the sea and seafaring, spoke of matters connected with navigation and naval warfare. The Vizier did, in fact, have a passionate love of the sea and of a sailor's life. Besides his secret shame over his failure in Egypt, he suffered most of all from the fact that he had been torn away from the sea and imprisoned in these cold, wild mountain regions. Deep down inside him the Vizier still nurtured the hope that one day he might succeed his great Kutchuk Hussein Pasha, and as Chief Lord of the Admiralty, pursue his plans and designs for the revival of the Turkish battle fleet.

After an hour and a half of conversation the Consul and the Vizier parted as old acquaintances, each believing that much might be achieved with the help of the other, each pleased with the other and with himself.

The Consul's leave-taking occasioned an even greater bustle and hubbub than before. Fur cloaks of really considerable value were brought out; sable for the Consul, coats of fox fur and cloth for his retinue. Someone voiced a prayer and invoked blessings on the imperial guest, and the others chorused after him. The high-ranking courtiers led Daville back to the mounting block in the middle of the inner courtyard; they all walked with open arms, as if bearing him along. Daville mounted his horse. The Vizier's sable cloak was slung over his greatcoat. Outside the Mamelukes were waiting, mounted and ready. The procession turned back the way it had come.

In spite of the heavy robe weighing him down, Daville shuddered a little at the thought of having to ride once more between those worn shutters and jutting windows grilles amid the cursing and contempt of the crowd; but, it seemed, his first public appearances in Travnik were to be full of surprises, even, sometimes, agreeable ones. True, the Turks in the shops along the way were sullen and impassive, their eyes conspicuously averted, but this time neither insults nor threats were heard from the houses. Arching against his will, Daville had a feeling that behind the wooden grilles many a curious and hostile pair of eyes watched him, although he heard no sound and saw no movement. It seemed almost as if the Vizier's cloak, were shielding him from the people, and he drew it instinctively tighter around him and sat up straight in the saddle and thus, with his head held high, he reached the walled courtyard of Joseph Baruch.

When at last he was alone in his warm room, he sat down on a hard couch, unbuttoned his uniform, and took a deep breath. He was worn out with excitement and tired in every part of his body. He felt empty, blunted, and confused, as if he'd been hurled down from a great height onto this hard settee and couldn't yet come to himself and grasp clearly where he was and what had happened. He was free at last, but had no idea what to do with his free time. He thought of resting and going to sleep, but his glance fell on the hanging fur cloak he had got from the Vizier a little while before, and all at once the thought came back to him, unwelcome and a little jolting, that he must write a report on all this to the Minister in Paris and the Ambassador at Istanbul. That meant he must live through the whole thing again and, moreover, paint a picture that would not be too damaging to his prestige but not too far from the truth either. This task now loomed before him like an impassable mountain that he must somehow negotiate. The Consul laid the palms of his hands on his eyes and pressed them. He sighed heavily a few more times and said under his breath: "Dear God. Dear God!" He remained sprawled like this on the settee, and there he slept and rested.

*   *   *

About the same time Desfosses had his talk with Cologna.

He went to see him one evening, around eight o'clock, accompanied by a *kavaz** and a groom carrying a lantern. The house stood

---

*guard; courier.

on one side of a steep rise, enveloped in a damp mist and thick darkness. Unseen waters from the spring of Shumech filled the night with a purl. This sound of water was muffled and transmuted by the darkness and magnified by the silence. The path was wet and slippery; in the meager, flickering light of the Turkish lantern it looked as new and unfamiliar as a forest glade trodden by human feet for the first time. The gate to the house appeared just as mysterious and unexpected. The threshold and the ringed doorknockers were illuminated, but everything else was in darkness; shapes and dimensions of objects stretched away into the night, defying identification. The door gave out a hard, hollow sound when the *kavaz* knocked. The noise struck Desfosses as somehow rude and out of place, almost a physical pain, and he winced at the man's excessive zeal, which seemed to him boorish and uncalled-for.

"Who's knocking?" The voice came from above, more like an echo of the *kavaz's* banging than a question in its own right.

"The young Consul. Open up!" shouted Ali, the *kavaz*, in that unpleasant, needlessly sharp voice in which young people are apt to talk to one another in the presence of a senior.

Male voices and the gurgle of water from afar—it was all like some casual and unexpected cries in a forest, without a known cause and without a visible effect. Finally there was the rattle of a chain, the creaking of a lock, and the noise of a latch. The gate opened slowly and behind it there stood a man with a lantern, pale and drowsy, wrapped in a shepherd's coat. Two lights of unequal intensity illuminated the sloping courtyard and the low dark windows of the ground floor of the house. The two servants' lanterns vied with each other to light the ground at the young Consul's feet. Bemused by this interplay of voices and flashing lights, Desfosses suddenly found himself before the wide, open door of a large ground-floor apartment, which was full of smoke and the heavy reek of tobacco floating on the moldy air.

In the middle of the room, by a large candelabrum, stood Cologna, tall and stooping, dressed in a weird assortment of Turkish and European garments. On his head was a small cap, from under which peeped long, sparse tufts of gray hair. The old man bowed deeply and spoke resonant greetings and compliments in that peculiar language of his which might have been either corrupt Italian or half-learned French, all of which sounded glib and stilted to the young man, empty conventions that were not only devoid of cordiality and genuine respect but lacked even the normal conviction a speaker might be expected to put behind his words. And then all at once everything he had encountered in that low-ceilinged, smoky apartment—the reek and the appearance of the room, the figure and the speech of the man—coalesced into a single word, so quickly, so vividly and clearly that he all but said it out aloud: age. Melancholy, toothless, forgetful, lonesome, earth-bound old age, which corroded, travestied, and embittered all things—thoughts, sights, movements, and sounds—all things, even light and smell themselves.

The old doctor ceremoniously offered the young man a seat but remained standing himself, explaining that he was merely observing an old Salernian rule: *Post prandium sta*—After a meal one should stand.

Desfosses sat down on a hard armless chair, but was filled with a sense of physical and mental superiority which made his mission appear easy and simple to him, almost pleasant. He began to speak in that tone of smug confidence which young men so often adopt in conversing with old men who seem to them outdated and at the end of their rope, quite forgetting that bodily infirmity and slowness of mind are often accompanied by vast experience and hard-won skill in handling human affairs. He delivered Daville's message to von Mitterer, trying to make it appear for what it was, namely a well-meant suggestion in their common interest and not a sign of weakness or fear. He concluded and was pleased with himself.

Cologna hastened to assure him that he was honored to have been chosen as an intermediary, that he would pass on the message conscientiously, that he fully appreciated the intentions and shared the opinion of M. Daville. He agreed that his own background, profession, and convictions made him the most suitable person for such a role.

Now, evidently, it was Cologna's turn to be pleased with himself.

The young man listened to him as he might have listened to the babble of water, gazing absently at his regular, long face with its lively round eyes, bloodless lips, and teeth that moved as he spoke. Old age! thought the young man. The worst of it was not that one suffered and died but that one grew old, for growing old was a malady for which there was no cure or hope; it was a long-dragged-out death.

Except that the young man did not think of aging in terms of a common human destiny, which included his own, but as an affliction that was peculiar to the doctor alone.

And Cologna said: "I don't need too many explanations. I understand the Consul's situation, as I understand the situation of every enlightened man from the West whose fate it is to live in these parts. For a man like that, living in Turkey means walking the sharp blade of a knife or roasting over a slow fire. I know it too well, for people like me are born on the knife's edge and we live and die on it. And in this fire we grow and burn ourselves to a cinder."

Through his musings about age and growing old, the young man began to listen with more attention and to grasp the doctor's words.

"No one knows what it means to be born and to live on the border-line between two worlds. What it means to know and understand the one and the other and yet be unable to do anything that might help them explain themselves to each other or bring them closer together. What it means to love and hate either, to waver between the two and imitate now one now the other. To have two homes and yet none, to be at home everywhere and yet remain a stranger forever. In short, to live crucified, but as victim and torturer at one and the same time."

The young man listened in amazement. These were no longer empty phrases and compliments; it was as if a third man had joined in the conversation and was now holding forth. Before him stood a man with flashing eyes and long thin arms outspread, demonstrating how one lived torn between two conflicting worlds.

As often happens with young people, Desfosses could not help feeling that this conversation was not entirely adventitious, that it was somehow, in a special and intimate way, linked with his own thoughts and with the book which he was preparing to write. There weren't too many opportunities in Travnik for conversations of this kind; he felt pleasantly stimulated and in his excitement began to ask questions, then to make observations of his own and describe his own impressions.

He spoke as much from inner necessity as from a desire to prolong discussion. But there was no need to prompt the old man to talk. He never as much as wandered from his main theme. Although, here and there, he was brought up short for want of a French phrase and sub-stituted an Italian one, he spoke like one inspired, almost as if he were reading from a prepared text: "Yes, these are the miseries which torment the Christians in the Levant and which you people from the Christian West will never be able to understand fully, just as the Turks cannot understand them. Such is the fate of a man from the Levant, for he is *poussiere humaine,* human dust, drifting wearily between East and West, belonging to neither and pulverized by both. These are people who speak many languages but have no language of their own, who are familiar with two religions but hold fast to neither. They are victims of the fatal division of mankind into Christian and non-Christian; eternal interpreters and go-betweens, who carry within them so much that is unclear and inarticulate; they are good connoisseurs of the East and West and of their customs and beliefs, but are equally despised and suspected by both. To them can be applied the words written six centuries ago by the great Dželaleddin, Dželaleddin Rumi: '. . . For I cannot tell who I am. I am neither a Christian, nor a Jew, nor a Parsee, nor a Mussulman. I am neither of the East nor of the West, neither from dry land nor from the sea." They are like that. They are a small mankind apart, stumbling under a double load of Eastern sin, that ought to be saved and redeemed a second time, though no one can say how or by whom. They are a frontier people, bodily and spiritually, from that black and bloody dividing line which through some terrible, absurd misunderstanding has been drawn between man and man, all creatures of God, between whom there should not and must not be any such lines. They are the pebble between the land and the sea, condemned to eternal swirling and pull. They are the *third world,* a repository of the curse and damnation which the cleaving of the earth into two worlds has left in its wake. They are. . ."

Excited, with shining eyes, Desfosses watched the transformed old man who, with his arms flung out so that he resembled a cross, vainly searched for words and then suddenly wound up in a broken voice: "It is heroism without glory, martyrdom without rewards. But at least you who are our kinsman and believe in the same God, you people of the West who are Christians by the same grace that we are, at least you should understand us and accept us and lighten our burden."

The doctor dropped his arms with an air of utter hopelessness, of anger almost. There was no vestige left of that queer, elusive "Illyrian doctor" Desfosses had known. Here stood a man who thought his own thoughts and expressed them forcefully. Desfosses burned with the desire to hear and learn more; he had quite forgotten his own feeling of superiority of a little while before and the house he was in and the business on which he had come. He knew that he had sat there far longer than he should have or had intended to, but he didn't get up.

The old man's eyes were on him with a look full of unspoken emotion, as though he were watching some one who was moving away out of reach and whose going saddened him. "Yes, monsieur, you may understand this life of ours, but to you it's only an uncomfortable dream. You're living here now, but you know it's only for a time and sooner or later you will go back to your country, where conditions are better and life has more dignity. You will rise up from this nightmare and walk with your head high once more, but we never shall, for to us it's the only life."

Toward the end of the conversation the doctor grew more and more subdued and queer. Now he too sat down, quite close to the young man, leaning toward him in an attitude of the most intimate confidence and motioning him with both hands to keep quiet, almost as if, by an inadvertent word or gesture, he might frighten and scare away something fragile, precious, and timid that was there, like a bird, on the floor at their feet. Staring fixedly at a spot on the carpet, he spoke in a whisper, yet also in a voice that was warm and soft with an inner sweetness. "In the end, when all is truly and finally said and done, everything is nevertheless good and works out for the best. It is true that here everything seems to be out of joint and snarled up beyond hope. '*Un jour tout sera bien, voila notre esperance*'—One day everything will be all right, that's our hope, as your philosopher has said. And it is hard to visualize it any other way. For, in the last instance, are my thoughts, which are good and right, worth any less than someone else's identical thoughts in Rome or Paris? Simply because I've conceived them in this mountain gorge known as Travnik? Certainly not. What is to prevent my thoughts from being jotted down and appearing between the covers of a book? Nothing! And even if things seem to be disjointed and chaotic, they are nevertheless linked together and interdependent. Not a single human thought, no enterprise of the mind, is ever lost. All of us are on the right road, we shall all be amazed when we meet eventually. And we shall meet and understand one another, no matter how scattered we may be now or how far we may have strayed. That will be a happy meeting indeed, a glorious surprise that will save us all."

The young man had trouble following the doctor's premise, but he was eager to hear him talk on. And Cologna did go on, in the same confidential tone of joyful excitement, even though what he said was at times not immediately pertinent. Desfosses nodded his approval, grew excited himself and now and then, unable to hold back, threw in some observations of his own. He told the old man about his discovery on the road at Turbe, where the telltale layers under the road's surface clearly indicated various historical epochs— the same story he had once told Daville, without much success.

"I know you look around you and notice things. You are interested in the past as well as the present. You know how to look," said the doctor approvingly. And, like a man divulging a secret of hidden treasure and letting his smiling eyes insinuate more than words can encompass, the old man said in a low but dramatic voice: "Next time you go through the bazaar, stop by the Yeni Mosque. There is a high wall around the whole area. Inside, under huge old trees, there are graves and no one can remember any longer whose they are. But the people still remember that once upon a time, before the Turks came to the country, the mosque used to be the Church of St. Catherine. And they believe that the sacristy stands to this day in one of the corners of the mosque and that no one can open it. If you look a little closer at the stones in the ancient wall, you will see that they were taken from Roman ruins and tomb monuments. And on one particular stone that has been built into the wall of the mosque enclosure you can read quite clearly several neat and regular Roman letters from a text fragment: '*Marco Flavio . . . optimo . . .*' And deep down below, in the hidden foundations, there are great big blocks of red granite, the remains of a much older cult, the former shrine of the god Mithras. On one of these blocks there is a mysterious relief, in which one can make out the young god of light killing a powerful wild boar in full flight. And who knows what else is hidden in those depths, under those foundations? No man can tell whose endeavors may be buried there or what traces may have been wiped out forever. And that is just one little plot of land, in this remote little town. Where are all the countless other great settlements the world over?"

Desfosses stared at the old man, expecting further confidences, but here the doctor suddenly changed his voice and began to speak much louder, as though any outsider were now allowed to hear what he was saying: "You understand, all these things are fitted one into another, bound together, and it is only to the outward eye that they appear lost and forgotten, scattered about and lacking a master plan. They all stretch away, quite unconsciously, toward a single goal, like rays converging on a distant, unknown focus. One should bear in mind that it is expressly written in the Koran: 'Perhaps one day God shall visit peace upon you and your adversaries and create friendship between you. He is mighty, gentle, and merciful.' So there's hope, and where there's hope . . . you understand?"

His eyes brightened with a meaningful, triumphant smile, the purport of which was to hearten and reassure the young man, and with his palms he outlined a round form in the air in front of his face, as if he wanted to show the closed circle of the universe.

"You understand?" the old man repeated meaningfully, with a touch of impatience, as though he considered it needless and redundant to search around for words to express anything so obvious and certain, anything so near and familiar to him.

And having said it, his whole tone changed again. Once more he rose, thin and erect, bowed unctuously and spoke sonorous hollow words, telling the young man how honored he felt by his visit and by the mission entrusted to him.

That was how they parted.

Joseph Hitrec

Miloš Crnjanski

(1893)

Crnjanski was born in Ilanča, Vojvodina. An ardent Serbian nationalist, he nevertheless had to serve in the Austro-Hungarian army at the Eastern front in World War I. The horrors of war so utterly disgusted him that he became a militant pacifist in his poetry, which began to appear immediately following the war. In the post-war years he worked as a journalist and served as a diplomat. Because of his antileftist views, he refused to return to his country for many years after World War II, living in London and working on various degrading jobs. He finally returned to Yugoslavia in 1965. He now lives in Belgrade, revered as one of the greatest contemporary Serbian writers.

His first work was a book of poetry, *Lirika Itake* (The Lyrics of Ithaca, 1919). It was followed by a short poetic novel, *Dnevnik o Čarnojeviću* (Diary About Čarnojević, 1921). In both works he displayed an unusual talent, strength of conviction, antiwar protest, and modernistic tendencies all of which made him one of the leading avant-garde poets. His best work, a two-volume novel *Seobe* (Migrations, 1929, 1962), depicts the fate of the Serbs in Vojvodina in the second half of the eighteenth century, who fought for their foreign rulers while constantly dreaming of the renaissance of their own nation or migration to Russia.

Crnjanski's powerful talent, vitality, and boldness in the use of the language have resulted in considerable influence among younger Serbian poets.

A TALE

All I remember is
that she was chaste and slender,
that her tresses
were warm as the soft
black silk upon her white bosom,
and that the break of day was fragrant
with the perfume of acacia.

This memory came back by chance,
came back to me with sadness,
as I shut my eyes in silence.

When once more, acacias breathe their scent,
who knows where I shall be?
But secretly I fear
that her name no longer I'll recall
no, not even her name.

A. Lenarčič

MIGRATIONS

(Excerpts)

The first day after her adultery seemed indeed insignificant to Madame Dafina Isaković. Towards evening she felt weak from the expectation that something unusual would happen.

The morning passed in crying, contemplation and primping, and the afternoon in waiting for Kir-Arandjel, who had gone across the river to Belgrade, to deliver to the Turks the horses with which he had almost drowned in the Danube.

But that afternoon in the big, yellow house filled with flour like a mill, passed very monotonously, too, accompanied only by the murmuring of the water flowing by, so that Madame Dafina felt like shouting, if only to break the silence that was stifling with the odor and dust of stale wheat and rye.

She was not sorry for having betrayed her husband, but she felt ill seeing that nothing was changed by that act. She had spent the night with her brother-in-law, but that did not move a single seed of oats in the attic above their heads. Having already sensed that, despite all her authority, she had been lying around the house like an object which everybody avoided quietly, she wished now that the house surrounding her would turn upside down. The dead things, motionless and always the same, enervated and disturbed her. She wished that her brother-in-law were there so that he could promise, above all, to marry her and to take her away from there, to a new home in Budim.

She ordered the maids to bring the children to her, but even that did not help.

The younger girl, covered with scabs, lay wrapped like an infant. Sucking her thumb, she stared at the ceiling with her yellowish eyes, wriggling her legs. She fixed her black-dotted eyes on the ceiling without noticing that she had been carried to another part of the house. The older girl at first fell into her mother's lap with violent joy but left her just as quickly, playing hide-and-seek among the multicolored dresses hanging behind the stove. Madame Dafina soon realized that she had nothing to say to these children and that she had no reason to look at them. As she observed them, they seemed to her silly and alien. All this time the children were not even aware of her presence. They were attracted by the colorful hanging rags, by the window bars, and especially by the burning stove with its crimson fire, but they did not notice her misery and her eyes swollen with tears at all. Even from her lap the children extended their arms towards distant objects, as if to the opposite shore, and struggled as if from the arms of a giant. So, at last, she sent them away, together with the maids and dogs.

She called the legitimate wife of Dimča Diamanti, who looked like a long black broom sweeping around the house all day long, always wrapped in many folds. This woman knew how to read cards and she liked to talk, constantly plucking at the same wart. But that, too, was in vain. Madame Finka Diamanti was only able to relate how, on the shore, one of the horses which had been involved in the drowning attacked her own husband, who had run to save the drowning people, especially his partner Arandjel Isaković. All of Zemun was talking about this incident. Immediately afterwards, Madame Finka departed.

And so, when it got dark, Madame Dafina was again alone. She was horrified by the boring, wet day from which only recently she had expected so much.

All she had done seemed to her somehow meaningless; yet, it would have seemed so even if she had not done it. Everything her brother-in-law Arandjel had been telling her for weeks seemed right to her now. Although she still remembered clearly that entire night of love, she felt that she could easily forget it and that it would never even cross her mind again, especially if her husband should suddenly return. She also realized that the adultery would not bring her any joy, that she could repeat it tomorrow, with anybody, and that it would not seem particularly important to her. She began to reflect upon and to console herself with the riches in which she would revel if she married her brother-in-law. She visualized the new dresses she would order; and, as if she already had one on, she began to feel the touch of the silk garment on her body. At that thought, however, she not only felt no specific pleasure but even anticipated some sort of sadness. It seemed the same to her whether she belonged to one brother or to the other; and it occurred to her that afternoon that, as far as she was concerned, she would consent to belonging to both. What is more, to others, too—to anybody.

Through the window she saw the entire huge twilight and the reflection of the cool, grey sky on the flood waters. The river was a murky yellow, full of mud, and the willow groves, whose buds had already begun to swell, were frozen in recent days that had suddenly turned cold. Above the islands, however, at the lower end of the sky, opened a large blue patch, on which the minarets and walls of Belgrade emerged clearly out of the moist, bright evening. The croaking of the frogs around the house began to roar and throb.

A large, bright piece of sky also lighted one wall in the room where Madame Dafina was tossing around from boredom and despair, almost in tears, having lost one of her gold-embroidered slippers behind the stove and the other by the door. Lying beneath a large, ancient icon of Christ, she felt a desire to put out the burning light but, unexpectedly, she became afraid of the descending darkness. Not daring to reach for her slippers, she hardly stirred, lying on her back on the pillows, in the intolerable haze from her incessant smoking. Since her head was heavy, she only now noticed that it was almost dark in the room. The darkness had already enveloped the objects and walls. Only toward the stove, the grey light of the dying evening glow from the river was falling on one wall and disappearing behind the curtain. A large, black trunk, filled with her dresses, rose darkly from the floor, like a high grave mound.

Through the smoke of the Turkish tobacco, Madame Dafina was staring at the light in the window as if mesmerized by the bright moon in the dark night. Tired from thinking, she suddenly heard behind her the running of mice. Only then did she become fully aware of the darkness in the room. She wanted to scream, but her voice choked in her throat.

Opening her eyes widely, she realized only now that she had not escaped in time from the darkness which had surrounded her and of which she was so dreadfully afraid. Except for the white stove, on which a bed sheet was drying like an apparition, and for the bright opening of the window, everything else in the big dark room had sunk into a dense murkiness, together with the murmuring of the water. Neither the tables nor the bed nor the door was visible any longer, and she noticed in horror that she could not even recognize her slippers on the rug. Dogs were howling outside.

Suffocating in the darkness and mortified by fear, she was not able to shout or move. She was shivering all over, and she felt an icy coldness beginning to creep up her legs. Sensing that her toes were stiffening, she still could not move her feet; on the contrary, wishing to get up and flee, she felt that she was sinking deeper and deeper into the pillows.

It seemed to her that the sheet on the stove was rising and that cold air was blowing through the curtain above the bed. Tense, trembling all over and with her eyes wide open, she saw how the mice were pouring forth and creeping up to her from the large, black trunk which held her dresses. Bending over her knees, with a shriek in her throat, she saw around the trunk frogs, snakes, and snails in the mud, coiled and pressing, treading upon each other, and swarming.

With her eyes almost popping out from under her eyelids, she saw how the white sheet from the stove was coming closer and closer. At the same time she sensed that somebody was standing behind the curtain in the darkness. Dishevelling her hair with trembling hands and shivering from the cold as if she were cast in ice, she saw a hand emerging from the dark.

Its fingers, white as chalk and contracting, were creeping closer and closer, each one separately. The hand descended from the illuminated wall like a white cat, crawling over the objects and the stove. At that moment, Madame Dafina noticed another hand which had approached her from behind and was reaching for and rumpling her dresses on the wall, throwing them around on the floor. Finally, screaming subduedly, she also saw in front of the curtain the huge belly of her husband, his mouth, eyes and nose, his entire image on the white sheet, bloody, with the throat slit and with his black military hat hovering above his head.

When the wall behind the apparition began to sway, she also discerned hills and golden ears of corn which spilled through the wall together with waves of wheat, rye and oats from the ceiling. Then entire constellations of stars flashed before her eyes, blue, purple and yellow; and unusually luke-warm waters, over which the skies were flowing, poured over her. Shrieking terribly and starting in the air she found herself face to face with her bloody and horrifying husband Vuk Isaković, and she saw him decompose before her eyes. It is thus that fleeing in a dream from wolves, and suddenly rushing in front of a rock, one sees a terrible bear.

And so Madame Dafina fell down, clasping her hands in the darkness the very first day after the adultery, hurting the unborn child she was carrying.

*   *   *

Isaković was—or at least he thought he was—at the end of his life here, before Strasbourg. His heavy boots had lost all color, and his trousers, bulging behind like a sack, all form. He had been darning them himself. His face had become copper-colored from walking, wind and sun and he was taut and sturdier from the strain. Then again, with his belly he would look like a heavy, filled barrel. Although he had become completely decrepit with age, after two days of sleep he began to squint after peasant women, despite all the sadness in his heart. Believing that he would die, he mellowed, but he still beat horses with his fists.

He did not shave at all and, therefore, his face became more serene, with an almost gentle expression. But when his regiment, too, was assigned a Catholic priest, his yellow eyes with small black dots acquired a feverish glow which they had not displayed during the journey. In these days, speaking differently from all other officers, soothingly, like a priest, he was selecting people who, he thought, should be sent home. "Read this with attention," he said to Captain Antonović, giving him the list he selected, "and correct me if you find a mistake.

Write: they passed through Lorrain like soldiers and fought a war; they came home and there they should continue to serve like soldiers. . . ." In fact, he was sorry that, sending his people to Varadin, he could not send them to Russia with his flowery signature.

For, tortured by illness, which he did not want to worry about, and disappointed in his expectation of promotion, maddened by the difficulties concerning the acquisition of flour and meat for his soldiers, the honorable Isaković, lying in his den, finally realized during the truce before Strasbourg that he had become a ludicrous and superfluous figure, like a senile, fat priest who keeps on preaching but who in reality is no longer worth anything. As sometimes happens with the onset of old age, a fathomless emptiness appeared clearly before his eyes.

Setting out for this war and seeing death for the fourth time in his life, he hoped that something interminable would finally come to an end and be fulfilled. He thought that he and his men, in some special army, would emerge from a fierce battle strong, glorious, and rewarded with something unknown but which he imagined as particularly pleasant and significant, both for himself and for them. On his departure, he had left behind a lot of worries, which were especially cumbersome this spring: the quarrel with his brother about his wife's money, a sick child with scabs over her entire body, a repulsive wife whom he could no longer subdue, and finally the entire village which had begun to build dirt homes in the mud near Varadin. The villagers had been complaining every day, expecting him to give them food, to find them beams and posts and to draft them into the army and at the same time migrating and fleeing from him into older villages and richer settlements nearby. Thus, plagued in the last days before the departure by the digging of a well in search of drinking water and by the building of a church in the middle of the village, Isaković left gladly, convinced that all this was miserable and worthless, whereas that which awaited him in the war was powerful and bright and might end in something wonderful, both for him and for all these people of his.

Before leaving, he was disgusted not only by deprivations and misery which he found in his own home, in his hut, cattle-yards and all around his village along the river up to Varadin, but also because of the unpleasantness which he had experienced with Marquis Guadagni, the commandant of Osek, while working on the new distribution of Slavonian villages. At the same time, he was involved in the solicitations and written petitions of Patriarch Šakabenta, so that it seemed to him that they all, like him, felt the futility of their living, settling, roaming, wailing and multiplying there on the shore of the Danube. Leaving the foggy evaporation of marshes and bogs and the immeasurable suffering, which repeated itself daily during the migrations, drowning of cattle, and ploughing in the mud and salt-springs, he imagined himself riding away on horseback on a warm spring morning to some high hill, where he would receive something that would help and cheer up every one. With forebodings that he would not come back, he still thought that upon his return, when he and his soldiers descended the other side of the hill, they would all ride home contented, finding everything changed and joyful. He used to leave his wife and children confidently in his brother's home; and as far as the settlement and those who remained at home were concerned, it seemed to him that somebody would take care of them too, so that he would find them in the tall wheat already growing on the plain, free from epidemics and disease. He thought that he would forget thefts and murders, which he had to argue about every day at home, and he hoped that God's or the Emperor's hand would be extended over all his soldiers and their wagons, along the entire journey to war. Therefore, he took special care that the names and conditions of individual villages and regiments be nicely written out on the roll which the commissary had to send by special courier to the War Council in Vienna.

Having grown up close to his father, who sold cattle even to Savoyski and who had pushed all his children, brothers, relatives and acquaintances into the Austrian army which was repelling the Turks, the young Isaković had led an almost pleasant life in the army. Spoiled and often rewarded, he harbored in himself a hazy but deep notion of happiness and pleasure, in the hope that all wars would end in a general peace and that afterwards he, his relatives, friends, and all his soldiers would be clothed in especially festive and showy attire and thus make a round of the battlefields and the Empire, before the eyes of the entire world which would exclaim, "Look, Serbs!"

Under the influence of his father's promises, which filled his head with the return to a burned, slaughtered, and deserted Serbia, he spent his life in the army not only at peace but also during all three wars, carefree and contented, constantly expecting something pleasant to happen to all of them. Sinking deeper and deeper into military life, colonization, censuses, concentration of people and livestock in fortresses and strategically situated villages, Isaković realized only after his father's death that nothing was becoming any better. Only then did he notice around him the muddy fields and marshes, the misery of his people, the monotonous, bitter life in villages and trenches, in homes on the water, in huts and cattle-yards, in holes dug in the ground.

And so in recent years he survived all the unpleasantness of the migrations and the service and all the disappointments of people older than he: those in military ranks as well as in the patriarch. In this war, however, from Pecuj on, he was trudging along with greater and greater difficulty, lost in the masses, slighted deliberately, it seemed to him.

He crossed the Rhine observing his actions as if they were done by someone else, stepping among corpses through the burning streets, as if in a dream. And only here, before Strasbourg, during that intolerable truce, did he finally feel that horrible, giddy emptiness before him, in which there was no longer anything.

Lying in the terrible heat and humidity on the ground, in the low hut covered with grass which, dried up, smelled intoxicating, he remained almost completely alone for days, with a jug of water, shifting on the cover and the saddle from the sunny to the shady side, removing ants with his palm from under his headrest. With his ailing stomach, which bothered him less since the beginning of the battles, he lay in this hut as in a grave, all day avoiding going into the camp built on the pasture-ground among the wagons—a real gypsy camp, in which the people were roaring, accompanied by gusle by the fire, more out of hunger than from drinking. Stretching his legs and spreading out his arms, Isaković imagined in his slumber that he was reaching all the way to the city entrenchments and to Baerenklau's tents, so that he could push the forts with his soles and strangle several Baerenklaus in the camp with his hands. He fell asleep several times, furious and desperate, and was awakened before evening by the singing of the soldiers and the beating of the drums.

In the darkening twilight, through the rattling and murmur of the camp, the clatter of hoofs, the cattle bells, the sound of blacksmiths' anvils, Isaković, bloated from sleep and rest, immersed himself with all his strength in the subdued, endless chirping of crickets over the whole wide field, in the fathomless nothingness and emptiness which he saw suddenly near him, before his old age. Afraid of being disturbed by his officers' problems, as well as by their feasts, he did not ask for them, and did not even go to Baerenklau's tent where gambling and carousing were in full swing. In his loneliness, his eyes filled only with the silhouettes of several miserable, motionless wagons, from which harnesses were hanging, and with long plains of scorched fields and the glowing sky, Isaković abruptly shook off everything he had hoped for until now. After his lieutenant-colonelship, he also renounced Baron Baerenklau, whom he had admired, and a whole group of spruced-up, wigged commanders. Not only did the entire army, which they were dragging behind them, clearing its path by slaughtering the enemy, seem not to worry him in the least now, but also his past appeared to him as an infinite madness. He hoped for nothing anymore, not even for his return; and all those people who had settled down there in the mud he now saw as changed, sad, and deceived.

But on abandoning and despising the entire army, he abandoned everything else forever: his wife and children, for whom he had been breaking his back for so long and who were not there to see, to touch or help him; all that mud to which he was supposed to return with his mad, empty, and worthless life; and all those affairs he still wanted to take car of.

That evening not only the hut in which he lay, but his entire life as well sank into the darkness and fathomless emptiness. It disappeared; he took it off as he used to take off his silver-embroidered clothes before women, tittering drunkenly. An old woman appeared instead of his first love, emptiness in place of cities where he had lived, traded, dug trenches, shot and beaten people.

Of his entire life there still remained bright in his memory only those shining, pure stars and silvery forest paths above which the April fog descended and on which he rode his horse in the first days of his marriage, living in that monotonous boredom of a small Slavonian garrison, hunting foxes. And in the future he saw only boundless Russia engulfed in snow, where he had thought of migrating, to live an easier life for once and to rest and settle down once and for all.

Vasa D. Mihailovich

Sima Pandurović

(1883–1960)

Pandurović was born in Belgrade, where he spent most of his life. Together with Vladislav Petković Dis, he became the leading representative of pessimistic, even decadent poetry. The dark mood is already evident in his first books of poems. *Posmrtne počasti* (Last Respects, 1908) and *Dani i noći* (Days and Nights, 1912). He continued in the same vein between the wars, working also as an editor, critic, and translator (Shakespeare). Although he died in 1960, he had practically ceased writing at the outbreak of World War II.

Pandurović's poetry is suffused with sorrow, pain, evil, and death. Even the fleeting moments of joy are mixed with despair. Hopelessness and alienation are the two conditions most frequently encountered in his poems. An erudite poet well versed in French Symbolist and decadent poetry, he adopted much of the same avant-garde spirit. At the same time his poetry is sincerely felt and ruthlessly honest, penetrating to the deepest recesses of mind, spirit, and heart. As such he struck a genuine and even original note in Serbian poetry, influencing a few of the younger poets.

His other books of poetry are: *U nemirnim senkama* (In Restless Shadows), *Iluzije sećanja i nada* (Illusions of Remembrance and Hope), *Tamne ispovesti* (Dark Confessions), and *Iskušenja* (Temptations).

A SONNET

O deaf midnight! Vain are the cries of pain!
No: icily the wind roars from the height;
Our eyes are blind with tears, and drought and blight
Shatter our earth and all our world of dreams.

The hangmen have gone mad; the mob blasphemes;
Who guards our shrines, so holy in our sight?
Our city gates? None but the cold midnight,
And evil mud chokes our pellucid streams.

233

O deaf midnight! Vain are the cries of pain!
All images once dear as our own breath
Have vanished out of sight like our own youth;

The paths we knew we will not tread again,
And devils dance the grisly dance of death
Before a brutal, bare, grimacing Truth.

G. Komai

Momčilo Nastasijević

(1894–1938)

Born in Gornji Milanovac in 1894, Nastasijević became a high school professor and spent most of his life in that capacity in Belgrade, where he died in 1938.

Nastasijević is perhaps the most enigmatic of Serbian poets. From the very beginning he endeavored to create his own idiom, to which he remained faithful all his, unfortunately brief, creative life. In his poetry and short stories he drew from the rich folklore and from the distant past, both of which he interpreted in his own way, as well as from his mystical outlook on life. He also attempted to formulate through his works a national and religious philosophy whose roots, again, he found in the dark recesses of the soul of his nation.

As a poet, Nastasijević remained a loner, understood and admired only by his closest friends. Lately, however, his work has began to exert a noticeable influence on younger Serbian poets.

TO THE LADY

Ever more alone.
You visit me in dreams, a stranger.
More sinful, I call you in my loneliness.
To children of others you have given the first cry.

Have pity.
Your physic poisons and does not heal.
You pierced me mightily with gall.
My wretched days, o Lady,
I squander in song.

I wail
but the voice trails off.
Mellifluous salvation is on some far-off star,
of which I, ailing singer, stammer here below.

There is no hand to loose our knot for us.
But even then, and for ever,
will your glance hurt?
Strange creatures born of you will I hold dear?

Have pity.
Your physic poisons and does not heal.
You pierced me mightily with gall.
My wretched days, o Lady,
I squander in song.

Vasa D. Mihailovich

Desanka Maksimović

(1898–   )

Born in Rabrovica near Valjevo, Maksimović studied in Belgrade and Paris and taught school for many years. Most of her life she spent in Belgrade, where she now lives and writes poetry.

Maksimović began to publish poetry after World War I. In the period between the two wars she wrote poetry and literature for children: *Pesme* (Poems, 1924), *Vrt detinjstva* (The Childhood Garden, 1927), *Zeleni vitez* (The Green Knight, 1930), and *Gozba na livadi* (The Feast on the Meadow, 1932). These poems are distinguished by strong lyricism, genuine emotions, an almost pantheistic closeness to nature, simplicity and immediacy, and refreshing images and metaphors. These characteristics remained the same throughout her creativity.

After World War II she wrote several poems in which she expressed her concern for her suffering poeple along with the hatred for the oppressors. In the last few years she has written perhaps her best poetry, evoking the glory of the Serbian distant past and searching in it for answers to present problems.

Her best postwar books of poetry are: *Pesnik i zavičaj* (Poet and His Native Land, 1946), *Miris zemlje* (The Scent of the Earth, 1955), and *Tražim pomilovanje* (I Seek Mercy, 1964).

A LEGEND OF BLOOD

(This poem refers to one of the most dastardly crimes committed by the Nazis in the Serbian town of Kragujevac where, as a reprisal, schoolboys were taken from their classes—along with their teachers— and executed with about seven thousand hostages.)

It happened in a far-off land of peasants,
among the Balkan hills, where
martyrdom befell
a class of schoolboys gay—
all on one day.

About the same year
were they born,
same were the days at school they spent,
same the celebrations
to which they went;
same was the date of vaccination,
and same the day their lives were spent.

It happened in a far-off land of peasants,
among the Balkan hills, where
martyrdom befell
a class of schoolboys gay
all on one day.
Five and fifty minutes back
before that fatal hour
still at their desks they sat,
a company of bodies small,
with eager answers to all
those questions difficult: How much,
if a traveller went on foot . . .
and many, many such.
Their thoughts were full of figures;
their satchels full of copy-books
with marks
both good and bad
a handful of dreams and secrets,
of love and loyalty,
stuffed into their pockets.
And it seemed to each of them
that still for long,
for very long,
they would all run beneath the sun,
until their tasks
were done

It happened in a far-off land of peasants
among the Balkan hills, where
heroic death befell

a class of schoolboys gay—
all on one day.

Out came the classmates small
holding each other by the hand;
their lessons but half done,
to the shooting place they went
in the silence—death to face:
schoolboys small,
one and all,
sent to their eternal dwelling-place.

A. Lenarčič and J. Lavrin

Branko Ćopić

(1915–   )

Ćopić was born in the Bosnian village of Hašani during World War I. He received his education at a teacher's school in Banjaluka and the University of Belgrade. He participated on the side of the partisans in World War II. Since the war, he has lived as a professional writer in Belgrade.

Ćopić is a prolific writer of short stories, novels, poems, plays, and children's books. He achieved early recognition, shortly before World War II, with his stories about the hard life of the Bosnians. His postwar novel *Prolom* (Breakthrough, 1952) is an epic tale about the partisan war, whereas his later novels, *Gluvi barut* (The Noiseless Gunpowder, 1957) and *Osma ofanziva* (The Eighth Offensive, 1964), depict the difficulties the victorious peasant partisans encountered in the cities after the war. The last war is still one of his main topics and he is able to spice it with genuine humor, as in *Doživljaji Nikoletine Bursaća* (Adventures of Nikoletina Bursać, 1955).

He is often satirical of the contemporary situation in his country. He is perhaps the most popular Serbian writer today, especially among children. The populist and somewhat superficial nature of his writings is compensated by his warm concern for people and by healthy humor.

His prewar collections of stories are: *Pod Grmečom* (At the Foot of the Grmeč Mountain) and *Borci i bjegunci* (Fighters and Deserters, 1939)—perhaps his best book of stories.

CRUEL HEART

The machinegunner, Nikoletina, was parting from his mother in the tiny, cluttered yard in front of the old house, with its sagging roof. His short leave was over, and he was hurrying to reach his unit, which had been fighting these days somewhere near Ključ, before dark.

It was a dry, cold morning in late autumn. There was no sun; and, in addition, a cold wind was blowing steadily. Nikoletina's frail, little mother seemed even smaller as she drew her head into her oversized man's overcoat. Huddled beside her big, awkward Nikoletina, she looked like a blue-lipped child.

"My Nidžo, my apple, take care of yourself, when you go away," said the mother worriedly, shivering constantly—partly from the cold, and partly from the self-supporting sorrow of old people. She spoke, not looking at her son, but at his pants, patched at the knees. If she had looked at his face, she knew well, she would have started crying and forgotten all her resolutions.

"Go to the devil, mother, what else would I do, but take care of myself?" responded Nikoletina morosely, and he carefully buttoned his bulging little army bag, out of which protruded a layer of greased paper.

"Take care of yourself, my happiness, be clever," the weeping old woman advised softly, taking a thread off his outgrown, wrinkled army overcoat, while Nikoletina sullenly replied:

"What is the matter with you, mother, do you think that I am crazy, instead of clever? What is with you this morning?"

Being used to his rugged nature, the old woman was not hurt by her son's rough answers, but advised him further, constantly afraid she would forget to tell him something important. She had been like this since the uprising started.

"Nidžo, my pigeon, I did not ask you what kind of quarters you have there where you are going to be."

"Well, mother, there are crazy people in the world, but you surpass them all! What quarters! Do you think that somebody makes a mattress for me? I lie on the ground, cover myself with the sky, and that is my lodging."

The dry, cold wind was blowing tirelessly over the bare hills and deserted fields which were covered with the first hoarfrost. The wind whistled sorrowfully in the orchard, chasing down the last few apple leaves and winding through the groves by the river, warning that unavoidable parting was upon them. The old woman sank even more deeply into the faded overcoat, and started to cry with tiny, stinging tears.

"My son, you are already leaving, and I haven't had a chance to look at you long enough!"

Nikoletina only scowled, avoiding the eyes of the crying old woman, and, with knitted brow, stared at a lonely tree on the nearby hill, and answered her roughly, almost angrily:

"Ach—to look long enough at me! Why the devil do you want to look at me? Do I have horns? You have really become childish."

"Ach, my son, a lot of mothers become childish nowadays," the old woman said bitterly and reproachfully, wiping her eyes with the little end of her black scarf, and Nikoletina no longer knew what to answer her, and he wiped his nose and said in a businesslike fashion:

"Mother, let's kiss each other and I will leave. I will be late."

Beginning to cry again, the old woman was barely able to kiss her son on his chin and shoulder before he pulled away from her embrace, saying good-bye dryly, and hurried down the road.

"Well, good luck, son! May God watch over you and keep you alive!" said the old woman with her last strength before her voice was choked by tears. Nikoletina did not hear her words anymore, but he knew well that his mother watched him with tearful eyes, and no matter what, he could not walk with a measured step, and he kept stumbling on the large dry clods on the road as he hurried to hide himself behind the hedge on the first curve.

Left in the deserted yard, the tiny, weak old woman strained herself to see once again her departing son through her tears, but Nikoletina's wide shoulders were disappearing with merciless speed around the bend.

The rugged and craggy mother Bosnia, rough and sharp in everything, does not let you, not even in the last minutes of a departure, look long enough at your most loved one: it wrenches him from you quickly and hides him from your eyes, just then when he is dearest to you. . . .

II

. . . Wet and sweating, all red in the face and with a curse on his lips, Nikoletina was running hastily with his helper to a low stony knoll from which the enemy was retreating, caught by fire from the side.

"Faster, Djurkan, faster! Are you having an attack of liver sickness? For heaven's sake!"

They reached the knoll quickly and lay down in a quarry full of low thorny bushes. Fortunately, he had time to place his machine gun suitably. He started shooting in short spurts at the retreating legionnaires who were running in groups over the rocky field, and already taking up positions at the edge of the first underbrush.

The enemy had been forced to retreat hastily from its former position as the partisans had driven a wedge into its overextended lines. They had been forced to retrench quickly and prepare for a new attack. They were confused and bewildered by the persistence of the partisans. It had not occurred to them that their opponents were fighting from the last suitable positions at the entrance to the wide valley, the birthplace of most of the partisans in this battalion. If the partisans had retreated from this place, the enemy would have had an open way to the lower villages. Each partisan fighter knew this, and, therefore, yesterday's hasty retreat had abruptly stopped as each partisan group had dug in, feeling there was no room for further retreat. To the enemy these were incomprehensible, sudden changes in the situation and the unexpected, persistent, counterattacks of the newly tempered partisan detachments had overwhelmed them. Deafened by their own guns, boiling with blind hate, they were fighting and storming, seeing in front of them not an ordinary enemy, but an odious and greedy plunderer, a thief, who like a greedy pig had attempted to break into their homes.

"Well, we wouldn't let you get by even if you had a star on your forehead."

Having fired on the last scattered groups of legionnaires, Nikoletina changed the hot barrel of his machine gun, wiped off the angry sweat, which was burning his eyes, and addressed himself to his assistant, Djukan:

"Fill up all the ammunition belts; they will come again. They really have gone blind, like hungry pigs before they get hit over their heads. They won't retreat."

Suddenly both of them started frightfully, as if somebody had shot behind their backs. Behind them, quite close, somebody called hesitatingly:

"Nidžo-o-o-o. . . . Nidžo!"

After a moment of speechlessness Nikola opened his mouth and then exclaimed:

"Look! . . . Where did you come from, mother? How you scared me!"

Hesitating, undecided, as if caught in a prohibited place, the tiny little woman, aged before her time, started slowly up the sloping ground, covering the several steps which separated her from the machine gun.

"Get down, get down! Sit here, you are revealing our position!" Nikoletina swore at her in a subdued voice and the old woman, confused and unsure, like a child, got down quickly and unnaturally, sitting on a stone near his legs, putting a little bag on her lap.

"Well, where did you come from?" Nikoletina yelled at her snappishly, coming to his senses.

"Well—I just came!" said the old woman modestly, still breathing heavily from the excitement and the distance she had covered. She gaped at her son with so much quiet and devoted joy that Nikoletina, touched, only turned his head and mumbled:

"You came! I can see myself that you came; I'm not blind."

"How did you learn that we were here?" said Djurkan surprised.

"It was easy, my son, I recognized your machine gun and I just went after it. I felt all the time: here must be my Nidžo."

"Ach, your Nidžo!" snubbed Nikoletina at her. "What the devil did you come here for?"

"Ach, my son, you are really a child," the old woman said reproachfully, shoving her hand into the little bag. "Well, mother came and brought a snack or two. Maybe you are hungry."

"Hmm, hungry! What else? Of course, we are hungry. Do you think that the enemy is treating us to roast chicken!" Nikoletina mumbled, and then still peevish, he sized up the little bag on mother's lap and said in a more conciliatory voice:

"Take out what you have and run home! . . . They are coming again, and when a bullet hits you. . . . hmm. . . ."

The old woman took out smoked bacon and a piece of unleavened cake, placing it on a stone near them, and the watchful Nikoletina, having noticed something suspicious among the enemy, gave a sign to his assistant and waved to the old woman.

"Go on, mother, go back quickly! Hurry, just get across the field to the road."

Kept busy with the enemy, Nikoletina was no longer morose, nor rough, and the old woman felt that it was something serious and that she should not bother them any more, and without taking leave she hurried down the hill.

The shooting started again. The enemy began a new attack. They were advancing in groups under the protection of their machine guns, not sparing their ammunition.

Nikoletina returned the fire and then turned for a moment, waving to the old woman, who stopped for a moment.

"Faster, faster! I will protect you with the fire!"

The black silhouette started walking again and almost crawled across the field.

Already hot from the fighting, Nikoletina fired again, and during the short rest he spoke tersely to his assistant:

"Take a look, Djurkan. Is the old woman getting away?"

"There she is—she is already half way across the field!" said the winded Djurkan, taking out the first round of cartridges.

The enemy was very persistent this time. Systematically and slowly, according to all the rules of warfare, they pushed forward.

"Look, ours are retreating from the right wing!" Djurkan said somewhat excitedly, pointing to the small groups of partisans who were running down from a low mountain range along the sparse little birchtree wood.

"We will have to retreat, too. They will hit us from the side."

"We are not retreating," Nikoletina replied shortly, shooting again at the nearest knoll, from which spat the sharp fiery tongues of the enemy's guns, hardly noticeable in the snow.

"Djurkan,—see where the old woman is!"

"There she is, almost at the end of the field. Just a bit and she will reach the road."

"A little bit longer, Djurkan," Nikoletina threw out almost apologetically, covered with sweat, and with red eyes, not listening to the courier, who angrily yelled, showing his round head from behind the pile of rocks on the left side.

"The machine gun! The machine gun! . . . Nikoletina, retreat to the old position by the beechtrees! The commander ordered it! . . ."

"Djurkan—the old woman? Take a look?"

"There she is, reaching the road!" said Djurkan relieved, and with this, Nikoletina let out the last long and joyful spurts, grabbed the machine gun and started walking back.

"Let's go, Djurkan, now we can go. Take the bacon with you! Ach, mother, you made me sweat today! . . ."

Above the steep edge of the road, which from this point led in curves down to the village, Nikola's mother stood. Hardly noticing her shivering, not hearing the bullets, which were singing high above her, she was holding the wet timber tree branch, watching two black silhouettes with tearful eyes—one bigger, one smaller, who were hurrying down the remote snowy mountain range. She shouted in her weak voice, although they couldn't have heard it down there:

"Hurry up, my Nikola, my apple. Here I am; I am safe! Do not worry about me; do not worry, my pigeon. . . ."

Branko Mikasinovich

Mihailo Lalić

(1914–   )

A native of Montenegro, Lalić was born in Trepča, near Andrijevica. As a law student at the University of Belgrade, he was often imprisoned for his communist activities. He fought as a partisan in World War II and spent time in a prisoners' camp. After the war he occupied many positions as an editor and journalist He has been a professional writer for the last several years.

His first book of short stories, *Izvidnica* (Reconnaisance Patrol), appeared in 1948, but it was not until a series of novels—*Svadba* (The Wedding, 1950), *Zlo proljeće* (The Evil Spring, 1953), *Raskid* (The Break, 1955), *Hajka* (The Chase, 1960), and his best work *Lelejska gora* (The Leleja Mountain, 1957, 1962)—that he received universal recognition as one of the best living Serbian writers. So far he remained a one-theme writer—the last war and the fratricidal struggle between the partisans and their opponents in Montenegro. But Lalić is not concerned with the realistic depiction of war as much as he is with man's behavior toward his fellow man. In *Lelejska gora* he follows the odyssey of a partisan leader left behind enemy lines and hunted like a wild animal, until he is freed of all restraints and concerns civilization had imposed upon him and is faced with the problem of naked existence.

Some of his other works are: short stories *Prvi snijeg* (The First Snow, 1951), *Gosti* (Guest, 1967), *Posljednje brdo* (The Last Hill, 1967); and his last novel *Pramen tame* (1970, A Patch of Darkness).

LELEJA MOUNTAIN

(Excerpts)

The Italian trucks were speeding one by one along the road past Breza. They passed by every day, bringing food to the idling troops and ammunition to the *Chetniks** defending them whether there were

---

*A guerrilla force opposing both the occupier and the partisans.

any attackers or not. In the afternoon they returned empty at much greater speed. From my observation point they were inaudible—probably that is why they seemed to be frightened and trembling as they began to descend into the abyss before them. Only after they rounded the sheltering bluff did their bluster and thunder come back to me. Much of life, perhaps everything, is like that: late, or never, we realize what we see; frightened by what is already over; in between, we love or hate the things and people we are thrown together with because we are unfamiliar with them.

Such empty thoughts are a nuisance because everything can be justified by them, and a man burdened by them might as well lie down, fold his arms and die. Well, I don't want to die: there's still half the summer to go, and perhaps even the autumn before me, and I've got a woman too. But I don't know her nor does she know me. We've seen each other by the light of the fireplace and stars, but never in the daytime. Perhaps we are destined not to see one another in the daytime, but only at night—a damned sneaking affair, Anyway. I can't stand being without her for long. Everything about me—the woods, clouds and rivers—is stale compared with her voice and laughter.

I hurried unnecessarily, arriving too early at the Jablan pastures, which were green after the recent rain. It was daylight and the view was uninteresting. The salt-licks were visible like scars, and there were stakes all over the place for tethering horses. A cowbell could be heard ringing at the farther end of the pastures. Should she chance along with her sheep, I would make my way over during the night and tomorrow I would see what she looked like in the daytime . . .Boredom made me go to have a look at the cave, which is actually a roomy corridor in the rock. Here and there are regular openings like rooms, and then pits with broken stone at the bottom. At one point the roof had caved in, and the distant sky, bluer and clearer than anywhere else, was visible through the chimneylike crevice.

The humidity and subdued movement of the air felt by the skin but inaudible to the ear soon got on my nerves. I went into the woods, to the hilltop, to wait for Neda, for she was sure to come to gather green oak leaves for the calves. I had not been waiting long when instead of her over the meadow came a tall man with a shotgun. He was erect and strong, his temples were grey and so was his moustache. He might have been her father-in-law, probably come to lay for a rabbit after the sun set. I waited for him behind a tree trunk; he changed his direction, deliberately, I should say. He reached a clearing, seated himself on a fallen tree trunk, rested his shotgun upon it and produced his tobacco box. I crept forward stealthily and stepped out in front of him with my pistol cocked. His features contorted, his cap stood up on his head, his black brows bristled.

"Don't move, old man," I said, "Only put up your hands!"

He spilled his tobacco, a breeze carried away the cigarette paper, but he refused to raise his hands, and his mouth twisted into a smile, Finally he recovered his voice.

"Who are you to give me orders?" he asked.

"Raise those paws of yours before I drill you!"

I pulled the Colt out of his belt and kicked the shotgun out of his reach. "That's right."

"Do you know what you're doing?" he exclaimed.

"I do. So will you, you'll be told by my superior. He's over in the cave, get on!"

He realized there was no talking with me; but he hoped he would find someone more reasonable in the cave. He got up, but irresolutely. I prodded him with the shotgun and roared as sentries and armed escorts usually do, in order to confuse him. He shook his head menacingly and went forward. Maybe he thought I belonged to one of those flying squads that have nothing better to do, or to those police patrols from other districts, unburdened by considerations of kinship —and so he proceeded. Superior officers are no problem; it's hard to deal with a man in a moment of irritation. We entered the cave and he looked about. Suddenly he stiffened.

"What does this mean?" he demanded, and his eyes bored through me like gimlets.

"You're going to pay your debt," I said throwing the shotgun to the ground.

"You're all wrong, I don't owe anyone anything!"

"Who informed against Veljo Plećović and raked in that money?"

His lips writhed as though there were an unpleasant taste in his mouth as he thought over my question.

"I did," he exclaimed, "not for the money, though, but because he had been living with my daughter-in-law."

I forgot where I was, and a mist came over my eyes. I felt as if I had been kicked in the head. And at that moment he really did hit me, in the chin, with a punch I hadn't seen coming. It was like the kick of a mule. He's a boxer, the thought flashed through my mind; he must have learned boxing in America. My pistol went flying through the air. I fell on my back, on my haversack of apples, where I had also stored his Colt, and I had no doubt that this was the end. Masnik would survive and Miklja would go on making money, and this dung, like any other dung, would go on polluting the earth. . . . Out of the haze I saw him bending over me to hit me again—I jerked my head aside and catching him between my legs pitched him over my head. He must have fallen on his head for he groaned.

"Had enough?" I shouted, though I was still unable to get up.

"You'll see who you're up against!"

"We'll see, all right!"

I felt for his shotgun, found it, and hit him over the head with it as hard as I could. The shotgun broke in two, and he staggered. I grabbed his hand and twisted his arm into a hammer lock—a short jab from him and I had to let go. To avoid a second blow I dived headlong into his ribs. I smelled the sweat of his body and felt his heart beating. Our fingers interlocked and we looked one another in the eyes, equals, our hair on end, and equally crazed by anger and fright. He had got it worse: his head was a shapeless sponge with blood flowing into it out of his left eye, but his hands were terribly strong. He was in every way stronger and he knew it. If I let him hit me only once more as he already had done—it would be the end. He was breaking my fingers. . . ! It seems I had had a premonition of what was coming when I ordered that coffin from Kacaranda for a joke. . . .

"You see, you see?" he roared, "I'm a Harpy—do you know what a Harpy is?"

"And I'm the Devil!" I returned. "Look where I've brought you!"

"I'll fix you like I would a snake, you s.o.b.!"

My mother was no bitch, went the thought through my mind as a strong wrench released my sweating fingers. I ducked to avoid the blow, clasped him around the hips and hurled him to the stony floor. To keep him from getting up I stepped on his right hand, clamped my hands around his neck and squeezed. He howled—from fear, or for help, or to scare me. For a time his howls were his only defense. He interrupted them only to gather strength for a blow. Thus I always knew when to protect my head. Finally his voice grew weak and turned into a dying moan. I decided to let him go and question him while he could still talk. I'd make him tell me everything he knew about Veljko and Nada. . . . Suddenly pain seared me below my belly: he had a grip and was squeezing.

"Now what?" he thundered in a ghoulish voice.

I sank to the ground in pain and unconsciously seized a sharp piece of long stone in order to have something in my hands.

"You are trying to measure wits with me, you bastard?" he said as he squeezed.

I stabbed at him with my stone—at his back, his hands—but my blows had no strength, and he did not notice them.

"This is how I castrate the devil," he crowed. "This is how! Like this! Like this! Like this!"

With a last glance, already at the edge of consciousness, I saw his neck and the back of his head in the distance. I wanted to hit him there with my stone and I believe I did make an effort to do so, and then everything faded out. I had been lying on my back for a long time, and the pain had moved upward into my head and teeth. I couldn't see anything, it was dark outside and in. He was still in the cave, I could hear him crawling towards me. I was lying on my haversack and his Colt was in it, but that was as far away as the mountains. I remembered I had Vanja Lopa's little pistol and I put my hand in my pocked. It was there. Perhaps it couldn't kill a Harpy, but at least it could scorch its skin. He sensed my intention, changed his direction and began to retreat.

"I'm here," I shouted, "where are you going?"

He hesitated for a moment, and then began to crawl, and a stone rolled off into the pit.

"Don't you want to start again?" I asked. "Everything has to be settled somehow."

Two or three pebbles rolled off into the pit, followed by something which thumped heavily like a sack. I started with fright: he must have thought of something, he had had more time in which to do so.

"I believe I've knocked one of your eyes lopsided," I said to enrage him. "It doesn't matter. I'll fix the other one too."

He said nothing. And I couldn't hear him crawling any more. We were silent and he seemed to be even more resistant in the silence.

I'd have to give in, I thought, if he was like that—one couldn't wait all night! I struck a match, the flame flickered and lighted a cave within a cave, one that was illumined against the trembling walls of darkness. He was invisible against those walls: there was nothing but stone, apples and pools of blood black as tar. The apples had spilled from my haversack when I fell the first time, and had rolled under our feet. Nor did the blood surprise me—it made no difference whether it was mine or his—I didn't know why he had fled or how it was that I had escaped with my life. . . .

I touched my swollen jaw—some tooth must have been knocked loose there. The bones were whole, but the jaw was numb. I got to my feet, but I was unable to stand erect—I was all broken. I dragged myself about almost on all fours—I found my gun; it was strange that he hadn't taken it. He must have been frightened by some devil and taken to his heels. It was beyond me what could have frightened him like that. I gave up thinking about it—I was so worn out. I slipped the haversack from my back—there were still a few crushed apples in it, the Colt and a piece of pine. The pine barely took fire because it was soaked in apple juice, and I went back to look for him.

A trail of blood, like a wounded snake, led over the stone floor. Following it, I came upon a small hollow leading into the pit. I held my burning pine torch over the pit, and the first thing I saw were his big feet in their *opanci**—they were at the edge of the hollow—and then his head, crushed almost beyond recognition, which seemed to be listening in silence to the pulsations of the earth. I called to him, I prodded him with my foot—there was no answer. I felt his hand—it was cold. Well, I was the lucky one! I said. I don't know if my luck will hold out, but for the time being I'm all for your being where you are instead of me. You wanted a rabbit but you came on something you didn't expect—it's you today, it will be me tomorrow—that's Life the Gambler for you. . . .

I went on looking for my pistol for some ten minutes. I found it at length amid the stones, trampled over and dusty as though it had been lost for a long time. As I dragged myself all broken up to the mouth of the cave, some people arrived through the woods from the pastures with torches in their hands: a man and two women, one of

---

*Opanak—Soft-soled peasant footwear.

them Neda. They stopped and called him, then waited in vain for his answering call. This waiting, silly as hop, enraged me, and I emitted a hoarse cry from the slope. I hurried away from the spot before they could reach it; then I let out a cry from my fresh position. They hesitated perplexed—and then they waved their torches and called no more.

I often happen to come upon a place I have not seen for a long time—a familiar cliff, a trail or a memorial fountain with an old through. The familiar objects shimmer in a dual light—that of the sunshine, and in the light of my memories. The joy that overcomes me is not as unreasonable as it might appear to be. In a particular object I sometimes find a friend such as I seek in vain among men, and it is the only faithful being that can be found in this unfaithtul world. Besides, it is evidence that in my mortal self there is a permanence of feeling, rather like the reflection on water, but which can compete with the permanence of the hills and rocks.

On the other hand, sometimes recognition is a nuisance. For instance, once I found myself in nameless streets with rotting walls and closed shutters. I recognized one, unfortunately, for whatever I see is merely the corroboration of a state of affairs which I have already seen somewhere, from which I have, I know not how, extricated myself with the hope that I shall never return to it. The two rows of rotting houses came together and parted and reared underneath the overhanging sky in convulsions like a scotched snake. I slowly came to the conclusion that it was a real snake and that I was inside it, observing it from within. I did not know where its end was, and I staggered through the fluid mud of its undigested food with no hope of ever finding it.

I went forward and then back, and then I realized it had joined its head and tail in a closed hollow circle of eternity. No one has ever come out of this gaol, I thought, and nor will I. . . . Let it digest me. . . ! I stopped and, as if to protract my sufferings, it changed again into a street adorned with butcher's meat hooks. Flies could be heard and people called to each other from time to time. It was evident from the calls that two warring factions were involved, the right and the left, which were trying to prove to one another their rights to the future.

Sometimes the walls parted and then disappeared entirely. There was grass and it was dark, and I believed I was in a field. I buried my head in the turf and rested and the sombre walls converged again from either side. The people seemed to have noticed me—they were shouting again. For some reason both sides were angry with me. They put out a dog-catcher's net for me—its frame fell just behind me, and since it scraped my crouching shadow, together with the mud and slime. I saw it writhing and straining for freedom for a few moments, and then it surrendered at the bottom of the net and went over the wall. The hunt was over and I decided that it was my shadow, not myself, that had annoyed them and, now that I no longer had a shadow, everything was all right, paid up and settled.

They were keeping silent now, in order to deceive and entrap one another. Meanwhile, each on his own side was whiling away the time with cards, lice and propaganda. Time was actually a beam, heavy and growing heavier, and its weight could not be endured unless it was shared by many shoulders. They had come to know somehow that I was carrying my beam alone, or had heard me groaning beneath its weight, and they accused me of being an isolationist and a solitary damned leper. It was in vain that I pulled off my shirt to show them that I had had only the mange—they couldn't get over the idea that it was leprosy, and because of their clamor I could not hear my own weak voice.

Something told me that it was daylight and that the rays of the sun were on the back of my head. I peered through the particles of dust in my eyes and with the tip of my tongue licked several glistening drops of dew, which helped me to gain my senses, to arrive at the vague idea that for some reason or other it was unhealthy to stay in the open. First I pulled my cap down to my brows to cover my face, then it occurred to me this would not be enough, and I started up the hill. I leaned against a branch and it moved to open a doorway. There was a shadow inside and some sort of green, untouched by light or wind. I was struck by the scent of vegetable oils and by the profound serenity of the eons when there was no human race on earth.

I stretched out on the brown carpet of needles and felt I was being rocked gently. In some places my aching body was numb, in others the pains continued to stab needlelike, and they were almost pleasant, especially when they collided with the waves of some odd sense of euphoria that comes over the drowning. The pains gradually subsided; it was as though Džana had soaked clean cool sheets underneath me in a balsam of lavender and myrtle. Everything became quiet and I slept like an uninhabited mute valley amid the mountains. Suddenly, the sooty stone of human voices began to tumble into the valley. A dream probably—and I awoke. As I did, the voices solidified and, linked up into a chain, echoed over the meadow.

"See, he isn't here," said one. "You've dragged me about through this hell all for nothing."

"Not here," added the other. "He was lying there where the grass is flattened down."

"The devil's flattened it down! It's flat everywhere."

"I saw him, I tell you. He looked dead, his head was hanging lower than his body. A live man never lies like that."

"Well, did the devil take him away?"

He must have, I thought, the devil takes care of himself as long as he can. I lined up three pistols on the ground to defend myself. The day was endless and they were crafty. It wouldn't be easy. If they would only go along the trail together, but they wouldn't. Perhaps they would leave one on guard while the others hurried after me. Fear, that old fear, began to twist me and raise me from the ground: it lifted me up and dropped me, it wore me out with waiting, and again dropped me. It let me realize that I am merely a vulnerable hunk of flesh; then it clouded my brain and shook up my joints beyond my control. I dug my elbows and then my knees and toes into the earth and clenched my teeth to keep them from chattering.

Their voices were growing louder: they were standing in the same place, murmuring something in wonder. Judging from their voices, they were afraid. Especially one of them. He kept repeating, "dancing-ground" in a strange tone of voice, and "fairy lights," and then warned his companion against touching the flattened grass, for it would knot up his brain. He lowered his voice to an ominous whisper and revealed that they, the Harpies, always died an unusual death, usually nothing remained of them. They were rare, he emphasized, and that was because they can't stand each other. When two met in the same place, they challenged each other to their Harpy duel without witnesses, and fought with clouds or whatever else they could pick up as a weapon. Sometimes both of them got hurt and never returned.

"Let's call him," said the other.

"No! They also called to him and he answered from different places to lure them on."

"Those are only fairy tales. He's been done in by the Plećovićs in revenge."

"The Plećovićs were all down below when it happened."

"Then someone else did—for his money."

I realized that they were looking for *him*. They had forgotten me as though I had never existed. I was sorry for a moment: the old brute had taken over my fame and pushed me into the background. Before this he had wanted to take that woman from me, now he lay in the pit with his whole weight on the pocketbook with the money in it. I should have taken the money from him to buy a soul or two with it. Now it was too late. Perhaps it was better this way. When they found him they would probably think that the Devil, that wild and popular devil, who was ignorant of the use of paper money, had personally done him in. . . . A different voice called from the slope; there was a black blot in the meadow in the valley, they would have to see what it was. . . .

They went to see, and the voices, subsiding gradually, vanished altogether. The air cleared of their stench and I inhaled till tears filled my eyes. I gazed at the branches, they were really slender and constantly outstretched in embrace. Their eyes, golden and green, regarded me with calm sorrow: you've wandered a lot, you're tired out, settle down for once! The gentle arches vaulting one over the other, a sky over a sky into infinity, swayed up and down. Sleep overcame me and I slowly forgot. Forgetting with one part of my being, I remembered with the other: Gluvlja, summer, when the grain was being brought in, and my mother sticking birch branches over my cradle to protect me from the sun.

Branches were again between me and the high sun. My mother was somewhere in the vicinity, gathering the crop and protecting me. I heard her sighing and seeking shelter in the shade to rest. I removed a branch in the mad hope that I would manage to see her before she disappeared, but she was not be to seen. As always, she was not visible, and it was no longer any surprise to me. Instead stood Leleja Mountain, washed in sunshine, up to its shoulders in green sheaves of foothills. You're not a good mother, I reproached it bitterly. You're evil: you're late to sow, your harvest is always green—and that's nothing to boast about! Your children squabble over bare bones or roam about the world, seeking shelter underneath foreign roofs, serve all and sundry, and every idiot regards them as an object of mirth. . . .

It was quiet, so quiet that the stillness silenced me. As I listened, the mountain seemed to grow, trembling in its growth. There was something living and something passionate in those tremors. It was alive in its own way and mad—it would seek to fly off and unite with the pure azure void. And it screamed with supersonic screams which I only indefinitely discerned—with the skin rather than with the ear. Long ago, from the bottom, perhaps the sea bottom, it had emerged and risen for this encounter. Whatever it possessed it sharpened and turned upwards: the trees to grow straight into the height; the eagles to fly towards the sun; men to dream like madmen about happiness that is unattainable on earth.

There is a period during the equinox when even snakes climb trees. Evidently the peak of a striving for the heights and of madness, for afterwards comes autumn with its burdens: the leaves fall, the Haiduks part, and flags are folded up. Age and fear are ushered in by hoarfrost, before the snows, and everything withdraws within itself and changes: the eagle devours its young in grottoes, and the rabbit endeavors to thump its woes to death; the snake finds itself a hole, and the chieftains of the Leleja Mountain valleys seek out the Vizier of Scutari or some other governor to bow before him and vow allegience in return for a jerkin and some cash.

Thus, whenever my thoughts, stirred by the idle breezes of leisure, seize upon something and wander off I know not where nor why, I ask myself in amazement whether I am completely mad or if madness is only setting in. Why do I endeavour to vindicate present hirelings and informers with natural laws and because they had predecessors a hundred years and more ago. . . ? How have they made me their debtor? Njegoš, a bishop of the Christian church, enticed these with the jerkins with the aid of the faith and godfatherhood, and annihilated them either in ambush or publicly, and afterwards he donned his vestments and in a hoarse voice sang the liturgy in church, and his soul seemed to be pure and sunny as a Saint George's Day morning in the mountains.

What is happening to our souls that they are so hopelessly soft and green, that they have become so childish and maidenish and timid? We prepared them for everything in those happy swarms of ours, except for one thing—for solitude, and it is solitude that has taken us by surprise. It affects us and so does its time, for there is much of it, and with its duration; with its weight it magnifies negligible things, making a beam out of mote. Out of a trifle, out of the shadow of a sound and pale memory—but away with such thoughts, for I am afraid, for they always lead me to a byway, and there is no one to show me the right road. I covered my eyes with my hands and withdrew my head underneath the branches. That was better. I timed my breath to their swaying rhythm—slowly, now very slowly, which is nothing compared with eternity, and even afterwards there is time.

All night long, in a fever, two women tormented me with some sort of new game, the rules of which they invented as we went along and as they saw fit. They stole my cap, tossed it to each other and hid it in the darkness underneath their skirts. The game began in the open, but later we retreated deep into the hawthorn and dog-rose thickets. Somehow I contrived to catch one of them, and left her screaming in the tangle of a thicket. The other burst out laughing—I recognized her by her voice, it was Neda! She had started it all, but it was Miklja who paid by being pushed into the thornwood. . . . And even now when I think I'm awake—because I notice the hills heaving and shivering at dawn—I feel it is so.

Perhaps it is not quite so, I tell myself in order to vindicate her. That thief of a father-in-law of hers from America, old and crafty as he was, had thought up the story about Veljko to confuse me. He had invented it as we went towards the cave, and it had come in handy. I refuse to think about it, to poison my mind further with it—he invented all, because of his suspicions and jealousy. Now that he was dead it was silly to infest myself with those suspicions where they could thrive like maggots. It was silly, I repeat; yet they continued to live and multiply whenever I began to think they were disappearing, for Veljko always kept some sort of woman, and Neda had wanted a child, and this child which was supposed to be mine was perhaps a pure deception.

What about my going to her and openly telling her so? But that would be merely a pretext to see her and succumb to her charms again. I got up to escape from these thoughts; I took the opposite way—lest my feet should carry me nearer to her. I was proceeding slantwise, I think, and in the wrong direction, but it didn't matter.

Suddenly I heard men, the poisonous beasts, shouting, and I hid. They weren't coming my way, they weren't thinking of me; they had climbed the trees, like snakes, each in his own wood, to cut branches. As they rested they called to each other from hill to hill. I listened and calmed down; they reminded me of my childhood, when Jovan Miletić and Gavro Grivić used to call to each other.

"Oh Markelez, you frog spawn, look and see why Masnik is so quiet!"

"You'd be quiet too if you had been lifting and rolling logs all night long. . . ."

"Logs all night long? What do you mean for God's sake?"

"Heavy ones too. The females in the neighborhood have drained him so dry his bones are breaking out through his skin."

"Oh Masnik, the devil take you, do you hear what Markelez says about you?"

"No, I don't! I'm not in the habit of listening to barking dogs like Markelez and you and company."

The hoarse dull voice dragged me with it before I realized that something about to happen where it came from was to be remembered so that something else could be forgotten. I made my way past Markelez through the virgin wood, and reached Masnik's area. He must have been working since before dawn—a whole patch of the wood had been laid bare by early autumn. Only naked skeletons were left of the trees, with sharply protruding stumps of what had been branches. I saw him high up in an oak tree, in the network of forks and antlers, and I hissed at him like a snake, one as big as he was, his equal. He looked down, saw me and realized everything at once.

"You've worked a lot," I said. "It's time you took a long, long rest from all this."

"I'll rest," he said derisively, "after you liberate me."

"That's why I've come from the cave. It's time I liberated someone at least."

"Well, you've talked a lot about liberation, but somehow everything's turned out wrong for you."

"It can't do otherwise when the world's all upside down."

He hid behind the tree trunk. He held on to a stump of a branch with his left hand; with his right he swung his pruning hook at my head. I stepped back, I was cool and I hated him no more than I hate the rain, the heat, the woods or some other natural phenomenon. He was natural where he was, and in the right, and he knew it, and I was an alien who wanted to disturb the natural course of things. I couldn't kill him, I hadn't the will or the strength to do so. It was always like that when men were concerned—the opposite of what I wanted to do. I'd let him live, for I was accustomed to his dodges and I'd miss them; but first I'd scare the wits out of him.

"Why did they take Vanja Lopa to jail?" I asked.

"How should I know? Someone ordered it and someone else acted on the first someone's orders."

"Yes. You wouldn't know. All you did was take the letter to the wrong address. Now, could you manage to get down out of that tree?"

"No," he said between clenched teeth. "I'm working, can't you see?"

"Then I'll bring you down quicker than you think."

I took aim, not at him but at the branch on which he was standing —between the tree trunk and his feet. Hit by the bullet, the branch broke under Masnik's weight and he scrabbled with his hands at the void. A protruding bough broke his fall; then, as he dropped to a lower one he screamed. He could have stopped there but his long legs flayed out as though he purposely wanted to lose his balance. He dropped again, but now more slowly, like a huge spider emitting the filament by which it suspends itself. At first I was frightened by his shadow, then I noticed the rope he had, and that it was unwinding from his stomach like a snake, simultaneously unwinding and distending.

He reached the lowest branch, grabbed it convulsively and hung over it. He was moaning and the coil of his intestines continued to unravel from his torn trousers. He stank, It made me sick to look at him. A bullet through his head would have ended his sufferings. I took aim, then I lowered my rifle: why should I end his sufferings? It was better as it was. The bullet I had fired had not touched him. It was not his fate to die by a bullet—he did not deserve the honor. He'd have done the same to me if he had had the chance, just as he had to Niko; so now let him suffer.

His strength forsook him, he slipped from the branch. He fell on his knees, cried, rolled over on his back to see the tree trunk bridled with his intestines. He contemplated it with hatred, as though it had been a horse that had thrown him. He thrashed with his hands in pain. Shaken by these movements, the long blue snake burst, spattering me with slime and filth. I wiped my face with a handful of dry leaves. I heard his name being called again. I replied for him with shouts that could not be recognized and meant nothing. He turned and looked at me—his face was livid and shiny with sweat. He moved his lips, whether he was swallowing or trying to throw up something, I could not tell.

"Kill me," he muttered at length.

"I'm no fool to owe blood. You'll croak as it is."

"Kill me, kill me; I'd do as much for you!"

"You would, with someone else's hand—I know you well."

"Pfuy!" he tried to spit on me, but he shut his eyes.

He was calm. I knew he was conscious and that it was by sheer willpower that he was keeping quiet, stifling the pain. There was not a sound, only the breeze disturbed the leaves of the lopped-off branches. In the trees there was nothing more for it to move except the blue stretch of intestines, at which Masnik would gnash his teeth and snarl through his nose. He continued to be quiet, he seemed to be sleeping spread out all over the place, in the air, the tree and on the ground, striving to cover as much space as possible, to tie it to himself and take it with him on his undesired journey. Even that was not enough: he tore up handfuls of earth with leaves and twigs and crushed them feverishly in his hands.

"You'll pay for this," he moaned with shut eyes.

"You fell yourself; why should I pay?"

"Someone will avenge me."

"Why, when a bullet didn't even nick you?"

"I'll tell how it was."

"I don't care if you do. I'm paying a lot as it is—what I owe and what I don't."

He probably hoped to provoke me with threats into finishing him off. When this hope was gone, he ground his teeth and covered his eyes with one hand. The sun was in his eyes, he tried to swish it away like a fly with his other hand. He mumbled something incoherent in a half tone—I couldn't make out whether he was praying or tallying up his crimes. Froth and blood had caked around his lips, out of which peered sparse gray hairs. His breath stank—to come closer to him was nauseating and if I stayed where I was I could hear nothing he said. And nothing more was audible. From the distant patches again came shouts of alarm, and Grivić called to Markelez,

"Run, man, and see! That wasn't his voice!"

"Run yourself, captain, if you're so anxious to see."

"Go on, you coward, maybe the man has hurt himself."

"It's none of my business. I've enough of my own troubles as it is."

"There was a shot, Markelez! He's had an accident."

"Well, I'm not going to match a pruning hook against a gun. You go, captain, if you want to be a hero."

They carried on like that for an hour. In the end they got together and began to approach noisily. Masnik raised the upper part of his body and fell back again. He raised himself once more and looked around. He was looking for something, maybe for a hole, like a snake. He could no longer lie still. He was moaning, breathing heavily, crawling towards the heap of branches he had prepared. He reached it, crawled underneath, only his legs remained exposed. The branches over him heaved and trembled and at length sank into stillness. I uncovered him. His eyes had glazed; he had paid his debt.

I should have gone, but something held me back. I could not say what it was, perhaps money and documents. Diving into his stench, I produced his pocketbook. Some small change—it was not worth taking. I took his Italian identity card and his Chetnik membership booklet. They might come in handy. I'd leave him an I.O.U., and I wrote out on a piece of paper, "Acknowledge receipt of the soul of the faithful Masnik—(signed) THE DEVIL." Stuffing the paper into his pocketbook, I put it back into his pocket. That would make them think!

Petar Mijuškovič

Stevan Raičković

(1928–   )

Raičković was born in Neresnica, Serbia, finished high school in Subotica, and studied literature at the University of Belgrade. He has been working in various institutions and publishing houses as editor. He is now an editor in the leading Belgrade publishing house "Prosveta."

Raičković has published several collections of poetry as well as books for children. Representing the neo-romantic current in contemporary Serbian poetry, he employs several basic motifs: nature as perfection, passion for loneliness, and yearning for soothing silence. His anxiety over man's losing ties with nature leads him sometimes to pessimism and retreat from the urban life. Simplicity, sincerity, and genuineness are his other traits.

His main books of poetry are: *Pesma tišine* (The Song of Silence, 1952), *Kasno leto* (Late Summer, 1958), *Kamena uspavanka* (The Stony Lullaby, 1963), *Stihovi* (Verses, 1964), and *Prolazi rekom ladja* (A Boat Sails Down the River, 1967).

AWARENESS OF AUTUMN

We have grown weary of looking at the cloud,
the grain,
the rain
and everything we know already out and out.

We wonder not at the swallows
as low they fly,
nor at the sunflower, turning
to the sun on high

We know the time when yellow grow the leaves
and know they needs must fall.

('Tis only love that may at times
come unexpected, after all.)

There is not anyone but knows
and fully knows,
how this little life of ours
goes and flows.

Why, then, where the green grass spreads
should we not rest our weary heads?

And why
you and I
should not dispel our grief
by the beauty of a single leaf?

A. Lenarčič

THE SONG OF THE GRASS

The grasses have a thought, a stone heavy thought.
They tell me: "There is no need for song.
Lie down, with hands beneath your head
in silence. And silent be till you forget your speech.
In quiet contemplate that hill, distant, blue,
wrapped in silence. Slowly raise your eyes
up to the cloud which roams so restless in the sky.
Then from the cloud look down into yourself. And pent up,
silent lie with inward gaze, beneath the cloud that's spread
        above the hill.

Bewildered by the darkness in yourself, look up to see the
        simple truth
(simple as a chance touch of the wind):

there is no longer any cloud above. The lonely hill
is silent, dimmed by the waning of the sun."
As I lie in the high grass I ponder vaguely.
An ant crawls upon my knee, like to a man upon a hill
Uneasily it crawls. Silent am I, silence is my song.
Absorbed in thought I lie; the grasses rustle their
    stone-heavy thoughts.

A. Lenarčič and Janko Lavrin

Miodrag Pavlović

(1928–   )

Pavlović was born in Novi Sad in 1928. He finished Medical School at the University of Belgrade and practiced medicine for several years. Later he turned to writing as his main vocation. Now he works as an editor in the publishing house "Prosveta."

He has written poetry, plays, short stories, and essays of literary criticism. His first collection of poems, 87*pesama* (87 Poems) appeared in 1952. His other books of poetry are: *Stub sećanja* (The Pillar of Memory, 1953), *Oktave* (Octaves, 1957), *Mleko iskoni* (Primeval Milk, 1962), and *Velika Skitija* (Great Wandering, 1969), For his prevalently contemplative poetry Pavlović found the sources in the Anglo-Saxon literature and in classical myths. Intellectual and neoclassical, he endeavors to overcome the romanticist, Bohemian tradition of overemotionalism. In his latest poems, he is turning more and more toward the old Serbian myths and legends, creating also his own, in an effort to find answers to the present problems.

Pavlović has also written short stories, *Most bez obale* (The Bridge Without Shores, 1956), and plays collected in *Igre bezimenih* (The Dance of the Nameless, 1963), *Koraci u drugoj sobi* (Steps in the Other Room, 1958), and *Put u neizvesnost* (The Road to the Unknown, 1958). His collection of essays *Rokovi poezije* (The Terms of Poetry, 1958) show him as an erudite and demanding literary critic.

THE EPITAPH OF AN ANCIENT SLAVIC POET

Because of our old poems
in this new faith
they called me a heretic and archenemy.
To consolidate their church
they weeded out the old refrains
and they hated me!

Buried at night
I passed into misery.
They dream of me as a magician
but I did not rise from the grave.

Nor do I rise now, when they awaken me—
is this the Last Judgement, or what?—
they're shouting at my unresponsive ears:
rise up, infidel, collect your body!
Where can I find it, I ask,
as if it were easy to remember
in this tumult that destroys the crevices of my mind.
Angels, put away your trumpets,
Soldiers of heaven,
don't trample my grave with your spurs!
I am staying where I am,
in the earth of my native tongue,
I don't want to be tried in your courts
and thrown below the open skies
on the cold sieve of Eternity.

Let others face the god,
I like my own big hole
where ancient words heal like runes
and the gusle under the earth is fertile with memories.

Biljana Šljivić-Šimšić

Vasko Popa

(1922–   )

A native of Vojvodina, Popa was born in Grebenci near Bela Crkva. He studied
in Vienna, Belgrade, and Bucharest, and graduated from the University of Belgrade. He has been active for many years as an editor in the publishing house
"Nolit." His poems have been translated into almost every European language.
In 1968 he received the National Austrian Prize for European Literature. He is
considered one of the leading poets in world poetry and certainly one of the best
poets in contemporary Serbian poetry.

Popa has published relatively little—only four collections of poetry: *Kora* (Crust,
1952), *Nepočin-polje* (Field of Sleeplessness, 1956), *Pesme* (Poems, 1965), and
Sporedno nebo (Secondary Sky, 1968). His poetry shows many unique features:
a predilection for concrete objects, a curt, crisp verse and, above all, a creation of
new myths. Despite seeming traditionalism and deceptive simplicity, everything
about Popa is unconventional, almost revolutionary. Even his patriotic poetry is
unlike any other. Concern for the universal and even metaphysical and an attempt
to pierce the crust of things make his poetry laden with meaning and symbols
and exciting to read and listen to. He likes to write poetry in cycles, several of
which are completed while others are still in the process.

Popa is also interested in folk literature, gathering and publishing unearthed
folk songs and tales, especially those with mythological connotations.

THE QUARTZ STONE

Without head without limbs
It appears
Through the exciting pulse of coincidence
It moves
With the shameless gait of time
It holds everything
In its passionate
Internal embrace

A white smooth innocent body
Smiles by way of the moon's eyebrow

Vasa D. Mihailovich

SOPOĆANI*

Rosy calm of strength
Mature calm of greatness

From the golden birds below earth
To the profusion of fruit in the heavens
All is within reach

The forms have knelt marvellously
In the eye of the artist

(Time has gnawed at it)

Young beauty of pride
Sleepwalker's certainty

The gates of eternal spring
And the bright weapons of happiness
All wait only for a sign

In the artist's right hand
Beat the pulses of the world

(Time has gnawed at it
And broken its teeth)

Anne Pennington

---

*Sopoćani (built about 1260-70) is a Serbian monastery famous for its frescoes.

Ivan V. Lalić

(1931)

Lalić was born in Belgrade, where he studied law. He spent a few years in Zagreb. Now he works in Belgrade as an editor.

Lalić began to publish poetry in 1952. His first book of poems, *Bivši dečak* (The Boy That Was) appeared in 1955. Since then he has published several collections of poetry. He is a poet of subdued pathos and great technical skill, inclining toward classical motifs and intellectualism. His verse is complex and refined and his poems are vehicles of his thoughts rather than emotions.

Among his other books of poetry are: *Argonauti i druge pesme* (Argonauts and Other Poems, 1961), *Vreme, vatre, vrtovi* (Time, Fires, Gardens, 1961), *Čin* (The Act, 1963), and *Izabrani stihovi* (Selected Verses, 1969).

THE STONEMASONS OF DUBROVNIK

In stone is the measure
and what the earth says
crumbles into the voices of chisels
that seek one another
in the resounding dust
like children's voices
in the rain.

Sometimes
we would catch an exclamation,
a particular word, would stop it,
hold it upright in the air.
In this way
we could find the measure
of a wall, the cry of a battlement

a smile, a vine, the movement
of an animal out of the stone
like a star from the sea
clean-washed and innocent.

With our tools,
with this imperfect love
we measure out the stones,
translated their curious language
into familiar images,
and charmed away (so we thought)
their deep fidelity
to a stronger measure.

But the earth shook—
somewhere we had made a mistake
we could not define,
not even in the glitter
        of the dust settling,
our words dissolving
as in water
to their beginnings.

After the blood dried
we began again

C. W. Truesdale

Miodrag Bulatović

(1930)

Bulatović was born in the small Montenegrin village of Omladina. World War II, which he experienced as a boy, left an indelible impression on him. After the war he found it difficult to adjust. After spending several years drifting from place to place, he began to write. He quickly became successful with his unorthodox short stories and novels and his fame crossed over the borders of his country. Next to Andrić, he is the most translated Serbian author. Today he is a professional writer in Ljubljana.

His first work, a book of short stories *Djavoli dolaze* (The Devils Are Coming, 1956), showed immediately his predilection for the unusual and even bizarre, his interest in, and concern for, the insulted and injured, for demented, drifting individuals at the bottom of society. In his novels, *Crveni petao leti prema nebu* (The Red Cock Flies to Heaven, 1959), *Heroj na magarcu* (The Hero on a Donkey, 1964), and *Rat je bio bolji* (War Was Better, 1968), he treats in an expressionistic manner the alienation of his characters, the evils of war, which he likens to pornography, and the inability of man to even recognize, let alone achieve happiness. This stark pessimistic tone is strengthened by the author's unbridled license and an uncanny sense for the dramatic.

In addition to these works, Bulatović has also written a short-story collection *Vuk i zvono* (The Wolf and the Bell, 1958) and a play *Godo je došao* (Godot Has Come, 1965), a take-off on the Godot theme.

THE RED COCK FLIES TO HEAVEN

(Excerpts)

Jovan saw Srećko and Ismet carry the stretcher into the graveyard. They vanished among the sparse briars and put down their burden. They were visible to Jovan from the waist up. Their heads were together, and they were staring at each other. They clinked their bottles and the brandy sparkled in the sun. Without taking his eyes off them, Jovan rubbed the bristles of his rusty beard.

Peter looked up at the sky and saw nothing. That thing above, the blue that men called the sky where the soul settled after the body's death, was nothing but a vacuum, an unsubstantial emptiness devoid of anything visible or real on which the human eye could fasten. Jovan saw Srećko and Ismet embrace.

Peter, who felt himself lying on the dusty ground, was tortured by hunger. This was a devil situated somewhere in his bowels, at the center of his being, a devil that kept turning over. He felt it equal in size to the whole of his stomach, a devil with feelers that sucked the strength, endurance, and will from every ounce of his exhausted body. He grabbed up fistful of dust and sand and pounded and kneaded them. Never had he felt such a burning in his stomach or such ashes in his throat or such a strange and tasteless dust on his lips and under his tongue.

Jovan stared through half-closed eyes into the sparse thornbushes behind which something was happening.

The buzz and singing of the wedding guests mingled with the clatter of dishes. From the table came an uproar of thumping, singing, and shouting. They were eating, Peter thought, beyond all measure. And the devil in his stomach grew more and more restive and drew a veil across his half-blinded eyes. "Hold on," he said to himself. "Hold on. There'll be a bone or two even for you. They won't eat it all."

"Look at those two singing," said Jovan, shaking his arm. "They're drinking too, look!"

"How can they drink on an empty stomach?" Peter asked without shifting his position.

"How do you know they're drinking on an empty stomach?" Jovan asked childishly, putting on a frown of importance.

Peter opened his eyes. The sky was lighter, as if all the fires on earth were up there pouring down their heat and burning ash into his eyes. He felt too that the clamor from the long table, the sated shouting and groaning, the banging of dishes and scraping of spoons, the whole of this overheated tumult, was coming from above, from the transparent and burning sky and not from the square, white house by the roadside.

To Peter's imagination it appeared thus: they were all of them up there in the sky. They were grinning at one another over a table laden with foodstuffs. A thick, dark broth poured from invisible dishes. The servants fought over the scraps. The sweating bride appeared unable to eat any more, yet still they went on stuffing her like a turkey hen. They forced her jaws apart and crammed her with hot potatoes, large chunks of meat, and slices of hard barley bread. They poured ever hotter broth and sweet sour milk into her so she would digest the meat and pastries better and, light as a feather, be the first to leap into the dance. Her belly was swollen to an unnatural size but no one seemed surprised. They were actually delighted by it. They danced around it and vanished from sight. They clanked their glasses, swilled their drinks, tapped her belly to see whether it was firm and rang; it rang like an empty barrel. Her belly grew and grew and the sun began to shine with a new light. Her belly grew larger every moment, and the wedding guests grew smaller, punier, and less noticeable. Everything at this wedding in the sky was sad save the bride whose body was soon to fill the entire celestial space. There were no more wedding songs, no more music or shouting. The domestics dashed around her, squabbling over the crusts, bones, and stinking dregs of broth. Everybody was looking upward but none could make out her wise head perched on its rounded beam of a neck.

Finally they all set off marching across the blue firmament, dragging the table in all directions. It came apart, but the tureen of broth and the bones remained aloft. They all departed, each taking his own road, leaving the bride alone in the sky. She was so large that she filled the whole of Peter's vision. Her blue-veined legs hung motionless. Her arms rested on the mountain tops. She was perched on a cloud like a bee on an apple blossom. Gnawed sheepsheads, untouched roast chicken with yellow backs and charred legs, a bloated goatskin—this was all that remained visible behind her.

Catching sight of the distant wedding table, Jovan grew sad. He raised himself a little so he could take them all in at one glance. Some were dancing and some were not. They were throwing bones and crusts of bread around them. He could not tell which of them was the most sated and replete. He looked longingly at the bride.

"God, I'm hungry!" he said, sniffing the air.

His words brought Peter back to earth: the wedding guests descended from the sky and resumed their clamor. Ivanka's belly went flat and the sky reassumed its vastness. Of the former picture in the sky there remained only a white smudge—the wedding guests running around the bride like circus clowns, admiring her and wiping their greasy faces on the hem of her many-colored dress.

"I've never been so hungry," said Jovan.

"Nor I," replied Peter, and only when he heard his own voice was he quite certain that he was back on earth.

"Do you think they know how hungry we are?" Jovan asked.

"Don't be a fool," said Peter. "When have you ever heard of the well-fed believing the hungry? They not only don't know we're hungry, but they think we're too full to get up."

"Peasant swine!" said Jovan.

Peter closed his eyes and dozed off again.

"What about going and begging a bit of bread and some bones from them?" Jovan whispered.

"Not on your life!" Peter snapped.

"It wouldn't be a bad idea," said Jovan in a singsong voice.

"It would be cowardly," interjected Peter.

"But I'd soon be back," Jovan blustered, "and then you'd bless me for it."

"Shut up and stay where you are," Peter replied.

"But what's there to stay for?" Jovan persisted.

"Them, of course," Peter said sleepily. "Maybe they'll remember to throw us the odd bone. Who knows?"

"But why?" Jovan objected. "Why should they? There's no reason why they should, is there?"

"All right, but is there any particular reason why they shouldn't?" Peter asked, half opening his eyes and seeing the desperate Jovan above him.

"No . . . that's true," Jovan said. "There certainly isn't . . . only . . . the devil alone knows."

"Well then, if there isn't, wait and see," Peter burst out in a deep voice. "Perhaps they'll realize we're too proud to beg."

"God, but will they though!" Jovan groaned, looking in the direction of the feast. "Oh God, if they don't, interrupt their feast for a few moments and tell them we're hungry, but that we refuse to beg!"

"They'll probably think of us," droned Peter sleepily. "They're peasants and you can never be surprised by anything peasants do."

"Oh God, will they remember though," Jovan repeated tearfully, biting his forefinger like a child. "Oh God, whisper to them so they don't forget. Say to them: My dear, well-fed people, pause in your guzzling a moment and see how hungry these brothers of yours are. Throw them what you don't want to eat yourselves and they'll be as satisfied and gentle as they always are . . . tell them that, oh God. We aren't asking much. Only that they pass by and throw us some bread and bones as they would to the dogs."

The replete and many-hued wedding party was reflected in Jovan's large, tear-filled eyes.

*   *   *

The crowd grew agitated and began to thin. The old man saw the Moslem cemetery overgrown with burrs and brambles. Among the headstones tottered the dark shapes of the gravediggers, unable to free themselves of their gleaming charge, which still lay on its planks. Even more clearly could he see the motionless vagrants under the pear tree; he wondered how they could lie so long in the burning sun without getting sunstroke. In the far distance, he could make out the stinking town of Bijelo Polje and was terrified at the echo of its bells which drifted from it in warm waves.

When he saw Mrkoje grab Muharem by the shirt front, he turned cold. "What do they want of him now?" he thought, and noted that two of the crowd carried guns on their shoulders. "Surely they're not going to kill him? Oh, God, give me my strength back so I can go and drive them away like dogs."

"Call the cockerel!" Mrkoje demanded inflexibly.

"It won't do any good," said Muharem, scarcely able to stand. "You've already seen."

"Call him, I tell you," Mrkoje growled.

"What are they for?" Muharem asked, catching sight of the guns.

Mrkoje bared his teeth, and Muharem thought he was about to spit in his face. He quickly lowered his head and murmured:

"But . . . he's quite happy up there where he is. . . ."

"If you don't get him down, we'll shoot," Mrkoje said.

"Tell me first why he's so important to you," said Muharem boldly, raising his head from his breast.

"The guests want to throw him alive into the boiling water," Mrkoje snarled drunkenly, letting go of him, "so it'll be better for you if you call him."

"I'm sorry for him," Muharem whispered.

"Do you want us to give you a hot bath and pluck you, instead of him?"

The old man could not hear what was being said, but he saw Muharem recoil from the crowd and gaze upward.

"Heh, Reddy, lad!" he called. "Reddy! You mustn't come down for anything. Stay up there forever. They want to put you in boiling water and pluck you. They want to have a bit of fun. So you stay where you are even if it means I can never hold you in my arms again." Mrkoje again grabbed Muharem by the breast and hurled him violently aside.

The old man saw that if some of the men had not caught him he would have fallen.

Muharem's eyes wandered over the crowd, which no longer wanted to play with him, and a damp smile of gratitude spread across the old man's lips.

But he soon saw one of the three men with guns spit at him and he felt like crying.

The man nearest Muharem took aim. The gun kicked in his shoulder. The shot had no effect on the mass of the crowd—they were watching the cherry tree. Muharem saw the cock give a jump at the shot and fly away. It appeared to be still crowing. He could not tell whether it had flown off before the shot or only after the bullet had hit it. He was numbed with fear.

"Perhaps you're only wounded," he whispered loudly enough for those near him to hear. "Hold on . . . don't fly to earth . . . the wounds are nothing . . . I know plenty of herbs that'll heal them . . . you just try to stay alive."

The old man saw Mrkoje take sight along his gun barrel. Then he smelled burning powder.

"Dogs!" he said to himself. "Lousy, rotten dogs!"

"Mrkoje didn't miss either," thought Muharem, beginning to wish a bullet would take him.

Still crowing, the cockerel gave a start in mid-air at the second shot and, for a moment, seemed to halt in its flight so that Muharem thought it was going to stay suspended there forever. But with a further crow, it tore itself away from the invisible ground on which it appeared to rest and flew higher and higher.

"He's going to fly right away," Muharem thought and was seized by a fit of trembling. "I'm afraid I shall lose him."

The crowd seethed. Many just went on dancing, but there were some who stopped to watch the cockerel and the stooping Muharem. The song died on their lips, their drunken shouts remained bottled up in their throats, and an expression of fear and wonder replaced their grimaces of fury and anger.

They twisted their red necks and gaped, trying to keep their feet while they did so. Across their broad faces, past eyes exhausted with brandy and dancing, the cock flew like a red comet. And who can say what strange position their tousled heads would have attained or how far their necks would have bent and twisted or how far the cock would have hurtled in its whistling trajectory, had not a third shot rung out?

Muharem could not see who had fired: Mrkoje, the two men behind him, or one of the other six who had appeared carrying guns. But he saw that the third shot had also found its mark. "As long as they don't get his heart," he thought, still not grasping what was happening.

At the shot, the cock once more halted a few seconds, long enough to see who it was that laughed and who had fired at it. It seemed to hang there some time, its head retracted, its wings outspread and feet extended. And when the third searing pellet pierced its plumage, it gave a start and soared straight up into the sky.

It might have fallen but for the volley of bullets that reached it. The men took aim, staggered and fired, yelled and catcalled, and the empty, smoking cartridges fell about their feet. They continued firing for a long time. Beside them the hot water steamed and the masculine women standing over the pails showed teeth that were gleaming white.

Struck by the pellets, the cock flew swifter and more madly than ever. It was so high above the earth and the crowd that no one, not even the terrified Muharem, could tell its wings from its legs, its head from its neck, or its tail from the rest of its plumage. All Muharem saw was a handful of fire, a red ball vanishing into the blue sky with an ever increasing velocity.

The air vibrated with song. The earth shook beneath the dancing. Muharem was horrified at the thought that the cock might go on flying upward until it reached the heavens themselves. "They'll never let him come down again," he whispered. "They'll want him there too and I'll be left on my own forever."

When the sun had hidden the cock, Muharem saw the faces of the crowd bathed in a red light. The sky itself had turned red and the hills that pierced it with their summits, the bare fields, the road and the river that hid among the alders and willows. Blood poured from the red dot and the tears gushed down Muharem's cheeks. Purple feathers flew everywhere, so many that he could make out none of the people standing near him. People tried to avoid them, but they rained down, covering them.

Somewhere amid the noisy crowd stood Muharem, helpless to stir from the spot. Through his tears he watched the red dot growing smaller and smaller and the men who continued to take aim and fire without pause. He had only one wish: to find the place where the cock would fall, to catch it in open arms and see whether or not the lead had shattered its heart.

But the cock flew faster and faster, not even flinching before the sun, without any thought of returning to earth. It scoured the heavens with the speed of a comet, vanishing from the sight of the startled people. The firebird!

Old Ilija, seated in his chair, gazed over the heads of Ivanka, Kajica, and the women who were emptying their pails of water. He saw Muharem weeping and hardly able to support himself.

"Calm yourself," he thought. "Calm yourself, boy. Don't take on so about your cockerel. I know you loved it. But try to forget it. There's nothing on this earth that a man can't get over and forget. So don't mourn your cockerel too much. I'll make a sign to these swine around me to get you another. Pull yourself together, for their game hasn't been entirely successful. The cock's escaped them . . . soared off to heaven and the devil himself couldn't get it down again. Look around you. See, they've been deceived. It's turned into the sun itself and is shining down on us, all bloody and ragged. So be calm, laddy, dry your tears and come and sit here beside my knee."

The men continued to shoot, at what they themselves probably had no idea. The kolo went on turning as before. The masculine women and the giants and dwarfs who had been hurling stones and sticks into the cherry tree had gone.

Nobody made any further mention of the cockerel—as if it had never crowed. The crowd seemed merrier than ever. Only Muharem stared at the red dot in the sky and whimpered like a puppy.

E. D. Goy

Introduction
Croatian Literature from 1800 to the Present

The Croatian literature of the nineteenth and twentieth centuries can be divided into the following periods:

The Illyrian Period, covering the first half of the nineteenth century;

The Period of Realism, occurring in the second half of the nineteenth century;

Croatian "Moderna," taking place from the late nineteenth century to the First World War;

The "Interim" literature between the two World Wars; and

The "Contemporary" literature, beginning after the Second World War and continuing to the present.

The Illyrian Movement is certainly the most important cultural phenomenon in the nineteenth century. It encompasses all aspects of life: economy, education, arts, literature, and the language itself. It revived the Croatian people and placed them among nations with an established national and cultural individuality. The avant-garde of this movement was a group of intellectuals, headed by Ljudevit Gaj. They were mainly younger people educated in Vienna, Budapest, Gratz and Prague, where they came in touch with liberal and progressive thinkers. In 1830 Ljudevit Gaj, under the influence of Jan Kollar, a well-known Slovak poet, published *A Short Basis of Croato-Slovenian Orthography,* expressing its concept of a united South Slavic language and people. In 1832 Count Janko Drašković, in his *Disertacija* proposed the most complete program of Croatian national revival stressing its national independence. The whole cultural and political concept of the Illyrian Movement was built mainly on Gaj's and Drašković's theses.

The struggle for the realization of their program lasted from 1835 to 1848. A number of important cultural achievements came about during this period. Ljudevit Gaj established newspapers printed in the people's language, *Croatian Papers* and *Danica*. In 1838, *Matica Hrvatska* was established, an association for the publishing of "useful books" (this institution later became one of the main centers for the cultivation and preservation of Croatian culture, and it is still in exisence). At the same time, the Illyrians fought for the use of the "people's language" in literature, stressing that speech, tradition, and a way of life are the main characteristics of a mature nation.

During this period, of all the genres patriotic poetry developed the most, having its roots in the deep faith of the Illyrians in the future of the Illyrian Movement and in Slavs generally. Ljudevit Gaj was the first to write patriotic poetry; his verse became very popular, mainly as a political and national manifestation of the Croatian people. As the Illyrian Movement progressed and underwent changes, so did the patriotic poetry, now with motifs to be found in the glory of the national past. In this respect, the literary contribution of Ljudevit Gaj is not too great, but his role as the organizer of the Illyrian Movement gives him the first place among many intellectuals in building the Croatian culture.

What Ljudevit Gaj did for the political orientation of the Illyrian Movement, Stanko Vraz did for the rebirth of Croatian literature. Of Slovenian origin, Vraz, enthusiastic about the ideas of Slavic unity, joined the Illyrian Movement and started writing in Serbo-Croatian. His first book of poetry, *Djulabije,* a collection of love poems, gave him immediate recognition among Croatian writers. As a literary critic, Vraz was the first to point out the extraordinary qualities of Njegoš's *The Mountain Wreath* and Mažuranić's *The Death of Smail-Aga Čengić*.

Preradović is considered, along with Vraz, to be one of the most distinguished poets of the Illyrian Movement. He wrote primarily love poetry and patriotic poems, and his poem "To Slavdom" serves as an outstanding example of the latter genre.

However, the greatest poet of this period is certainly Ivan Mažuranić. After moving to Karlovac in 1840, Mažuranić intensified his writing, and it is here that he wrote most of his poetry, including *The Death of Smail-Aga Čengić*, which placed him among the greatest poets in Yugoslav literature. The plot of this epic poem was taken from a historic event—the death of Smail-Aga Čengić, who was killed by Montenegrins in 1840.

In the second half of the nineteenth century, particularly after the revolution of 1848, the Illyrian Movement showed weaknesses: the leaders of the movement, its main force, became divorced from the masses and were soon to experience a political defeat. Ljudevit Gaj, for example, became isolated and soon forgotten, and many of the other leaders abandoned politics and poetry altogether. Facing a new situation, Croatian literature began to change and, having to cope with new problems, became more adaptable and realistic. Thus, the Croatian literature of the sixties and seventies changed from Romanticism to Realism. Its most distinguished representative at this time was August Šenoa. He wrote prose and poetry; as a poet he continued in the Illyrian tradition, while his novels, dealing primarily with social and historical topics, mark the beginning of Croatian realism.

The strong development of the middle class and the influence of Western European literature helped create Croatian realism. Opposing Romantic one-sidedness and idealization, Šenoa and other realists asked that literature describe everyday life and come closer to the masses.

Parallel with the influence of Western European literature, the influence of Russian realism (Turgenev, Gogol, Tolstoy, and Dostoevsky) gained momentum and gradually became a conditioning factor, especially in the works of Ksaver Šandor Djalski, one of the best nineteenth-century prose writers. Being of noble origin like Turgenev, Djalski described the life of the Croatian upper classes and nobility, as well as the peasantry.

Because of historical events in the period after 1895, a new trend known as Croatian "Moderna" could be discerned. Under the rigorous rule of Khuen Hedervary, many intellectuals and, especially students escaped abroad to study. There they engaged in a vigorous cultural activity along national lines, which strongly influenced Croatia itself. After the fall of Hedervary in 1903, a sharp polemic developed among Croatian writers, splitting them into two opposing groups, "the young ones" and "the old ones." "The young ones," being attracted by modern French literature, rejected the Romantic-Illyrian and folklore-realistic approach to literature and demanded that literature become an expression of one's subjective state. Among the critics and writers of "Moderna," advocating Symbolism and Impressionism, Antun Gustav Matoš played a particularly important role. However, this tendency of "the young ones" did not last long; still, the Croatian "Moderna" was able to attract later such writers as Kozarac, Novak, Vojnović, Kranjčević, and others.

Josip Kozarac wrote with excitement about his birth place, Slavonija, its forests, villages and inhabitants, delving into social problems of the villages and the destructive influence of the cities on them, especially on the female population in his short story "Tena." Vjenceslav Novak wrote in almost the same vein, except that he described the moral and social problems of Croatian cities and the decay and the gradual disappearance of the nobility, as in his novel *The Last of the Stipančići*.

Although Ivo Vojnović belongs to the most fruitful period of Croatain realism, he nevertheless was closer to "Moderna" than to realism. He had his greatest success with his *Dubrovnik Trilogy*. This dramatic chronicle deals with the moral and political agony of the Dubrovnik nobility around the turn of the century.

In the Croatian poetry of this period, Silvije Strahimir Kranjčević is certainly the best poet. He introduced new ways and methods in his poetry, building it on contemporary motifs. His predominant topics are those of human pain and suffering as in "The Painting of Christ" and "Moses."

During and after World War I, Expressionism, as a literary movement, was an attempt to cope with the intellectual crises of Europe; in literature it manifested itself in individuality, in highly subjective expression freed of all moral and social obligations, and in a revolt against all that was traditional. It came to Croatia from Germany, and its most important representative was Antun Branko Šimić.

Šimić was a poet of extraordinary sensibility and subjective disposition. His short life was spent in agonizing inner conflicts, which is illustrated in his collection of poetry *Metamorphosis* (1920). Under the influence of the German expressionists, he created a new modern poetry, with completely free form, deliberately ignoring the accepted ways of writing. He presented in it the drama of his chaotic and wounded life. His education in Catholic schools left deep scars on his personality, making him an even darker and more pessimistic poet. Eventually, Šimić was able to cast aside the mystic and religious influences in his poetry, in order to approach more realistic topics, even antireligious ones ("Earth").

In this period Croatian prose, especially the novel, underwent an important change: fragmentation. In this technique, the writer described only one aspect of life in a typically expressionistic way: loudly, nervously and anarchicaly.

In the midst of this movement, during World War I, appeared the most important living Croatian writer Miroslav Krleža, who, in this period of confusion, expressed his antiwar feelings in his cycle of short stories *Croatian God Mars* (1922). This prolific writer has proven himself in almost all literary genres. His literary activity started with poetry, which can be considered to be the first stage of his literary development. His principal books of poetry are: *Pan* (1917), *Three Symphonies* (1917), *A Book of Lyrics* (1932), and *Poems in the Darkness* (1937). During this period Krleža also wrote romantic dramas: *The Legend* (1914), *Christopher Columbus* (1918), *Adam and Eve* (1922), and others.

The Legend is Krleža's first drama, a romantic work depicting conversations about biblical personalities, and a man who, in spite of all misfortunes and abuses, remains a convinced idealist, not acknowledging to himself "the dark side of life." *Christopher Columbus* is a romantic version of human conflicts in flux, inspired by Lenin and the Russian October Revolution.

The second period of Krleža's development is characteristic for his war stories from *Croatian God Mars* (1922), *In the Camp* (1920), *The Wolfhound* (1923) and *Golgotha* (1922), as well as for a number of poems, essays and polemical articles. At the same time, Krleža had either initiated or contributed to a number of literary journals: *The Flame, The Literary Republic, Today,* and *The Republic.*

In Krleža's third creative period, he wrote prose and drama, which are his most important types of work. Krleža's novels and short stories are: *Three Suitors of Miss Melanija* (1920), *Stories* (1924), *The Return of Philip Latinovicz* (1932), *A Thousand and One Deaths* (1933), *On the Brink of Reason* (1938) and *Banquet in Blitva* (1939). His main plays are: *In agony* (1928), *The Glembajs* (1929) and *Leda* (1930).

In his descriptions of the Croatian bourgeoisie, especially in his drama on the Glembajs, he follows them from their beginning, ascendance and success to their physical and psychological degradation and fall. In interpreting them, Krleža applied a method of psychological realism, thus creating one of the major books in Croatian literature.

Krleža's associate August Cesarec, along with Krleža, did much to help orient Croatian literature toward a greater attention to social problems. Cesarec was first influenced by German expressionists and Dostoevsky, but toward the end of his life found his own way, describing the unbearably miserable working class. His main novels are: *The Emperor's Realm* (1925) and *The Golden Youth* (1928).

Besides Krleža and Cesarec, Vladimir Nazor enriched the literature of the beginning of the twentieth century with his writings. Croatian poetry at this time, imbued with nihilism and decadence, found in Nazor a new tendency, a healthy poetry of joy and beauty.

Other important writers of this period are: Ivan Dončević, Vjekoslav Koleb, and Ivan Goran Kovačić.

Dončević is primarily known as a short story writer, depicting "the small man" in anecdotal style. His stories are full of vivid facts and emotions. In his prose writing up to the Second World War, he wrote mainly about peasants from his village, Moslavina. He was involved in the war, and his personal experiences inspired him to write on new topics, such as in his novel *Nameless* (1945).

Kaleb depicts his native Dalmatia, mainly its peasants and villages, as well as war themes. He is simple in style so that one may have the false impression that he is naive. However, he does this deliberately in order to achieve the most convincing and realistic presentation. His most successful novel *The Beauty of Dust* (1954), describes only two characters: a political commissar, who is a student, and a peasant. Both with great difficulty escape their enemies and death. Kaleb describes both of his heroes in their daily hardships, showing their inner strength and stability.

In his relatively short life, Kovačić wrote poetry, short stories, criticism, and two unfinished novels. He also translated from English, French, Russian and Slovenian. In his poetry, he wrote on patriotic and social themes, expressing his love for the fatherland and his attachment to the poor, especially the peasants. His poetry dating from World War II is particularly impressive. In his poem *The Pit* Kovačić created a unique work, protesting crimes against man.

After World War II, a trend imitating the Soviet brand of Socialist Realism was introduced into Croatian literature. Many of the writers could not cope with the demands of Socialist Realism, which required that a writer depict the idealized life of the future, neglecting the real problems of individuals, society and reality. However, after 1950, this literary dogma began to lose its importance and Croatian writers started looking for a new and more realistic approach to literature. This period of liberalization produced a number of good writers, among whom the most notable are Ranko Marinković and Vladan Desnica.

Marinković is a dependable psychoanalyst, probing the intimate relations of his heroes, their dreams and impulses. The inspiration for his prose and drama writings, Marinković found in his birthplace and its people. His best known novel is *Cyclops* (1965), contemplative prose, analyzing the psychological make-up of present day man and his life. In this novel, as well as in his short stories, Marinković presents himself as a modern and original writer.

Desnica is another poet and short story writer from Dalmatia. He is known for using the inner human monologues as a means of unveiling one's state of mind. In his literary works he focuses on "human shipwrecks," on those who cannot realize their goals, who lose their ambition and desires, and simply exist monotonously. His writing is in the best tradition of Croatian realism; his literary expression is modeled after Western European standards. He attracted most attention with his novel *The Springs of Ivan Galeb* (1957), in which he gives way to his inclination toward meditation and contemplation on philosophical, religious, political and esthetic questions concerning man.

One should at least mention other Croatian writers of this period: Vesna Parun is one of the leading and most original postwar Croatian poets. She is a poet of youth and love. Her poetry treats the problems of motherhood, the relationship between a man and a woman, and complete identification of man with nature. As time went on, she became more pessimistic, turning from the poetry of love to meditative poetry. She published several important collections: *Dawns and Gales* (1947), *Poems* (1955), *The Black Olive Tree* (1954) and others.

Jure Kaštelan is known for his warm and patriotic poetic treatment of themes from the Second World War of which the best known collections are: *A Cock on the Roof* (1950), and *A Few Stones and Many Dreams* (1957).

Vlado Gotovac is an example of a poet who concentrates on ideas. Thus, he is called "a poet-philosopher"; he dwells on philosophy, on the ideas of Hussar, Heidegger, Sartre, and Camus. His latest and very successful collection of poetry is *Recasting Poems by Memory* (1969).

What is essential to the poetry of Slavko Mihalić is his manipulation of language, his interesting technique and poetic expression of philosophical ideas. The main theme of his poetry is that of defeat.

Petar Šegedin's novel *The Lonely Ones* (1947 and 1960) is an analysis of the disoriented intellectuals of prewar Yugoslavia, and it belongs to his better prose works. Some of his collections of short stories are: *The Dead Sea* (1953) and *Prose* (1953).

In conclusion, we can assert that contemporary Croatian literature is contributing its full share to the family of Yugoslav literatures.

Ivan Mažuranić

(1814–1890)

Ivan Mažuranić is one of the greatest poets of Croatia. Born in Novi Vinodol, he was educated at the high school in Rijeka, supporting himself by tutoring other students. He learned German when he was in Novi Vinodol and acquired a good knowledge of Italian and Latin in high school. Later on, he learned Hungarian, French, and English, along with all the Slavic languages.

After finishing high school, Mažuranić studied philosophy at the University of Zagreb. Here, he came in touch with the Illyrian Movement and its participants. Having changed his field of study from philosophy to law, he graduated from the University of Zagreb and in 1840 moved to Karlovac, working as an attorney and writing. He wrote his famous *Smrt Smail-age Čengića* (The Death of Smail-Aga Čengić) in Karlovac.

During the revolutionary year 1848, Mažuranić went to Zagreb to help Ljudevit Gaj and Jelačić in the Illyrian Movement, advocating Croatian independence from Hungary.

In 1873 he became governor of Croatia; he was criticized by a group around Ante Starčević for his meek and conciliatory policy towards Austria. He died in Zagreb in 1890.

Mažuranić started writing poetry as a high school student and his first poem was completed in 1835. Enthused with Byron and Pushkin, he wrote romantic, patriotic and love poetry. His best achievement, *The Death of Smail-Aga Čengić*, ranks second in epic poetry in Yugoslav literature to Njegoš's *The Mountain Wreath*.

THE DEATH OF SMAIL-AGA ČENGIĆ

(Excerpts)

III: THE BAND

Now doth the day begin to redden,
While all around o'er neighboring hills

Thou hear'st the shepherd call his flock,
To whom there cometh gentle answer
From the leader's tinkling bell.

When, lo, another shepherd comes,
Who humbly walketh to his sheep;
Neither gold nor silver decks him,
Only virtue and black robe;
Bright procession he hath not
With burning lamps and candles holy,
Nor sound rich bells from any tower;
Escort enough, the golden sinking sun,
While from the hills the gentle sheep-bell calls.

His church, the glorious vault of heaven;
His altar holy, hill and vale;
As incense fragrant rises the perfume,
From herb and flower and all the sunlit world
Of martyr blood outpoured for the Cross.

To the Band he draweth nearer
Servant true of truer Master,
He greeteth them: "All help from God!"
These knightly souls around he gathers,
And steppeth up upon cold stone—
The stone is cold, but warm his heart—
Then to the troop doth preach the good old man:

"Children mine, ye bravely fight
For this the land which gave you light;
Rugged it is, but to you golden,
For here were all your grandsires born,
Your fathers, too, they were born here,
And ye yourselves here, too, were born;
For you no fairer place in all the world.

" 'Twas here your grandsires outpour'd blood,
'Twas here your sires pour'd out their blood,

And here ye also shed your blood;
In all the world no dearer place for you.
'Mid crags the eagle weaves his nest,
Since vain on plain is Freedom's quest.

"Ye who know well this land of ours,
No careless days are yours, I trow!
But what mind ye when rocks yield wine?
What mind ye when stony lands give wheat?
What mind ye, if 'mong the rocks there's silk?
Or while from springs ye still draw ice-cold water,
While in the vales still bellow hairy herds,
While on the hills the sheep do gently bleat?

"Of shot and powder sure ye have good store;
The hero's hand, it sure is strong enough,
And 'neath bold brow gleams falcon eye,
While warm heart beats within each breast;
Steadfast in faith, who would turn renegade;
With brother-love thy comrade loveth thee;
Faithful husband faithful spouse embraces;
As heritage thou hast all noble song;
Wantest thou arms, the Turks for thee them save!
Say, is there more the heart of man could crave?

"But what 'bove all the jewel of this land?
It is the Holy Cross which rises over all,
That Cross imparting comfort 'mid all tears,
Gift of God's grace, and lasting strength for fleeting years.

"Oh, may tribes of earth, may they all see,
From their low levels where they blindly stray,
This glorious Cross which must victorious be,
On Lovtchen's height uprising to the sky.
And may they know how doth the monstrous Turk
In his great maw strive e'er to gulp it up,
Though on these rocks he vainly breaks his teeth!
Not idly longer would they fold their hands

While ye do bear all sorrows for the Cross;
Who'd dare you 'Barbarians' name?
Ye gave your lives while others slept in shame!

"Aye, for the holy Cross e'er ready ye to die;
And for the Cross, indeed, begin ye now to die,
Avengers true of God's own righteous ire,
But who would serve his God in faithful part
Must service render from a cleansed heart;
In truth, all clean of soul must be that man
Who executes on Earth decrees of Heaven.

"Hath one of you perchance his brother wronged?
Or put upon his soul dark stain
By taking from weak rival his dear life?
Or hath one shut his door against the traveller?
Hath one gone back upon his word of honor?
Or from the hungry kept the call'd-for food?
Or for the wounded bound not up the wound?
This all is sin; these all are acts that harden.
Without repentance God to none gives pardon.

"Repent ye, then, while yet ye may!
Children, in time, repent this day!
Repent ere thou receiv'st the call
Unto they soul from Him Who shaketh all;
Repent ye, for our earthly race
Runs out in arrow-flight, repent!
Repent ye, for the morrow's dawn
May many find where they must ever stay.
Repent; again, repent I say!"

But in the throat . . .
The good old man his words they stopped;
On his grey beard there glistening dropp'd
Something that in the sun's ray shone
Shone like a pearl minute;
It may be that his youthful days

Still burn with bitter memories,
That, healing wounds amongst his flock,
He brings to mind his own heart's pains;
Good shepherd he; what he to others preaches
He maketh sure his own example teaches!

IV

TAX GATHERING

Gatsko Field, how fair art thou,
When no famine is upon thee,
No hunger cruel, nor cruel want!
But now, alas, thou art o'errun
By bloody men in armor bright,
With heavy irons and cruel chains,
With furious steeds and tents all white.

What would these men? Wherefore these shining arms?
Why all these horses, and why all these tents?
Why all these heavy irons and cruel chains?
Smail Aga now demands the bloody tax
From Gatsko and the countryside.
In the field's center he hath pitched his tent,
Whence come forth his brazen-faced collectors.
(May the hungry wolves devour them!
These from each man demand a golden coin,
They from each home a goodly sheep devour,
And every night do spoil some fresh girl-flower.

Out from the east tax-gatherers wildly gallop,
And naked rayas bind unto their horses' tails;
Out from the west tax-gatherers wildly gallop,
And naked rayas bind unto their horses' tails;
Out from the north and south the dragons gallop wildly

Bind the naked rayas to their horses' tails.
Then the wretched creatures, hands fast bound behind,
Close on the horses' heels are dragg'd with ropes.
Dear God, what has the raya done,
Must he make answer for the villain Turk,
Is it his crime the Turks are vile,
Or this his crime, that he is just alive?—
And that he has not what the Turks would have,
The yellow gold and loaves of good white bread?

Aga meanwhile his goodly horse
Before the tents doth exercise,
And with his javelin tests his clear, keen eyes,
And what of strength there is in his right hand.
He jumps now higher than all others,
With his fleet steed in prowess all surpasses—
A goodly knight, were he as good a man!

Then as he sees what booty
The fierce collectors gain,
He rushes like an arrow
On his fine, fiery steed,
And while he gallops, just in sport,
His javelin casts with reckless aim,
Directions giving toward some raya head.

But the hero's skillful hand
May fail at times in every land.
So it was, as luck would have it,
His nimble steed that moment stumbled,
The flexible shaft went whizzing through the air,
On wing most light, but not in steady flight.
For the lamb it did not strike,
But the old brown wolf, brave Saphir,
Who, dragging 'hind his horse a raya,
Lost from his head a star!
His out-thrust eye on the green grass did cry,
And he was overspatter'd with red blood.

As were he angry snake the Turk cried out;
While Aga flar'd up like a living flame.
Shame it were on such a hero,
To gather taxes, yet to get no tax;
To aim a javelin, yet not strike the mark.
More shame to blind a Turk stead of a raya,
And yet more shame that Christian dogs should mock!
Then Aga flar'd up like a living flame;
Alas! Oh God, what will from henceforth be,
When from some guilt the raya ne'er is free!

"Mouyo, Hasso, Omer, Yashar,
Set your good dogs and fiery horses
A-gallop round the level field,
That we may see how Christians run!"
Thus roar'd Aga like wild bull.

Servants quick more quickly do obey,
Good horses gallop o'er the field;
Now servants shouting as they ride,
Now horses plunging 'neath their men,
Now rayas screaming 'hind the horses.
At first you say the lissom raya
Must, swallow-like, o'ertake the horses;
A moment more, scarce canst thou say
Which is quicker, horse or raya.
One moment more, the horses draw away,
The hapless raya must now fall behind;
One instant later, and what dost thou see?
The hapless raya falleth to the ground,
And winged horses trail him as they bound:
At heel they drag him through the dust and mud.
Hectors are they, beneath the walls of Troy
When Troy already by the gods is doom'd.

Where Aga stands, the other Turks stand too.
Upon this sight most pitiful
They feed a greedy eye,

And their insatiate thirst for blood
From raya veins do satisfy with raya pains.
Their hearts beat fast with cruel glee;
With loud guffaw they laugh;
It is to them fair sight to see
These dogs of rayas bleeding on black ground.
With such accursed laugh might Hell itself resound
At sinners writhing with an eternal wound.

J. W. Willes

Stanko Vraz

(1810–1851)

Vraz was the leading personality of his time in Croatian literature. Of Slovenian origin, he was early enchanted with the Illyrian Movement. Born in a rich family in Cerovac, he studied in the German high school in Maribor and then studied law and philosophy at the University of Gratz.

As a student, he learned most of the European languages, reading Homer, Dante, Petrarch, Goethe, Pushkin, Byron and other great writers. When Ljudevit Gaj started publishing *Danica* in Zagreb, Vraz became its permanent contributor. Having become very attached to the Illyrian movement, Vraz moved to Zagreb in 1838, where he lived until his death in 1851.

Vraz published three books of poetry: *Djulabije* in 1840; *Glasi iz dubrave Žerovinske* (Voices from Dubrava Žerovinska, 1841); and *Gusle i tambure* (Fiddles and Guitars, 1845). In his literary development two trends can be felt: the first from his student days to the age of thirty, as a poet who wrote in Slovenian, and the second, from his 30's until his death, as a poet who wrote in Serbo-Croatian. In his Slovenian poetry the themes are patriotic, expressed most often in a sentimental and sad fashion. His Croatian poetry is dominated with the theme of love, especially in the first collection, *Djulabije*. His "Love" and "Rose Apples" are fine examples of this period.

LOVE

What is love? 'T is just a zephyr
Born when springtimes come.
What is love? It is the storm-wind
Unrestrainable and restless.
It kills flowers and oak trees, too.
What is love? It is the light's kiss
Waking countless flowers to life.
What is love? It is a fire-ball

Which turns flowers and oaks to ashes.
What is love? Heaven's stairway
Down which angles their blessings,
And poor mortals given gold sandals,
Try to climb to heaven again.
What is love: It is a demon
Who turns all that's good to evil,
Robs the soul of prayer and peace!

Let your love, Dear One, I beg you,
Keep the spring-wind's gentleness,
Calling only flowers to bloom.

E. W. Underwood

ROSE APPLES

Why do I look
    In your eyes so black,
When all that I get
    Is but grief, alack?

Eyes, O Dear Eyes,
    So cruel, so sweet,
I'm a vagabond for you,
    My ruin is complete!

Even death will be good,
    For it comes without woe,
And your white hands
    Will touch me where I lie low.

E. W. Underwood

Petar Preradović

(1818–1872)

Preradović was one of the most notable poets of the Illyrian Movement. He was born in the village of Grabovnica, into a poor family, and his father died early. On the request of his mother, he was accepted at the Military Academy in Vienna. He started writing his poetry in Austria in German, a language which never ceased to affect him.

Preradović became seriously interested in the Illyrian Movement under the influence of Ivan Kukuljević Sakcinski in Milan. Preradović had forgotten his native language by then, and had to study it again by translating Gundulić's poem "Osman." His whole life was full of misfortunes: he was often ill and some of his children died. When he was 40 years old, he felt like an old man, and started writing religious poetry. After having gotten in touch with the Illyrian Croats, Preradović changed completely as a man, and as a poet. Having accepted his native language and the idea of Slavic greatness, he soon developed into one of the best Croatian poets.

He appeared in Illyrian literature for the first time with his poem "Zora Puca" (Dawn), which brought him such success that he wrote only in his native Croatian from then on.

Preradović wrote primarily patriotic and love poetry. His best known poems are: "Rodu o jeziku" (To Slavdom), "Putnik" (A Traveler), "Dvije Ptice" (Two Birds), "Pozdrav domovini" (A Greeting to the Fatherland), "Jezik roda moga" (The Language of My People) and "Djed i unuk" (Grandfather and his Grandchild).

TO SLAVDOM

With gesture of obeisance I bow myself down unto thy black earth,
Having set foot on thy domain, riddle of all the world,
Glorious, might, renowned, omnipotent Slavdom!
With eagerness my spirit trembles, unfurling its wings
And dauntless of eye, clutches at the hollow heavens,
Desiring now for glory of thee to soar loftily.

But how should my voice be upraised high enough for thy world,
Where shall I, faced by thee, find strings potent enough not to
      be rended,
When my soul, enkindled with the flash of thy radiance,
Begins to thunder above? O would that, after my desire, I were able
To weave threads from the golden fabric of sunbeams,
That from shore to shore I might span them over the wan ocean,
And that I might take for my bow the gleaming rainbow aloft;
Then when I drew it across the strings, the ocean-depths should
      resound
With the immense roar of thy hidden powers, and the waves
Should be mingled above in that graceful allurement of Nature
With which breezes rustle and birds carol,
And the vault of heaven should re-echo it to me a hundred fold,
Uniting it all again in mighty harmony.
Then, O then only, were it mine to fashion
Such a song as is meet for the rapture and glory within thee,
Thy bygone years, thy greater years to come. Whither has thy girth
O might Slavdom, surged up? Like to an ocean,
The hand of God has poured thee out in earth's bosom, and although
Foreignness with many and many a gulf eats into thy soil,
Yet art thou still ample enough, that when thou but stirrest,
With any limb of thine, all the earth is aquiver.
The stranger stands, dismay in his eyes, his hands crossed,
Upon thy coasts, and thanklessly marvels at thee
And shudders with foreboding of terror. Wherefore is he affrighted?
O, from thy greatness an unswerving conscience metes out unto him
Requital which is his due for monstrous transgressions against thee.
A pirate he cruised through thy waters; the banner of the cross
Was his ensign, enlightenment the feigned beacon he steered for!
But his sails were swollen with the foul breath of greed,
His hull guided by the hand of one rapaciously exulting in plunder,
A sword was his oar, a spear his plummet for thy depths,
And behind his vessel ever floated in blood a cluster of corpses—
Thy slain. Heaven itself would have wept
To behold the fruit of its gentle labors on the field of mankind,
Happiest race of them all, when a black curse
Mowed it down, and to behold the outcome of its tending,

Greatest in number of dwellers, when virulent savagery
Harried it to the bane of ages; in fine, to behold
An image most like unto itself upon earth, when in God's name
Godlessness evilly vexed it, and for the sake of the cross
Nailed, as it were to the cross, the gentlest of tribes.
The devoutest on earth.
But wherewith, O Slavdom, didst thou requite
This bloody debt unto the foreigner? Verily, by blood,
But by the blood of thy heroes in many a contest
With the sinister wildness of Asia, which with darkness
Threatened to quench even that tiny ray of twilight
Which flickered in the west of the World, Even then, conceiving
Thy task magnificent as befits thy potency, thou didst not strive
Many a time for vengeance when hazard favored thee;
The best hazard didst thou shape for thyself, as a mediator
Towards a seeing and a sightless world—to be intercessor
For the one, and against onslaughts of the other
To hold out thine heroic breast as a shield.
      And as thou stoodest proud
In twofold glory, so now thou standest on the marge
Of these two worlds as a giant whose stature can cope with
The supreme mission on earth: with one hand thou clutchest
Western stars of enlightenment, with the other thou sheddest them
Over the gloom of the east; but this is not thy sole renown;
With yet greater pride canst thou upraise thy chivalrous head
Heavenwards. Upraise it, upraise it, undaunted and joyous
For the world to behold, that everywhere it may see upon thine
      heroic brow
The kiss of light wherewith God's love hallows thee
For his holy toil here below. Over the unbounded expanse of heaven
The Creator has inscribed by the stars the statute of Love,
And by the eternal course of His decrees through eternity
Has ordained its potence. Thus as His minister,
Everywhere and ever Love labors unfalteringly; it moulds, beautifies,
Softens and smooths, pacifies, tames and subjugates,
Assuages, ennobles, sanctifies, makes like God
All that is God's in the world—thee He chooses and empowers
From among the race of mankind to be hero

And idol of her. Ah, it fares ill upon earth
With those favored by heaven: for heaven they are in travail, and
     of hell
They cannot long elude the toils; thus already
Thou bindest upon the thread of thy life
Ages of suffering, and upon each limb of thy huge body
Thou feelest all human griefs diversely grievous.
Thou art mauled by hatred, selfishness and discord, by wrath,
By evil and envy art thou mauled, every passion engrafted
Upon thy weal by alien blood. Thy blood ever seethes in thee
With poisoned ferment, through it all thy bowels
Are set astir, thou reelest, swoonest, and mutely art stunned;
But yet with no step dost thou cease from advancing
Further upon the path to Unity; not to that one
Where treacherous foes unceasingly slander thee, nor to that one
Whose token is one head adorned by an all-embracing crown
Which outrages all (under such a crown
Every human head would droop) but to that one, which must needs
     be crowned
By the garland of hundred-fold federation, the concord
Of all wills, since it bestows happiness on all.
          Concord is dawn, proclaiming
The eternal day of love; already thy countenance is aglow
With the flush of health—thy countenance which was pallid
From grievous slumber. Already unto thee
          Krkonoše, Triglav, Tatra, the Balkans,
Ural and Velebit are aflame like new Horebs
Where the spirit of God is speaking afresh; already unto thee, Volga,
Vistula, and Danube, Vltave, Save and Drave are gleaming
Like new Jordans, wherein are baptised the newborn thoughts
Of the new age; already the dew of thy tears is everywhere radiant
With hope of solace at hand; hazes of morning
Already converse with thee in golden images of coming lustre;
Early breezes, a gentle foreboding of joy, already with their pinions
Fan thy bosom and brow, setting aquiver thy ponderings,
And mustering little by little thy chaotic emotions;
Thy spirit is striving against its last slumber, thy heart
Is grappling with its last weariness, thou shakest and heavest,

Strainest and rubbest thine eyes, already thou art at the point
Of rousing thee, of gazing in concord upon
God's beauteous day, whereof love is the sunrise: oh, ere long,
Ere long thy tribes shall rally them, shall arise and clasp
One the hand of the other, with a kiss they shall evoke happiness
And heroic prowess, one the other; ere long shall love
Blaze up as an overwhelming pyre of happiness, and all thy broad
      focus
Shall be its domain, with every heart that is thine
For its fuel; resplendent shall be its example
And hitherto unheard of, unseen in the world;
The world to its utmost shall be amazed thereat, and shall marvel,
Gazing and gazing; till, dazzled by this torrent it shall surrender.
And with it shall merge into a single realm of love, into that realm
Which upon earth is foretold by the divine books.
Thus in the world's mighty design thou hast set thee astir
Potently, in mankind's eternal contest for advancement,
Its strong protector, the hem of whose garment
All tribes upon earth should kiss in thanksgiving!
      But so long as
This prison-planet, the which is called black by its captives,
So long as it shall engender all dismay and wretchedness,
Whereby it needs must punish its captives, cherish not
Hopes that it will show itself beholden to thee:
      because of the very keys that thou bearest,
Its bondsmen shall call their jailer, and shall hate thee; only when
A worthier humanity renders it softer, when the world
Gazes forth, unwaveringly discerns and verily traces
Heavenly order on earth, then only shall they acknowledge thee
And ever extol thee as key-bearer of heaven. But for now,
Only thy young generation together about the tomb
Of fallen biases are linked in a single chain
And with a tumult, whereby the pulsing spirit of time
Thunderingly heralds the march of humanity, will fashion a psalm
Of praise unto thee, and with this melody already
The world on all four sides is re-echoing.

                               P. Selver

August Šenoa

(1838–1881)

Šenoa was born in Zagreb. His father was a Germanized Czech who wanted to make his son a good and obedient Austrian official. Šenoa studied in Zagreb under markedly patriotically disposed professors such as Adolf Veber, Tkalčević, Antun Mažuranić, a poet and short story writer, and Matija Mešić, a historian, so that he became a passionate Croat, contrary to his father's desires.

After finishing high school, Šenoa studied philosophy at the University of Zagreb. He distinguished himself as an excellent student and Bishop Štrosmajer sent him to Prague to study law. There Šenoa learned Czech, Polish and Russian. Upon his return to Zagreb he became an editor of the daily *Pozor*, an organ of the Peoples Party of Štrosmajer. As a critic, theoretician and writer, Šenoa represents the end of Croatian Romanticism and the start of Croatian Realism.

Šenoa did not contribute anything new to Croatian poetry. He only continued the Illyrian tradition, so that his real innovative talent lies in his prose. In 1871 he published *Zlatarevo zlato* (The Goldsmith's Gold), followed by several other major novels: *Čuvaj se senjske ruke* (Beware of the Hand of Senj), *Seljačka buna* (The Peasant Uprising), *Diogenes*, *Kletva* (A Curse) and *Baron Ivica*. His novels deal almost exclusively with social or historical topics.

SONG

In a gay little flowery garden,
    A castle stood stately and fair;
Tall trees threw down their shadows
    And blossoms scented the air.

Here the nightingale's voice was ringing,
    And pleasure was soul of the place;
Yet the castle fell into ruin
    Since time must all things efface.

> One flower alone was left blooming
>   In the ancient garden-close;
> Your name in my memory, Sweetheart,
>   Shines like a red, red rose.

E. W. Underwood

THE PALE MOON

"Fertig!" called out the conductor at the Agram station. The steam began to hiss, the train started. It went faster and faster, off towards Styria.

"Damn it!" exclaimed one of the three youths that were standing on the platform, and hurled to the ground his burning cigar. He was a darkskinned, tall, well-built man,—in short, a fine specimen of a Croatian.

"What hurts you, Djuka, Djuka?" asked his friend, a slender, trim-looking fellow with a goatee, frisking about on his thin legs like a doll at the puppet show.

"Jozica!" replied the third young man to the second, as he leaned against a pillar and peacefully smoked, "Jozica, your head is always full of higher politics, but you are as blind as that blackened meerschaum dummy on your pipe. Did you not notice that beautiful blonde in the third carriage, from whom Djuka could not tear his eyes away? How that rogue did smile to him, until that accursed whistle took her away to Styria."

"My sweetheart has gone berries for to pick," Jozica declaimed, and looked at his meerschaum pipe.

"Damn it!" was all Djuka said as he looked gloomily at the whitish smoke of the locomotive that was gradually lost toward Styria.

At the "Golden Filly" Djuka soon drowned, with his two friends, his sweet memory of the golden-haired Vila* in golden wine.

*   *   *

---

*South-Slavic fairy.

And soon Djuka's time came to be carried away from Agram by the accursed whistle. Whither? To Vienna, to study medicine.

His sister sent him on his way with sweet cakes and a hearty embrace; his mother gave him a roast turkey and a sincere blessing, and also some good instructions, and what is most important, a big package of those colored bills whose divine power is greatly in demand with Plener, the Minister of Finance, and also with young prospective "doctors," particularly if they are Croats.

And Djuka went forth "berries for to pick."

Young "doctors" are great gentlemen, and Plener's bills, though you can't classify them zoologically, belong, according to their nature, to the order of winged birds. The logical conclusion of these two premises is generally a darkness in doctoral pockets. And because of this, the young gentlemen must often enter into diplomatic relations with the kind of a shark whom other mortals label a broker, but prospective "doctors" call a "Manichean," in order to satisfy their various needs.

And Djuka, too, had his "Manichean"; but especially one who was not merely a heretic, but an outright pagan.

That pagan's full title was Mr. Vendelin Venclíček, "*tailleur des habits pour messieurs*," or, in plain language, tailor.

Mr. Venclíček was a small man, with a fleshy snub nose, heavy bristling eyebrows, and an eternally smiling face; he wore no mustache, but was bearded *a la* gorilla, and was the "corporeal" tailor of the faculty of medicine, and a Manichean *par excellence.*

Mr. Venclíček—stubby, mustacheless Mr. Venclíček—wound himself around the young doctors like a blood-sucking spider around poor flies.

Our Djuka was an especially unfortunate fly, and his name adorned the pages of Vendelin's black book.

Mr. Venclíček was at heart as good a Slav as Djuka, but tailors' bills are unfortunately not paid in Slavic sympathies.

Other Manicheans called on Djuka, and they used to call during regular visiting hours. But every blessed day when the sun was barely shining into Djuka's windows, Venclícek was at his door, asking the "doctor" in a piping voice whether the "fat" letter had arrived from Agram.

Djuka once grew angry, and he planned an escape from the tailor's attack.

"I had better get up early in the mornings and go to the Prater. Vencliček's nets won't reach me there," thought Djuka.

One day—it was in the afternoon—Djuka was walking leisurely through the Prater, and who should suddenly stand before him but that beautiful blonde, with whom he had fallen in love at the station in Agram.

"Ah!" Djuka exclaimed joyfully, without noticing the old woman at her side.

The blonde smiled sweetly; but the old woman led her away to the omnibus, for it began to rain.

Djuka wanted to get into the same omnibus; but just as he stepped on the platform, he noticed through the window a fleshy nose,— Vendelin Vencliček's; and he started to run.

It is all right to pass your time in the Prater in nice weather, but as it was raining, he had to find shelter.

He couldn't go home, for there he would find Vencliček lying in wait for him; nor did he want to pass his time in a coffeehouse, and it was a pouring rainday. Where could he go?

Where, but to Milan's? And he lived near by.

Milan was an old fellow. He never spoke a word in his house, went his way without looking to the right or to the left, but was a true son of a brave country.

Djuka confided his sorrow in him, and begged him to protect him from the Arch-Manichean Vendelin.

"Well, stay here! Here is a book, a cigar; I have to go to the University. Bye-bye!" said Milan, putting on his hat, and went out.

Djuka lit his cigar, lay down on the sofa, and began to examine the room. To the left of him was a door, through which he could hear from time to time the rustling of woman's dress and nothing more.

Djuka took a Croatian novel from the table and began to read.

"Pshaw!" he cried, and threw down the book. His cigar burned poorly.

"Pshaw!" he exclaimed, and he threw away his cigar.

On the ceiling was painted a colored star.

Djuka fixed his eyes upon it and began to count its rays.

At the third ray he thought of the blonde, of Vendelin and the omnibus, and again called out "Pshaw!" and went on counting.

"You see," he began to reason, "if I were not so lazy, I could go and see my relative Milica. I have never seen her. She is young. She stays in Vienna with her aunt. Dad keeps on writing to me that I should go and see her. But where the devil does she live? Dad gave me her address, but I have lost it. Pshaw!"

Just then the clock in the adjoining room began to strike, and then it played out the tune of "—Pale Moon! I accuse you—."

Djuka pricked his ears to listen to the musical clock. And then it stopped.

Djuka again counted the rays, and he whistled "Pale Moon."

And there came back from the other room a soft feminine voice that sang "Pale moon" in Croatian.

"Pale Moon? The devil! A Croatian woman?" and Djuka jumped up.

He could hear someone winding up the musical clock in the next room. The clock played the tune, Djuka whistled, a soft Croatian voice sang—and thus, two, three, four, five times.

Djuka tried to look through the keyhole, but there was a cupboard on the other side.

Finally he took courage and asked: "Pardon me, dear country-woman, what time is it?"

"Five o'clock, Mr. Countryman!" was the reply of the gentle voice.

Djuka wanted to continue his conversation, but someone entered the other room—evidently an old woman, to judge by the voice—and told the young woman to get ready to go out.

Djuka flew down the stairs, hoping to catch a glimpse of his country-woman through the window.

He watched the window sharply. Then the shutters were slowly opened, a white hand appeared, and then there appeared—around the corner of the street, and hop, hop, towards Djuka—Vendelin Venclíček.

And unfortunate Djuka? Spun around, and ran!

The next morning Djuka again came to Milan.

"Milan! Tell me, who is your landlady? Does she have a daughter? Tell me quickly?"

"Just two hours ago she went away to live in the country," answered Milan.

"Oh, pshaw! Don't you know their name? That young woman's name?"

"Well, I don't know. I never asked them."

"And you have been here these two months!"

"Oh, I have seen the old woman, but I don't know the young one."

"Pshaw!" exclaimed Djuka, and struck his brow with his hand.

"What of it?" Milan remarked coolly.

* * *

The tailor's attacks no longer annoyed Djuka: a lot of Plener's bills soothed him.

One morning someone knocked at Djuka's door. The young doctor thought it was some Manichean, but it was his father.

They embraced warmly, and the father at once demanded:

"Djuka! Take me to Milica right away. I am her guardian now!"

"Dear father!" and the young "doctor" hesitated.

"You have never been at her house? Wretch! That's what I thought. Come along! Now you will have to go. She lives in the country, in Dornbach."

At the summer residence they were received by the old aunt.

Milica was not there; she had gone out for a walk in the park.

Djuka did not know what to do and how to answer the aunt's questions. But he was still more embarrassed when the clock began to play, "Pale moon!" The aunt sent someone to find Milica.

Suddenly a gentle voice was heard in the yard, and in came Milica —that beautiful blonde of the Agram station and Milan's neighbor; and she called out smilingly:

"Dear uncle! And Mr. Djuka! I recognize you from your picture, from the Agram station, and from the 'Pale Moon'!"

"Yes, the 'Pale Moon'!" Djuka said, embarrassed.

* * *

When, later, Djuka and Milica, after their marriage, looked at the bright moon, the young wife would say, "Look there! There is the 'Pale moon'!"

"Yes, but I do not accuse it now!" and he kissed his wife.

Leo Wiener

Ksaver Sandor Djalski

(1854–1935)

In the literary work of Djalski, born in Zagorje of noble origin, prevail topics depicting the Croatian nobility in an idealized way, although realizing their social and economic decay.

He was a fruitful and influential writer, a man of cultured background and one who knew European literature well. He enjoyed Russian literature, especially Turgenev. There is, actually, a great deal of similarity between Djalski and Turgenev in their approach to the peasantry and nobility, so that sometimes he is called "the Croatian Turgenev."

Djalski started his literary career with a collection of short stories, *Illustrissimus Bathoryč* (1848), followed by *Pod starim krovovima* (Under Old Roofs, 1886): *Tri pripovjesti bez naslova* (Three Stories Without Title, 1887), and *Bijedne priče* (The Stories of Misery, 1888).

Some of his novels are: *U noći* (In the Night, 1886); *Osvit* (Dawn, 1892); and *Djurdjica Agićeva*. The story *Moj susjed Dobromir Bosiljković* (My Neighbor Dobromir Bosiljković) is a fine example of his craftsmanship.

MY NEIGHBOR DOBROMIR BOSILJKOVIĆ

One morning in May I suffered a slight mishap just outside Brezovica, my mare Rachel casting a shoe. I was forced to dismount and walk up the hill to the manor, to have another shoe put on. At the manor of Brezovica, you must know, in accordance with the ancient custom of Croatian gentlemen, illustrissimus Batorić had, even after the abolition of villeinage, retained in his service his own manorial wheelwright and his own manorial smith, and even a special manorial cooper, who was at the same time charged with the special task of keeping an eye on the wine-cellar and supervising the handling of the wine. Hence I was quite certain that my need would be supplied without delay. Besides, I never regretted an opportunity of visiting Brezovica.

When I arrived I was met by old Vanko the butler, who informed me that he had just that moment been setting out for my home, on the squire's instructions, with an invitation to Brezovica for that very day. "Having some people, eh?" I inquired carelessly. But when the old man went on to say that the squire of Remetinec had announced his intention of calling that day, I was no little surprised. I knew that this was no ordinary visit. In days gone by, at the time of the Illyrian movement, Batorić and Bosiljković, squire of Remetinec, had been great antagonists, Bosiljković being an ardent Illyrian and Batorić a fervent supporter of *sacra regni corona.*[1]

Bosiljković I knew merely by hearsay, never having had occasion to make his personal acquaintance. But I had, of course, heard all sorts of things about him. I remembered from my earliest days tales about this ardent Illyrian patriot. While the supporters of Josipović and Briglević had only the worst to say of him, and at the best referred to him as "that Illyrian donkey" or "that pro-Russian idiot," Gaj's partisans could scarcely find epithets adequate for Bosiljković, "the great patriot and nationalist."

I found Batorić in his dimly-lit room, though the weather was beautiful and the young May day, brilliant with blue and golden light, was exhaling the perfume of its fresh breath and rejoicing high and low with the song of nightingale and lark and finch. The old man sat in his Voltaire chair, at a small table on which he was setting out a patience.

"Vanko tells me you're expecting a guest, *illustrissime,*" I said when I had greeted the old man and shaken him by the hand.

"And so I am! Bosiljković wrote me yesterday saying he wanted to see me, and asking whether I should be at home today, for instance," replied Batorić in Latin. "*Naturaliter,* I answered at once to the effect that I expected him today. I shall be delighted to see him after all

---

[1]The Croatian nationalists of the 'thirties and 'forties, led by Count Drašković and Ljudevit Gaj, laid great stress on the unity of all Slavs and wished to establish an Illyrian Kingdom, stretching from the Slovene Alps to the Black Sea. Their opponents, the Unionists, wished Croatia to remain in union with the Holy Crown of St. Stephen, i.e. with Hungary.

these years. *Meus carissimus amicus Titus* is certainly a great fantast, but truth must have its due; he is *homo honestissimus ac celeberrimus.*"[2]

"Latin today, *illustrissime*, when you are expecting a guest who, you know, led such a campaign against the use of that language?" I asked with a smile.

"*Ecce, revera*! As a matter of fact, that had not occurred to me. Of course, you young people from the new schools are not quite so much at home with the 'language of clerks.' Very well then, my dear fellow, let us talk our language," he went on in Croatian with a twinkle in his eye, intentionally assuming the broad brogue of the frontier folk.

Our talk naturally turned for the most part on the awaited guest. Batorić praised him sincerely, though he called him a fanatic, and simply could not and would not understand the other's Slavonic aspirations.

"*Per amorem Christi*!—To have one's glorious Croatian homeland— a kingdom ten centuries old!—and to be in alliance with the sacred crown; and yet to dream of some nebulous Yugoslavia, Illyria or Russia! It's inconceivable! We Croats are the only Slavs to have maintained uninterrupted one and the same kingdom, from Krešimir till today. More than a thousand years, and what difficult and terrible years they have been; and yet we have filled them with glory, and protected the royal crown of Croatia! Why, that's the best proof, if proof were needed, that we have the strength and the power and the conditions necessary to maintain our existence and to live as a people —but as a people of Croats, and not flying like bats after some will-o'-the-wisp that flickers for a moment only to vanish again, like your Yugoslavias and Illyrias. No, no! I refuse to abdicate from my position of priority as a Croat in favour of any Muscovite barbarians or, worse still, some wretched troglodytes down yonder in the shadow of the Turkish dragon!" cried the old Unionist Batorić, growing quite heated. And he would certainly have continued his philippic, had he not perceived through the open window the arrival of a carriage. At the sight he threw down his cards and stepped with me to the window.

From the carriage there descended an old gentleman of middle height, dressed in a brown Croatian jacket adorned with light blue

---

[2]Latin was the official language of Hungary and Croatia till 1840, and was widely used in conversation by the gentry class.

braid, which was also sewn down the sides of his trousers. His white waistcoat was fastened with laces, and around his soft grey hat there ran not the customary band, but a tricolored ribbon. Beneath the hat was to be seen fairly thick, snow-white hair, cut rather long at the back.

His voice was exceptionally pleasing, and quite free from the quaver of advanced years. It reached us sonorously from the yard as he inquired for the master of the house.

"He still wears that absurd Illyrian jacket, that everybody else has given up!" exclaimed Batorić, looking down into the courtyard at the newcomer. And in truth it also struck me strangely to behold such a costume, for I had not for years seen anyone similarly garbed; but in my case the impression was by no means unpleasant. On the contrary, I felt as though I were looking at a ghost, from a long-departed era that we shall never be able to praise sufficiently.

We hurried into the hall to meet the visitor, and found Vanko the butler in the act of flinging wide the door and bowing him in.

"Here I am, *illustrissime domine, servus humillimus*! I trust you are well, my dear Cornelius!" cried the newcomer with feeling, approaching his host with open arms. The old men embraced, kissed one another and clasped hands. I waited till they had given vent to their emotion before venturing to approach.

"This is my neighbor Vladimir. I knew his father; he was an Illyrian like you," said Batorić, introducing me.

"Why, of course!" said Bosiljković, extending both hands to me. Then with a laugh he added:

"At least I shall not be alone with my stubborn Unionist or, as the simple folk say, Magyarone. I shall have a supporter when we start to discuss national affairs."

"Do not let us embark upon politics today!" protested Batorić. "Let us rather, my dear Titus, talk of the days when you and I were law-students together in Pozun,[3] and used not to quarrel—how shall I put it?—over the beard of St. Peter or St. Paul."

"Come, come, you mustn't set limits to our talk! It is no mere question of politics, if we discuss our people and the sacred aims and tasks of our national endeavor. We can never talk enough about *them*.

---

[3]Pozsony (Pressburg or Bratsilava).

And, after all, that is precisely why I have come!" returned Bosiljković with an amiable smile.

He had only uttered a few words, and already I was compelled to feel admiration for the old man of seventy. At the sound of those words there seemed to pass before my inner eye all the great strength and beauty of the Illyrian days.

Batorić now summoned us to the table, upon which Vanko had set out sandwiches and bottles of old plum-brandy.

"I should really have welcomed you, my dear *magnificus,* enthusiastic Slavophile as you are, with bread and salt; but no doubt you will permit me to keep to the custom of my ancient manor, and offer you a glass of old plum-brandy and a sandwich."

"Why, that's a Slavic custom, too, for it is a Croatian custom!" cried Bosiljković, and with an easy and almost elegant gesture he took up his little glass to toast Batorić and me. "*Bonum silvarium*! as our friend Kuntek would say.

"You know, *illustrissime domine,* when I am in this old house, under these blackened roof-beams, I am irresistibly reminded of my travels through Poland, Lithuania and Russia," he went on, gazing around the room. "Little I encountered there that was not just as it is in your house, in old Croatian Brezovica. And yet you are surprised at my being a Slav—a Slav—and again a Slav!"

"You will sooner find something similar in Hungary, I should imagine," said Batorić.

"No, no! Perhaps at the first glance; but just look a little more closely, and you'll see at once that it's not the same by a long chalk! I, too, have been among the Magyars, and their things are not ours— they are alien; and I have been in distant Lithuania—nature quite different, everything quite different, and you go into the house of a Pole, and at once you feel as though you had been sent a greeting from home. And why? Because they're Slavs like ourselves. It's no joke; as we used to say, blood is not water! Why, it was in Russia that I once couldn't help thinking of this Brezovica of yours. I encountered there, on a nobleman's estate, just outside his dwelling, exactly the same sort of lime-trees as you have here.[4] And I told him so. It is true that he, sad to relate, didn't even know we existed. *Ad*

---

[4]The lime is the Slavic tree, as the oak is the English.

propositum lime-trees, what are we sitting indoors for? A beautiful old garden just outside the windows, and you not enjoying it? Your wonderful lime-trees are still standing, I suppose?"

"*Naturaliter!* Though they have several times suffered from the lightning, still they stand, unbroken."

"Just like our Croatia! How many times has she suffered terrible blows, and still, as we Illyrians used to sing, Croatia has not yet perished."

"Yes, yes, Croatia—but not your Illyria!" retorted Batorić.

"It's the same thing, my dear *illustrissimus!* The only difference is that Croatia, Croatia alone, may serve all sorts of aims, including non-Croatian ones, whereas Illyria or Yugoslavia can only serve the idea of our freedom. But let us drop politics, as you suggested just now; let us rather go out under the lime-tree, my dear Cornelius—our beloved Slavic lime-tree! The day is so beautiful, and there's still time before lunch."

"*Bene, bene!*" gladly agreed Batorić. "*Fine, finaliter* I will tell my man Vanko to let the other gentlemen know where to find us."

"What gentlemen?" asked Bosiljković and I.

"I also wrote to Petrović and Ercigonja, and to Kuntek, too. Petrović would not have forgiven me on his deathbed if I had failed to invite him when I had so dear and rare a guest as his *magnificus* Bosiljković, who was his ideal and apostle and all."

"Well, well—old Petrović! We've long been friends and comrades," said Bosiljković, moving towards the door. "We did great work together for the national cause."

In the old garden of Brezovica, kept just as it had been in the days of Batorić's grandfather or great-grandfather, we at once made our way to the venerable lime-tree. Beneath its far-spreading branches, around the huge trunk, a wooden bench had been fixed in the ground.

Bosiljković stepped under its shade with almost religious awe. His kindly dark eyes lingered on the lofty crown and the great branches, from which there descended bluish twilight and cool freshness, while every twig, every quivering leaf seemed to give forth the murmur of hundreds of tiny voices—a sort of faint, continual summons.

"Oh, how wonderful! In truth it is the best of trees; not for nothing did the Slavs choose the lime as their own and consecrate it to the god Svetovid or Perun. It is Slavic, it is our tree!" cried Bosiljković, standing by the bench with his hat in his hand and looking up at the magnificent expanse of the ancient tree. And it was only to be expected that there should start to flow from his lips eloquent words about Slavdom, its grandeur, its great and glorious future; a dithyramb on that great block of humanity that stretches from the eternal ice to the burning coasts of the Black Sea and the Adriatic, from the Danube to the Volga and thence across the Urals to the furthest lands of the East.

And as I listened to his words, I understood the success of the Illyrian epoch. Presented with such wonderful prospects, men's minds could not but have been captured, the deepest slumber broken.

Illustrissimus Batorić himself did not venture to interrupt the old man's intoxicated words. In the shade of the Slavonic lime he, too, seemed spellbound by the magic of the great idea, enthralled by its strength and truth.

"*Ecce poeta—meus carissimus Titus!*" he said at length.

" How is it, *illustrissime domine,* that you will never call me by my national name? To the Latin Titus corresponds our Slavonic Dobromir; that's how I have signed and called myself for years, and that's the name everyone knows me by."

"As you will, but let me at least call you Titek, just as I used to when we were law-students," returned Batorić.

It then occurred to me that Bosiljković had not merely changed his name Titus into Dobromir, guiding himself by some old Zagreb calendar published by the Illyrians in the forties, but had also turned his wife Juliana into Slavica, and had his children christened with nought but Slavonic names. Thus he had in his family a Miloš, an Uroš, a Ljubomir and a Dušan, and of his daughters one was called Olga and the other Milica. Among his servants, too, he had turned many a rustic Stefeka, Jankic and Martin into Krunoslava, Vitomir or Svetozar. And when he acted as godfather to his villagers, he regularly demanded of the priest at the baptism that he should give national names. Fortunately his priest was body and soul an Illyrian, and thus the surroundings of Remetinec began to stand out among neighboring districts by the disappearance among the peasants of Jankos, Tincas and Ursalas, and the frequency of names that in all probability had been out of use for four hundred years. Bosiljković liked to take names from old local documents, and in this way there were revived names like Stojislav, Vučeta, Mutimir, Dragilo, Gudislav, Stanko, such as are to be found in the ancient parish records of our mountain regions.

Bosiljković was emitting a great torrent of words with which he was demonstrating to Batorić how one and the same people stretched from Carinthia to Adrianople, when in front of the lime-tree appeared the other awaited guests. Both Petrović and Ercigonja almost wept with delight when they perceived the orator. Their joy was truly enormous, and clearly came from the heart.

"So at long last you have returned, *magnifice*!" cried Petrović. "I'm sure you have plenty to tell us about our brothers yonder!"

"That I have, gentlemen! And here, beneath this old Slavic lime, my words will flow all the easier."

Bosiljković, you must know, had during the course of his long life traveled far and wide through the Slavic world, and particularly in the Balkans. His heart was always drawing him "thither," where "Slavic speech resounds." He had passed through nearly all the Slavic districts, and that more than once. While still a young man he had traveled the length and breadth of Slovakia, and visited all the districts in Hungary where Croats and Serbs dwell; and at an equally early date he had made his way to Bohemia and Moravia, to pay his respects to the magnificence of Golden Prague and to the lands that had given mankind the great Hussite movement, that first uprising of humanity against the darkness of the Middle Ages. Then he had gone to Bosnia-to see the home of his ancestors. In the company of the Croatian poet Mihanović he had traversed Serbia, Macedonia and Bulgaria from end to end. To Russia he had proceeded immediately after 1848, and had traveled it from Odessa to Petrograd; and only recently, when in his seventieth year, he had gone there for a second time. On this occasion he had approached it from the South, He had passed through all Dalmatia, Herzegovina, Bosnia, Bulgaria and Serbia, spending almost a year on the journey.

It was quite natural that we should overwhelm him with questions about our brothers. And Bosiljković replied with the greatest readiness. His words flowed like a great river in the sweet shade of the lime-tree, from which there descended the scent of its blossom, while all around there continually sounded the humming of bees and wasps. And from somewhere right at the top of the tree the old man's words were accompanied by the loud song of some little bird.

He told us enthusiastically, in his pleasant and almost youthful voice, about the places through which in years gone by the national kings of Croatia had passed, leaving traces of their rule. He told us of Bosnia and Herzegovina and Turkish Croatia, where the Moslem folk had spoken just as loudly to his heart as patriotic frater and heroic Christian. With religious fervor he recalled how he had stood on the field of Kosovo,[5] and beheld in those parts unperishing evidence of the power and greatness of the Serbian empire. With emotion he spoke of the great sufferings of the Bulgarians, and also of their exceptional worth and national strength.

"And everywhere—everywhere I felt at home; everywhere I encountered men like myself, and continually received confirmation of my conviction that we are one and the same people. What a delicious feeling swept over my heart when, in the marketplace at Sofia, a Bulgarian peasant came up to me and offered me something for sale, saying 'Take it, sir; you can have it for a copper' ('*Gospodin, zemi, dam za groš*')! I was quite startled, and had to look at him well to make sure a man from Remetinec hadn't popped up before me—the same dialect, the same words! And the great truth that we are one and the same, from the Alps to the Bosphorus, once more shot with radiant clarity through my soul, and warmed a heart bruised and tortured by all the sufferings and injustices endured by that people —and why? Because it has not yet realized that unity, or been allowed by its bitter enemies even to approach that goal!

"And as in Sofia, so too, and even more so, in Macedonia, in Old Serbia, I constantly came across something that seemed to take me straight home. I would hear the names of villages and farms that were exactly the same as those here in Zagorje: Prosenik, named just like my nearest village, Brezovo, Zlatar, Krapina. . . . Always the same. A peasant tells me something about the field he has been working at, and out comes the same word, the same expression as we use up here in our parts. Something is always turning up that makes you forget that you are hundreds of miles from home. Recently I was walking through the main market at Belgrade. The peasants whose faces reminded me of our own country-folk in the Jelačić Market at Zagreb were Serbs, and those that struck me as foreign were Germans or

---

[5]The famous battlefield of 1389, on which the Turks overthrew the Serbs under Tsar Lazar.—ED.

Magyars from Syrmia and the Banat. Again I must say: the same world, the same folk. How, then, can you lose faith in the future? How can there fail to stir in your heart all the hopes of our Illyrian days? How can you then fail to preceive, with triumphant joy, that we are the same, one and the same; that we belong together, and needs must dance the same *kolo*?"

The old man's words were imbued with youthful vigor, and his every syllable resounded with ardor and trembled with emotion.

"And listen; it is precisely you, Cornelius, I must tell that in Bosnia, among the beys, I came on the trace of your own blood. I met a bey whose surname was once borne by your family—and, upon my word, I could almost fancy I perceived a family likeness. And then there was the time I met a bey who had the same surname as I. Believe me, this is no joke or figment of the imagination, but the absolute truth. I had quite a shock when he was pointed out to me, even before they told me his name was Bosiljković. I could have sworn I saw before me my late-lamented Uncle Janko. So it wasn't the surname made me see the resemblance. After all, blood is blood! And thus at every step I obtained proofs that we are the same people. Yonder, too, there are those opposed to this unity; but we, in whom flows pure Slavic blood, we are all for that unity, for we bear it in ourselves. Just as with us various Jakabfis, Mayers, Freys *et cetera ceterorum* are the bitterest opponents of unity and the protagonists of Croatian, Slavonian, Dalmatian and all the other separatisms, so too with them the same elements are opposed to it, save that for centuries past they have borne such names as Kristomanos, Georgios and God knows what!"

And while the old man was being swept along on the intoxicating current of his thoughts, over the fence there came echoing to us, from somewhere in the fields, the sound of peasant girls singing. The lingering harmony fitted in perfectly with the beauty of the May day and with the old man's ardent words. And he, too, listened awhile to the singing, and then, quite moved, more to himself than to us, softly hummed the same tune. And he told us how that peasant song of Zagorje carried him away to the Drina, the Maritsa, the Dnieper—why, "everywhere Slavonic speech resounds."

And Bosiljković's fervor seized our souls too. As though the shade of the great, wide-spreading lime-tree had somehow quite bewitched us, as though at that moment there came floating to us the great spirit of the noble Illyrian days, to awaken in our souls far-reaching vistas of Slav reciprocity and the freeing of our enslaved brothers, there crept into our souls sweet dreams, and into our hearts there seemed to pour a great wave of love for everything akin to us, Slavic, ours by blood, by speech, by the community of fate!

Not even illustrissimus Batorić himself could at that moment resist the appeal of Bosiljković's panegyric of Illyrism and the unity of the Yugoslavs. . . . .

When old Vanko, wearing his best uniform, came to announce that dinner was served, we all felt sorry that the conversation must end. And when, over the roast, illustrissimus Batorić raised his glass to his guest, and particularly to Bosiljković, and handed over the management of the table to his "perpetuus" Ercigonja, it was not long before the two old men had become so carried away by their exchanges that they had to give vent to their emotion in song.

And now the old manor of Brezovica resounded with the songs of the Illyrian campaign, and the almost opaque, greenish windowpanes trembled in sympathy with Slavonic melody. The old voices revealed an almost youthful vigor as "Ho Slavs, still alive," was followed by "Croatia has not yet perished," "This is the threshhold of the dear Serbian land," the Czech "Where is my homeland?" the Slovene "Forward the standard of glory"—one after another, all the dear songs of the Illyrian days of long ago.

We were all very moved and carried away. Night had long since covered the earth and we were still together, listening to Bosiljković, who told us story after story about his travels through the Slav world. And it was with genuine emotion that we responded when he suggested we should make a collection for the cause of "Yugoslav agreement." In a trice all our purses were emptied and our contribution made to the "sacred cause of Yugoslav progress and the liberation of our still enslaved brothers," as Bosiljković put it.

Batorić himself sent Vanko with a key to the iron-bound cupboard in the back room, in which he kept ready money. His generous contribution made Bosiljković embrace him heartily. And when he was saying good-bye he cried once more:

"I knew that I shouldn't come to Brezovica in vain!"

* * *

I seized the earliest opportunity of paying a visit to Remetinec, and was rewarded by the delight with which Magnificus Bosiljković welcomed me. I found him outside his manor, a large brick building around which many lime-trees grew. The house was an old building dating from the eighteenth century; one perceived at once that the limes were of a later day. Bosiljković himself had planted them. Some were already spreading trees, others still quite young.

"You're looking at my lime-trees!" cried the old man as he led me towards the house. "Well, my dear fellow, it was my hand planted them all, and each was planted in commemoration of some memorable Slavic day or to the glory of some great Slav. Look, the oldest and biggest one there was planted in honor of Kollar, and the one beside it in memory of my famous and never-to-be-forgotten Ljudevit Gaj. This one near us celebrates the day when Stanko Vraz first visited Remetinec. The one next to it is to the memory of the occasion when we elected Jelačić as our Ban! And so on and so forth; you shall see them all later on, but now I must take you indoors."

In a trice all the members of the large family had gathered around me: the lady of the house, two married daughters with their husbands and children, and a son. When the introductions had been made and the first words exchanged, I felt obliged to glance around the room. Everything was arranged according to the dictates of Bosiljković the Slavophil.

The spacious, lengthy room, with its Biedermeier furniture of the 'thirties and occasional tables and mirrors in the Rococo and Empire styles, was filled on every wall and in every corner with pictures and souvenirs of the Slav world. The portrait of Jan Kollar hung on the center wall in a rich gilt frame, beside it Ljudevit Gaj;[6] then came Palacky, Pushkin, Šafarik, Karadjordjević, Obrenović, Karadžić, Mickiewicz,[7] and other famous men of Slavdom. I do not think the

---

[6]Kollar, the Slovak poet and apostle of Panslavism, was on close terms with Gaj, the Illyrian leader.

[7]Palacky, the Czech historian and statesman; Pushkin, the Russian romantic poet; Šafarik, the Slovak philogist and author of the epoch-making "Slavic Antiquities"; Kara-George and Obrenović, the two leaders of Serbian independence after 1804; Karadžić, known as "the Serbian Grimm," collector of folksongs and proverbs; Mickiewicz, the Polish "Messianic" poet.

portrait of a single distinguished Slav was lacking. On the opposite wall I saw lithographs of the famous Ragusans from Gundulić to Pucić,[8] and farther off pictures of Peter the Great, George of Podiebrad, John Sobieski, Zrinjski, Frankopan, and so on. In the corners stood busts of great Slavs, and in glass cases were displayed china figures of Yugoslav types, Slovak wiremakers, Poles in green coats, Russians in red shirts.

On every side Slavic *motifs*! So much for a beginning; but when he took me into his own room I was almost overwhelmed by the multitude of things Slav. First of all, of course, he pointed to his books. Here were all the Illyrian and Serbian editions in rich, gleaming bindings. Then books in Russian and Czech and Polish. And in special cases in the corners were set out practically all the Slavic national costumes. And the splendor of all the rich colors and designs, of delicate fabrics and heavy woolen stuffs, exerted quite a spellbinding effect, and lost nothing of its strength even in the semiobscurity of the room.

Bosiljković interpreted everything to me with obvious delight. His words grew quite fervent as he drew my attention to this or that choice object. And from this esthetic enjoyment he soon sailed off on the rolling waves of his hopes for the future of Slavdom and his views on the greatness of the Slavic world. And the Lord only knows how long we should have remained there, if his good lady had not come into the room and conducted us once more to the parlor, where we found a tall dark man with a goatee beard, the shortness of whose sleeves and trousers threw into relief his huge red paws and his still huger feet in heavy dust-caked shoes. He had just arrived at Remetinec.

Bosiljković seemed rather taken aback at the sight of him.

"Ah, it's you, sir!" he said, extending his hand to the newcomer. "I know—I know why have you come! But, my dear sir, prices have fallen as low as they well could, nothing can find a buyer—how then can a man be expected to pay his taxes?"

"Quite so, your honor. We know that better than anyone, and I told the tax-inspector myself not to send me up here for a while; but he said—the tax-inspector did—that it was high time; he'd received

---

[8]Gundulić (d. 1630) and Pucić (d. 1882) were the two chief poets of Dubrovnik.

another reminder from head office. And so, your honor, I must ask you at least to pay a little on account."

I felt quite embarrassed at having come at such an inopportune moment, but Bosiljković did not seem too much put out. He sent a man down to the village to ask a merchant to send him up some money, and asked the tax-offical to stay to dinner; and it was not long before he was off again on his beloved subject.

The official proved to be a native of Lika, thereby considerably sweetening Bosiljković's bitter pill; he spoke like a folksong, which greatly took the old man. By the second course he had quite forgotten why the fellow had come, and addressed him solely as his "dear Mile." And Mile had to tell him all about life in Lika and his youthful experiences in Italy, where from Verona to Bologna he had everywhere been known as "il grande Croato."

This obviously upset Bosiljković's son-in-law, Toša Nedeljković, a Serb from Syrmia established in Zagreb as a high legal official, who had by his name recognized in Mile Kalemberović a brother Serb from Lika. And he could no longer control himself when Mile began to stress his Croatian nationality, and to point out that Lika folk of the Orthodox persuasion had always been more ardent Croats than the Likan adherents of the Roman Church.

Councillor Toša was up in arms at his, and began to demonstrate to Mile the official, almost in the voice of superior officer, that he simply wasn't a Croat, but a Serb and nothing but a Serb.

Bosiljković began to wave his arms in annoyance, murmuring that Croat or Serb was all one, since the correct name was the collective Yugoslav or Illyrian.

But not so his son Ljubomir! He at once started to argue with the Councillor, and to defend Mile for taking his stand as a Croat. Ljubomir, Bosiljković's youngest son, had already in his youth experienced the ebb-tide of Illyrian ardor, and seen Serbian separatism answered by Croat separatism, the Serbian slogan "Serbs and nought but Serbs!" by a louder and louder "Long live Croatia!" After the Serbian Karadzićes, Subotićes, Nenadovićes, there had appeared Starčevićes, Kvaterniks, Matoks,[9] who no longer viewed the Croatian world merely in the narrow boundaries drawn by a mournful history, but perceived it

---

[9]Rival champions of the strictly Serbian and the strictly Croat point of view.

all around them, wherever Yugoslav speech resounds, and as far as the powerful Croatian kings had once ruled.

A regular dispute arose, almost a quarrel. Mile prudently hunched himself up on his chair and was as silent as a fish. Old Bosiljković, for his part, was almost paralyzed with grief, and, just like an ancient Hebrew prophet by the waters of Babylon, began to lament such "blindness and barbarism." Just when the uproar was reaching its climax, when the Councillor was absolutely roaring that it was the duty of every Serb to preserve his Serbian traditions, the sacred things of the Serbs such as the Cyrillic alphabet, and Ljubomir was yelling that a man born in Croatia and speaking the same tongue as the Croats could not and should not be anything but a Croat—just at this moment the door opened, and on the threshold appeared a stranger.

It was obvious at the first glance that he was from the south. He was, it is true, clothed in everyday garments, and he bore in his hand an ordinary broad-brimmed hat; but by the features of his brown face one immediately recognized a man from down yonder in the neighborhood of the Balkan Mountains. And in fact his first words revealed that he had come from the regions where the Maritca roars.

The stoutly-built, broad-shouldered, shortish man at once went up to Bosiljković as though he knew him. And Bosiljković soon convinced himself that he had already met the man somewhere. The stranger reminded him that it had been in Plovdiv, and added that his name was Penčo Popov. He had with him a letter of introduction from Bishop Strossmayer, and soon revealed the object that had brought him to these parts.

When he declared that he was collecting contributions for schools in Thrace and Macedonia, and for the freeing of the enslaved regions, Toša Nedeljković at once asked whether he was collecting for Serbian schools and the liberation of the Serbs in Old Serbia, Bosnia and Herzegovina.

The Bulgarian was somewhat taken aback, but soon collected himself, and averred that he really could not say whether the money would go to Serbian or to Bulgarian schools. But he knew that the money was being collected for schools in all the regions where Slavs were under the Turks.

Thereupon Nedeljković turned his back, in order to continue his argument with Ljubomir, who for his part asked the Bulgarian whether any of the money would go to the Croatian schools in Bosnia and Herzegovina.

Old Bosiljković alone did not inquire whether the contributions were being gathered for Bularians, for Serbs or for Croats. The old man began once more to preach unity in the Slavic south, and almost embraced Popov, so carried away was he by the idea that energy and thought were being devoted to the liberation of the Slavic regions from the Turkish terror and the tyranny of the Phanariotes.

Encouraged by this, and despite Nedeljković's abuse and the insistence of Ljubomir, Popov began to defend his purpose with boldness and eloquence, and finally summoned Bosiljković to enter his contribution in the book he carried with him, in which he pointed out the names of well-known Croatian patriots, further producing the postal receipts in evidence of the fact that the money was being sent to the right quarter. Bosiljković was already taking from Penčo's hand the *karandash* (as Popov called the pencil) to enter his contribution, when his good lady suddenly appeared and told him not to forget that Kalemberović was there, and why.

So Bosiljković put the pencil down again. Just at that moment his man returned from the village, bearing a bundle of large bank-notes. He stood in hesitation by the door, as though wondering what he should do with the money and the note from the merchant. The old man beckoned him over, and took possession of the remittance *coram publico*. He did not stop to inquire how the man had arranged the matter, and thrust the merchant's letter unread in his pocket.

"And now, your honor," began Kalemberović, taking out his receiptbook. But Bosiljković appeared not to have heard, and, the money still in his hand, was listening intently to the dispute between Nedeljković and Ljubomir, who were arguing about the nature of Croatism and Serbism, and demonstrating to Penčo that they didn't care a fig for his Bulgarians.

"Wretched men!" cried Bosiljković. "While such as you exist, shall we ever witness the dawn of freedom for native soil and mother tongue? Never, never! You will always remain separated, thus tortured by mutual hatred, you will continue to serve alien blood, alien speech— alien profit. On the back of such 'patriots' as you Turk, Greek and Rumanian will ever cling, and the Slav will continue to be nought but a tool!"

And with these words he thrust at Penčo Popov all the money he held in his hand.

"Your honor!" protested Kalemberović, holding aloft his receipt-book.

"Let me be!" cried Bosiljković. "There, Penčo, I give you all this money for the cause of Yugoslav freedom!"

All looked at him in amazement. And as for me, I felt I wanted to run over to him and kiss his hand.

Walter Morison

August Harambašić

(1861—1911)

Harambašić wrote a great number of patriotic and love poems and some poetry for children. He was also a newspaperman and an editor of the newspapers *Hvratske Vile* (Croatian Fairies) and *Balkans*.

Among his published works are: *Sitne pjesme* (The Tiny Poems, 1893); *Tugomilke* (Laments, 1887); and *Slobodarke* (Poems to Liberty, 1883). He also wrote *Pripovjesti* (Stories, 1883) and *Pjesničke pripovjesti* (Poetic Stories, 1889) in prose.

Harambašić's patriotic poetry, similar to Zmaj's and Jakšić's, was an expression of his sincere national feelings. He was a "poet of freedom," and directly continued Šenoa's tradition.

On the other hand, his love poetry is somewhat weaker because of the lack of real inspiration. Only in the final stages of his career, when he was experiencing personal unhappiness, did his poetry show the skill and strength of real poetic expression.

THE CHAPEL

My heart is a poor little chapel
Where an altar stands lonely and grand,
Upon it as long as my life lasts
Lies love for the Croatian Land.

Unto it I sacrifice daily
    That sometime my race may be free,
There I have gathered dreams and my longings,
    May God hear the voice of me!

But beneath, black, a grave lies open,
    Wherein half of my life I place,

O! my heart is a poor, little chapel,
   The altar . . . the good of my race.

On the grave I have set now a cross up,
   But within love keeps its dream,
Cruel Fate may rob me of fortune
   But it can not my heart of its gleam.

                                        E. W. Underwood

SONG

Blossom, blossom
   Little Rose,
In the sunny
   Garden-close,
Soon your leaves
   Will fall below,
You into the
   Grave will go,
Fading, withering
   Away;
Not my love thus—
   No, no, no!—
Love has come to
   Me to stay!

                                        E. W. Underwood

Vjenceslav Novak

(1859–1905)

At the end of the nineteenth century the most fruitful Croatian writer was Vjenceslav Novak. He described the conditions of the various social classes.

Novak was born in Senj. His father was of Czech origin and his mother was Croat. He graduated from a teacher's college in Zagreb and taught in Senj for five years. He then went to Prague to study music and returned to Zagreb to spend the rest of his life teaching music.

As a writer, Novak fought against the oppressive regime of Khuen Hedervary, who suppressed any nationalistic activity of the Croats with police force. Novak himself was a witness of this difficult period when many noble and old families decayed in the rough fight for existence, as is described in his *Poslednji Stipančići* (The Last of the Stipančići).

Novak is exclusively a prose writer, with seven novels and about one hundred stories to his credit.

THE LAST OF THE STIPANČIĆI

(Excerpt)

One more year had passed during which Stipančić had waited in vain for his son to finish school.

The son had constantly excused himself, declaring that even with the best intentions he could not subject himself to the examinations and promised at the same time that in three months at the latest he would return as a ready man to the house of his father. Stipančić had not lost faith in his son; how could he? Despite a lost law-suit, he had still considered himself a nobleman, and had looked disapprovingly at heads of noble families who were forced to struggle for their daily bread. He had not budged an inch since he had lost the election against Čolić for a seat in the court.

His fortune was rapidly disappearing, but his eyes had remained fixed on his son Juraj, by whose efforts the name of Stipančići would be seen in a better light than ever before. When he had become worried because the time had come to spend the last of his wealth, and from thinking that Lucija had nothing of her dowry, when Valpruga, as a mother, had turned the conversation to how this and that young man had become interested in Lucija's beauty, he would become carried away in his imagination with Juraj, gazing at him fondly in his elegant nobleman's suit, handsome and wise, with the city bowing in front of him, the country and the leading men; and then his thoughts would end with some rich and powerful aristocratic family somewhere in Budapest or Vienna, where Juraj would become engaged to the only daughter, returning richly to his home that money which had been spent on him. Those beautiful thoughts, which had enlivened the old man's fantasy, had been stimulated by his son's great talent and desire for knowledge, in his perfect education and finally in the practicality of Juraj's spirit, of which he had convinced himself by lengthy monologues in Hungarian. . . .   .

"He turned out to be a failure!" said Stipančić in the same unbearable voice. Valpruga reached under the pillow and took the letter without his resisting. Through tears, she hardly recognized the words in the letter, which she read with astonishment: "To my very kind father, Mr. Ante Stipančić. It is my duty to inform you that I finished my studies by throwing the books in the corner, for my overly kind father did not consider it worthwhile to support his son for the next few months at the university. Three days ago I began a new career with which my father's noble heart will have to make friends—I have been accepted in the service of tavern waiters. If my noble father's heart feels sorry that I descended from the threshold of high doctoral honor to a waiter, a very handsome consolation remains for him,— that his son is probably the most intelligent waiter in Europe. To tell the truth, I have to admit that I took this step with a heavy feeling in my soul. But at the time, I had to choose between either jumping into the Danube, or remaining alive as an honest waiter. This much to my noble father, with a humble request that he forget everything regarding me that he dreamed in his generosity about me and with me. I remain with due gratitude and with respects to my noble father . . . Juraj Stipančić, former doctoral law degree candidate, waiter."

Valpruga, after having read the letter, was consoled after her initial fear. "As long as he is alive," she whispered to herself. Then, she asked her husband quietly: "You even denied him money?"

Stipančić did not answer for a long time. When he lifted his hands from his eyes, he said in a deep voice, as if reproaching her with all of his feelings.

"What do you mean by 'denied'? Do you know what it meant to send whatever amount of money he asked for in the course of eight years? You wash your hands, and blame somebody else. Well, you say "denied"?

"I don't know. . . . I understood something like this from his letter."

"Do you think that this came suddenly? Not ten, but twenty times he wrote to me that this time it would be the last sacrifice he would ask of me. After all, I could not have hoped for anything better. But on the contrary, I saw that my property was not enough for him any more. When I finally saw all this and became convinced that there was no way out, I wrote him the truth: 'Only this spring, and after that do not count on me any more, for I don't have it. This time limit passed; I didn't even answer the last two letters. This morning I received this. . . . He proved himself a failure and ruined us. . . . Ach, this shame, ach this shame! . . ."

Branko Mikasinovich

Josip Kozarac

(1858–1905)

The economic strivings of the Croatian bourgeoisie have their best literary representative in Josip Kozarac.

Kozarac was born in Vinkovci. After graduating from high school he went to Vienna to study at the University. He was particularly influenced by Adam Smith and Charles Darwin. During Kozarac's life, Slavonia underwent significant social and economic change. Its rich land was still in the hands of the nobility and it was being cut into small, unproductive farms. As a result, Slavonians were getting poorer and more frequently left their land and went to the cities, never to return.

In his short stories, besides describing Slavonian forests, villages and people, Kozarac penetrates the problems of the villages and their gradual destruction. The village was sinking into immorality, which had been introduced by foreigners— merchants, soldiers, and clerks. He pointed out especially the moral decay of the peasant woman ("Tena"), who neglected her field work, ruining herself in the indulgence of immorality.

His novels are *Mrtvi kapitali* (Dead Capitals, 1889) and *Medju svijetlom i tminom* (Between Light and Darkness, 1891).

TENA

(Excerpt)

In her sixteenth year, she was tall and slender, as if she had sprung out of the water. It even seemed that she would be too tall and her girlfriends started giving her some mean names. Her face was a somewhat indistinct ashen color, so that one could not know if she would turn a pale swarthy, or a rosy white. Being so underdeveloped, she was not especially liked by anybody; but if one looked at her more attentively, it was evident that her facial features were regular in every respect—nose straight and tiny, forehead like her mother's, and the lower part of her face somewhat extended and just starting to round out. Not one bone or line clouded this tender, regular harmony, yet her face was dead, without inspiration; only her dark, shiny eyes, like the premature scent of a half-green fruit-tree, betrayed that those regular features, when filled and revived with the color of real youth, would create a beauty with which nature rewards only a few women. Anyone who saw her hot from heat or work would without hesitation say that she would be a beauty; and anyone who, on the other hand, caught her chilled and blue, would take pity on her, as if he were looking at a very sick woman. She was not one of those premature beauties, but one of those who mature later, but with more perfection. . . .

When she was seventeen years old, she started blossoming so abruptly that she was different every day; every day she became more beautiful. All the dormant life-power within her rushed into bloom. She did not grow any more but only rounded out, until her fullness was in complete harmony with her height.

The young men of the village noticed her and began active pursuit. Her mother knew when opportunity knocked and watched out for her as best she could. Some bachelors offered Tena marriage, but one was like the other to her. The mother waited for a time to see whom she was going to chose, and finally when she became convinced that her daughter's heart remained unmoved, she chose Jovo Matijević, respected enough and well-to-do. Tena was neither especially happy, nor did she protest her mother's choice; her mother did not exactly like her detachment at a time when she should have been ecstatic, but, nevertheless, she felt relieved, knowing that Jovo loved her and that the Matijevićs liked her.

Shortly after this the mother died.

Tena did not mourn her very much; it was not in her nature to cry. and also, she felt in her heart like a strong horse who had escaped and flown to the spacious plains, to golden liberty. . . .

Leon often studied her, skillfully analyzing her feelings and her thoughts. He noticed that her crudity and bashfulness were slowly giving way to new feelings. These were the moments when many a woman fell with trembling knees before the glitter of wealth. He noticed correctly that she admired this glitter more than she cared for him; he was of secondary importance, only the possessor of all of this, but he knew that it could not be otherwise, when one buys love.

"How do you like it?" he asked her, certain that she was already won over.

"Good. Better than you."

He would burst into laughter, kissing her lips. She resented that kiss in her soul, but her expression hardly revealed that the kiss was unanticipated. . . .

"If all of you were as rich as Leon, then I would be yours." This sentiment echoed in the depth of her soul, whenever she saw a man's eye lusting for her. It was the same now as before, when she had not wanted to hear about anybody but her corporal. She felt more clearly everyday that she did not belong to one man alone. To belong to one man when so many offered themselves seemed to her unjust. That holy flame was disappearing from her soul which guarded the picture of only one man, not letting any other near. In her heart, in her understanding of people and life, her feeling began crystalizing in a new form, and that form seemed to her more natural than her feelings when she had loved the corporal.

Leon noticed these new feelings, for he followed not only the anatomic beauty of her body, but followed the development of her thoughts in detail. Although he and she became closer and closer, he noticed nevertheless how she spoke more freely, how her feelings became wilder, how with every day those soft bashful expressions with which a woman wraps the nakedness of her body and her soul disappeared.

He did not care much about this; he was not in love with her; she was not his wife; to him she was the same as any other woman, with the one difference that the beauty of her body pleased not only his eye, but his spirit as well. He did not care whether she loved him or not; she was his ninth; he knew he could enjoy her as he pleased.

"Do you love me?" he would ask her at times, caressing her with his white round hands.

"How do I know to tell you! I just think now and then how nice and good it is here, while that soldier had nothing and nevertheless, I loved him. I don't know why myself. My God, was I crazy! . . ."

Branko Mikasinovich

Silvije Strahimir Kranjčević

(1865–1908)

Silvije Strahimir Kranjčević is the best realist poet of nineteenth century Croatian literature. He introduced realism, based on motifs from contemporary life, into Croatian literature.

Kranjčević was born in Senj where he received his elementary and high school education. Without getting his baccalaureate because of disagreements with the school authorities, he went to Rome to become a priest. His inclinations were different, however, and half a year later he left Rome and went to Zagreb where he finished a teacher's college, afterward getting a teaching post in Mostar.

In 1893 he received a post in Sarajevo, again as a teacher, and also became an editor of a magazine, *Nada* (Hope), on which he worked until his death.

Kranjčević's teacher and poetic idol was Šenoa, to whom Kranjčević dedicated his first collection of poetry *Bugarkinje* (1895). One can also detect the influences of Preradović and the Serbian Romantic poets—J. J. Zmaj and Dj. Jakšić. Until the appearance of Kranjčević, Croatian poetry was fairly monotonous in its form and motifs of love and patriotism. Kranjčević slowly moved away from these topics and began writing meditative poetry, searching for the meaning of life on earth. His meditative poetry concentrates on social injustices and in many respects it is the peak of Croatian verse of the twentieth century.

He published two additional collections of poetry: *Izabrane pjesme* (Selected Poems, 1898); and *Trzaji* (Twitches, 1902).

MOSES

". . .Lead my people out, O Lord.
Lead them out of doleful bondage.
And cast off from drowsy lids
Scales encrusted, scales still direful
That now shackle up their eyes!
Call to mind how cheerless slavery

Like that ponderous tombstone there
Weighed upon my brother's shoulders;
How our torturers condemned
In our women's wombs our children:
Great Jehovah! Be thou kind!
Cast a curse on torturing tyrants
And my people save, O Lord!"

"Mad wish! But how like man!
Cast a curse on torturing tyrants?
This folk slay for that folk's sake?
O my creatures! Why should I
For one, some other creature crush?
See where West lies, East arises.
There the North and here the South loom:
All, all this have I replenished
With the spawn of life: each doing
Drawing equal breath, holds life dear.

Now thou bidst that I transgress
This my greatest law in nature.
Couldst thou take but here thy stand
Whence for me the vista opens,
Thou wouldst see how mean and petty
This bloodstained wish of man is.
From these heights, thou human wretch,
Jutting pyramids lie as low
As nameless mole-hills.
Vain, presumptuous is thy plea."

I. Titunik

THE PAINTING OF CHRIST

Painted one bitter day His holy face
On the bare rock, how long ago? They lay
And looked at Him, and sweet was His embrace
To sufferers who came to gaze and pray.

And every day the sun came gently down,
So rich and warm, to ease, caress, adore;
To give His cruel wounds a golden crown,
An aureole: to pray forever more.

Gentle His smile, sweetly He spoke as of old;
Love and forgiveness— they were always there,
As on the mountain when He would enfold
The world, or when He touched the children's hair.

But dark the day when men came with the rain
To build a great cathedral on the height;
The sun assailed the prison walls in vain,
No more to aureole His head with light.

Alas! He is inanimate, who shone,
Painted one bitter day by one unknown;
He hangs now lifeless, cold; His smile has gone—
Lost in the shadows of the church of stone.

G. Komai

LOVE'S DESIRE

O come, I know not, love, from where;
O come to me one summer's night,
So warm, impetuous and bright,
As sweet as lime upon the air,
And wild the blood with love's delight!

Your name, your face, I do not know,
I know them not, yet they enthrall,
And like a nightingale I call
Where flowers on the branches blow;
I call for you, for love is all.

And always it has been my fate
To long for you, who are the sum
Of longing hearts—my heart is dumb—
Of life itself—my heart must wait;
My tender love, and will you come?

I sing of all the warmth you bring,
My longed-for one, O would you stay!
But not for you this mortal clay,
And like a cloud upon the wing
Beyond the hill you will away.

O come, a sweet breeze from afar—
If only I could see your face!—
And let our hands at last enlace;
Come on the beams of moon and star
And greet me in a mute embrace.

G. Komai

Ivo Vojnović

(1857–1929)

Vojnović was born in Dubrovnik into an aristocratic family, which enabled him to acquire a good education. He studied in Split and Zagreb and received his law degree from the University of Vienna. Afterwards he worked as a lawyer in Zagreb and later as an administrative clerk in Dubrovnik.

Vojnović started his literary career as a short story writer, but became famous by writing drama. His first short story *Geranium* was published in 1880; a collection, *Ksanta*, in 1886; a comedy, *Psyche*, in 1899; and the dramas, *Ekvinocij*, (1895); *Dubrovačka trilogija* (The Dubrovnik Trilogy, 1900–1903); *Smrt majke Jugovića* (The Death of the Mother of Jugovići, 1907); *Lazarevo vaskresenje* (The Resurrection of Lazar, 1913); *Akordi* (Accords, 1918); and *Imperatrix* (1919).

Count Vojnović's most popular work is *The Dubrovnik Trilogy*, in which he pictured the hopelessly degenerate nobles of Dubrovnik, among whom only a few were attempting to remain free from foreign domination. Orsat, the hero of the work, has vainly striven to arouse his fellow senators to resist the French. *Allons Enfants* is the first part of this trilogy; *Twilight*, the second and *On the Terrace*, the third.

"A TRILOGY OF DUBROVNIK"
ALLONS ENFANTS!

Characters of the Play

The Prince	72 years old

Noblemen of Dubrovnik

Senator Orsat	41 years old
Senator Nikša	60 years old
Senator Marko	36 years old
Senator Niko	33 years old

Senator Lukša	42 years old
Senator Vlaho	27 years old
Senator Mato	70 years old
Senator Gjivo	60 years old
Senator Gjono	52 years old
Senator Karlo	30 years old
Senator Jero	29 years old
Senator Tomo	30 years old
Senator Palo	34 years old
Senator Sabo	60 years old
Senator Luco	58 years old
Senator Antun	48 years old
Senator Miho	50 years old
Senator Šiško	82 years old
Senator Luko	50 years old
Senator Vlagj	26 years old

Three Boys, Servants to Senator Orsat.
Two Members of the Body Guard.

Lady Ane Menze-Bobali, Orast's aunt	69 years old
Lady Deša Palmotica, Lady Ane's niece	27 years old
Kristina, maid to Lady Ane	16 years old
Lucija, a serving maid in Orsat's house	60 years old

Scene: House of Orsat, near the Church of Our Lady.

Time: May 27, 1806, between four and seven-thirty in the afternoon.

ACT I.

Apartment in the palace of ORSAT THE GREAT. *The walls are hung with crimson tapestry. In the center are large white monumental rococo doors. Along the wall in a row are placed several Louis XVI chairs (red, white, and gold). At the left is a large Louis XIII secretary of ebony and ivory. At the side of the secretary toward the left there are more Louis XVI chairs. On the secretaty rests a new Empire clock with alabaster columns and a gold and black face. On top of the clock is a golden Napoleonic eagle. The pendulum, a large ball, is also of gold. On the walls hang several portraits of the family ancestors. There are two smaller doors, one at the right and one at the left; but less ornamental than that in the center. Toward the left side of the stage is a large Empire writing desk, and on it two or three books and a gold inkstand with a quill pen. Close to the desk are two large Louis XIV tables covered with dark gobelins. At the right, between the door and the side wall, is a large open window. Not far from the writing desk is a large gilded "Empire-console," with a large mirror in a gold frame. The top of the "Empire-console" is of marble and on it rest a silver candlestick and two Greek bronze figures: the heads of Agrippina and of Alexander. The floor is of Venetian mosaic, uncovered. An atmosphere of richness and order pervades the room. The door at the center is closed; those at the left and right are open, but the crimson silk curtains bar any view. The warm rays of the May sun enter through the window; and as the sun declines to its setting, they move slowly upward from the floor to the writing desk and to the wall, the tapestry becoming redder where the rays touch it. With the afternoon sunbeams comes in the twittering of black swallows that are flying in the spring air, foraging merrily around the Church of Our Lady and of St. Blaise. At times a noise disturbs the stillness of the room. This noise is caused by passers-by under the window, or by the echo of some distant bell from the neighboring suburb of Konal, or by the cooing of the pigeons from their nests in the old palace; or by the faint low murmuring of voices that penetrates through the large white doors. The room behind the white doors is evidently heavily draped in curtains of tapestry, for although the struggle that is going on must be bitter and loud, the faint murmuring of voices hardly reaches us. But in the ancient stillness of this house even the faint murmuring of turbulent voices is lost. The sobbing and lamentation for the death of* SENATOR BRNJA, *father of* DESA ALMOTICA, *and brother-in-law of* LADY ANE MENZEBOBALI, *seem to be still hovering. (You fancy that you still catch the fragrance of incense from the time when the canons removed his body.) Then the swallows twitter wildly and the peasant girl selling lettuce cries in the deserted street and the warm afternoon, "Lettuce, Ladies."*

This undisturbed succession of mere noises and of the mute conversation of speechless objects lasts long enough to allow one to inspect the room and behold the splendid azure sky that extends to the regions beyond, laughing mockingly at the ill-fated city. Then—the large white doors open, an invisible hand has parted them. Like the hiss of escaping steam from a boiling kettle when its cover is raised to keep it from overflowing into the fire, an outburst of passionate voices from invisible mouths issues through the open door.

VOICES (*broken and intermingled*): It is no use! It is no use!—Who can believe them? Too late!—Listen to him now!—Ha! ha! ha!—It was easy for Kaboga to do that![1]—But we are helpless now!— O Orsat! . . . Orsat! . . . *Che tipi!*[2] Stop talking!—Why?—The same old story!—Speak up! speak up!

From this tumult LUCIJA, *an old serving maid, emerges. She carries a large silver tray loaded with glasses, coffee cups, and sweetbread. It is easy to see that the glasses and cups were drained, but that the bread was hardly touched.* LUCIJA *is wearing a balck dress cut like that of peasant girls from the neighboring village of Župa. Her grizzled hair is twined with a black ribbon. Under the short dress a pair of white stocking and open black sandals are conspicuous. With bent brows and frightened face she lays the loaded tray carefully on the table and sighs.*

VOICES (*growing louder*): Who told you? Ah!—Read! read!—*Mon Dieu!* That cannot be true!—Why not!—Liberty first! What a wonderful liberty with just a couple of guards to protect us!

(LUCIJA *goes back to the white door and for a moment lowers her head as if listening, then closes the door softly and shakes her old head disapprovingly. She then goes back to the tray, gesticulating with her hands. Her behavior shows that, if she dared, she would shout, "Stop that nonsense inside." As soon as the door is closed, the oppressive silence ensues once more.* LUCIJA *takes the tray, and trembling with*

---

[1]Marojica Kaboga (or Kabužić, 1630–92), when twenty-five years of age, murdered a faithless guardian. Released from prison by the great earthquake of 1667, he helped bring about peace and order in the ruined city; in particular, he repulsed an attack by the surrounding mountaineers. Ten years later he was of great service when the Turks made exaggerated demands on Dubrovnik. Sent as ambassador to Constantinople, he was imprisoned there until the Turkish defeat before Vienna in 1683. Writing from prison, he urged his fellow citizens not to give in. After his return home he continued his efforts for the rebuilding of Dubrovnik. The speaker contrasts Kaboga's exploits with the present helplessness of the Dubrovnik patricians.

[2]What types!

anxiety and old age goes toward the door at the right. Thereupon is heard):

VOICE OF THE LETTUCE SELLER (*under the window*): Lettuce, ladies!

LUCIJA (*close to the door, angrily*)! You here, too! (*Goes out. From behind the large closed door at the center, one voice louder than the rest is heard.*)

VOICE OF ORSAT THE GREAT: Shall I invite him?

VOICES: No! No! Yes! Yes! (*Pause; low murmuring.*)

VOICE OF LADY ANE (*from the room on the left; feeble, querulous, and colorless*): Lucija! . . . Lucija!

ORSAT THE GREAT (*suddenly opens the large white doors, as if he wished to fly through them; then quickly turns back toward the black opening; and, holding with the heavy curtains that cover the entrance of the unseen room, speaks to the invisible audience; each word is hard, bitter and burning as the blood that has rushed to his face, and as the terrible anger that has convulsed his innermost being and contracted his black eyebrows, under which flash a pair of large, eager, gray eyes. He wears an Empire costume such as the young men of that period affected. He is smooth shaven except for the side-whiskers extending half way down his cheeks. His hair is thick and sprinkled with gray. His large mouth, which seems moulded of bronze, droops scornfully in a deep line. His whole bearing betrays great suppressed anger, and shows great intellectuality and ideal ambition mixed with the firmness of an unbending aristocrat*): You do not wish me to? Naturally! How could a plebian —a Jacobin— a freemason—enter here—in the sancta sanctorum where you meet—you!

VOICES (*angry, uncertain and alarmed*): You are in your own house! . . . He is mad! . . . Now? . . . at the eleventh hour! . . . No! . . . No!

ORSAT (*as before. His head disappears behind the curtains; then in a loud voice*): Mad! . . . Maniac! . . . Idiot! . . . Yes . . . yes . . . that and worse; but if I wish it . . . I wish it. (*Suddenly draws back with a single movement slams the doors. Absorbed deeply in his thoughts, he walks to the center of the room, where he stops with a shiver. Like a man that has suddenly returned from darkness to a glowing light, incautious and bewildered, but still trembling from the fear and suffering that he has endured in the darkness,*ORSAT *composes himself, and with an indescribable glance filled with anxiety and prayer encircles the silent aristocratic emptiness. His sight becoming clouded, he leans heavily on the desk,* *and closes his eyes only to reopen them at once. Involuntarily, he passes his hands over his brow; then plunges his cramped fingers into his thick curly hair. Two lines that seem moulded of iron, give his face an old, bitterly sad expression. Then he directs his glance dully to empty space and whispers*): And why all this? . . . (*His expression stiffens. Involuntarily he takes a step forward and whispers, hoarsely, mysteriously*): "*Lazare, . . . veni foras,*"[3] he spoke, and the dead came to life! (*His muscles relax, and the faint shadow of a bitter smile passes over his frightened face. He nods slightly and folds his arms.*) He! . . . was God. —But I?—The dead sleep and come back to life. But if the living wish to die . . . (*Noise behind the white door*) if they wish!

LADY ANE (*short and stout; dressed in black silk a la Louis XVI. Her white locks are coiled in a high chignon. She wears a pair of long openwork silk gloves, and holds an exquisite lace handkerchief in her hand. She passes from the left to the right, walking as if propelling a bicycle. She looks neither to the left nor to the right. Her face is pale, sleepy and expressionless. Everything about her is strange and ancient, almost grotesque; but the historic greatness of her name and her time-honored, aristocratic bearing and mannerisms make her a captivating and enigmatic picture. It seems as if one of the dusty portraits hanging on the wall had suddenly left its frame and come to life, finding itself among strange, petty surroundings of an unknown period. When she reaches the door at the right, she calls again in the same querulous, distant and colorless voice*): Lucija! . . . Lucija!

(ORSAT, *after her entrance, although still pursuing the course of his stormy thoughts, follows her every movement. Then as if tired he sits down at the desk and starts writing, but still watches* LADY ANE *carefully*.)

VOICE OF LUCIJA (*from the right*): Did you call me, Lady Ane?

LADY ANE (*still more peevishly and harshly*): Come down!

VOICE OF LUCIJA: I am coming! . . . Right away!

(LADY ANE *goes back whence she came, sleepy and aged, as if following an invisible procession.*)

ORAST (*rises, holding a letter in his hand, and looks involuntarily at the black silhouette of the old lady*): Do you wish anything, Aunt Ane?

LADY ANE (*close to the door at the left, without turning back or*

---

[3]Lazarus, come forth.

stopping, and without looking at him, in the same hard and querulous voice): Nothing. (*Goes out.*)

ORSAT (*follows her with his eyes, and when she disappears says bitterly*): It had to come to this!

LUCIJA (*enters hurriedly from the right, but sulkily*). Here I am. (*Sees* ORSAT.) Ah! (*Becomes silent and hurries away.*)

ORSAT (*as before*): Why did she call you?

LUCIJA (*looks at him quickly and furtively as if she wished to say something that she dares not*). Why? (*Murmurs and starts away.*) It is probably the same thing today as yesterday and the day before (*calmer, but more angrily*) and forever—amen!

ORSAT (*somewhat disturbed, looking at the letter. His thoughts are outside the room*): And what's troubling her?

LUCIJA: You know, master—when she gets some notion into her head! (*Comes to the door, then suddenly turns back toward her master, looking him straight in the eyes.*) She wants milk from Petrovaselo! She doesn't like ours from Konal any more.

ORSAT (*as before, absent-mindedly looking at her*): Why don't you give it to her?

LUCIJA (*as before, motionless at the threshold, in a slow drawling voice*): Why? (*Looking at him reproachfully*). Tell the French not to drink it.

ORSAT (*rigid and motionless, scowling, says dryly and curtly*): Go! . . . Lady Ane needs you. (*Goes hurriedly to the door at the right and calls in a loud and angry voice.*) Ivan! . . . Nikola! . . . Pero! . . . where are you? (*Goes back, sulky and excited, evidently suppressing angry speeches.*) All! . . . all! . . . cowards! . . . running away!

LUCIJA (*has not moved from the door, but has been gazing at him with lowered head, silently and almost sadly*). Master!

ORSAT (*sternly, rudely, as if seeing her for the first time*): What are you doing here?

LUCIJA (*as before. In a low voice*): I wanted to tell you. . . . You sent them to guard the city gate. (*Still lower, almost confused.*) Today it is their turn.

ORSAT (*closes his eyes for an instant, as if in great weariness; then sits down, resting his head on his hand, and speaks in a slow, dull and indifferent voice*): Satisfy her first—then come!

LUCIJA (*quietly*): I will, master. (*Goes out.*)

ORSAT (*alone, still sitting in the same position, unable to arise, to emerge from the bitter weakness that has so suddenly settled upon him. He speaks as if in sleep*): Deša! Deša dearest! . . . Cruel destiny would not let us realize our dream! Let me invoke your help: "Help me to bear this heavy cross that has crushed me to the ground!" No—no! . . . She would not even answer. (*Bitterly and contemptuously, reflecting upon the new idea that is torturing him.*) Oh! . . . how ugly it is to look at this frightful and dishonorable death—the death of dotards!

VOICES (*louder and louder from within*): What liberty! . . . What independence!—Ha! ha! ha! . . . Mouse and elephant! . . . You say that? . . . And I?

ORSAT (*motionless, but an expression of extreme scorn suffuses his face. His head bows lower and lower; his eyes sink more and more; his mouth twitches, between his teeth he mutters*): Serpents! . . . Nest of serpents exposed to sunshine . . . So! . . . Destroy each other!

LUCIJA (*enters from the left and looks sadly at him. She comes closer to him and says in a simple way, as if ignorant of everything*): Do you wish anything, master?

ORSAT (*slowly composes himself, passes his hands over his brow, and, rising with dignity, quietly and indifferently (but with sadness, gives her the letter*): Go to Rado Andrović: Give him this letter.

LUCIJA (*as before*): Shall I wait?

ORSAT (*pausing for a moment; then speaks, his glance directed to empty space*): Tell him: "Senator Orsat summons you!" Then come back at once.

LUCIJA (*approaches and takes the letter*): I will, master.

ORSAT (*motionless, his eyes meeting hers*): Where is Lady Deša?

LUCIJA (*draws back, holding the letter to her bosom with both hands*): Praying in the Chapel. (*Pause.*) Shall I call her?

ORSAT (*quietly*): Let her alone! Go. (LUCIJA *goes out without turning back.*)

The white doors suddenly open and all the suppressed tumult of unintelligible words and exclamations bursts into the room.

MARKO (*young, slender, and full of life, holds the door and calls excitedly, angrily, while behind him three agitated and excited faces protrude*): Orsat, where are you?

ORSAT (*he neither turns his eyes nor moves his arms. Scornfully, and as if speaking to himself*): You could kill me now, but I would not move!

MARKO, NIKO, VLAHO (*hurry from the white doors, which close behind them. Angrily, in a group, they rush to* ORSAT *and take him by the hands and shoulders boisterously and excitedly, face to face as if they would melt him in the flame of their anger*): What is the matter with you?—Where is Andrović?—Why did you invite us, then?—Speak!—Be yourself!—Come!

ORSAT (*as before*): What are they still saying inside there?

MARKO: They are crying that Napoleon is—God!

NIKO: And that you are—mad!

ORSAT (*as before, more and more firmly and contemptuously*): Have they read the letters from Fonton and Sinjavin?

VLAHO: That idiot Gjivo cried, "Morte ai Cosacchi!"[4]

NIKO: And the Salamanca party: reiterated[5] "We are not Serbs."[6]

ORSAT (*as before, smiling bitterly*): It is a pity we are not!

LUKSA -*opens the white doors, through which the noise rushes again, and cries*): The French are here!

ORSAT (*his whole body trembling, flies to* LUKSA; *and gripping him with both hands by the shoulders, drags him to the center of the stage. The doors close*): You fool! . . . Who? . . . Who told you?

LUKSA: Tomo has just arrived and brought a farmer who says that he saw bayonets at the Church of the Annunciation![7]

ORSAT (*pacing the room convulsively*): No, no, that cannot be!

MARKO: We are too late!

NIKO: Who is going to convince those dotards?

VLAHO: And the plebeians?

ALL FOUR (*encircling* ORSAT, *speak more and more piercingly and desperately*): They tremble before you!—Let's lock them up!—Then

---

[4]Death to the Cossacks!

[5]The Salamanca party was that of the old nobility, nurtured on the conservative, reactionary ideas of the University of Salamanca in Spain. Their opponents, the Sorbonne party, followed the more liberal principle of the Sorbonne in Paris.

[6]The word is used derisively, in allusion to the fact that the Serbs, like the Russians, are members of the Orthodox, not the Catholic Church.

[7]Less than two miles from Dubrovnik.

to go the city walls!—And throw the keys in the harbor!—Quickly— quickly—Orsat!

ORSAT (*as if listening to a voice mightier than theirs, he motions them away from him; then, as if hearing something terrible, he puts his finger on his lips in a quiet and mysterious manner*): Pssst! . . . Silence!

ALL FOUR (*frightened, follow him quietly*): What is the matter with you?

ORSAT (*looks around him, then directs his glance to the closed white doors that have suddenly become silent as those of a grave, With wide open eyes he stares at his companions and speaks in a slow and hoarse voice, as if in terror*): They are silent!

ALL (*turn pale and gather closely in a group, then direct their glances toward the door as if frightened, as if silence had been transformed into a human being whose steps they heard*): What is that?

MATO (*opens the door, from which no further sound comes forth. He is tall, pale and grizzled, He puts his hand on his mouth and speaks slowly, with a drawl*): The Prince sends word—that he will be here presently!

ORSAT (*grasps rigidly the hands of his friends and looks at them as if he saw then for the first time*): That means death![8]

ALL: Let us go! (*They all depart hurriedly through the white doors, which close behind them. A faint murmuring of voices is heard, but muffled and very distant. The Empire clock strikes five, producing a thin, penetrating, and metallic sound.*)

LADY ANE (*at the fifth stroke she enters from the left. Her bearing is as before: colorless, dreamy, and rigid. She goes to the desk and sits down, laying her hands in her lap; then turning her head, first to the right, then to the left, as if searching for something, she murmurs peevishly, like a person who suffers from a host of annoyances*): What's happening today? . . . Deša is not here—nor Lucija (*looking at the clock*), nor Kristina! (*Wailing like a small child left alone in the darkness.*) Oh, dear, no one pays any attention—no one!

KRISTINA (*she is a very young girl with rosy cheeks, dressed in a modest but tasteful Empire dress of white jaconet marked with small*

---

[8]The Prince of Dubrovnik held office for only a month, and was forbidden by law to leave his palace. His departure from it would mean that he had lost hope of saving the Republic.

polka dots; at her girdle is fastened a red rose. She has been running and is out of breath; all her body vibrates with youthful merriment and confusion, from her dark tresses and dark eyes down even to the little open, black sandals, through which protrude, or you might say, laugh, white openwork stockings. When she sees LADY ANE, *she stops and, bringing her hand to her heart, says*): Oh, my, Lady Ane!

LADY ANE (*without turning back or looking at her, curtly*): Kristina! . . . What time is it?

KRISTINA (*casts a hurried glance at the clock; then coming to the desk, says in an anxious voice*): Ah! . . . I know: five minutes after five! (*Searches for a book, then draws nearer to* LADY ANE *as if she had something important to confide.*) Ah! . . . You ought to see, Lady Ane!—You ought to see what's happening outside!

LADY ANE *(as before):* Kristina, where is my footstool?

KRISTINA (*stoops down and finds the stool under the desk, then places it under* LADY ANE'S *feet. She remains kneeling before her, and continues with gay animation, laughing and disclosing her white teeth*) Everybody is running—gathering together!—Everybody is rushing toward the city gate.—The young men have cockades on their hats! . . . and ladies decorated with fans and plumes are waiting at the windows!

LADY ANE (*as if looking for something that annoys her*): Kristina! . . . I smell something here!

KRISTINA (*searching around for a moment*): You smell something? . . . What? (*Remembering her rose, she takes it from her girdle.*) Ah! . . . My rose, Lady Ane!

LADY ANE (*harshly and colorlessly*): Throw it away, Kristina! . . . It will make my head ache!

KRISTINA (*putting the rose in her pocket, with petulant naivete*): Let it stay here!—Let it sleep.—You'll pardon me, Lady Ane! . . . You know! . . . The French are coming!

LADY ANE (*motionless as an ivory idol; harshly, emphasizing each syllable*): The French are on-ly pass-ing!

KRISTINA (*close to* LADY ANE, *with childish anxiety*). They won't remain here?

LADY ANE (*as before*): By no means!

KRISTINA (*taking a thick book, with a sigh*): What a pity!

LADY ANE (*leaning lightly on the chair; reproachfully*): Kristina, where is the Metastasio?

KRISTINA (*quietly, as if all her former enthusiasm had died; opens the book indifferently and sits down on the other side of the writing desk*): Here it is, here!

LADY ANE (*tired*): Before I fall asleep—how does the passage go?

(*Declaims in the old Dubrovnik style, without even moving her eyebrows.*)[9]

Non vi piacque ingiusti Dei
Che io nascessi—

KRISTINA (*who knows the passage by heart, keeps the book open, and looks straight before her. She shakes her head sadly and continues with true dramatic force*):

—pastorella,
Altra pena or non avrei
Che la cura d'un agnella.

LADY ANE and KRISTINA: *Che l'affetto d'un pastor!*[10] (*A smothered murmur comes from the adjoining room.*

KRISTINA (*raises her head like a bird and listens, then asks*): Lady Ane!

LADY ANE (*as if awakening from sleep*): What is it?

KRISTINA (*indicating the closed white doors*): Why do they clamor?

LADY ANE (*as before*): Read me Metastasio!

KRISTINA (*turns several pages quickly, then reads in an ill-humored voice*):

Nascesti alle pene,
Mio povero cuore,
Amar ti conviene—

(*Stopping suddenly, as if a thought had occurred to her.*) Lady Ane!

LADY ANE (*starts; in a surprised voice*): Ah!

KRISTINA (*intent on her idea, asks affectionately*): Is it true, Lady Ane, that in France even serfs become nobles?

---

[9]To declaim in the old Dubrovnik style is to stand stiffly, "without moving one eyebrow," and utter with pathos the Italian words, misaccenting them in Serbian fashion: for instance, *ingiusti, nascessi, conviene* will all be accented on the first syllable.

[10]"It has not pleased you, cruel gods, that I should be born a shepherdess; then I should have no other troubles than the care of a lamb and the love of a shepherd." (From the melodrama *Arsace*, by Metastasio.)

LADY ANE (*rising with alarm, almost to her full height*): By no means!

KRISTINA (*sighing*): There you are! (*Almost sadly, to herself*). Well! —It makes no difference—they are only passing.

LADY ANE (*sits down again and says peevishly*): Well, Kristina! Where is the Metastasio?

KRISTINA (*nods and continues more sadly*):
> Amar ti conviene
> Chi, tutto rigore,

(*Noise from the room.* KRISTINA *looks inquisitively at the door and listens, and at the same time continues the passage, which she knows by heart.*)
> Per farti contento
> Ti vuol infedel.[11]

(*Murmuring of voices and merry exclamations come in from the street.* KRISTINA, *startled, listens first to the noise that comes through the door; then to that from the street. She is evidently anxious to get up, but LADY ANA starts to recite dreamily.*)

LADY ANE: *Vado! . . . Ma dove? Oh! Dio!*

KRISTINA (*frightened, turns several leaves rapidly and continues in a quick, constrained voice, more and more forcibly*): Resto . . . Ma qui . . . che fo? (*The noise from the street grows louder.* LADY ANE *has fallen asleep.* KRISTINA *looks at her and, continuing her declamation, rises and leaps to the window like a sparrow.*) Dunque morir . . . dovrò![12] (*Coming to the window, she looks outside.*) Ah!

VOICES FROM THE STREET: Let us go to see them! . . . They are behind Three Churches! . . . No! . . . no!—They are coming down the Pasat. Move on, Mary! . . . Ha! Ha!—Girls!—It seems like the feast of Saint Blaise!

KRISTINA (*comes to the center of the stage, merry and impatient*). The French are coming! . . . And I here . . . ah! (LUCIJA *enters hurriedly from the right, with a worried look on her face.*)

---

[11] "Thou wert born to suffer, my poor heart, since thou must love one who in his sternness wishes thee to attain happiness by being faithless." (From the melodrama *Sirve*.)

[12] "I go! . . . But where? O God! I remain . . . but here . . . what do I? . . . Then I must die!" (From the melodrama, *Didone abbandonata*.)

KRISTINA (*runs to her and embraces her*): Ah! Lucija, dear! . . . Let's go to see the French!

LUCIJA (*surprised; then angrily*): What nonsense she is talking about the French! . . . You'd better help me take Lady Ane away!

A VOICE FROM THE STREET: Kristina! . . . Come home, quickly!

KRISTINA (*beaming with joy*): I am coming! I am coming! (*Takes the rose from her pocket and, blowing in it, fastens it in her girdle.*) Ah, there you are! . . . If Napoleon sees me! . . . Who knows! . . . Ha! ha! ha! (*Runs then embraces and kisses LUCIJA passionately.*) Ah, Lucija, dear! . . . Joy is coming! . . . (*Looking at her sleeping mistress.*) Poor Lady Ane! . . . This is not for her! (*Dances her way to the door.*) Good-bye, Lucija! Good-bye! (*Puts her head through the door and laughs with the careless abandon of youth.*) If they remain—I əm a noblewoman! Ha ha!! (*Vanishes.*)

LUCIJA (*has remained speechless during* KRISTINA's *merry outburst, and now crosses herself*): Ah! (*Almost scornfully and angrily.*) Oh, well! . . . A plebeian remains always a plebeian! (*Draws nearer to* LADY ANE, *looks at her and shakes her head.*) Eh! . . . Were it not for us serfs, you would have disappeared long ago! (*Uneasily.*) But now?—I must take her away!—That she may not see, that she may not hear!—(*Calls softly.*) Lady Ane!

LADY ANE (*as before, raising herself slowly; then in a distant, far-away voice*): Has the sun set?

LUCIJA (*helps her to get up, then accompanies her toward the door at the left*): It will soon, Lady Ane! . . . It is time to go to your room and tell your beads.

TWO BOYS (*they are from the valley of konavlje*[13], *serfs of* SENATOR ORSAT. *They enter running from the left, sweating and breathless, without taking their hats off*): Senator? . . . Where is he? . . . Lucija?—For the Lord's sake! . . . Tell us! . . . Quick!

LADY ANE (*turns around and looks at them amazed and wrathful; and, majestic in her melancholy helplessness, exclaims*): What manners are these? . . . You ass!

TWO BOYS (*stop and take their hats off, trembling with excitement and fear*): The French are . . . at the gate!

LUCIJA (*anxious to take* LADY ANE *away*): Let's go, Lady Ane!

---

[13]A peasant district, seven miles from Dubrovnik.

LADY ANE (*looking at the boys fixedly and piercingly*): Even if they be Turks—this is not the way to appear before the Senator! (*Turns and starts to go out with* LUCIJA.) What an idea! Eh? Just because the French are passing. (*Turns toward the boys, who wait humbly and turn their hats awkwardly in their hands.*) Hm! . . . Has it come to this! (*Goes out on the left with* LUCIJA. *A loud noise is heard behind the white door.*)

FIRST BOY (*listening*): They are inside!

SECOND BOY: They are still howling!

FIRST BOY: I am going to tell the Senator!

SECOND BOY: Eh! Worse for them! (*They go out hurriedly through the doors at the center, which slam after them. A short pause, then a loud shout, evidently from the mouths of all those present in the room, is heard; then again deep silence ensues.*)

LUCIJA (*enters hurriedly from the left and takes a letter out of her pocket*): Now is the time to give it to him! (*Moves toward the white doors.*)

ORSAT THE GREAT (*rushes through the door. His face is burning, his eyes flashing. A deep frown contracts his brows and forehead. He drags after him the two boys, holding them by the shoulders with an iron grip and shaking them brutally, full of grief and agitation*): You! . . . You! . . . You have seen them? . . . How many of them? . . . A multitude—a multitude, is it? . . . The air is bristling with bayonets! And the gate? . . . Speak up! . . . You fool! . . . Speak up!

TWO BOYS (*greatly frightened*): Closed, Senator!

ORSAT THE GREAT (*shakes them, then tosses them away like a handful of chaff*) :Still closed! (*The boys run toward the right and disappear.* ORSAT *sees* LUCIJA *and, still full of anger and fright, grins at her derisively*). And you? . . . What are you doing here? . . . Why do you look at me? . . . I am handsome, am I not handsome?

LUCIJA (*quietly handing him the letter*): From Rado Androvich!

ORSAT (*grasping her hand and facing her*). You too, old Lucija, bring misfortune, do you?

LUCIJA (*looking at him calmly*): He only said: "I am sorry for your master."

ORSAT (*releases her hand, as if peace had suddenly entered his soul. His face brightens; only a firm lofty pride is reflected in his every feature and motion. Then he says, almost smilingly*): Who is he that may pity me? (*Opens the letter and reads.—For a moment he frowns, but soon the indication of displeasure gives away to a deep contempt on his pale lips. He folds the letter calmly and shows it to* LUCIJA *with an indescribable expression of sadness and fineness.*) If you could only read, Lucija, you would soon learn the meaning of the word, "senator"! (*Stops, then bitterly, as if to himself.*) He invites me to attend the ball that the plebeians and some . . . others . . . are giving in honor of the French! (*Remains absorbed in thought, nodding his head disdainfully.*)

(LUCIJA *involuntarily draws near to him and gently kisses his hand.*)

ORSAT (*growing calm and cool; casts a glance at her — then says indifferently*): And she? . . . Still praying?

LUCIJA (*shrugs her shoulders and closes her eyes*): You . . . know her master! (*The white doors are slowly opened from the other side.*)

ORSAT (*looks at the doors, then starts slightly and says calmly to* LUCIJA): Tell her to come! . . . Go! (LUCIJA *goes out, casting a long glance at* ORSAT).

(*The white doors open, and one after the other, enter the Senators. Some are old, some middle-aged, some young; some short and stout, some well-built, others decrepit. But all of them to a greater or less degree bear distinctive marks of ancient lineage and have the features of men who for centuries have dispensed justice to others. A long period of power and irreproachable aristocratic marriages have left on them an imprint of peculiar individuality, worn out but sharp. Some of them are odd in their gait and dress. There are old men who still wear Louis XVI wigs. The younger are faultlessly attired in the Empire fashion even to the cut of their hair. But each one of them is a distinctive type, especially now when they are alone, immune from criticism of the plebeians; now when a significant history-making moment discloses the secret spots and hidden crevices of their exhausted characters and crushed souls. Now their every nod, every murmur, every faint voice has a marked infallible and truthful significance. A great hurricane is shaking the dried leaves of the ancient republican oak and shows us, little by little, all the joints, the notches, the holes, and the crevices of its dead trunk, laying naked the bareness of its distorted, peeled and mangled branches. The skeleton is already grinning under the dried skin of mouldering antiquity.*

The senators enter discoursing with moderated animation. Many hold their hats in their hands, others under their arms. As they walk they lean on their long canes with round handles of gold or ivory. NIKO *and* MARKO *hurry to* ORSAT, *who has not even moved, but has remained leaning on the desk, with his arms folded, gloomy and mute.*

NIKO, MARKO (*in a low hurried voice to* ORSAT): The Prince has sent word that he knows what his duty is!

ORSAT (*as before*): How I wish it were true!

GJIVO (*tall and robust, with stooping shoulders. His head is very large. His green eyes sparkle; his hair is gray. He wears an Empire costume, and in his handsome white hands holds a long cane. His large scornful mouth, his impudently hard glance, and his flaming red skin give the impression of a violent and savage disposition. He comes to* ORSAT *and speaks clamly and naturally, in a coarse and stuttering voice, with a broken and confused accent, at times looking askance at him. His arms are folded behind him*): You see, Orsat, I guessed it! They came sooner than we expected. But . . . you will understand.— He who crossed St. Bernard and had marched in triumph . . . hm!

ORSAT (*motionless as a statue, speaks in a voice sharp as a glittering dagger*): Beneath the Pyramids, Gjivo!

GJIVO (*glancing swiftly at him to see whether he is joking; then calmly, but in a slightly trembling voice*): Yes! . . . precisely.—Beneath the Pyramids; mi capite?[14]—Then he can do anything! (*In a somewhat lower tone and in a friendly, almost good-natured manner.*) So we must not deceive ourselves! . . . Everything is in vain now—and too late. (*Murmur from the group around* ORSAT. GJIVO *looks at them sharply, then continues more clearly and harshly.*) Everything! . . . I said, everything! (*Continues again more in a natural voice.*) We have spoken enough, we have shouted and said all kinds of things—

NIKSHA (*seated in a chair, with a delicate smile*): But it must be as we wish, Gjivo! (*Takes a little old book from his pocket and starts reading it.*)

GJIVO (*starts, then says with heat*): As I wish, dear Niksha (*anger tortures him*), for I am shouting and yelling to you and, if you wish, imposing my opinion on you—

GJONO (*shrewd, short, with a large nose and eyeglasses with a gold frame, speaks to* NIKSHA, *slowly and disdainfully*): He doesn't lack sincerity.

---

[14]Do you understand me?

GJIVO (*almost furiously*):—but what I think I say.

LUCO (*takes snuff. He is extremely thin. He closes his eyes as if to give his bearing an expression of inexorable grandeur, and says in a hardly audible voice*): Purtroppo![15] (*Quiet laughter in different groups.*)

GJIVO: And I don't care a rap for stale wine, mi capite?—Ah! . . . (*More calmly, but with flashing eyes.*) Therefore, according to the decision of the Senate, we will remain neutral.

VLAHO (*tall, handsome, with black hair, flashes out*): Wonderful neutrality! . . . To let in the French!

GJONO (*ironically*): . . . to march across the Placa!

KARLO (*tall and stout, with classic profile: a true type of Napoleonic hero. Hurriedly*): Marmont has promised that he will leave the city— and we believe him! Were it not so, we all should be with Orsat.

MARKO, LUCO, NIKO (*to one another*): Ha! ha! ha! Believe the French!—They promised that to everybody!

JERO, TOMO, LUKO (*to one another*): Suppose they have! We prefer them to the savage Cossacks!

MARKO, VLAHO (*to each other*): What is the price of the keys! Traitors in Napoleon's pay!

(ORSAT, *motionless as a bronze statue, contracts his eyebrows and closes his eyes as if a strong light were piercing them.*)

GJIVO (*angry, because interrupted in his speech, he pounds on the floor with his cane; then says in a loud voice*): You have started again, eh? We had plenty of time, it seems to me!—Three days of discussion in the Senate, and today, all day, here! (ORSAT, *more hastily, almost good-naturedly.*) Dunque,[16] as I said, *mi capite*; To there is no need for excitement because a battalion passes toward Boka. (*Murmur, and restlessness.*) And when they have passed . . .

NIKSA (*looks at him through his glasses, stops reading for a minute, and says maliciously*): If they pass! (*Continues to read.*)

GJIVO (*disregarding the remark, continues*): . . . then, Orsat, we will discuss the things that you proposed to do! (*Surprised because* ORSAT *does not move, says naturally and kindly.*) If we did argue a little. . . .

LUKSA (*refined and tasteful, as if he had stepped out of a painting by Boucher; to* GJIVO *with a smile*). You call it "a little"!

---

[15]Too much so!
[16]Then.

GJIVO: . . . forget it as we all do. Such we are! . . . *Cosa volete!*[17] Much ado about nothing—then—*mi capite* . . . my Italian friends . . . (*Laughing noisily.*) Ha! ha! . . . ha!

MATO (*very thin and dignified, with compressed lips. He directs his glance far away and, chewing slowly some pills that he has taken from a small gold box, says*). Pardon me, dear Gjivo, *non vi capisco!*[18] (GJIVO *walks lazily to* MATO; *they converse.* MARKO, NIKO, VLAHO, *and* GJIVO, *gathered around* ORSAT, *engage in an animated conversation. It seems as if they wished to warm him with their breath.*)

SABO (*tall, old, with wrinkled brows and dull eyes. His lower lip, indicating a boundless, almost naive vanity, falls in a manner that indicated his ancient lineage. He speaks to* PALO *and* TOMO, *slowly and indifferently*): *Sicuro!*[19] When the Emperor Francis, in Vienna, asked me to go to Napoleon as *cavalier d'onore dell' Eccellentissima Republica*,[20] I told him (*speaking still more slowly*): "Pardon me, Sire! . . . One who is born a nobleman, as we are, cannot condescend to escort one *che non e mio pari!*"[21] (*Slowly takes snuff.*)

TOMO, VLAHO, MIHO (*surprised, as if they did not believe in the possibility of so much vanity*): Oh!

ANTON (*gloomy, stooping, and near-sighted*): And . . . why do you receive him now, Sabo? (*Laughter in that group.*)

SABO (*as before. Speaks to* ANTUN *with great ennui*): In the first place . . . because since somebody must pass—it is better that this somebody be the French than the Russians.

MIHO (*fat and simple, as if he had come from a farm*): And in the second place?

SABO (*drawling his words and looking backward as if he wished to go out*): And in the second place . . . because it pleases me. (*Murmur, conversation and quiet laughter.* ORSAT *looks involuntarily at the clock, as if he had just awakened from a long sleep.*)

ORSAT (*almost calmly, but with an iron energy; only his eyes flash, cry, and thunder. He feels this, and from time to time his inward struggle*

---

[17]What would you have!

[18]I don't understand you.

[19]Certainly.

[20]Honorary chevalier of the Most Excellent Republic.

[21]Who is not my equal.

to conquer their flame may be perceived. He speaks and instantly becomes the dominating figure): You think that we have come to an understanding, and that since the Senate has said: "Pass!"—we ought to shout, "And help yourselves!"

KARLO and JERO: Law is law. We have made it, we must obey it!

ANTUN, MIHO, LUKO: Oh! there he is!—Starting again!

SHISHKO (*old and extremely fat. Until now he has been dozing in his chair. He speaks to* LUCO): *Che seccatore!*[22]

VLAGJ (*young, sentimental, and restless*): My Made, she is waiting for me!

GJIVO (*to* ORSAT, *almost ironically, but with suppressed anger, leaning heavily on his cane*). Of course . . . "Help yourself; welcome!" Ha! ha! ha!—and pray God that they do not eat you out of house and home!

ORSAT (*as before; in a voice more and more harsh, hurried, and resounding*): And all that we have been discussing here—and what I have told you about the letter of Admiral Sinyavin who writes to me from Slano: "Do not give up, we will be there!"

KARLO: Ha! ha! They'll be there!

JERO, PALO, TOMO (*laughing*): *Les Cosaques!*[23]

ORSAT (*pounding the table with his fist; he directs a severe glance at them. Hard as flint, he continues inexorably, as if cutting with an axe*): And the message from Fonton!

GJIVO (*pounding with his fist*): That scoundrel! (*Loud murmur.*)

ORSAT (*as before, but still more loudly and energetically*): And Uhlans from Sarajevo, and the message from Constantinople declaring that they will help us as at the time of the earthquake!

NIKO, MARKO, VLAHO, LUKSA (*hurriedly, one after the other, like rifle shots*): And they will! The Turk is better than the Christian!

ORSAT: And the letter from the prince bishop of Cetinje.

JERO, LUCO, GJIVO, MIHO: *Graeca fides!*[24]

NIKSA: It is also said: "You can't trust a Latin!"

NIKO, MARKO, VLAHO: Bravo! bravo! That's true!

---

[22]What a pest!

[23]The Cossacks!

[24]Greek loyalty!

LUKSA (*yells*): If you had received the Russians, you would not have Lauriston before your gates now![25]

ORSAT (*as before*): Nothing could persuade you—because he is here! —He!—Napoleon!—God! And when you heard his name it seemed to you that it was a river that overwhelmed, a whirlwind that swept everything before it, and a thunderbolt that crashed.

KARLO (*harshly*): Are we stronger than Venice? . . . than the Pope? . . . eh?

PERO: Or than the Roman Emperor?

TOMO: And than Spain, *di grazia*![26]

ORSAT (*more rapidly and passionately*): We are, we are; if we have behind us him who has set the trap into which your God will fall. (*Loud murmur.*)

GJIVO (*laughing boisterously*): And who is he?

ORSAT: He who sends the message to you, "Wait, I am near!"—He who sent the ships to Rijeka.[27]

GJIVO (*as before*): And Fonton to our city!

KARLO, TOMO, PALO (*with great noise, amid laughter and murmur*): Ha! ha! two karavels! It is true! . . . true!

ORSAT: Yes! yes! . . . And Fonton, who cried to you, *in tutti i toni*,[28] "When the Emperor is in the dust, you will have to deal with us!"

VOICES (*from all the group*): That's true! . . . Again the same nonsense! . . . Alas! Orsat, finish it!—Speak!—Yes! Why? (*Loud murmur and crowding around* ORSAT.)

NIKSA (*with a beatific smile to* MIHO, *indicating something in the book that he is reading*): What do you think of this! *"Non jam regnare pudebit! Nec imperii, nec frons erit ulla senatus!"*[29] Ah? Sublime!

---

[25]An allusion to a dispute with Russia in 1772 as to the building of an Orthodox church.

[26]If you please.

[27]Fiume.

[28]With endless variations.

[29]Lucan, "Pharsalia" ix. 206, 207, from the speech of Cato after the death of Pompey: "No tyrant need blush in future: there will be no pretense of military command, and the senate will never again be used as a screen." (translation by J. D. Duff). There is a grim humor in helpless old Nikša's quotation from the indictment of tyranny by the helpless young Lucan.

MIHO: Maybe! . . . But I would not trade a verse of Ovid for all the work of your famous Lucan! . . . *Per esempio*,[30] listen to this . . . (*Takes a book from his pocket and declaims slowly.*)

THIRD BOY (*enters perspiring and breathless, without his hat. He almost falls exhausted near* ORSAT): Ah! master . . . master!

ORSAT (*with a terrible glance, seizes him with both hands as if with pincers*): Who are you? . . . What do you want?

THIRD BOY (*as before*): They have come—all together . . . Posat and Bersalje are covered with them.—Everything is darkened with horses, soldiers and cannon.

ALL: Ah!

ORSAT (*clutching at his breast*): And the bridge? . . . the bridge?

THIRD BOY: It is still raised, but . . .

ORSAT (*releases the boy, who runs away; then, as if his flood of passion had suddenly broken all barriers, his agonizing struggle rises to its summit, and his idea is flashed into words*): Ah! . . . Listen! Listen! . . . Between these foreigners, their Emperor, and us, miserable handful of old republicans, us, ancient freemen, there is still a barrier, an abyss! . . . The bridge is still raised! . . . Oh! Blessed be your mouths, my people! . . . Still we may fasten its chains on our holy walls, still we may die in harmony and freedom!

NIKO, NIKSA, MARKO, VLAHO: Let's go! Let's go!

ORSAT: Still we may be independent, our own masters!

GJIVO (*brutally*): Can you stop the mouths of their cannons?

KARLO (*also brutally*): Do you want to drive away this new liberty that knocks at our door?

SABO (*mercilessly*): Do you want them to bombard us?

MIHO (*close to him, angrily, emphasizing every syllable*): We do! We do!

MARKO: We are able to hold out for eight days.

PALO, MIHO, ANTUN (*retort ironically*): Why not fourteen? . . . Ha! Ha![31]

ORSAT (*as before, tensely and excitedly*): Longer . . . longer!—Until

---

[30]For example.

[31]When the French entered, they found in the city two old cannon and seven kegs of powder. That was the entire arsenal of the Dubrovnik nobility. (Lisichar.)

all our villages gather their forces, until the men from Boka and Montenegro come, until the Russians come!

GJIVO (*ironically and loudly*): And then they'll set fire to our homes and plunder us!

ORSAT (*facing* GJIVO, *retorts with extreme cruelty*): They will! They will be justified in hanging us on the cross-beams of the gate, if we help the enemy of our liberty! (*Loud noise. A wide circle surrounds* ORSAT. *It seems as if a disaster had occurred.*)

LUKO (*timid, modest, and respectful, asks* PALO): Is it proper to address Lauriston as "Excellency"?

PALO (*a true Parisian type of Napoleonic courtier. He speaks with a half-French accent*): *Non, mon cher!*[32] Only Marmont.

VLAGJ (*to* PALO): It will be necessary *col tempo*[33] to pay a few visits.

PALO: Oh, *vous verrez*[34] . . . They'll come themselves! . . . What a cultured class they are!

GJIVO (*breaking the circle, red in the face, pounds the floor with his cane*): Ah! . . . So you propose to dismiss the Senate and receive the plebeians?

ALL: Ah!

GJIVO: Say, then, that you wish revolution!

ORSAT (*folding his arms, he goes to him and looks at him with a piercing glance*): And if I say "Yes"—would you forbid it?

GJIVO (*looking at him like a lynx*): I! . . . *Perl'appunto.*—[35] I!—As long as the Prince and the Senate continue to exist. As long as we, who have decided to let the French enter the city, continue to exist! As long as we are the majority.

KARLO, JERO, TOMO, PALO, ANTUN: Yes! Yes!

ORSAT (*as before, still closer to him and still paler*): Who is "we"?

GJIVO (*as before*): We senators!—who will break you if you attempt to disregard the decisions of the Republic—*Mi capite?*

NIKO, MARKO, VLAHO: How do you say that?

---

[32]No, my dear.
[33]In time.
[34]You will see.
[35]Exactly

LUKSA (*with great reproach in his voice*): Gjivo! But the Republic is dying!

ORSAT (*with unrestrained irony, motionless, surveys* GJIVO *from head to foot*): Who can say to Gjivo, "Gjivo may live!" when Gjivo wishes to die!

GJIVO (*hoarsely, angrily*): Orsat!

ORSAT (*as before*): How could we of the royal blood sit in the Senate together with Stullis, Vodopiches, and Vlajkos—when plebeians have nothing but their heads. (*Murmur and exclamations.* ORSAT *continues with the terrible severity of a judge.*) But do you know why we receive foreign sansculottes and Jacobins?—Ah! . . . Because when the emperor is hungry for more land—first of all he buys nobility!

GJIVO, PALO, TOMO, MIHO, VLAGJ (*as if they wished to rush at him*): Oh! That is infamy!— That's a lie! . . . You have become mad! Mad!

NIKO, MARKO, VLAHO (*contemptuously, laughing uproariously*): Imperial eunuchs!

ANTUN, JERO, SABO, LUKO: Serbian women!

LUKSA (*to* GJIVO *and his followers in a loud voice*): You'll be worse than the Dalmatians! (*Great confusion reigns; taunts, insults, disputes and jests fly thick and fast in the smoky air. All at once the clock strikes six, gently but piercingly. The thin sound rises above the storm; and at the sixth stroke silence ensues involuntarily, silence filled with tremor in which only the agitated breathing of the senators is heard. This lasts but an instant; then a red apparition, like fate itself, appears at the door.*)

ALL: The Prince! (*Silence ensues, again, as if a great black bird had broken its wings and were floating dying, upon black water.*)

(*The PRINCE enters clad in the red gown of state, with gold lace on his shoulders, under which is seen a red Louis XV costume of satin with diamond buttons. He wears white stockings and small black shoes. His head is covered with a white "alonge" wig. His face, clean shaven, sad, old, bears the impress of ancient ancestry. His eyes seem sewed up in in sacks, and his lower lip droops. In his hand he holds a gold-headed staff. Behind him, in the darker part of the room two body guards stand waiting.*)

VOICES FROM THE STREET (*penetrate the deathlike silence of that moment*): Quick! . . . Quick! . . . They haven't come yet!—Why don't they let them enter!—*Liberte! Fraternite! Egalite!*—Mary, move on! (*Uproarious laughter in the street, then a pause.*)

Voices of the Senators (*gently, like the rustling of dried leaves*):
Who ever saw a prince act in this manner! . . . Who authorized him!
. . . To leave the palace . . . with his official gown! . . . *Che scandalo!*[36]
The end has surely come!

The Prince (*comes to the center of the room, walking slowly, with
short dragging steps. He pays no attention to the senators, who look at
him with different expressions of astonishment and curiosity. He is
evidently concerned only with an insignificant, almost ridiculous matter.
His drooping lips move and a peculiar smile passes over them. When he
comes to* NIKŠA, *who has discontinued his reading and who looks
at him ironically through his glasses, the* PRINCE *glances at him for
a moment, then laughs more loudly and shakes his head, indicating the
open letter in his hand*): Here is the letter from Antun Largo in
Paris. I found it!—Ha! . . . *vale la pena*[37] to read it.—Especially now!
—Listen how it begins. (*He laughs gently to himself, but a cough chokes
him slightly.*) Ah! . . . my Mara laughed her head off! . . . Imagine!
(*Reads the letter through a large golden monocle that hangs beneath
his gown.*) "*Excellentissimo Signor Principe*[38] My dear Maro, hasn't
the devil taken you yet!" (*Murmur. The* PRINCE *laughs to himself
and continues to read.*)—Then . . . "The Republic, then, is still alive!"
. . . etc! etc! . . . (*With a senile, coughing laughter*) What a devil of a
man he is! (*As if remembering something*) Ah! . . . Let me not forget
it . . . (*Turning toward the various groups*) Karlo and Tomo . . . Yes!
it seems to me I came to remind you what to do . . .

(ORSAT *would like to stop him, but the* PRINCE *looks at him
curiously, coldly, absent-mindedly; then continues quite simply and
naturally.*)

The Prince: Lauriston is at Pila; he cried to Luko over the city
gates: "What is your answer?—Are you going to let us pass through
the city?" Luko told him to wait, and came to see me. (*Noise on the
street.*)

Voices (*coming from the street*): Why don't they let them enter the
city! . . . Have they gone to sleep?

The Prince (*takes snuff, then carefully dusts off his white jabot and*

---

[36]What a scandal.
[37]It is worth while.
[38]Your Excellency the Prince.

his red gown, so that no particle remains. He then continues between coughs, but always frankly): That's why I thought it necessary to dress and come to tell you.

LUCO (*to* SABO, *aside*): Really he could have stayed at home!

SABO (*slowly and ironically, to* ANTUN): "The gown is worth more—"

ANTUN (*laughing, to* SABO): "Than Tinto and the branch."[39] Ha! ha! ha!

ORSAT (*trembling with anger*): But you will not, Your Grace, like that—now!

THE PRINCE (*not understanding*): What's on your mind! I will wait for him in the Palace, with all of you . . . in gran pompa[40] . . . and Tomo and Karlo will go to Pila and tell him that we protest—that we are neutral —and at the same time that they may pass. Eh?

KARLO, TOMO. We are ready.

THE PRINCE (*as before*): I have given orders to raise the flag in front of St. Blaise's Church, when you leave, and to place soldiers and guards around it.

NIKSA (*ironically and slowly, to* MATO): Oh! *che bella festa!* . . . Oh! *che bella festa!*[41]

MATO (*slowly and ironically, to* NIKŠA): The only thing tacking is an illumination!

THE PRINCE (*bowing slowly to the left and right*): And now . . . Eccellentissimi[42] . . . come with me! . . . We must show Lauriston with whom he has to deal!—(*With his former smile*) And when they pass, I'll answer Antun. (*Laughing to himself*) What a witty fellow he is!— He! he!—"We are alive and the devil hasn't taken us yet!" (*Turns to go, and bows again, this time more profoundly, to all the senators*) My lords! (*Goes to the door. All senators bow.*)

---

[39]Sabo and Antun are quoting from a Dubrovnik jingle that in translation runs thus: Tinto sits on a branch:In a red gown. The gown is worth more. Than Tinto and the branch.

This jingle is a riddle, to which the answer is, a cherry stone. Sabo and Antun sarcastically intimate that the prince's red gown is worth more than the prince himself and the office that he holds.

[40]With great ceremony.

[41]What a lovely festival!

[42]Your Honors.

ORSAT (*who until now has been pacified by his immediate friends, suddenly rushes and closes the large white doors, places himself in front of them, firm and great, like Orlando, face to face with the* PRINCE): No!

ALL (*with mingled feelings, in unison*): Orsat!

GJIVO (*in a loud voice, as if he wished to attack* ORSAT): Let him go!

ORSAT (*motionless, glorious as St. Michael on the threshold of Paradise, in a resounding, terrible voice*): No!—This is my house! This is my door! I am master here!

THE PRINCE (*trembling, almost frightened, but not without a sort of wretched dignity*): Orsat!—I am your Prince!

ORSAT (*with an indescribable sadness*): Because you are my Prince, I fall—on my knees before you! (*Rushes to him and kneels down.*)

ALL: Ah! . . . rise! . . . Sublime!—That's a man! . . . What has happened to him?—*Che ciarlatano!*[43]

ORSAT (*as before. In the course of his speech he weeps and makes a last impassioned plea for liberty*): And I kiss your gown as I kissed my dead mother, and I say to Your Grace, "Do not heed us and our ignominy, do not look at our wretched and exhausted faces; think in this hour of judgment that we are not equal to you, no—but your slaves and servants!"

GJIVO (*runs among the senators as if beside himself*): Do you hear! . . . He is insulting us nobles!

ORSAT (*becomes more and more dominating, more and more eloquent, as if he wished, with the fire of his word, to melt the ice that has frozen every soul*): And consider that we have forgotten all that our fathers have done since they came to these cliffs—and that our souls have frozen; and that we no longer remember who were our sages, our poets, our navigators, and our martyrs, who have transformed this nest into an altar, who have saved the honor of our oppressed race! . . . (*More and more penetratingly, clinging to him as if to the cross, until every face, every hand, every breath trembles and flames around him*) Say from the depth of your soul that we are the last relics of ancient selected generations, without will, without blood, and without brains— and after you have acknowledged all this, Your Grace, say only one word . . . only one!

---

[43]What a charlatan.

THE PRINCE (*unwillingly, all confused, does not understand him; looks all around him as if searching for one who could interpret this enigma*): What word? . . . What?

ORSAT (*on his knees in supplication, and with prayer in his voice*): "I am master!"

ALL (*in great confusion, with extreme contrast of feeling in their voices*): Passionate! . . . Wonderful! . . . Orsat!—Stop—Speak!—Speak!

ORSAT (*rising slowly, as if transformed*): Give orders to chain the bridge; proclaim that the senators do not exist, only the people and you!—Then imprison all of us. Ring the bell of Our Lady—and sit, Your Grace, with your people, under the arches of the palace. If you wish, be another Marino Faliero.[44] . . . Only save the Republic—save it from ourselves!

GJIVO (*like a lynx*): And we tolerate these insults!

GJIVO'S FOLLOWERS: Let us leave this house . . . let us leave this house.—The Senate is the master! . . . The Senate!

ORSAT'S FOLLOWERS: (*gather around him as if perplexed. They wish to bring him back to his senses, which, they think, he has lost*): Orsat! . . . Orsat! . . . Come to your senses! It is in vain!

ORSAT (*looks before him with a wild, threatening glance. He struggles to free himself from all of them*): I am alive! . . . I am alive! . . . Do you hear? . . . (*Looks at the* PRINCE *as if seeing him for the first time*): Why is he red? Why? When there is no more of that noble warm blood that washes away all sins, when there are no tears, when there is no suffering—when all this perishes in mud, in shame, in ignominy! . . . Ah! (*Shudders as if he were viewing fathomless depths from the peak of a mountain*) There . . . there . . . the gate is being opened—the bridge descends—they enter . . . they enter! . . . Such a multitude! . . . The French first! All is gold, plumes, and banners! . . . Fine men! . . . All hungry for glory, all hungry for women! . . . Then the others, others! Ah! . . . They are worse, uglier!—Wretched, poor, savage! They all want to pass through the gate! . . . They are all laughing, spitting at

---

[44]Marino Faliero (or Falieri: c. 1275–1355) after a brilliant military career was elected doge of Venice. Angered at a personal insult, he plotted to exterminate the whole body of the nobility, who were hated by the populace. His plot was discovered and he was executed. Byron based a tragedy on his story.

the black walls, they all growl! "Where is your crown? Where is your liberty? You are as we are!" Oh!

(*While* ORSAT *is under the spell of his passion, the* PRINCE *accompanied by* TOMO *and* KARLO, *leaves the room.* GJIVO *and his followers accompany them closely to the door; then they remain at the rear of the room, listening angrily, and smiling venomously at* ORSAT'S *wailing.*)

ORSAT (*he seems to have regained his senses, but the idea that has brought him to the summit of his feverish outburst has changed its course and he looks at them to see if he can find other channels to their sleeping souls*): We are still a power! . . . I . . . You . . . We! . . . We kings!— We masters!— Wherever we appear even emperors stand behind us! . . . Our sea and our fortress—and our churches—and the Palace,—everything is still here, alive,—alive! Shall we allow all this to disappear!— And our children to forget even the symbol of liberty—and force them to emigrate and seek for a name, justice, and power elsewhere, in ignorance that here is our country, our free country, and that everything else is slavery, dreadful slavery! (*Goes from one senator to another with gay, youthful enthusiam, but his eyes are questioning and doubtful, fearing that his word may be impotent and useless.*) If this ancient lad of liberty must be subjugated, let us go! . . . Brothers—children! There in the harbor are our ships. Let us take our flag and St. Blaise and sail, as our ancestors did!—Oh! Happy sailing! . . . Let us go! Let us go! The sea gulls and the clouds will ask us, "Who are you? Whom do you seek?"—And our sails will answer, "Dubrovnik on the sea . . . Dubrovnik again seeks desert cliffs on which to her hide liberty! . . . Show them to us, O clouds! . . . Conduct us to the beautiful Grecian land, the land of gods!" . . . (*All the senators draw near. They are all excited, moved. Some of them have tears in their eyes.* GJIVO *shivers involuntarily.*) Oh! (ORSAT *is in supreme happiness, because his word has produced the desired effect.*) Oh! . . . Blessed be those tears! . . . Quick, quick! . . . Run . . . Hold the keys! . . . Oh! we are saved . . . we are saved! (*A cannon shot is heard.*)

ALL (*shuddering*): What is that? . . . Roaring of cannon!

GJIVO (*for some reason confused*): That is the signal.

ORSAT (*with a terrible suspicion*): The signal? . . . Signal? . . . And the Prince? . . . and Karlo? . . . and Tomo? . . . Where are they? (*perceives a malicious smile on his lips of* GJIVO, *who leans on the cane, swaying with an air of indifference.*) Ah! . . . (*Understands.*) Traitors! (*He is about to attack* GJIVO, *but his friends restrain him.*)

GJIVO (*coldly, in a calm, deep voice, like a different man*): You cannot complain, Orsat! . . . You have said all you wished, no one interfered! (*Turns toward the others, like a man of affairs*) First signal, *mi capite?* Lauriston receives our ambassadors. (*A second report. Pause filled with fateful silence.* GJIVO *continues in a lower voice, as if speaking to himself.*) And . . . the second! . . . The French enter.

ALL (*with dull surprise, fright, suspense, and relief*): Ah!

ORSAT (*composes himself with a supernatural effort. Like a statue of bronze he remains erect, alone, and motionless in the center of the room. One can just perceive in the furious flashing of his eyes, in the convulsive motion of his mouth, and in the threatening coldness of his voice, that a passionate storm is sweeping his soul; but that he is master of this tempest. In a natural voice, with a contemptuous smile and a dignified aristocratic manner he turns toward all the groups and motions gallantly with his hand as if bidding them farewell*). Yes!—Pardon me for detaining you—but I did not realize that it was too late.

NIKO, MARKO, LUKSA, MATO (*all shake his hand and look into his eyes. They all would like to embrace and kiss him, but to them his soul is strange and inexplicable*): Oh! Beloved Orsat! . . . What shall we do now?

ORSAT (*as before, looking at them condescendingly, with overpowering irony*). Thank God we did not decapitate them!—(*closes his eyes from terrible pain*) Go! . . . Go! . . . Leave me alone.

GJIVO (*approaches him in confusion, but almost with good humor*): Orsat! . . . Now that it is all over, let us forget everything!

ORSAT (*looks at him piercingly, and slowly mutters through half-closed lips*): Begone at once! . . . Let me see no more of you! (GJIVO *seems on the point of explosion.*) You are in my house . . . Do you understand?

GJIVO (*with flashing eyes, mutters as if to himself*): A family of charlatans! (*Goes out.*)

NIKSA (*with delicate irony, placing the book in his bosom*). I am curious, Orsat, to know what kind of faces we shall have tomorrow when we wake up.

ORSAT (*as before*): Purtroppo!⁴⁵—the same!

MATO, LUCO, VLAGJ, PALO, SERO, LUKO (*shake* ORSAT'S *hand silently and start away slowly, conversing in low voices*): Veramente,⁴⁶ he speaks nicely!—Somewhat too theatrically!—He is so annoying!— His discourse is unworthy of a senator!—I am sorry for him!—Let us hurry, we may miss our chance of seeing the general!—He has as grand ideas as his late mother!

SISKO (*sluggish and peevish; he has been sleeping during the entire scene. Starting away, he asks* MIHO): Is it certain that Napoleon will abolish the confidential agents?

MIHO: Certainly! . . . Right away, too!

SISKO (*casting an angry and scornful glance at* ORSAT): Why does he howl so much, then? (*Goes out.*)

LUKSA (*starting out, with a bitter smile, to* NIKSA): Do you know how all this is going to end? . . . Con un ballo all' ungherese!⁴⁷ He! he! . . . It will! it will! (*Senators depart from the room one by one. The large white doors remain open, revealing the black entrance of the silent room.*)

ORSAT THE GREAT (*alone. Pale, broken, choking, his hair ruffled. He advances slowly to the large open doors and directs a vacant and furious glance all around him. He hears the last steps of the departing senators, the merry noise from the street, and the twittering of the swallows. All his bitterness rises to his lips, and, in spite of his strength and his will, something seems to be strangling, crushing him. He speaks in a heavy, hoarse, trembling voice*): No . . . no . . . I will not . . . Everything is over! . . . everything . . . everything! (*With great wailing, as if all his strength were failing him*) Alas! mother dear!⁴⁸ (*With all the weight of his large body he sinks in the chair near the desk, buries his face in his arms like a small child, and weeps bitterly. in the stillness of the desolated house is heard only his pitiful sobbing, like the*

---

⁴⁵For pity's sake.

⁴⁶In truth.

⁴⁷"With ball in Hungarian style;" that is, "We shall dance to Hungarian music." (An historic phrase of Count Lukša Gozza.)

⁴⁸These words are the typical cry of pain of a Dubrovnik child when struck on the head by a stone.

wailing of a slaughtered animal.—In the darkness behind the open door there becomes outlined the figure of a woman.)

DEŠA *remains dark and mysterious as if on the very threshold of death, without making a step forward. Her long black dress falls down her tall figure in heavy, even folds, and envelops her in a cloak of sadness. Around her short bodice is wrapped a transparent white fichu a la Marie Antoinette, disclosing her delicately moulded neck. From the short black sleeves emerge her white arms. Beautiful blond hair, a little powdered, crowns her head with a tragic halo. Her long oval face, that gives her compressed mouth an expression of haughtiness, and deep blue eyes, remind one of Delaroche's portrait of Marie Antoinette, especially now when she stands here like the fulfillment of fate. Pale, calm, and cold, with a mysterious glance she stops and gazes, gazes at the downfall of a man—*ORSAT THE GREAT. *Her hands hang at her sides; in one she holds her prayer book, in the other a white handkerchief,*)

ORSAT (*raises his head, showing a face suffering from great pain. He shakes his head desperately, then lays it back on his clenched fist.*) Nothing, nothing! . . . Neither my prayers—nor my curses—nor my tears! . . . Oh! for shame!— Orsat weeps! . . . Orsat! . . . Nothing—could help! They fly, fly, then they flutter aimlessly around the flame!—Yes! Their wings are singed! . . . Frozen souls! . . . empty hearts! . . . Even common sense was of no avail . . . nor interest . . . nor fear! (*Inexorable, as if he were viewing them all before him*). Nor pride that until now covered their wretched bones! . . . They are still vivid in my memory . . . and will remain there until doomsday. (*Shuddering*) Oh! How small they were . . . empty! . . . How they hated me because I saw their ugly, hidden thoughts that crawled over their brows, but which they had no courage to speak out!—Oh! their eyes, their silence, their smiles! All that spoke, cried: "Why do you hold us? . . . Why do you strip us? We are naked, naked!" Oh! (*Shivers from bitterness, and with a far-away look in his eyes continues in a still more distant voice*) And I thought, like an idiot . . . what? . . . that my word could bring the dead back to life. (*His glance becomes harder.*) Lazarus! . . . Lazarus! (*Rises slowly as if bewitched and plunges his hand into his hair. The sun is setting. The clock strikes seven, but he does not hear it. The warm rays of the sun fall on him from the side. He speaks as if in a dream.*) Not even He, Christ, could melt frozen souls!—He himself could not! (*Shakes his head and shoulders involuntarily. His consciousness returns and with it all the misery of bitter and inexorable reality. His voice is fainter.*) Strange! . . . I feel cold! (*Looks around him. Only the swallows twitter before returning to their nests.*) I am alone! . . . all alone! . . . Everyone has deserted me—as if I were to blame for everything!—And she!—My beloved! . . . Great heart, the only being!—My only faith—she, too!

DESA (*still in the same place, in the same position, but yet paler*): I am here!

ORSAT (*turns quickly toward her, and remains petrified by her appearance. Pause. Then they look at each other's distressed faces until* ORSAT *slowly breaks the silence*). Oh! . . . Why are you so pale?

DESA (*clutching at the door jamb with one hand*): I have seen death! (*Starts to move away.*)

ORSAT (*as before; quickly, almost imploringly*): Ah! do not move! . . . You come from the depths of my yearnings. (*More slowly, gazing steadily at her*) You are beautiful as death! . . . and as disdainful!— The same contemptuous lips that are not to be kissed—and the same marble white hands that pluck the flowers of life. (*With desperate calmness*) You—you are the only one—who should be here now—to look at me—to call me!

DESA (*advances to him and takes him by both hands, directing a steady glance at his bedimmed eyes*): I—or—death?

ORSAT (*hoarsely, in exhaustion, freeing his hands*): Why have you come, then?

DESA (*leans gently on his shoulder. The last rays of the setting sun illumine them with bloody light. Slowly, feelingly, she points to the radiant sunset framed by the window*): Do you not see?

ORSAT (*exclaims, grasping her hand and looking at the declining sun*): Oh! . . . The sun is setting!

DESA: The sun of freedom! (*Almost embracing each other, mute, they stand before the open balcony.*)

ORSAT (*with great calmness*): How peacefully it is setting!

DESA (*laying her hand on his shoulder*): Will it ever return?

ORSAT (*as before, very slowly*): That sun—never!

DESA (*extends her hand toward the sun and fixes her eager eyes on it*): Look . . . look . . . it has not yet disappeared. There is still a trace left.

ORSAT (*as if in a dream*): Still . . . still!

(DEŠA, *freeing herself from him, steps forward toward the sun and oins her hands as if in prayer.*)

ORSAT (*lays both hands on her shoulders, then rests his head on her shoulder. His face becomes more gentle and he utters only a single sigh. The sun has set*): Ah!

DESA (*crosses herself and draws close to him. Shivers pass over her body. She speaks very slowly, as if frightened*). It is gone!

ORSAT (*steps forward, absorbed in his thoughts, but calm*): Tomorrow, when it rises again, it will not recognize us! (*A loud noise in the distance and the singing of a great multitude are heard.*)

DESA (*approaches the window as if she suddenly wished to close it, shuddering and casting a quick glance at* ORSAT): Oh! My God!

ORSAT (*stands erect and looks at her. They understand each other. A deathlike sweat covers his brow, on which there is no longer warmth, nor wrath, nor flame.—The sun has set!—Bitter sadness, like night, has darkened his soul. He breathes calmly, but slowly*). It is they!

DESA (*frightened, draws back from the window, and points with trembling hands to the distance*): They . . . they!

ORSAT (*sits down; then speaks very slowly, as if in a dream*): Come! —here!—near me! (*The singing draws nearer.*)

DESA (*comes to him and bends down as if to kneel. He embraces her as though he wished to protect her with his tenderness. She speaks with suppressed fury*). Cursed song!

ORSAT (*as before*): Ah! do not curse! . . . Listen! (*Then the song of the revolution hovers majestic and triumphant in the twilight. The whole army sing it. All the doves and swallows have awakened and now fly frightened over the city. The two sufferers draw nearer to each other, and involuntarily rise, as if the beautiful melody had inspired them. They remain embraced like a statue. Warm tears flow down* DESA'S *face. The song becomes fainter and fainter, as if the army had turned to some other part of the city.*)

ORSAT (*entranced with the glorious song, shakes his head bitterly and whispers*): Oh . . . how beautiful it is!

DESA: Do you know it?

ORSAT: I heard it in Paris—when the king's head fell! (*Pensively, in a lower voice*) As do ours today!

DESA (*with a terrified glance, as if she were standing before a fathom-*

less abyss. The song is completely lost in the distance. She speaks slowly and mysteriously, almost to herself): What are we now, Orsat?

ORSAT: Slaves.

DESA (*involuntarily draws back, shudders, and exclaims*): Oh! Then, no!

ORSAT (*bewildered*): What is the matter with you?

DESA (*looking penetratingly at him*): I am thinking—shall we ever be happy after this day?

ORSAT: Yes—if we forget!

DESA (*draws back from him, full of mystery*): Who could do so?

ORSAT (*hurries to her and takes her forcibly in his arms, looking passionately at her lips*): You are leaving me.

DESA (*pale, exhausted, but firm*): No.

ORSAT (*holds her by the hand, and looks eagerly at her*): So much bitterness! . . . So much misery! And now we have reached the very threshold of our wretched happiness.

DESA (*her lips near his, gazing into his eyes*): I love you!

ORSAT (*a terrible suspicion takes possession of his soul; he grasps her face with both hands and looks at her as Oedipus at the Sphinx*): Then why do you refuse to be mine? (*Closes her lips with his hand*) Yes! . . . yes! . . . I see that in your eyes—on your lips! . . . You refuse! . . . And why?

DESA (*with her whole being*): Will our children be slaves as we are?

ORSAT (*calmly releases her and says with great bitterness*): Then— choose! ORSAT (*turns and remains before her, frightened, in ecstasy, full of dread and sadness; then speaks as if to himself*). Wretched— charming—majestic as death! (*Rushes to her and taking her in his arms presses his lips on hers in a long, passionate kiss. Then they draw apart as if exhuasted; he, motionless and sad, but inexplicably calm, says sharply and courageously*) No!

DESA (*pale as death, she grasps his hand, then taking her prayer book she goes to the doors. On reaching them she turns and asks him in an indifferent, weary voice*): Shall I close the doors?

ORSAT (*leaning against the chair, fixes his eyes on DESA and, shrugging his shoulders, says, smiling bitterly*): One need not close the dwelling of the dead. (DESA *motions with her heavy hand, as if bidding farewell, from the threshold of death, to those who have remained on the other side of the dark river of life—and goes out.* ORSAT *bows his head and sinks slowly into the chair, broken and dumb.*)

VOICE OF MILK SELLER (*down the street*). Milk, ladies!

VOICE OF LADY ANE (*from the room at the left*): Lucija! . . . Lucija!

ORSAT (*hears and understands the sounds of the undying life of the city. Folds his arms on his breast and, nodding his head, whispers to himself*): And now? (*Remains absorbed in thought.*)

VOICE OF MILK SELLER (*lost in the merry uproar of the streets teeming with life; in a distant, frawling tone*): Milk, ladies!

(THE CURTAIN FALLS)

John J. Batistich and George Rapall Noyes

Antun Gustav Matoš

(1873–1914)

A. G. Matoš was the most temperamental and lively exponent of turn-of-the century Croatian cultural and literary life.

Born in Srem, he attended high school in Zagreb and University in Vienna, studying music. Never settling down, he deserted from the army and went to Belgrade and then Paris. On his return from Paris, he lived in Belgrade for several years and then went to Zagreb, remaining there until his death.

Matoš's main works are: *Iverje* (Chippings, 1899); *Novo iverje* (Further Chippings, 1900); *Ogledi* (Essays, 1905); *Vidici i putevi* (Vistas and Roads, 1907); *Umorne priče* (Weary Stories, 1909); *Naši ljudi i krajevi* (Our Folk and Our Regions, 1910); *Pečalba* (Migrant's Labor, 1913); and *Pjesme* (Songs, 1913). His complete works were published in seventeen volumes in Zagreb between 1935 and 1940.

Although under the strong influence of the decadents and the French Symbolists, he found inspiration in his native country and believed "that only a merging of the past with the vigor of the present could produce the strength required for national survival, so that his literary work transcended the boundaries of literature, for which reasons many regarded him both as a literary and as a national teacher."[1]

THE NEIGHBOR

He was very tired. While cooling himself at a window of his apartment on the second floor, his thoughts wandered afar. He had had to leave his country on account of debts. His family had turned him away, not without giving him the necessary expenses for his journey to America. He stopped off at Geneva and began gambling, winning at poker from the Slavic, especially the Bulgarian, students. When one of the students committed suicide, because of his losses, by drowning

---

[1]Kadić, Ante, *Modern Yugoslav Literature*, University of California Syllabus Series No. 347, p. 155.

himself in the lake, Tkalac stopped gambling and conceived a happy thought: he would rent a larger apartment, buy a few mats and start giving lessons in fencing and later on in boxing (having learned his latter sport from a Parisian expert).

By means of the sword he made his way into the highest social circles, securing excellent recommendations. After the wonderful match placed him among the world champions, he made preparations to move to Paris. For the first time in his life he had managed to save money. The young, eccentric, cosmopolitan ladies, in particular, were paying him in a princely fashion. He started paying off his debts in his native country. Everyone was won over by his behavior, which was undeniably good, being a heritage from a long line of heroic border-land officers, noblemen of Laudon's time. Like most of our frivolous men, he remained good at heart—a childish, almost girlish soul shining from his yellowish, eagle-like eyes; and a black, manly beard accentuated his rapacious profile, as it does in all our mountaineer descendants of *hajduks* and *uskoks*. Though he loved much, he did not like a single woman, because at heart he remained somewhat of a Don Quixote, dreaming of the ideal woman like all men who are brought up on the ideals of chivalry.

An agreeable breeze wafted from the huge yard which was transformed into a garden. A canary was heard singing from a nearby window, and elsewhere a sweetly grieving strain from a Chopin ballade was audible. Tkalac followed the curling smoke of his cigarette, dreaming, with eyes open, like a savage. Suddenly he winced. On his bare, perspiring neck, he felt some drops. He wiped them off with his handkerchief, but, alas, rain again, and from a clear June sky. The young man turned his head, and above, from the upper window among the flower pots and blossoms, there blushed a beautiful woman who lacked words to excuse herself and was powerless to turn her eyes from his confused countenance.

"Along with your beautiful flowers, you are also watering nettle, madame," he finally said in his foreign French which, reminding them so much of a child's prattle, caused him to be well liked by the ladies.

"I am too far away to be hurt," she retorted, continuing to observe him with childish surprise.

"But there is also nettle without thorns."

"I am quite poor in botany, but I am willing to accept what you say."

"Please do not go, madame; it is so wonderful to look up to heaven and you in that blue sky surrounded by those beautiful flowers."

"You are a foreigner, I gather, from your accent and manner of speech."

"I am, to my sorrow. I am an army officer who has failed and, as you doubtless know, I teach fencing and boxing."

"Yes, I have read about you in the newspapers. You are on the path of glory."

"Miserable glory! But even that is better than stealing. What can one do? A man must work. Should my plans succeed, I shall go to Paris and, besides, teach horseback-riding. I am a passionate equestrian, and you cannot understand how I feel here without my horse. At the sight of a fine horse I become as sad as a Bedouin. We horsemen alone know that a horse and a horseman may become one; not a horse's soul in a human body—naturally!"

"You are a survival of extinct centaurs! And have you found an Amazon?"

Tkalac noticed how suddenly she paled and then blushed, and his eyes darkening, filled with a surprising moisture, which confused her. He wanted to reply with warmth and great affection, but among the flowers there remained only a short greeting and a suppressed and sirenlike giggle.

Thus they became acquainted.

In the evening, Tkalac did not wish to go to the city for dinner. He felt ashamed about something. The presence of a stranger embarrassed him. In the evening, in the dark room, lying on a leather sofa which served also as a bed, he felt utterly unhappy and alone. He thought of his dead mother who had spoiled him—her only child; even as a cadet he had had to go to her bed every morning before she arose. His memories turned to his father, a colonel, the real "bruder Jovo," red of face with a white mustache, hard as a provost's stick, wearing his civilian clothes as though they were on a hanger, and those red, dilapidated morning slippers. Even as an officer he dared not light a cigarette in the presence of his father without first asking for permission. He remembered, when taking his departure, the sudden burst of tears which flowed like molten iron, the burning of which he still felt on his cheeks.

"Be righteous, Pero, if you are not successful as a soldier. Even be a laborer, but remain honest like all your ancestors. Here is a revolver which may be of use to you, even for yourself, in case of any shame you may commit, to yourself or to me. It is better to die honorably than to live in disgrace."

And Tkalac found, in the disorder of his luggage, which was like that of a gipsy's, a photograph, and although it was quite dark, a lady, somewhat gray-haired, stepped out of the picture—she was still of a girlish build, pale, attractive, dark-eyed, with a permanent, sad smile—and this foreigner, after two years of dissipation, pressed this dear, lifeless relic to his lips, weeping like a child before going to sleep, great big tears; and consoled by the shadow of his dead mother, he fell asleep without so much as removing his clothes.

He was abruptly awakened by a tapping on the window. Knowing every emotion except fear, he was greatly surprised and though he was suffering from hallucinations. The tapping on the window was repeated, once, twice, three times. He rose, approached, and noticed a key dangling from a string which had been lowered from the floor above. Fastened on the key was a gingerbread heart bought at a fair. It was then near midnight. Silence reigned everywhere with the exception of the sound of a passing automobile on the street and the singing, accompanied by a mandolin, of some Italian laborers in the distance.

"We went to a fair on the French border, and remembering that you were alone, I brought you this present. This is not my home. I am a Frenchwoman who considers loneliness a misfortune and really believe that you are very unhappy alone there in the darkness of your gloomy, empty rooms."

"Thank you, thank you," he said, untying the gift, and still under the sway of the memories that had lulled him to sleep. His voice trembled with restrained sobs. Leaning back over the window sill and untying the string, he looked up at her, transformed in the soft and tepid light of the gentle full moon.

"Oh, how beautiful you are, my charming neighbor! If you could only realize what a gift you have made and what happiness you have brought to me by this cookie, you would, perhaps, have reconsidered your act, because, in holding this dry heart, I feel as though I had a part of your heart and your soul."

"Ah, speak quietly, lest the neighbors should hear."

"Do not fear! The people who live below are always traveling."

Tkalac then leaped up and with the hand of a gymnast, took hold of the ledge of the outer window, hanging with his back and his whole body over the deep, dark, and black yard as over an abyss.

"Ah, for God's sake! What are you doing, you maniac? Should this old rotted wood give, you would break your neck. I beg you, as a brother, a son, a god, I implore you, enter your room! Have mercy!"

Suddenly she began weeping and, his grasp loosening, he almost fell from the window. He felt a warm moisture upon his forehead, like a tear.

"Oh, my dear, my charming, kind neighbor, were I not afraid of grieving you, I would this instant dive into the abyss as into a pool of water, because something fell on my forehead like a dewdrop, from that beautiful, refreshing heaven of yours.

"Mercy, mercy! Have mercy on me and yourself, you madman," she proceeded to beg, hardly able, out of great fear and sympathy, to utter a sound. "I will allow you everything, everything, you understand, if you will enter your room and be sensible."

As the wood of the window creaked and broke, she uttered a suppressed screech, while he, with one great swing, fell into his room with a loud and cheerful laugh.

"Until now I hung heavily between you and darkness, between life and death, and now life and happiness look upon me from your moonlit window, my dear beautiful neighbor!"

As before, he lay on the window sill, looking at her, her shadow, interwoven in the moonlight, surrounded by warm and luminous stars, and she silently observed this new, unusual man. They conversed in silence, with their eyes, for a long time, until finally she said:

"I like you because you have not insisted upon my word and do not ask anything of me. Good night; it is necessary to save those minutes. Good night and thank you, my neighbor!"

"Ah, stay a little longer! Tell me, at least, what your name is."

"Valentina."

"Beautiful name! Once Upon a time, if I remember correctly, a beautiful princess was called thus."

"Yes, Valentina of Milan. And what is your name?"

"Peter, common Peter."

"Goodnight, dear Mr. Peter, and 'au revoir.' Soon my husband will come."

"Who?"

"My husband!"

"Eh! Good night!"

Husband! He had never thought of that. Suddenly a cold sweat appeared on his brow. He went out and roamed until dawn around the quiet moonlit lake, filled with the reflection of bright stars which resembled greenish sparkling fireflies.

He was just about to lie down, when a tap, tap, tap sounded on the windowpane. His charming neighbor appeared, just like the dawn, golden and blushing, roselike and white, in a lace morning gown, her lovely blue eyes still heavy with sleep. She held a little finger to her red, sinful lips, luscious and sanguine, as a sign of silence.

"I spent a restless night," he whispered, pale and weary.

"Do not fear. I understand you. Do not fear, Peter; I am true to you alone!"

And only the trembling of a flower from her breath remained, as Tkalac extended his hungry arms toward the quiet, blooming window, lit by the first rays of the sun, while from above was heard the unpleasant voice of a man, severely rolling his r's.

This was repeated daily for two weeks.

Valentina was very much surprised when Tkalac disappeared without leaving a trace. She became ill from worry and torment. One rainy evening her husband told her in a puzzling way that he was awaiting a very important guest and that they would remain alone. She thought it would be some tiresome business matter, some tedious signing of papers; and while at supper, she almost fainted on hearing Peter's steps on the upper floor. Notwithstanding all her questioning, her husband refused to explain this unexpected visit.

Like a thunderbolt from a clear sky, the servant announced that "Monsieur Kalak" sends his card and wishes to enter.

She did not recognize him at first; so emaciated had he become in the last few days. Her husband arose, changed the expression on his bloated, otherwise quite pleasing face adorned with spectacles and a blond moustache, wiped his bald head and wheezed harshly, like one suffering from asthma. The visitor bowed courteously and in military fashion, kissed with visible embarrassment the hand of his hostess, sat down, and, after a brief, unpleasant silence, addressed his host.

"I am very glad, Monsieur Colignon, that you received me so gallantly, and, as I see, you have not advised madame regarding my coming. If there still exists some knighthood these days, it consists in that honorable and sensible people eliminate every unpleasantness with as little trouble as possible."

"Very well, very well," broke in the host, breathing heavily. "I have thoroughly inquired and learned all about you today, and I know that your affairs are in good condition and that you have a glorious future before you, though, relatively, very difficult. As a man of affairs and business, I guess your intention and the cause for your presence. You have no acquaintance here nor any countrymen of yours; in your native country, you have no reason, I presume, to look for help. Therefore, as your neighbor, you wish to turn to me. offering no more security than your energy and your indubitable honesty. You have begged me for the presence of my wife to show me that in such a delicate matter you fear not even such a—pardon!—embarrassing witness. I have, sir, no children from heaven, and although a man of means, I sympathize with everything young and fit for life!"

"But pardon me."

"Allow me, allow me, my dear 'Kalak.' I am really not as wealthy as they say, but I will always have enough to help you in your eventual establishment. It is known to me that your institution prospers excellently, and I feel proud that you should, notwithstanding your great acquaintance with foreign, especially Slavic, aristocracy, turn to me, an ordinary citizen and business man."

You are absolutely wrong, my dear neighbor," the young man gasped with difficulty, and paled as though he were going to fall from his chair.

Deep, asthmatic breathing. The ticking of a clock mingled with the wild, loud throbbing of hearts. Valentina's eyes became glassy.

"From your words, dear neighbor, I see that you are better than I ever dreamed, and my mission, therefore, is so much more painful and distressing. If I had known this, I never would have determined to undertake this step," came Tkalac as from a tomb, and Colignon began to look around fearfully, thinking that he must be dealing with a dangerous, gorillalike lunatic.

"Well, what is it? What is it?" he breathed with great effort, while kicking his petrified wife underneath the table to convey his alarm. She did not feel his nudges, so paralyzed was her moral and physical strength.

"No, sir, I have not come for money, but I came for her, for your wife, for Valentina, for my dear—"

"Are you sane?" sighed the host, rushing toward the window as if wanting to cry "Fire." Tkalac almost brought him back to his chair with his burning, feverish gaze.

"Yes, sir, you have spoken correctly. I am an honest man, so honest that I am unable to lie, and I would kill and I would die before stealing another man's wife, robbing the love that belongs to another, especially of such a sympathetic man as you. I love your wife, your wife loves me, and I came tonight to tell you this honestly and openly, and to take her with me," continued Tkalac, placing a revolver on the table. "Here, sir, do not fear! I am no lunatic, I am not a criminal, and you may, if you find no other exit, take this gun and shoot me, like an ordinary vagabond and burglar."

And again there was a painful, grievous, fatal silence; difficult, asthmatic breathing, then the ticking of watches as of hearts, and the beating of hearts as of watches.

"Why, what do I hear? Is all this possible; tell me, tell me, Valentina? Why, it is not, it cannot be true; say it isn't, Valentina, my dear little Valentina," sobbed the husband.

"Peter Tkalac, peer of Zvečaj castle, is poor, no longer has a uniform, but he remains an officer and never tells lies!" The young man, with his chest expanded, spoke energetically, as if commanding his troops. Valentina's glassy eyes revived; slowly, as if awakening, she arose and stepped toward Peter and said, looking at him from head to foot:

"Whether you are an Austrian, Hungarian, Slovak, or whatnot, you should know that I am a Frenchwoman, and that in France it is not customary for lovers to denounce their sweethearts to their husbands. Monsieur Colignon, I have in fact liked his type, although I have not given myself to him; but from now on I hate him deeply and let that foreigner consider himself slapped. Good-bye, sir"—and she swept from the room.

"Noble sir, Monsieur 'Kalak,' do you need any help? I am at your service," said Colignon to the young man, who staggered out of the room as though he were drunk and feeling like a whipped cur.

The servant ran after him into the hallway.

"Pardon, sir, you have forgotten your revolver!"

Ivan Mladineo

Vladimir Nazor

(1876–1949)

In the course of half a century of literary activity, Vladimir Nazor played an important role in introducing sound poetry into Croatian literature, and bringing together the Yugoslav peoples through his modern conception of nationalism.

He was born in Postira, on the island of Brač. Nazor graduated from high school in Split and received his university degree from Gratz. After graduation he was a high school teacher in different parts of Yugoslavia.

Nazor started his literary activity in the nineties of the last century. Fed up with the literary values of the time, he joined a group of other dissatisfied poets who left the traditional realistic schools and turned toward Slavic mythology and folk poetry.

Nazor's mature work includes a number of works of beauty and optimism: *Slavenske legende* (Slavic Legends, 1900); *Lirika* (Lyrics, 1910); *Nove pesme* (New Poems, 1913); *Hrvatski kraljevi* (Croatian Kings, 1912); *Medvjed Brundo* (The Bear Brundo, 1915); *Knjige pjesama* (The Books of Poetry, 1942) and others.

THE BAY

When the last ray of sunlight shivers—as a spear
    Stabs to the lifeblood, by some furious giant cast,—
    Over the water's face a secret sigh has passed,
And the wave's wail at eve sounds muffled to our ear.

Amidst the vale, the quiet Night has made her seat
    Just where the rocks arise—and now has loosed her hair.
    She scatters myriad stars on groves of seaweed there
Which from those deeps unseen are surging to her feet.

> Behold how, all unveiled and glittering, rocks the bay,
>> While from her boulder watches Night, alone and dumb.
>> From somewhere far amongst the gullies, murmurs come
> Of water, whose lamenting softly dies away.

Oliver Elton

MY DESTINED ONE

> Deep in my heart's most secret, holiest shrine,
>> And where my veins flow purest,—yes, and where,
>> Veiled in their light, abide all dreams of mine,
> And in my being's essence, still I bear

> Thee with me, sweetest secret of my heart,
>> Through all my changes, guises manifold,
>> Pure image, dream of fable that thou art,
> Mine from unknown, forgotten days of old!

> Thou, whom it never was my lot to see,
>> I know thee, none the less! . . . And shall I meet
>> Thee by some green hedge, ere my youth be past,
>> Or, bowed and ancient, on some dusty street,
>> And light on thee, thou miracle, at last?
> Ah when, in what existence, may that be?

Oliver Elton

Antun Branko Šimić

(1898–1925)

Šimić was born in Drinovci, Herzegovina, was an exceptionally gifted poet of great sensibility and subjectivity. He appeared in Croatian literature at the end of the First World War. His expressionistic collection of poetry *Preobraženja* (Transfiguration), indicated the heavy influence of his Catholic education and his pessimistic nature. In it he expressed the drama of his chaotic and wounded life with new, modern lyrics, in a free style, deliberately ignoring the established forms.

Later, Šimić freed himself from expressionistic influence, embracing more realistic poetry, free of religion. This antireligious feeling was particularly noticeable in his poem, "Zemlja" (Earth).

EARTH

For many a century good folks believed in heaven.
A place of brief sojourn was earth to them
to be exchanged for life eternal yonder.

For many a century folks went into heaven—
migrating millions' flight beyond the stars.
Their souls like birds kept soaring from the globe
into eternity.

Yet creeds too die, each in its turn,
and we have learned there is no heaven,
no upward soaring flight, no resurrection.
Earth is our home for all eternity.

On earth we are to stay for ever.
We, animals and plants are all one family,
the stone is but our distant brother.
Death makes us all alike.

J. Lavrin

THE SLEEPWALKER

The god of night
the moon
descends from heaven
and softly walks towards the house.

He climbs upon my window
and rests his eye on me
entices me into the night
I rise . . . and my white face . . . is smiling.

In sleep I step along the edges of the roof
and through the night I walk on high
The arms of the moon hold me aloft—

Light . . . unearthly . . . soaring
on a tree-leaf I could stand

But do not call: a voice from earth below
would kill my heavenly state
High above the earth I soar through the spheres.

J. Lavrin

Miroslav Krleža

(1893–   )

In contemporary Croatian literature, Miroslav Krleža can be considered the best writer. He was born in Zagreb where he attended high school, and then went to the Military Academy in Budapest in 1912.

As a young idealist, he at one point volunteered to serve in the Serbian army during the Balkan wars, placing high hopes in Serbia for the future of the Southern Slavs. But, the Serbian authorities did not understand young Krleža and after jailing him and suspecting him of being an Austrian spy, he was returned to the Austrians, who in turn suspected him of being a Serbian spy. As a result of this, during the First World War, he served as a simple soldier. Between the two world wars he was opposed to King Alexander's dictatorship. When Fascists occupied Croatia in 1941 he stayed in hiding. In postwar Yugoslavia he became vice-president of the Yugoslav Academy of Arts and Sciences, and Editor in Chief of the Yugoslav Encyclopedia.

Krleža has published more than fifty volumes of poetry and prose. His trilogy, *Gospoda Glembajevi* (The Glembays, 1929); *U Agoniji* (In Agony, 1928), and *Leda* (Leda, 1930), is representative of the very best in modern Yugoslav drama. In his stories *Hrvatski Bog Mars* (The Croatian God Mars, 1922), Krleža describes the tragic destiny of a Croatian soldier who fought for the interests of Austria; and in his *Povratak Filipa Latinovicza* (The Return of Philip Latinovicz, 1932), a prodigal son return to his native Croatia after twenty-two years.

We present a short story of Krleža's choice, "The Cricket Under the Waterfall."

THE CRICKET UNDER THE
WATERFALL

Lately I've been living with the dead and for entire nights I talk to them and that is my secret, that conversations with the dead are infinitely more lively to me than all my relationships with the people surrounding me who are supposedly alive, and the doctor curing me, who because of professional interest anxiously worries about my nerves, maintains that this is just a case of "shattered nerves," and that all this has no "deep and important significance." It is some kind of exhaustion which will disappear with time.

I don't eat, don't sleep, I ache all over, I am fretting away, and I really feel tired, and even without expert medical advice it's clear to me that in my case it's a question of "shattered nerves," only I can't understand how "my exhaustion will disappear" when instead it keeps growing, when insomnia and headaches multiply, and everything is becoming more dismal and it's becoming increasingly clear that there's no way out. I live in doctors' anterooms and waiting rooms and here in these gloomy, unpleasant, stale rooms I leaf through pamphlets from travel and tourist agencies and skim old, shabby, torn journals in which for the most part there is nothing particularly interesting: boring and untalented poems, quarrels about literature, "should literature be tendentious or not," and I, shabby as I have been lately, quite exhausted by my own treatment, a helpless tramp, really, with torn pockets, in what relation do I stand toward those aimless literary quarrels and how does it affect me whether "literature be tendentious or not?" I am called and most hospitably invited by those tourist pamphlets from travel agencies to spend Easter in Florence or Christmas in Egypt, and it's not heated here in the anteroom; one can hear a little pot behind the wall in a certain water closet,[1] like a waterfall resounding in the distance, the smell of galoshes and melted snow, in journals they write about tendentiousness in artistic creation, and the table is piled up with advertisements for medicine and over 20,000 medicines are recommended to patients for their pleasure and for their complete recovery. Really, to celebrate Christmas in Aswan is not to be despised, nor would Easter be bad in Florence, especially if it is not rainy, but 20,000 medicines in cellophane, in tinfoil, 20,000 medicines served just like prewar Gerbaud bonbons, Egyptian moonlight, Florentine Easter, boats, women, cheerfulness, wafers, tablets, thin silver pipes, all this means freedom from despair, health in a word, recovery, that magic, unearthly recovery for all us wretched persons who eavesdrop on the noise of a water closet pot in the distance, wrinkled, gray, tired, in the

---

[1] "W.C." in Serbo-Croatian is a borrowing from the English "water closet," and so this translation seemed more appropriate if less "American" than *toilet*.

ashy light of a dismal anteroom, where it looks like hell: mouldy, wet rags of rotten newspapers, wet umbrellas, and one old woman who sighs, massaging her lips with the index finger and thumb of her left hand from corner to corner, mashing her mucous like an old plumb, the skin of her lips swollen between her bony fingers resembles a crack in flesh which opened like a poisoned, rotten, terrible wound.

The mysterious wallpapered door of the doctor's office opened; in it appeared a man in a white doctor's gown, a nearsighted man, magical (the main character in this enchanted theater, illuminated by a strong, pale shaft of light), the doctor personally appeared in the doorway and with a cold, barely perceptible wet touch of his palm on my cheeks, he actually transported me somewhere far away, to another shore, to that other side of the wallpapered door, into his room, with all my nerves entangled, with my aching teeth and bowels, with my murky prelife, with all that aching chaos in me (which is only data for diagnosis to a doctor). He really floated with me from the waiting room into his office, and once again I found myself in front of him here, and without any idea how I got up and how we shook hands, I only remember that I really felt weightless as if I were floating, and now I am here in front of him, put into his hands like a body, like a subject for diagnosis, like an object in strange hands.

"Well, my friend, have there been any new moments since our last meeting?"

"No particularly new moments, doctor, really, I tell you there were none, but my dead still keep on appearing to me, with the same clarity and the same intensity. I spoke with one of them in the moonlight last night; there was wonderful summer moonlight, and he was eating cherries and talking to me about the Immaculate Conception of the blessed Virgin as if he were talking about a religious secret which remained clear to him up to the very last moment and in which there was never any doubt, not for a single instant. I could not quote his words to you verbatim, but I remember certain details! His front left incisor tooth had turned so gray that it seemed to be made of lead, and the fact that his tooth was gray and his hands were covered with cold sweat and that the cherries which he ate were wrapped in newspaper (still wet from the dew of a summer night in June), those are approximately the things which stayed in my memory. More yet, the color of his voice, a bit consumptive, a bitten-off sound, turbid, shabby,

lips turning black from the large black cherries and words about the
blessed Virgin, to whom he had been engaged from childhood, and he
wore light blue congregational lace around his neck even on those
days long ago when we went fishing in dirty water and played under
the old walnut tree as children.

"Perhaps you once stole something from your late childhood friend?
It is quite unimportant what, perhaps some insignificant trifle? An
eraser or pen?"

"I steal from him? No! As far as I remember, I never stole anything
from him. On the contrary he stole a watercolor of mine! I painted
the moon just as it comes out in the evening: in gray ashy mists over
ploughed fields an orangish dark yellow moon slab is born, and on the
left in the foreground stands a pine tree, and he stole that watercolor
from me, took it home and nailed it to the wall next to the "Timetable,"
as if it were "his work" and he even boasted in front of his father
that this watercolor was "his work," and I never betrayed him, and you
are the first person I've confessed this secret to. His father was a shoemaker, with a light greenish shoemaker's apron, had a moustache
thick and silky, and with a glittering sharp shoemaker's knife his hand
noiselessly would slide along the smelly and smooth goatskin, quite
inaudibly and with unusual vigor. His father was a specialist in orthopedic shoes, and in the glass storewindow of their shop several plaster
feet were displayed, deformed, disfigured, tinged a light rose, with
bloody swellings and sores, and those sores, disgusting, disfigured
plaster orthopedic models, that quiet movement of his father's hand
with a bare knife along the surface of the goatskin, that moonlight
and that consumptive voice, these are all that is left of him for me, and
all that is slowly dying and is out turning gray and finally will be all
gray. Everything will turn gray. And then he laughed loudly in the
moonlight and he ate cherries and in the front door through which
one entered their place, over the entrance archway were two little
plaster angels and an oval surface resembling a blind plaster mirror,
ornamented with pears, grapes, and melons and all the other usual
decorative symbols of fertility and plenty which were strewn over the
entrance vault of that huge portal, where the muffled stamping of
hooves was forever resounding because in the courtyard of that house
stood a cab. And so, doctor, you see the way things stand with me
today: today my life looks to me like a glimpse into a room of which

the door is slowly closing, quietly, inaudibly; that crack of the half-opened door is becoming narrower and narrower and everything is less visible and everything is less audible from that other side where there was a lot of laughter and movement and voices, and now the door is closing in a persistently merciless way, and today in that twilight I was devoured in anxiety, overhearing the voices of dead people who believed in the Immaculate Conception of the Virgin, and today they are no longer among the living, and, nevertheless, I hear them because their voices still endure inside of me forever, but there is one thing which is not at all clear to me, and I beg you to explain it to me! Why have I started with this huge pile of dead people within me, doctor? Many of them died in a lunatic asylum, and almost all wrote poems and boozed in bars. They walked along dirty, like scarecrows in wrinkled clothing, with shabby heels and greasy ribbons on their hats, and among them there were even certain free thinkers who confessed and took communion before their deaths. One of them had a forehead barely a thumb high, thick hair, stiff, bristly, curly like a faun, that is, a man who, while talking with him, one had the idea that from that thick, dark, opaque, bristly mass protruded two horns, so that this head acted stubbornly. But he was an impotent, trembling weakling who kept proving to me how filthy life is, like all its events, so that only with gloves should one handle all life's phenomena: aristocratically! And really! That gray, hungry tramp in thorn shoes and in a stinking shirt with a collar as gray as the collars of travellers on morning trains after sleepless nights, that bareheaded, dreamy fellow, shattered, wore gray woolen gloves, and on his left wrist a silver bracelet with a scarab poured out from hollow tin, that is, this bug on his bracelet looked bulging and swollen, greenish, like a small tree frog with wide-open glass eyes. When they were burying him, it grew cloudy in the rain, and frogs (in fact) croaked in the young juicy grass, and I myself had the impression it was the croaking of the frog from his bracelet. Someone spoke over that fresh grave, someone actually read a funeral oration, and all that was quite ridiculous, as usually happens in such cases: the tombstone speaker has a top hat, good digestion, the chance of a pension, and it is most likely that he is not unusually intelligent because otherwise how could he speak over an open grave? One of them played the flute. . . .

"Excuse me, please, forgive me if I'm interrupting you! I don't understand. Who is that 'one of them' who played the flute?"

"Well, one of my dead people, doctor, the dead people whom I was speaking about at the beginning! He played the flute, but was extremely stupid and in his house they had "linzer"—small cakes tasting like pig's fat, which reeked disgustingly of beastly urine. The raspberry juice in that house was insipid, and the peacock feathers stuck in vases were undoubtedly an omen of gloomy unhappiness: the tenant of that room was killed in the corn stalks, and the man who found him where he lay in the mud told me how it happened: it was a warm Indian summer, a quiet sunny afternoon, almost silent, and a single shot echoed across the forest expanses and for a long, long time soared like an echo over the whole region, as if it were slowly floating under a small parachute."

"That means: he was shot in the war?"

"That means: he was shot, but how and where, that is really quite unimportant to me!"

"I understand, For you those peacock feathers are much more important than his death!"

"No, doctor! On the contrary: for me his death is much more important than peacock feathers, and I will explain that to you immediately, if you have nothing against it. That dead man of mine, the player on the flute who was shot, was married to one Zosia D., a very blond woman, who had the coloring of a weak-blooded newborn babe, and who, nevertheless, is just as dead today as her spouse, whom they killed among the corn stalks like a rabbit. Zosia D. is dead, and she was photographed with her spouse coming out of church in her wedding gown; he was pale, and on the knees of his good black pants (which he paid to have made like a reserve officer's exclusively for that occasion) two gray circles remained from kneeling before the altar. In church we all stood with bowed heads with the presentiment that a war wedding, contracted so to speak in one night, in a hurry, like some kind of warlike improvisation, in a Lvov hotel, could not be happy; and nonetheless, if it had been happy, still according to our pessimistic expectation, it did not last long because they killed him, which is natural, if taken correctly, because in war soldiers don't pay any particular attention to bridegrooms! I sat with Zosia D. and with that now deceased flutist in a cafe on the eve of their wedding trip to death. I didn't know Polish, and Zosia D. didn't have a notion of any other language, and I sat with them myself like some kind of best man, confused, absent-minded, convinced that this was a question of a very dangerous and truly fatal game. Nor did the deceased groom know a single word of her mother tongue, but the two of them, stammering, trying to come to some understanding with gestures and motions, in that quite deaf and dumb sadness, were happy. I sat with them in the cafe in which I have been sitting for years with different sufferers, passers-by, bridegrooms, adventurers, with people who grieve over their oppressive state of affairs, and then curse their fate, preparing themselves for a distant journey, and all those who have died with whom I have sat down at that same cafe table (where we celebrated Zosia's wedding with two "ham and eggs[2]") will appear in your office unexpectedly, your office would be filled up with dead people, your whole apartment, your whole repulsive little building, this whole section of the city would swarm with processions of the dead, on all sides endless columns of the dead would march by, everything would hum with their voices, everything would be upset by their numbers, they would carry us away with them, they would raise us like a flood, they march, they pass, they drum all around us, doctor, listen, they are clinking their weapons, they are playing, doctor!

Enough. That moment from the street along with the quiet vibration of transparent glass, the thundering drumming of a single troop was heard which passed rigid, stiff, under helmets, in a parade with flags and, doctor, looked at me compassionately and kindly with its well-intentioned glance from under glasses, after I noticed with a lofty grin that these were not dead people but soldiers!

"Yes, doctor, these are soldiers, that I know! These are soldiers who are returning like an honored squad from a funeral procession. For the time being only one among them has died, doctor!"

"You are not an unintelligent person and you will understand that one dies in life, and that this is actually quite a natural phenomenon. Life is a kind of pendulum which swings between two pendulums: one is called life, the other death."

"Yes. But one of them had angina pectoris and was eating a red

---

[2]This phrase appears in English in the Croatian original.

orange and while deeply breathing, spoke about how difficult it was to breathe because he had angina pectoris, and this is approximately the same thing you wish to explain to me with your pendulum. We die because that is the law of nature. And how is it that this night music was playing all around me and there was singing accompanied by a guitar, when one of my neighbors had been poisoned in the last room down the corridor? Never, neither before nor after, did anyone sing all around me in my room (because my life by itself is so gray and so meaningless that it never occured to anyone to sing to me), but that night my guests sang, and one girl struck the guitar, when out of the room near us an uproar was heard, and when we reached it everything had already been done: a yellow quilt, the trembling gleam of a candle, the lower jaw duly bound and smeared with salve, and crying in the semidark room. One of them was a pimply, monstrously ugly drunkard, odd, quite gloomy, and it was not known how the young man had died. And the other again was old, old like a shrieking jay, and when I recall him, I don't know why a picture of a quiet summer's noon in a meadow always appears to me in glassy clearness, and from the distant vineyard you hear the warbling of birds and the songs of crickets from above, and unmown grass. I was never with that deceased fellow in a sunny meadow, and in his apartment stood jars of compote on top of a wardrobe and it smelled of cats, and so to me he meant uncomfortable minutes in an old mouldy lair, and along with his remembrance, a joyful, summer, serene sunny flood of voices resounds in me, clouds, and the warble of birds. I have parted with many of them standing in mud, and we were all gray, somber, dark in terror in front of the cannons, muddy and embittered, and as they pushed off into the mud, one felt they were leaving with difficulty and with an evil premonition, as if they were moving off beyond return. I spent nights and nights with many of them at a tablecloth filthy with ashes and spilled wine, in smoky, moist groundfloor rooms, where stuffed birds hovered on pedestals along the walls, and in goldframed pictures a Negro tells a white lady about his adventures, and so in such a city, where gondolas sail under balconies (at least according to a story in Venice), well, if everything were added up, we were howling out in the wine and the smoke —and in the disturbance of uneasy digestion there would be clouds of thoughts and ideas and of dreams which evaporate from us like sweat, and they are really nothing but steam and the breath from drunken heads. And this is what is really the matter with me, doctor! I'm tired, I'm quite fed up with the war, little by little I've been getting drunk, and it's boring for me to keep writing in offices for a poor salary, and besides that, one thought of mine keeps gnawing at me: that in spite of everything one finally dies, and that occurs even before one's final death. So many have died before us, and all their rooms, all the birthdays of their children with tortes and new toys, all their books and words and vibrating candles on the ceilings of their apartments and the ringing of the bells on their doors, all of this keeps on moving inside of me and is alive in me, and just as my voices and my movements died with them in their minds, so they still live in my pictures, and it would be difficult to determine what is here in me of theirs, and what was mine inside of them, because all this is eternally interwoven in a most vivid fashion, and because all that surges and moves, because all that still flows in by bloodstream and beats in my heart, when that frog's gland flows out one day, all their shadows will finally turn gray inside of me, will grow dark and evaporate like the repulsive smell of a closed trunk But while I am still breathing and still moving, I'm irresistibly bound to them, and in that enormous procession in which I even once happened to be a passerby, the innumerable faces of those numberless deceased actually outrun me. They started on a journey according to another timetable, like that small, dear, pale, fatally wounded standard bearer who slept on top of me in the Red Cross wagon on the road between Galicia and Vienna on the sixteenth of October, that fellow who startled me out of a deep sleep to give him a glass goose, and, still drowsy and confused, barely able to last, I got up to give him that glass goose, and he filled it up to the throat with something flowing and as transparent as distilled water, and leaning his head suddenly at that very moment he mechanically fell asleep, and only by the monotonous and deathlike swing of his childlike hand which accompanied the movement of the wagon in a monotonous tempo could one observe that he had fallen asleep forever, and that he would no longer awaken from that sleep. He died with pictures of my childhood which I had related to him just several minutes before his death, not surmising that I was confessing to a person who was dying, and the death of that unknown youth was really just like the death of my childhood, because I doubt that all those pictures of my own childhood will ever live through the intense life which they lived through that night when I kept vigil by the dying of an unknown child, confessing as if I had the presentiment that my voice was penetrating through the shell of that dying ear up to those spaces which are not more enigmatic than our most everyday reality, but which are just as unknown to us as reality itself. Many of them disappeared before we had explained ourselves to each other, and certain strange upspoken words kept continuously separating us, words which often (for nights) seemed to us like questions without answers and were quite as dismal as treelined avenues when it is cloudy and quite dark and a train is heard in the distance. We think about many with hatred even years afterwards, as we do about Latin hypothetical sentences in written school work which are composed and assigned in such a perfidiously nasty way that we are not able to figure them out at all, and when one of our acquaintances parts company with us and we learn that he moved away, we cold-bloodedly abandon him from the list of the living, just as we abandon calendar pages, in helpless devotion bowing our head before the inevitable. There are fresh dead in our consciousnesses, just as fresh impressions of early morning newspaper surprises, and there are faces faded, gray like old unpaid debts, which we don't remember having paid or not. I ate jelly doughnuts with one of them, it was Carnival night, we drank brandy, it was wartime, and a hot wind blew and disappeared and today I vaguely remember only that one detail, that he had angina, that he was sick, and that over his headboard stretched a wet sheet so he would not get pneumonia, but he was already dead. The room was on the ground floor, you could hear the steps of passers-by from the street, and I thought to him the best food of all was baked turkey and pate stuffing and how much he liked Hajdin cornmush with sour cream.

"Good, my friend, all those details are interesting and quite edifying, but until today in our conversations I've never succeeded in establishing exactly when that interesting idea of yours actually appeared to you for the first time, that the dead live with you, and also that their life is really more important for us than our own?"

"That was in Paris, more than some three years ago, some time at the beginning of autumn. If you're interested, doctor, I can tell you about it, because I remember every detail well, indeed even those which at first glance seem the most insignificant."

"Autumn in Paris is gentle and quiet, and those autumns all smell of bloody venison in a distant damp forest. Along the ancient narrow streets in the shadow of the Saint-Germain Tower appeared an unusual multitude of peeled rabbits and dead pheasants which, by the sick color of their transparent pastel mother-of-pearl eyelids which had turned blue reminded one so unpleasantly of the grayish color of preservatives. In the mass of dark violet peeled rabbit sinews and bloody necks, those funny rabbit faces stood out like the good-natured physiognomies of those a bit stupid, adorned with fur collars, *bon-vivante* forms (whom monocles and the posthumous honors of a respected civil official would suit amazingly well), amidst that bloody slaughter which was evaporating on the sooty streets like a symbol of early city autumn, about which the neurasthenic passer-by could ponder, if not about the futile sterility of rabbit life, then about how man is indeed a strange beast who, believing in cut rabbits and in the honor of holy Catherine of Sienna, sells wagonloads of chyrsan-themums; All Saints Day is approaching, already crepes are baking in authentic French houses, cold rain arrives, in the morning the crackling and continual sighing of iron steam pipes began, resounding in the walls of a hotel room, and last night over the Seine a dog's howl rang out which was so sad, so deeply melancholy, as if life could not have any deeper, hidden meaning than those bloody markets of dead birds and shot rabbits. Amidst the gray mass of bloody roe bucks and pheasant eyes, from the other side of the street, I felt some-one's glance so piercing and so intense that it seemed as if scenes from distant murky pictures were contained in the circle of that my-sterious glance; there across, on the other side of the sidewalk in front of the cafe under the orange blue stretched linen cafe awning, in a straw armchair, sat a gentleman and lady: he was sipping on a short straw, and the lady was looking towards me with great interest.

"Fog. Distance. Autumn in one of those greasy, narrow, filthy streets on the Left Bank, which is always dark gray, like the tar-smeared pavement of street pissoirs, somewhere an accordian accompanying a woman's voice was heard: *"Parlez moi d'amour"* and the sound of horseshoes on granite. A pause.

"Where did I meet that man? Ten, twenty years ago, twenty bloody years, twenty miserably bloody and desperate years, wars, shipwrecks, rebellions, whole processions of dead, one immense mob of living and deceased acquaintances, and here someone's eye appears in that mass of bloody rabbit heads and touches me with its magnetic gleam, and perhaps all this is only nerves and neurasthenic phantoms? A foreigner with his female visited the room in which Wilde died, or Delacroix's garret, they rest themselves, drink an aperitif like so many thousands of foreigners, the play of illusion, the completely chance touch of a glance, one vibration of an illusion, nothing!

"In the storewindow in front of which that event stopped me stood a huge aquarium. Striped brown flat fish noiselessly moved and circled around in the dark green mass of water disturbed by the spraying and the noisy grapes of oxygen, and in front of the storewindow of the fish shop, like a small illuminated stage, was the space of a lady secondhand dealer: the reflection of the dark yellow silky lamp poured out along the surface of the golden-streaked woven fabric: a boar hunt in the twilight copper partial glimmer of a forest waterfall, with the dim green expanse of a forest glade, clouds, twilight, bloody rabbits, huge flat fish in emerald green water, the sob of the accordian, and from above all this the gleam of an unknown glance, like a sign of light in the darkness, which began to shine and having shone, dies out. A pause. Having discreetly turned away from the fish storewindow, shyly, imperceptively, so I would not catch anyone's eye, I again threw a glance at the cafe terrace under the orange blue sail, where that foreigner and his lady sat motionless, watching my appearance in front of the restless fish which deaf mutely kept moving about under the frothy jets of air in the aquarium just like under glittering glass treetops of a swampy treelined avenue, between moss and shells. The stranger kept cold-bloodedly sipping on his little straw, bearded, paritally gray, elegant, in an armchair of red straw, and his lady, light-blond, young, unaffected in the English manner, with cigarette in mouth, particularly interested by my appearance, warned undoubtedly by her companion about my insignificance, looked motionlessly over to the other side of the street where there was an alley choked up with whole baskets of oysters artichokes, and snails.

"Where could I have met that person and when? Several thousand persons have I met in my wanderings, and in that endless series of forgotten eyes what does one unknown glance mean? Perhaps it was the steward on a ship of one of the South American lines, when that madman threw himself among the alligators, only making the water bleed under the paddle of the steamship which peacefully sailed on as if nothing had happened. Perhaps it is that Italian marksman with a machine gun of point 312 at Gorica, who was peacefully sipping hot black coffee from his thermos when we fell into an ambush. It's useless, otherwise, to stop on the street just because of the unexpected appearance of some unknown glance which means nothing more than the glance of those dark metal flat fish under the waterfall which all in the foam of oxygen swallow their own sick intestines, stirring in mouths like a rotten moustache, and the fish think they're warm. Bewildered and uneasy I stopped still again in front of the secondhand lady's storewindow, absent-minded, mechanically looking every which way amidst the silver baroque candlesticks at a red mahogany framed series of colored lithographs published in the honor and glory of the French king's visit to the English queen, showing Her Majesty of Great Britain Victoria, while on marble stairs under a purple canopy His Imperial Emperor Napoleon the Third waits, and having been startled, I started out and hurriedly wound my way down the street when that stranger got up and started after me. I observed only that his gait was extremely supple, that his pants were nicely pressed, that his whole way of moving was energetic, muscular, vigorous, as old swordsmen move, then, after throwing one more uneasy and helpless glance toward that blond woman under the cafe umbrella on the other side of the sidewalk, I felt the juicy lips of that man on my warm lips. Cramped by that slim and virile appearance, really proud of his light and lofty laugh, at that moment I recognized that it was the Pole Christian K. whom we called Gattamelat, the first conscious star among us, *"embevido de las estrellas"* "drunk from the stars," like a Spaniard declaiming himself the ecstatic descendant of Colombus, that fireworks of our Sorbonne days, that flaming anxiety amidst our anxieties, a premature world anarchist and individualist among us confused lads, Christian, my friend, whom I had not seen for twenty years, witness to my one duel in the Vincennes forest, my favorite postillion, my good old friend, with whom so many times I shared a box of sardines in my garret on Bonaparte Street just off Rue Jacob several meters from that place! My God, it was really him, Christian, the man from those gloomy Eastern distances, where different strange peoples are interwoven: Slavs, Gipsies, Hussars, Mongols, Bohemians, my good friend from Poland, where things are always exploding and rebelling as they do in Ireland, who secretly plotted among various Russian and Mongol closed circles (and I remember: once he hid several kilograms of explosives at my place in a woman's hatbox, and he strewed moss over all that and on the top of the box he put a live turtle, then the whole night in fear I overheard the turtle crawling on the box, positive that we'd all fly into the air, both the turtle and Jacob Street and the old tower on the corner of Bonaparte Street), my dear old C. who "momentarily" never had a minute of free time, who was always interweaving among at least three women, who not even at that moment, after twenty years, had "a moment" of time either, because he was "momentarily" prevented by some unpleasant thing, but he was so happy to see me, he was so joyful that he had met me, it would be unusually nice for him if I would pay attention to him and devote several minutes to him at the soiree of the Polish Embassy...

"I suggested that we get together after the soiree, if he was obliged to go to that soiree according to some agreement, but he stubbornly stuck to his proposal.

"He didn't know whether that would be technically possible to do, that in spite of all his noblest intentions he could not free himself from his arrangements made within the framework of that boring evening soiree, but it had been inexpressibly wonderful for him that we had met, that this meeting was above all a valuable and marvelous surprise for him (that is to say, he had heard about me, that I had been killed), he was sure that I was dead, and when here just a little before, when he saw me there in front of those fish, he thought he was dreaming and wasn't able to recognize me; unfortunately time had flowed by imperceptibly, our teeth had already fallen out, and our beards had turned gray, the first undoubted shadow of death had appeared, but nevermind, we are young yet, we still walk erect! Do I remember his words, when in the moonlight at the foot of the Belfort Lion he made a bet with me for a bottle of champagne, that for Europe, that whore, a death sentence had been signed. That was in the twilight of the European crash, and I left him the bottle of champagne I owed him (because from birth I have been naive and have absolutely no particular sense of reality), and now this evening also I would have the honor to pay! Oh, those wonderful moonlit nights at the Montparnasse grave when we played the guitar, and in Passy when we stole a whole basket of hot madeleines[3] from that fat, asthmatic, stingy baker, which today (unfortunately) are apparently no longer baked! And do I remember how we got drenched the whole night under the chestnuts of Aragon Boulevard in order to see the guillotine and death of some criminal type, and we saw nothing, only drums rumbled! So in a word: he "momentarily" had no time, he was occupied with some kind of "second rate absurdities," but he surely had undeniably considered that he would not be refused these trifles, that this evening we would still see each other one more time, indeed, however, only for a few minutes, because that would not be difficult for me if I were free, and he hoped that nevertheless, in spite of everything, he would be able to pull out if things took such a turn, then, if there would be no possibility of us conversing together this evening, we would at least make an arrangement for our following meeting to spend a whole day riding in Chantilly where we shot a fat old greasy Bonaparte carp in the lake with a revolver, either St.-Germaine or Chantilly, it was all the same to him, not one nook was there in those forests where there weren't innumerable memories of our childhood; but if I'm not officially bound, he would be leaving in three or four days for London to buy some submarines, I could go with him, he invited me as a guest, he is the head of one of the trade missions here, it is important that we confer this evening, and eventually the possibility was not eliminated that in spite of everything he would be free.

"In that torrent of words and pictures and smoke and ectasy (real), joy and a handshake, he dragged out one of his visiting cards from his wallet (at any rate, because of the idiotic diplomatic service, he can be excused) and wrote several words on this visiting card, waving the calling card around in the air still wet from the ink, all in a joyful movement, in a laugh, in heartfelt sincerity, he filled me up like thunder, dominated me, and just at that moment before I had a chance to ask him one logical question, what I would actually do at that soiree, he had already returned to that strange light-blond lady under the cafe awning and disappeared with her and her Chinese spitz in a cloud of benzine smoke from his huge Spanish-Suez car in the chaos of the city street.

"Fish, flat, repulsive, odd fish circled around in the light green box

---

[3]French sponge cake.

of the storewindow of the fish store in the light aquarium among those bloody rabbits and dead birds, and I, still bewildered, kept gaping at that queer visiting card which this evening should have opened the door of the embassy on Yokohamska Avenue.

"Well, good, did you go to that soiree in the embassy on Yokohamska Avenue?"

"Of course I went, doctor!"

"And did you meet your friend there? Did you identify yourself with this visiting card?"

"I didn't find him there because he didn't appear. They told me that Colonel Christian Kavaljerski fell at Warsaw on July 20th, and it seemed odd to them that someone was looking for him in the Paris embassy thirteen years after his legendary and heroic death, celebrated in all Polish elementary-school readers."

"And what happened with his visiting card? Was it really some kind of summons, just as they told you when you wanted to enter with the visiting card of a dead person?"

"I never showed anyone at all, under the hypothesis that no one would believe a word and would shut me up like a madman!"

"More like a naive person who fell for a bad joke! And where is that calling card of that colonel?"

I don't have it with me, doctor, but I can bring it to you whenever you want."

At that moment our glances met, and I maintain that the doctor didn't believe a single word, that all this was like an old routine, quite boring, that he viewed me as a harmless fool whom it would be best to humor in a harmless way, and in that same moment it became clear to me how naive it is when a person looks for warm understanding from this gentleman in a white doctor's gown regarding that mad game of falsehood and phantom and shadow in our brains, and so we were both relieved when we passed on to the real part of our conversation: how things stood with digestive disturbances since we last met, whether my feces were still always hard, irritability, anxiety, insomnia, apathy, a surprising beating of the heart, pain in the head, pain in the feet, constant indisposition, staleness in the mouth, fatigue from smoking, lack of appetite in general, etc., etc.—and so he wrote out a new prescription and bill for 75 dinars for that day's visit and in the nicest way said good-bye to me at the wallpapered door: "See you soon, I swear, my fine man, good-bye!"

Outside on the street rain was pouring in torrents. To move in the rain under the murky gas lamps, to look at the panes of someone else's windows hung with curtains, to sleep under the arches of gloomy rented rooms, to fill oneself slowly like a cursed vessel with sighs and tired movements and then even more tiredly to roam distant, muddy, dismal streets, to listen to how rain sobs, to buy medicine, to wait at drugstores, that is by and large the like of man in a small city. The old tree trunks, gloomy and at first glance incomprehensible like all the disgusting, demonic, depraved phenomena of reality, deaf and dumb tree trunks on a treelined avenue in the rain are as threatening as sick insides, as old, smoked, swollen, bloated pig's intestines in the storewindows of drymeat markets, and along that huge callous elephant leg slid the rain like a thread of black tar and greasy, and everything around the black treelined avenue in the rain looked like the flood and chaos of a catastrophe. Rotten southern fruit, a drenched newspaper with a picture of a girl trampled on the tracks, dog's tracks, soaked cigarette butts, all that stood on the surface of the sidewalk just like on a deep black mirror where everything exists for only one moment, just as short as a distant echo and an unknown sound which surges into countlessly many circles and disappears like a drop of rain which very simply and naturally reaches its destination from an incomprehensibly strong vertical of the sky and here restlessly meanders around the rotten peel of a trampled orange, and now moves across the black asphalt in order to again tumble down to the underground, where the filthy water under our feet resounds and gurgles.

Winecellars reek along the graves even on sunny days, and all human apartments are full of the smell of toilets—of shells and old unventilated wardrobes, but nothing in the world is as pitiful as a white silken shoe under the glass of a shoemaker's little cabinet when rain is falling. That white, maidenlike lonely object, pointed, old-fashioned, with a high heel, that dream of a young bride and the white picture of first communion, there, in that wet wardrobe, in that glass box in the rain, lit up like the trunk of Snow White, it stands so lonely, cut off from the whole restless condition surrounding it, so hopelessly isolated and in that rain so inexpressibly meaningless, as meaningless as is everything thrown away and forgotten. Rain falls and falls and all things are sad and soaked: horses and sparrows in treetops, and even the lonely monument in the damp shadow of pine-trees; the glass in windows is murky and so gray that all those rooms look like sunken spaces, immeasurably and incomprehensibly far away drowned in the bottom, where time disappears and where nothing moves, only gray drowned rooms framed in glass stand gray in the rain like empty illuminated boxes, and among them is one quite modest and completely unseen, in which motionless a white silken woman's shoe keeps silent. The rain flows along the old roofs of quite strange, incomprehensibly stupid and gray houses, rain gambols along the tiles and gutters, along old garrets and along completely empty balconies, like a tear over a blind girlish head (over the main staircase), one little drop creeps through between the plaster coiffeur and now slides down the cold classical form of a woman's face which stands correct and exalted above all earthly existence like a mask above the main door, decorated by laurel, and by that tragic feminine physiognomy crouches a little wet dove, tucking its head under its wing and becoming soaked. Who founded those small, empty cities with proper treelined avenues, those stupid balconies and those unlit apartments, that autumn rain and that boredom of a small city which stands in the rain as if it were dying out, and where there is no none, absolutely no one, only rain can be heard, as the twilight resounds in gloomy veils. A man passes on the empty treelined avenue, carries a package and groans, his cigarette is catching fire under his nose and leaving behind a cloud of warm smoke, disappears in the semidarkness like a reddish hor-izontal. One perceives behind the passer-by the stench of tired feet, an unwashed body, soaked rags and warm smoke, and he carries the package and moves down the treelined avenue toward the vestibule of the train station, which, with its perpendicular orangish lit glass, looks like a huge greenhouse, warm, dewy, full of rotten steam, in which unusually fleshy plants bloom. The tired passer-by travels, walks with bowed head, naked, gloomy, as if carrying his own epitaph with the inscription: so he lived, traveled, moved, and carried a package along small, unknown cities, having departed one day never to return, absorbed by his last unhealthy thought, how he could wash his feet, and didn't do that, and wanted to and thought about how good and necessary it would be ("in any case"), and so parted from the earth dirty and unwashed, just as he had lived in dirt and just as it stands written in the books from the beginning. Not a trace remained behind of this tired insignificant person, only a melancholy shadow in our brain, and he departed for somewhere far away into the lightblue, pastel greenish sunlit distance, where some kind of sunny city stood in the plantlike gleam of a summer day: ants flowed between their anthills, cats snoozed in the warm shadows, sparrows chirped, and from one balcony flickered a dark blue silk flag with a Swedish cross, as transparent as a woman's blouse, but its tiny, ever tinier folds in tbe summer breeze in the quiet sultriness seemed as refreshing as the murmur of a waterfall.

"And what are you doing, may I ask, in this rain?"

"Ah so! Nothing! I am fantasizing about the dead summer, I am feeling sorry for summer which, unfortunately, will never return again. I'm waiting (besides) for them to boil my medicine in the drugstore! I'm being cured! I'm bored!"

"Good evening! I'm pleased to see you! It's not a stupid thing to feel sorry for summer. For years I've not experienced a worthy summer like a true proper man. In general summer as such doesn't exist; summer is an illusion which expires in the fourth or fifth grade of the gymnasium. In the unusually melancholy hum of flies near the cafe window in the midst of winter you can experience glades and distances, quiet, blue scenes, hills, sheep, more strongly than in the first foolish summer when man had his first gonorrhea. What does "summer" generally mean for a neurasthenic city among cities? Gray, dusty, unwashed glass in the windows, removed shutters, napthalene carpets, gigantic preparations, lamps in the storewindows of stationers' shops and two or three vagrants. 'Pomme de paille' 'homme de paille' straw an sich! In general: a weekly summer afternoon in our small city, does anything more senseless and shabbier exist in the cosmos? Really, is there anyone alive who could explain, in the sense of some high universal order, the deeper significance of our weekly summer afternoons when, let's say, the street is overcrowded with hellish phenomena, like photographs of maids in the black framed little cabinets of photographers?"

"And a bit earlier, you see, I thought over how sad that lonely white woman's shoe is in that shoemaker's storewindow in the rain! It seemed to me that really this shoe is the saddest thing in the whole world!"

"You're right! That shoe of yours is sadder than my photo! That's right! It wouldn't be pleasant for this bronze friar to get soaked on this granite, what do you think? But imagine that friar on a vacation, when it is thirty-seven degrees centigrade in the shade, if he were standing displayed in that divine sun, bareheaded, with book in hand, and near him small women typists were licking ice cream! Even more unpleasant! And you, you say, are waiting for them to boil medicine for you? Have you been at L. W.'s? I've even been at his place! He told me about your case! You know: we're friends from the clinic! He is my Maecenus today! Today he so to speak keeps me! He is a hundred per cent cretin, and he has no concept of medicine. Let that medicine of yours go to the devil which L. W. prescribed for you! Come on, let's drink half a liter of dingač[4], that will be infinitely more intelligent!"

That was Doctor Siroček, but he is a chapter in himself.

Doctor Siroček is my acquaintance, how should I put it, our relationship is a delicate one, but it is true that we became close after meeting in the pissoirs of repulsive taverns, and in that dismal, thick, exitless drunken darkness of our domestic vagrancy, when a person keeps getting drunk, the memory becomes intoxicated, the heart is poisoned, when a person boozes from a self-destructive need in order to croak as soon as possible to be relieved of this depression of ours, of this absurdity of ours, of our nihilism, in a word: of our life as such. In these repulsive places, in which along the stench, along the tar and asphalt and along the black walls flows water murmuring in veils like a transparent curtain which overflows across filthy walls, there for years I have been getting together with Doctor Siroček, where we murmured as everything murmurs and flows in human life because everything is only a fleshy bladder and kidney and everything flows through us from a cloud into rivers and streams and city canals, and if it is taken right, even above our earthly existence we will still be merely fleshy bladder veins, some kind of heavenly judgments, through whom heavenly water flows and flows into porcelain shells, and we surge like kidneys on the bottom of a cloudy mass and blossom here like pale swamp flowers, murmuring, damp, blind and completely confused both when we are drunk and when we are sober, drowning

---

[4]Dalmatian red wine.

all the more sick in our own pools of tears or intestinal chills. Meeting with that unhappy Siroček for years with mathematical regularity always in that very same spot, in that too human almost drowned circumstance, like two tried watersprites we exchanged several empty, gray, insignificant, almost conventional words and returning again to the wine, to the smoke, to the tavern, to the fog of my own table, at the beginning I still had the secure feeling that this Doctor Siroček belongs among nice, well-intentioned, harmless, positive people, that he, however, is quite logically that type of ours who with mathematical certainty must be trampled upon. From those palefaced, lyrically surging, gifted personalities, certainly confused, but in their glances and convictions quite inconsistent, from that drunken state the stomach would regularly begin to speak from memory, while that invisible orator declared itself from the depths of his digestion (more like indistinct grunting than like a human voice), in spite of this glasslike glance and feverish hand, in spite of a burning cigarette glued to his lower lip, in spite of those noisy intestines and drunken bowels from the underground of his body constitution, that drunkard in the mixture of memory and in stirred-up wine babbled about himself and about his higher, poetic calling in this puddle of ours with such ecstasy and with such self-confidence, that those drunken monologues of his in pissoirs remain booming in my head, just as muscial motifs remain which are never forgotten. Once in that glorious Adamlike pose, helpless as a newborn child, he related his whole novel to me about some naked woman, and by his own confession he copied that novel seventeen times word for word, and is still dissatisfied because he did not succeed at all in describing the movement of that naked woman who, while squatting over laurel, washes her belly with a sponge, and when it appeared in our journals, people noticed it, but you heard the unanimous opinion from every direction that he was mad, and what he proclaimed under his pseudonym was merely the most typical example of Stenjevac literature. He was a doctor by profession, a man who stood before "a most glittering academic career," a young man who already in his twenty-sixth year as the assistant of an international genius in Paris had achieved a respectable name in scientific publications, there is even a scholarly medical method of some special surgical cut of the nerves named after him, "ssirotschechiana," that so famous bearer of a scholarly predicate was lost unexpectedly during that famous rise of his, got entangled with certain dubious women, became an alcoholic, became demoralized, became a libertine, sensualist, pander, beat up his Berlin "Herr Professor," was bedridden in sanatoriums for several years and returned to our small corner like a completely shipwrecked person. He did not last here as a practicing doctor and after entangling himself in an affair with dubious patients, he began to argue fiercely in newspapers about the eminence of the medical profession, beat up one of our famous doctors, a professor, our local genius, was in Stenjevac for observation and is now again getting drunk in gloomy wine cellars with dingač, starving for an announcement of a fragment of his unusual, strange, and confused prose, a poet who is homeless, actually living off the donations of his doctor friends, who treat him as lost sons are treated who like slops and food from pig troughs more than from richly set tables of proper civic patriarchal families, where the conquered and tamed are persecuted and where false authorities are regarded with the highest esteem, even at the cost of one's better belief. L. W. (my doctor who has been curing me for over a year) surely told him about "my case," and surely Doctor Siroček today, several minutes after me, visited Doctor L. W. to pump him for several dinars; they, of course, certainly spoke about me, since Siroček was unusually interested in how I myself am interpreting "my case," because Doctor L. W. is a cretin, that it was "his case" was for us beyond doubt, and to debate about it seemed to be quite superfluous to us. Having another liter of dingač in a Dalmatian wine cellar among barrels just like in some kind of underground pirate saloon, after I had returned from the drugstore with a whole package of medicine which Doctor L. W. had newly prescribed for me, Siroček and I were already agreeing that certainly "my case" was not only "mine" but also "his," that they were really "two identical cases," significant not only for us "as patients" so much as for the caveman, troglodyte, cannibal milieu which surrounded us.

"It seems your dead people disturb you like old governors, and those idiots of yours massage the indigestion! That is "our science," you see! Your basic idea, that we are dying before our actual death in the consciousnesses of those dead people who died before us, well, that is the most normal and most basic and most logical hypothesis of every most primitive meditation on death! One would need to go on a pilgrimage from grave to grave and kindle candles of comprehension and experience in those countless calamaties of those extinguished lives. All those deceased consumptives, widows, beggars, slain wounded men on clinic tables, all those could and would know how to tell us and confess in one or two shining and true words, and each light of wisdom, even the most obscure, would illuminate our darkness: it would make our own darkness of disorientation before strangers seem all the less obscure to us, because it would show that everyone is more similar to each other than it appears at first glance. Those before us have already passed examination, and we would become aware that this examination is not as difficult as it looks to us who do not have a pure conscience in front of that last stupid examination commission. Of course, those gentlemen are sick according to the doctors, for a gentleman of neurology that is a Stenjevac way of thinking, anything that has even the most insignificant nuance of lofty inspiration is for the gentleman specialist, Doctor L. W., "a pathological case."

"All that is only a pile of garbage and rubbish for us, and that "science" of ours is rubbish, and I don't know if you observed one everyday fact, that after all, in general, all cities are in garbage and rubbish heaps! Coachmen come with florins and raise our urban city level only so they can carry their fill of garbage: laurel, sacks, cardboard, old rotten spoons, boxes with women's hats, stinking rags which smell of burning, and then on those decayed newspapers they build the pavilion of our so-called domestic culture! In those tents created from old bags and from small decayed toothbrushes, in those gypsy tents of plaster of paris and of rags, in that filth and those huts dwell our civilization, and here amidst the rest dwells our medical science also, here ruminate our Mandarin authorities, and I tell you, and pay attention, please, because I won't be a wicked prophet: all that stands among us like paper scenery which is only waiting for the first whistling of the wind and for the first whistle of a grenade, and everything will be as it was: old punctured laurel, a shattered bowl, a smashed night pot, and a can of preserves. All of these fortresses of ours built on newspaper the wind will blow away, and all that will at once disappear somewhere, and it will not be known where, because our citizens wipe their buttocks with newspaper and so themselves will devour their own glory like Saturn! Besides, I already wrote all that to a gentleman and signed it, and therefore they have liquidated me like a Stenjevac personage, and what can I do today with those noisy phonographs of our science, I, who am like a subject led as Stenjevac evidence? I declared to them in public under my full doctor's signature: if one, even most superficial glance would be thrown at our surgery, at our laringology, at our neurology, then all that put together from a scientific point of view is nothing but humble government office work done in the uniforms of generals, none of us appear before international forums, and in the eyes of European science we are still the provinces! Experimental effort, original discovery, scientific initiative, all that is simply nothing. Me, if you please, the small provincial practitioners, wrapped up in academic togas, do not importune, me the plagiarists do not importune, who are occupied more by politics than science, and I wrote that to them, that they have completely turned into commercial employees of Indantren and Aspirin and Pirmidon, yes, really: commercial agents of great European chemical cartels, that and nothing else! Besides, please let me see what that sage of yours prescribed for you, just for a moment!"

I handed over Doctor L. W.'s prescription to Doctor Siroček and he flew over it with lofty ironic scorn like a strict professor when he takes in hand the written work of a notorious third-rater. But we'll see!

> Rx Infusion of senna 30.0
>   Sodium senna 30.0
>   Sodium chlorate 30.0
>   5–3 times daily
>   2–1 large spoons
>   Gardenal tablets
>   ½ 3 x daily
>   Probilin p.
>   ¾ x daily
>   a. before sleeping at night
>   b. in the morning before eating one hour of fast
>   Sodium chlorate 15.0
>   Sodium sulphur 40.0
>   Sodium bicarbonate 50.0
>   Calcium sulphate 5.0
>   M.F.p. 110.0

D. S. ½ coffee spoon in 4 tenths boiled water with
pills in the evening and in the morning.
Caffein sodiumsalicitate 0.15
Ergotin Bonjouan 0.2
Acid acetylosalicide 0.4
In capsule analaceis
D.D.t.d. No. 15
D.S. after coffee in the morning and after dinner.

Doctor Siroček again flew over that quite extensive prescription
with a single glance (for which I'd paid 176 dinars and 70 paras in
the drugstore), and then with his long, spiderlike fingers yellowed by
tobacco he touched my hands, and I felt how cold were the tips of
his weakblooded, nervous, arachnoid fingers, as cold as cocain.

"How much did you pay for this cretinism?"

"One hundred seventy-six dinars and seventy paras. Besides, the
druggist marked the bill in detail."

"Yes. And how much did you give his apprentice?"

"Seventy-five dinars."

"That means 251 dinars you payed for this Molier-like prescription.
A renowned doctor once said that the difference between doctors and
veterinarians is only in the patient! And do you know what he prescribed for you? Only purgatives! Senna leaves, that is an extract
which acts on the smooth muscle casing and hastens poisoning. He
prescribed one such sacramental diarrhea for you, so you'll go made if
you swallow that Egyptian absurdity. In Senegal and in Egypt they
cure trochema with it Folia Sennae, these are white leaves, greenish,
woolen, unusually soft to one's touch like tissue, it is a tropical flower
which blooms yellow, and the fragrance of the flower is quite un-
endurable, it is a kind of Cesalpiniaceae, which acts like a full and
sodden fruit, like a berry, and is called manna, heavenly, biblical
manna, and once in Paris at the "Foire de puces"[5] I heard a black
Senegalese recommending that fruit as the most infallible medicine
against gonorrhea. So, as you can see, the thinking in the scientific
world about the healing property of this Biedermier roguery has been
spread about and you probably don't have a hard stool.

---

[5]The French flea market.

"No! I suffer from diarrhea cronically."

"So, it is unbelievable, simply unbelievable! Cardenal tablets, that is the most common crap, it is what I call a commercial transaction in the Bayer line, but Probilin is a preparation which quickens the secretion of bile. Sodium, calcium, caffein, all that acts against headaches, and you, when you head aches, what do you take?"

"Veramon!"

"Of course. What should I do with you, go to the devil, 'half a coffee spoon in four-tenths boiled water along with Probilin pills at night and in the morning,' when your head generally doesn't hurt, when you suffer from nervous melancholic depression, because all in all you don't have a regular sex life. When was the last time you slept with a woman!"

"Well, I had the opportunity half a year ago."

"Of course! You need a woman, my friend, not 'half a coffee spoon in four-tenths boiled water with Probilin pills, three to four pills, and that twice a day!' He is a madman and it is L. W. who needs momentarily to be shut up in Stenjevac. Besides, I don't want to be alarmed! I told all that to this gentleman under my full signature, and why am I fruitlessly getting flustered? Someone who gets upset because of a madman doesn't deserve anything better than being crammed into a straight-jacket! I beg of you: sodium sulphate hastens the function of the liver, and you, if you swallow that mass of sulphur plaster, will impair your digestion so definitely that never will any dingač be poured for you! According to that prescription from now up to the end of three weeks you would not have any other obligation than between five and six diarrheas daily to swallow three big and small spoons of that rubbish, and then five times daily two spoons sodium sulphate in the morning, and in the evening sodium chlorate, and after coffee and after dinner Ergotin bonjouani and acid acetyl-salicylicide, which you can take in the form of common aspirin or some other kind of childish bonbon against worms. How much did you say you paid that idiot? Seventy-five dinars? I pumped him for a whole hundred, that means he returned your money to me, and we'll spend that on drink. Halo! Give us another liter of dingač!"

Nervous as a gentleman's dog, Doctor Siroček jumped with one short sprint up to the small iron stove which was smoking in the corner of the wine cellar blushing all over as if it were crimson, and with one elegant gesture he threw into the stove that small package of mine with the medicine which had lain in front of him on the overturned barrel, and then came back and victoriously tapped me lightly on the shoulder like an old intimate friend.

"Here we've liquidated the absurdity, and you, my friend, you've only one duty in the interest of your health, to find yourself a woman! Here is a new liter of dingač! To your health!"

We drank ourselves to oblivion and Doctor Siroček spoke about women the whole night. About how women rot like figs, and how we all cling to that feminine fig, we sink into that rotten fruit and no one has the strength to recognize that we are restless larva and we don't know anything except that we cling to those rotten figs like uneasy worms and so time flows by for us in that wormy rot, and cannons thunder around us and we prop ourselves up for centuries in that bloody pathos of thundering cannons and clattering trumpets, and he, Doctor Siroček, feels only one thing clearly: how terrible it is for him, but how wonderful it would be if he could sneak into the chaos of one woman's intestines, just as from that same intestine he once filtered out somewhere, once somewhere infinitely long ago and infinitely far away, on some kind of downy blanket in the dark, along with the squeaking noise of a bed, the whistle of the wind, when snow was falling, wet, dirty, sticky, misty, endlessly boring. His personal life is composed of the most petty and most stupid calamities: of endless cold and the empty knelling of church bells (which ring with one muffled, hundred-headed idea, and it would be really very difficult to decide what that idea represents), of women who are moving around him for the last time, and one of those scrofulous females wearing black stockings called Musja, a waitress somewhere in the barracks section of the city, far over on the periphery, in a small tavern where noncommissioned officers often go for goulash. No one else in the entire female cosmos, really, except that scrofulous Musja, that one who bears that secret intenstines toward which Doctor Siroček creeps like a snail, moves like a worm along the grooved expanses of her intestines, which seemed to me to be like some kind of naked unearthly Dantesque dismal underground.

"It's warm in a female's intestines and a man can drown hopelessly in that twilight and disappear as a person and cease being an object and turn into something which according to the measure of his dignity is less significant and stammers more than any newborn child in swaddling clothes drawing itself back into primordial matter to turn into some kind of cosmic slimy snot, so it exists just in order to feel the warm intestines, moves, is reduced to something which has no reason, no logic, no memory, to a deaf and dumb state of warm meat without even the palest thought of death, of transitoriness, of the dead around us, and of that academic educated reality around us. Because what is real in our everyday life? Streets? Are streets actually real phenomena? Telephones? (I heard a telephone somewhere far away as if it were ringing in emptiness.) A Dalmatian tavern? The administrative net over all that? The movement of the gnawed branches of my lungs? I moved along streets quite insignificant, so insignificant that in all likelihood I was invisible, and I really was transparent and glittered a greenish color like retorts in electric transformers and conversed with the stars and sang like my cricket there below in the pissoir! I discovered the cricket in the water closet, my dear gentlemen, there below in the water closet I discovered the cricket! Under the waterfall of those stinking asphalt walls where citrus peels float, and ammonia bites your nostrils as it does in a laboratory, there, on the bottom of this human rubbish one night I heard the sound of a cricket. Not even a dog was in the tavern, the wind howled as if it were raging, and there in the rubbish of the pissoir the voice of late summer, the smell of August, the distance of meadows which surge like woven green cloth, the voice of a cricket out of the urine and rubbish, the voice of nature which transforms even stinking city water closets into starry twilights, when mills clatter in dark gray distances, the first crickets appear like a sign of early autumn ... Here, I've brought it some sweet cake, come, let's go visit him!"

As helpless as a child, Doctor Siroček dragged a full palm of crumbled sweet cake out of his pocket and stopped short as if in that sick gesture with crumbs in his palm, holding his hand motionless and level for quite a while as if he were being lulled to sleep, and his eyes gleamed full of tears.

The cricket did not appear. The quiet was interrupted by a murmur which oozed across the asphalt walls like a trembling veil.

Having pricked up his ears, with a glance which was losing itself far above everything which has been determined as reality, Doctor Siroček lingered like this in that sourish hell for several minutes with bowed head, and then having moved his hand away he threw away his burning cigarette butt which, after crackling, went out in the water like a rocket.

"We are all butts in urine"—he said sentimentally and scattered the sweet cake, after turning out the lining of his left pocket, after brushing the cricket crumbs with four fingers of his left hand like a dog, while he scratched himself behind his ear.

Roberta Reeder

August Tin Ujević

(1891–1955)

Ujević was born in Vrgovac, near Makarska. He studied philosophy in Zagreb, Belgrade, and Paris. An original and powerful talent, he soon developed into a poet, critic, essayist, and a knowledgeable translator.

In the years before the First World War, Ujević was among the very active Yugoslav-oriented revolutionary youth. However, the horrors of the war, the chaotic political and social situation in the newly created kingdom of Serbs, Croats and Slovenians, made Ujević a bitter poet.

Ujević published the following books of poetry: *Lelek Sebra* (1920); *Kolajna* (1926); *Dva glavna bogumila* (Two Main Bigots, 1931); *Auto na korzu* (A Car in Corzo, 1931); *Ljudi na vratima gostinice* (People at the Door of a Tavern, 1931) and *Žedan kamen na studencu* (A Thirsty Stone on the Well, 1954).

A COSMIC WANDERER

I have a hundred selves and cry
For each and all a hundredfold
That I will not be broken by
Strange heavy tidings still untold

A hundred voices sing as one
Out of the depths of wave on wave
I will not let myself be done
To death, though freedom be a slave!

And O my soul is strangely wise:
Rebellious my heart's refrain;
Perhaps Assyria will rise
Or Egypt come to life again.

417

And like a stream my thoughts they race;
The strength is coming back to be;
And in the well I see my face;
And in my tomb I breathe and see.

Too narrow for these lands I tread;
Too frail these hands: I could become
An outlaw! Bitter crusts of bread
And bitter still each stony crumb!

I roam the ocean of the sky
And would the Milky Way ensnare;
Brother to sun and moon am I,
And bright stars keep me in their care.

For those who fight, a horse! For all
Who go to sea, a sail! She sings—
The mermaid, and bewitched I call
Across the azure, "Give me wings!"

G. Komai

Gustav Krklec

(1899–   )

Gustav Krklec is exclusively a poet. Born in Udbina, his literary activity has already lasted forty years. At present he is an editor in Zagreb's publishing house Zora.

He has published *Lirika* (Lyrics, 1919); *Srebrna cesta* (The Silver Road, 1921); *Tamnica vremena* (The Prison of Time, 1944); *Izabrane pjesme* (Selected Poems, 1947). Together with Slavko Ješić he also published *An Anthology of World Lyrics* in 1957.

Krklec's poetry is characterized by its picturesqueness and musicality. In the lyrics of his youth, he wrote about the natural beauty of his native Zagorje—the smell of grass, a flight of birds and so on. In this poetry there was no pain and death. During World War II, his poetry expressed sorrow of the country's devastation and suffering. He returned to happy topics after the country was liberated.

He is particularly well known as a translator from the other Slavic languages, as well as from German.

FEAR

The sky is dead. No bird is on the wing.
The reapers' songs are no more echoing.

No sickles cut the ripe corn anywhere.
The sun is gone. No voices cleave the air.

The light is fading, fading is all sound.
A misty shroud creeps on the paths around.

The sapless wood is still, the grass is sere.
All through the twilight crawls unrest and fear.

And he who rides triumphantly arrayed
Through alien fields, of shadows is afraid.

A. Lenarčič and J. Lavrin

THRALLDOM

Can this be life? To loiter at the gate
athirst, and for a quickening drop to wait;

far from the sun, the stars, or lights aglow
in one's own home to be enthralled by woe.

To quench all passions, wishes and delights,
and drift through all these cheerless days and nights.

To be an ant upon a path and feel
an aimless prey, crushed by an alien heel,

and yet afire, with righteous intent—
a dagger of revenge one cannot vent.

A. Lenarčič and J. Lavrin

Ivan Goran Kovačić

(1913–1943)

Kovačić was born in Lukovac, a picturesque village in Gorski Kotar. By conviction a Yugoslav, he expressed his feeling of love toward Serbian and Slovenian literatures through a cooperation in their periodicals of the time.

As a student at the University of Zagreb, Kovačić showed his leftist orientation and expressed it in his poetry. As a high school student, he had published his poems *Lirika* (Lyrics, 1932), and several of his short stories were published afterwards under the title *Dani gnjeva* (Days of Anger).

During the Second World War Kovačić actively participated in fighting against the Fascists. In 1943, in the town of Livno, he wrote his famous poem *Jama* (The Pit), protesting the bloody massacres and crimes against humanity. At the end of that year he was unexpectedly killed near the river of Sutjeska.

After the war his collected works were published and acclaimed primarily for his treatment of social problems in Croatia.

MY GRAVE

Let my grave be on a mountain peak—
with howling wolves around, trees bare and bleak;

where in the summer storms and winter's frost
access to it will be forbidding, lost.

Let it stand high like a throne, a cloud—
out of the reach of bells, however loud;

out of the reach of voices which repine,
and pray from fear, or for salvation whine.

On my grave let grass and sharp thorn grow.
Let it be too steep for those below.

My only friend the path to it may find.
and then—returning—leave no trace behind.

J. Lavrin

THE PIT

(Excerpt)

Blood is all my darkness and my light,
For now the clawed-out sockets of my eyes
Are void of sight and all the bliss of night.
Inside my brain a bloody eyeball cries,
Kindled from day-drops to a burning brand.
My eyes lie quenched upon my upturned hand.

　　Surely inside them like bright flecks of foam
　　Birds fluttered in the mild revolving sky.
　　I felt my bloody face and the sky's blue dome
　　Had blended in the deep depths of the eye.
　　And in my upturned hand my eyes laughed loud,
　　Mocking the sun's bright beams,—but no tears flowed.

But warm, thick blood-drops through my fingers dripped,
Which from the gaping sockets of my eyes
The anguish-thirsty executioner ripped—
Then stabbed my neck to make a sweet surprise.
Yet these thick drops of blood gave me delight;
They felt like warm tears falling in the night.

　　The last light seen before terrible night
　　Was the flash of a knife in lightning-strike,
　　A scream that lingered into blindness—white,
　　And bright, white skin; for the executioners all alike
　　Stood stripped to the waist; their stark, white skins
　　Dazzled the eyes like white-hot pins.

Oh, agony of light that never yet
Has burned so sharp and bright—at dawn, from pyre
Or lightning flash; it was as though my wet
Tears were live flames that set their holes on fire,
And through this hell the lightnings flashed their fires,
And screams rang out from all the tortured choirs.

I do not know how long the fires had burned
When suddenly hard, horrible lumps began to grow
Inside the sockets;—I stood limp and stunned,
My jellied eyeballs in my hand. "Oh,
Mother dear! I'm blind," I cried in pain.
"No tears for you can ever flow again.

And mighty light, like a peal of a hundred bells
In a white bell-tower, shone madly in the mind.
Light from Zion and the surrounding hills!
Glorious light—light giving light to the blind!
Bright bird! bright wood and river—shining silk!
Bright moon! Light bright as mother's milk!

But such an agony I had not thought would come;
The torturer said, "Now squeeze your eyeballs in your hand!"
I nearly knelt before him, stupefied and dumb.
And then a spasm of thick slime drenched my hand.
And senseless, like a man struck dead, I fell
To the bottomless depths of some dark hell.

D. Cooke

Ranko Marinković

(1914–   )

Ranko Marinković is one of the outstanding Croatian story writers who established themselves after the war. Although he was a promising writer before the war, it was only in 1953, when he published a collection of short stories entitled *Ruke* (Hands), that he gained recognition and received the 1953 award of the Federation of Writers of Yugoslavia.

Marinković was born in 1914 on the island of Vis. At the beginning of his career as a writer he took his themes almost exclusively from his native region, but, with *Hands*, he switched to more general and profoundly human themes of lasting value.

In addition to writing stories, Ranko Marinković is involved with the theater. He has written a play called *Albatros* (Albatross, 1953), and a number of dramatic reviews and criticisms. He also teaches at the Academy of Drama in Zagreb.

THE HANDS

I contemplated them, interlocked behind his back, the left hand lying snugly in the palm of the defter, stronger, wiser, more serious right. I might add "older," had I not known that they were conceived together and born of one mother (indeed, of one father, too), and now left by their parents to knead a clod of soil into a crust of bread.

They were the offspring of desire, of strange ramblings in the dead of one night, in the blackout of reason, and now they roved here and there in their embrace, full of love for each other, inseparable. The right hand hugged the left, carrying it with care and solicitude, as a bitch her pups between her teeth. The left lay snug in the embrace of the right, amusing itself at its leisure, its thumb tripping from fingertip to fingertip to the soft tune of do-re-mi-fa . . . fa-mi-re-do . . ., and then to another strain drummed in march rhythm.

"What are you doing?" asked the right hand.

"What do you think? Singing," said the left hand.

"What are you singing?"

"Do-re-mi-fa and 'Onward Christian Soldiers' . . ."

" 'Onward Christian Soldiers!' Nonsense!" retorted the right hand with an unconcealed smile of contempt. "You're not a soldier."

"It isn't only soldiers that sing 'Onward Christian Soldiers.' . . . Children sing it too."

"But you're not a child."

"I'm neither a soldier nor a child. But why is it nonsense to sing?" asked the left hand with a flash of irritation in its voice. "I will sing if I want to," and then burst out with,

"Every letter, big and small,
I can read and write them all;
Numbers also—one, two, three
Won't you come and read with me?"

"Do you mean to say you can write?" asked the right hand in an exasperated voice.

"Oh, dammit, I can't go about silent, or only counting on my fingers like a moneylender!"

"Are you saying I'm a moneylender?"

"You don't count on your fingers."

"What do I do then?"

"You work and act, as an illiterate fool has already observed before me."

"How do you know those were the words of an illiterate fool? You can't read?

"Neither can you."

"But I can write."

"You can't read, though."

"At least I can turn the pages of a book; you can't even do that much. All you can do is hold the book while I turn the pages. He reads, I turn the pages, you hold the book like a bookstand. That's all you can do. You've never looked in a book. You know books from their weight, but you haven't got the faintest idea of what's in them."

"I can turn the pages too. And if he were lefthanded, I could write."

"Write; yes, but how?"

"Like you do. And maybe even better. If he were lefthanded, I'd be able to do everything you do, and perhaps even better than you!"

"Would you know how to pull puppet strings?"

"Yes."

"And paint?"

"And paint."

"And draw three hares on the nail of my liitle finger?"

"And draw three hares on the nail of your little finger. And two chicks as well! By the way, why on your nail? I'd draw them on my own."

"Drivel! Even I can't do that. No one can."

"I could, though."

"It means you'd be able to cut your own nails?"

"Of course. I cut yours, don't I?"

"Yes, you cut mine, but I'm talking about yours. No one can do that."

"Stop saying, 'No one can do that!' I could"

"All you do is boast, but you couldn't even catch a flea."

"Rot! As if I never caught a flea!"

"Would you sew?"

"I'd sew too."

"But how about threading the needle? I'd have to do that for you."

"I'd thread the needle. I'd do everything myself."

"And tie a tie?"

"And tie a tie."

"And drop drops in his eye?"

"And drop drops in his eye."

"And shave him?"

"And shave him."

"But he wouldn't let you shave him."

"Why not? I'd shave him better than you do."

"You'd cut his throat."

"I'm not a murderer! You might do that. Anyway, you did try to do it once."

Silence. The right hand was at a loss as to what to say. It shook at those words, as though an odious memory coursed through its veins.

"But I thought he was serious about it," came the meek voice with a hint of guilt in it. "I only wanted to do what he said. . . ."

"Do what he said? He didn't ask you to kill him, surely?"

"His every wish is my command. I thought it was really his wish."

"Aha, you mean he is insincere? Who told you he wished to do that?"

"I thought he did . . . He was in trouble. He hadn't slept a wink all night. I'd wiped his moist forehead, lit cigarette after cigarette for him, and wrote his good-bye letter. He groaned, sighed, wrestled with his pillow . . . and then whispered, 'I must end it all, I can't go on like this!' And then he took me to his razor.''

"And straight off you took that to mean he wanted to cut my wrist!"

"Don't torment me! What else could I do when he kept saying . . ."

"What did he keep saying? That he couldn't go on like that, that he must end it all. . . . But those are only words! Words aren't fathered by wishes but by the tongue. It's easy for the tongue to play the fool, and harm comes of it only in those books whose pages you turn. The tongue splutters forth its words (always the same, by the way, and known for ever so long) and they melt away like smoke. Nothing happens: the earth keeps on spinning, people eat, smoke, and sleep, and speak the words again, and still nothing happens. People like to talk, but their words do not show their wishes; in fact, words even hide them. Words are a screen. So that proves he didn't mean what he said!"

"How can we know what he means, if not from his words?"

"Least of all from his words. He said, 'I must end it all,' but he didn't mean it. Even I knew that much."

"Where did you get that from?"

"Oh, you know: I'm clumsy, weak, and a fool. Yes, and fickle. And words are as strange to me as light is to the ear and sound to the eye, and I don't know one from the other, or sweet from bitter, they're all the same to me, and I don't believe any of them.

"I don't know how to follow words, I can't keep my balance along the circles and ellipses, parabolas and spirals of words; I can't twist and turn and swing like a teetotum and slide over the ice of conversation, drawing fancy figures, turning somersaults, doing monkey business like a monkey in the circus, and pat shoulders and diplomatically shake the right hand of a diplomatic enemy, and raise another gallantly to his lips to kiss. I'm neither a *preziosa* nor a *cicisbeo,* I'm neither a lady nor high society, I'm neither an academy nor a buffoon; I'm Molière."

"Molière." And what else?

"A fig in the pocket. Or out of the pocket—whichever you wish. Because I'm as insolent as Figaro. I'm your lackey: while you prostitute yourself naked in all sorts of handshakes, I hold your glove like a

Roman slave. I'm supposed to bear your train, to trot and trip after you while you carry on conversations, broaden horizons, build worlds. For you are a mason, a genius, a Demiurge; you're his pride, his strength, wisdom, skill: a Hand, in a word!"

"And what are you?"

"I? I'm only a holder. I'm still a kind of walker, a foreleg, a feeler, a pseudopodium, or something like that. I keep him in touch with the earth, like a foot, but still I know how to walk. At night I dream of running, of climbing trees, or jumping over chasms, and then I feel the toughness of matter and strength in my nails. For me things are as muddy as clay, hard as stone, hot as fire, or wet as water; for you they are terracotta, Corinthian vases, Venuses, rockets, or H_2O. That's why I know he wants water when he's thirsty, that he wants joy when he's sad, that he wants to live when he speaks of ending everything."

"Yes; but he's thirsty, I gave him water."

"You? No; you only turn on the tap or work the handle on the pump; but it's from my palm that he drinks; water pours on me and I feel its coolness, its wetness, and hear the gurgling sound it makes in his throat, and know the pleasure he feels after he has quenched his thirst. You say you give him water when he's thirsty? No; all you give him is a glass. You even cast thirst in a form and fashion a style for drinking. You step in between him and nature, like a self-styled arbiter and censor, like a master of ceremonies; in fact, like a filter. Whatever wants to approach him must go through your fingers; you have to touch, feel,examine everything,you have to suit everything to your taste, whether it pleases him or not. You have to stamp your pretentious thumb, the seal of your taboo, on everything!"

"You don't expect him to graze, or gnaw the bark of the trees, do you? After all, nature doesn't pet him as it is."

"Of course I don't. And then you had to come along and 'vanquish' it for his benefit. You've 'leveled mountains' and 'tamed the waters' and 'captured thunderbolts,' and now you wield terrific forces with which, they say, you can destroy the world as easily as you can snap your fingers. The earth lies in your palm like a ball that you can throw out into the universe. Well, why don't you, Omnipotence? Throw the ball away among the stars to dissolve into dust? Why don't you con-summate your Great Deed?

"I don't want to destroy the earth."

"How generous! Is there a century that you have not carved up with knives and riddled with bullets? It was not words, but your five fingers that were at work."

"There were words first."

"Yes, according to John the Baptist. But what would words have done if it hadn't been for you? Words would have quarreled, they would have clashed, the vanquished would have fallen, but no one would have been the worse."

"What about honor?"

"Honor? Whose honor? Define that chivalrous word. Your honor? When your palm itches, when your pulse quickens, when your fingers tremble and frantically seek the hilt of your dagger; when your finger is ready on the trigger, when you make the sign of the Cross and pray for God's blessing to alight upon the barrel of your gun, when your two fingers and thumb hold the pen that kills—is that what you mean by honor?"

"What pen?"

"The judge's fountain pen. Have you forgotten? The defendant was sitting in front of us because of some words. Not because of something his hands had done, but because of words. You didn't care to know what had made those words burst forth from his tongue; you simply took down the facts. He had said them and admitted them: that was all you wanted to know. He was pale, his lips were trembling as though he were freezing. He was counting his last seconds. . . . He stared at you with horror in his eyes, he followed every movement of your fingers, as though they could kill him. You were known as 'The Fist of Steel' and 'The Bloody Hand.' The iridium tip of your fountain pen was already thin with murder. That tiny speck of precious metal slid wearily along the paper, as though it were present at an uninteresting and tiring board meeting, and was doodling away its time drawing idyllic little houses with gardens and fences, and smoke rising out of the chimney. Your iridium tip, however, killed the idyllic little house with the garden and fence with a volley, and all that remained of the idyll was the smoke from the rifles. . . . You had already taken the pen between your ill-famed fingers and thumb and dropped resolutely to the paper. I jumped on you and, not knowing what to do, began to rub a smudge of ink off your forefinger. As I rubbed your forefinger with my thumb, I said, 'But he didn't do anything to you. Look how pale he is. He's trembling. Isn't that enough for you? He's listening to his last heartbeats and counting. . . . Don't stop him!' "

"Heartbeats, nonsense! He's fishing for pity with his pale look. That's an old ruse!"

"But your hand was like stone. Can't you shake instead of being so impassive, as though you were giving a pupil bad marks at an exam?"

"I've no reason to shake. I'm doing my duty."

"Then you began to write your well-known D, the first letter of violent and criminal death, with slow, painstaking, calligraphic strokes. And then you added four more letters to your D to complete the word 'death.' And you didn't shake in the least. That same evening (you hadn't even washed) you tangled her silky hair and caressed her face, and your fingers trembled with love. Those fingers, that never trembled before death, trembled that night with love. Now, who can say that love is not stronger than death, especially that our love is not stronger than someone else's death?"

"How can you speak about love? You don't know what love is. That first touch, when the fingers grope for each other in the dark, and suddenly touching, tremble as though two electric poles charged with power had come together. . . ."

"Yes, and a spark leaps: a short circuit and a blackout. And that's the end of love. What then? Duty? The gold pen dripping death?"

"You're erratic and crazy!"

"And I suppose you're rational and wise! That's the difference. Let me go!" and the left hand angrily endeavored to shake off the embrace of the right.

"What's come over you all of a sudden. Always behaving scandalously in the streets!"

"Don't touch me! Let me go! I won't have anything to do with you!"

"Whom are you going with then? The feet?"

"Even with the feet! At least they've got some idea of honor. They're at least noble as a horse. You're as cunning and venomous as a serpent."

"Yes, and they're as stupid as horses, too. All they do is walk and tug loads. You can't go with them. After all, you are a hand, you know!"

"I'm not a hand, and I won't be one! I'm ashamed of being a hand!"

"What do you want to be? a foreleg?"

"Anything, anything, only not a hand!"

"All the same, you're a hand like me."

"Like you? No! Let me go!"

And the left hand wrenched itself from the embrace of the right and crept into its own pocket, where it angrily rummaged about pretending to search for something, Finding nothing, it emerged, dropped defiantly to his side, and nervously twiddled its fingers.

The right hand remained a moment longer behind his back, empty and thoughtful. Then, snapping its thumb and dropping to his side, it fell in rhythm with the feet.

I watched the two hands, bad-tempered as they were, unable to believe my eyes. They were like two symbiotic animals or plants. The right hand was right: they were alike, they were both hands.

Two children were approaching them, a boy and a girl. They were holding hands and singing. But as they drew near, they dropped into silence, like crickets when someone is near, and separated. The girl passed the right hand, softly, as though she had done something wrong. It patted the girl's blond head. The girl returned the pat with a glance of gratitude.

The boy passed the left hand recklessly. He threw it an insolent stare, as though it were something lying in the road. It tweaked his nose awkwardly with its thumb and forefinger. The boy spat at it. It rose instinctively and made a palyful feint over the boy's head as though driving flies away. But the right hand rose and slapped the boy. He yelled.

"Why did you strike the boy?" asked the left hand.

"Because he spat at you!"

"But he spat at me, not at you!"

"He shouldn't have spat!"

"It must have hurt him. I was clumsy. . . ."

"You would be! . . . But still he shouldn't have spat. Disgusting!"

"To hit someone on the nose is the peak of refinement, I suppose!"

"You didn't hit him, you only tweaked his nose. That's not the same thing at all. Anyway, it isn't as if you had cut his nose off."

"Why should I mind if he spat at me?"

"To spit at someone is an insult!"

"To one's dignity!"

"Yes, to one's dignity!" retorted the right hand, already at the end of its patience.

The boy was screaming about the resounding insult to his cheek.

In a moment two glistening streams flowed from his nostrils and dropped to his chin, where they reached flooding level.

"Look at the little rascal, what a row he's kicking up!" remarked the right hand, astonished at the row. Then it turned to the left hand. "Let me wipe you."

"It's all right, I've already done so."

"But you had to do it on his trousers!"

"No, I didn't. I wiped myself on his coat! Look, here comes the boy's father!"

The boys' father came rushing out of the house in his shirt sleeves. His white-collar hands with their blue, timid veins were delicate and pale.

"Why did you hit my son?" asked the father coldly, like a judge contemplating sentence.

"Because he's rude and impudent!" replied the right hand with a note of challenge in its voice.

"What did he do?" the father went on, now really offended.

"He spat at me!" said the right hand bitterly, almost believing he really had.

"He spat at me, not you," said the left hand in a tone of righteousness.

"It doesn't matter at whom he spat; the fact is that he spat," exclaimed the right firmly.

"Spat for no reason at all?" continued the father, now realizing he would have to fight.

"I didn't, Daddy! This hand hit me on the nose . . ." interrupted the boy tearfully.

"Only tweaked his nose playfully," said the right hand, "and he up and spat."

"Serves you right!" shouted the father in such a rage that a flood of fury seemed to burst from him. "I can spit too!" and he spat. "Murderers!" he shrieked.

The right hand rose and swung with all its strength. The boy's father, warding off the blow, swung his own fist and caught the right hand a cuff on the thumb. The right hand groaned.

Then the left hand went into action. It grabbed the boy's father by his shirt. The right hand acted as swiftly and, clenching its fingers into a fist, began to pummel his face.

Blood streamed from his nose onto the left hand, which was holding his shirt front. The right hand, which repeatedly struck the father's bloody face, was also a gory mess.

Seeing her father's blood dripping to the ground, the girl screamed and flew forward to catch the drops. The boy hurled himself into the fray, grabbed the left hand, and sank his teeth into its forearm.

The left hand howled with pain and loosened its grip. The father took advantage of the momentary lull to take to his heels, a vanquished pulp, disgraced before his children.

The boy loosed his teeth from the left hand, which now struck him on the head. The boy received the blow hardily.

Then the legs, like obedient horses, started after the boy's father. The boy threw himself before them, not to implore mercy for his father, but to trip them up.

And, indeed, the left and the right hand suddenly found themselves in the dust.

"Oh-h-h!" groaned the right. Its thumb hurt.

. . . Two bloody hands on the asphalt. They lay in disgrace in the street, side by side, helpless, like cast-off gloves.

"The damned rascal!" muttered the left between its fingers as it got up.

"Serves you right for not giving him a good one!"

"But I did!"

"Yes, like a softy! help me up. I think my thumb is broken."

"Does it hurt?"

"Terribly!"

The left hand was gentle, like a sister . . .

They got up, leaving bloody blotches on the pavement. But they did not turn back to look at them; they rubbed each other, shaking in their desire for revenge.

Then the Face spat into their palms and wiped the blood and dirt off them.

Petar Mijušković

THE CYCLOPS

(Excerpt)

Isn't it your head that they want? A secret political conspiracy in a dark cellar by an oil lamp: three unshaven characters deliberate how to decapitate you. The knives are stabbed into the table, sharp, shiny. On them is inscribed Rostfrei–Solingen and they have a groove on their points, just butcher knives. (At the first occasion should you ask a specialist of slaughtering why that groove on butcher knives?)

They will surprise you in a dark street, at night, when you pass by, pounding your fingers distractedly on the wall. . . . Nevertheless, you do not understand why someone would chop off your head? And especially for political reasons? It's true, you have your own conviction, but this is . . . so . . . a conviction.

"Well, gentlemen (what sort of gentlemen are they?), can't I have my conviction? And already you are afraid that those over there know about your miserable conviction, that they even measured its strength with a special instrument and that you are done for. For, those dreams, the dreams that torment you! . . . No, it must be that those over there have spotted you, that your name was mentioned and even put on lists, on records."

He stands with Ugo beside the invalid's scale and waves his hands explaining: "Humanity, dear Parampion, humanity!" An elegant gentlemen in a raincoat who until than appeared to be waiting for the streetcar came up to them. Pointing a pipe which he took from his pocket at Melchior, he asked with great authority:

"Did you shout 'humanity'?"

"No, brother, I have discretely said 'humanity,' without any particular reasons. Simply so, out of humanitarianism . . . and brotherhood."

"Out of humanitarianism? Brotherhood? An internationalist?"

"O, no, on the contrary! I am . . . for the defense, for resistance as a nation, till the last drop! . . ."

"For resistance?"

"Yes, not to let go, wouldn't you agree, my dear colleague?"

But the colleague had already sneaked away, and the gentleman who was waiting for the streetcar took Melchior by the arm and went for a walk with him. . . .

A knife fight, shooting in the dark, running away, falling from heights—that was the program for his brief morning sleep. After Vivere.

They chase him with shiny butcher knives around the University Library. He climbs on a green copper roof and hides his head behind one of the four bronze owls. Each owl is trampling over a book. Suddenly they send him on razor blades of all kinds and dimensions. The shiny flocks of blades clatter and buzz in thick offensive formations descending upon the bronze owl. They squawk and splatter on the owl's head. She spreads out her wings maternally protecting Melchior, the fugitive, from the sharp flying edges. Ugo's mocking face emerges from the other side of the roof, behind the other owl: "Let go, ATMA is in charge of things. Cviker is in the headquarters. Maestro has killed himself and Vivian has entered the nunnery. . . ." He glanced down, but both eyes fell out of his head. Brotherly united by a nerve, as if holding hands and like twin soap bubbles, they slowly fall on the ground. They gaze at each other and from each drops a tear.

Recasting.

He sits on a cannon barrel. Next to him is a man—the soldier Garcia (that's his rank), who doesn't speak any of the known languages. Further on, behind large trunks are enemy positions. All is still at the front. From the pockets of his shirt, Garcia takes out words and lines them out on his palm. Then he stuffs them into the rifle. He studies languages. Suddenly, Garcia is no longer there on the cannon. Garcia's head shouts from the cannon barrel: "Moroccans! Moroccans!"* The cannon detonates frightfully. The words fly, shout, scream—murderers! Shots. The words are dying. Silence. Darkness. One cannot see the sky.

You run. You trample over dead things and dead people. Helmets, pots, broken bathroom porcelain. Any moment you expect a knife in the back. Merhum Melchior.

Merhaba!—Someone catches up with you, jabs you in the back with his finger, and you already think—merhum! . . . But this skinny, toothless and altogether funny man who had overtaken you, asks you promptly with apprehension: "We are retreating, *n'est ce pas?*"

---

*Moroccans of the dream.

One can tell, an intellectual.

"Yes, professor, a tactical move. García said so. But ours hold on, by the gods!"

"Polytheism?"—grins the toothless one with quiet satisfaction.

In the next sequence you find yourselves in a narrow school toilet (for teachers), posted with old newspapers containing pictures of many living kings. All of a sudden a terrible howling is heard, horse hooves, breaking of glass, a terrible confusion. Then, victorious drums, brass music, shouts: "Mamma! *Cara* mamma!" and "*Sieg-heil!*" Lastly, the song "*Vento, vento, poria mi con te.*" . . .

The old professor—even though he was, it seems, a solider—could not calm his knees which quivered as if carrying I don't know what weight. At last the professor sat on the porcelain seat and, after relieving himself, sighed: "O my career! My career!"

"Professor, professor, do you have any pesetas?"

"Seven hundred . . . and, here, forty centimos more. Will you take them away from me?"

"Yes. In order to throw them through the window, to the ones below."

"And then?"

"Then? Wipe away your career—and let's run!"

And, while below, the victors fight over a fistfull of money, with changing luck you squeeze through intricate, dark corridors. You would surely have escaped if you could have run. . . . But the Cannibals are already here from all sides. Surrounded! Caught! The Maestro (for that was he)—as one says in novels where for awhile they hide the identity of a person—is discarded right away as unsuitable for eating. (They make a little incision in him; the knife got stained—morbus lues, poisonous, said the redhead Asklepije), and they throw you into the boiler for breakfast. Foma Fomich Opiskin was making the fire under the kettle (as a slave, of course, with certain rights of dissatisfaction, and grumbled: "They persecute me. I am earning my bread!" Here appeared the redhead Asklepije looking like Sartorius the critic, smiling complacently: "And he says that he isn't under the influence of Dostoevsky! Disgusting lies, lies, lies. . . ."

A cut in the set.

The shore of a place on the sea. Along the shore barges and fishermen's boats. On the mainland barrels with wine and spread out nets.

No one is around. The time is indeterminable, morning or noon, one can't say. The hands of the clock on the bell tower fell out. Its face is rusty.

You are alone (. . . he is, we are, you are, they are . . . one can hear the old school echo, the choir of children's voices). In your hand you carry an empty ink bottle and sudenly remember that you could wash it in the sea. You descend two steps, you are closer to the water, you kneel down . . . but the bottle no longer interests you. Out of the pocket you take a knife, a big pocket knife. You open it and, seizing your hair with the left hand, you cut off your head with a very natural and light move. Simply, like decapitating a hen. Then, instead of the bottle you wash your own head: up and down, splash—splash. A clear picture of a beheading: a body without a head, the head in the hands and in it open, indifferent eyes. Suddenly, the head slips out of your hands and rolls down into the water. You can't catch it. You call it, beg it to return, but it looks at you in a lingering and offended manner. Then it smiles sadly and closes its eyes as if from unexpected pain. With some sort of a stick you try to draw it toward you, but it only turns like a pumpkin and doesn't come any closer. Finally it looks at you with a dreadfully painful, parting glance and says mournfully (bug as if reproaching you for this sadness): "Farewell, I am off." and you hear how it starts to sob. Then it dives deeply and disappears.

Behind you, on the shore stands a feeble-minded fellow who observed you grinning idiotically. When the head dived in, he said:
"You could have given it to me. My old lady's sister died, the deaf one."

"The deaf one," heard Melchior when he had already opened his eyes.

What is this? he said loudly.

A light is burning in the room.—"Who is here?"— he asks the room.

The room is silent. It diverts his look down, to the bed, to him, to his legs, the belly, the chest, and even closer, closer . . . it would like to show him the head.

The look is frightened. It discovered you on the bed in suit and shoes, and now it observes you surprised as if you were a stranger—a revelation.

You show it your hands. First the one, then the other. The look stares at them without emotion; "hands" it states indifferently. The hands do not interest it. It shortens the range, it looks for a closer aim. It closes up and crosses, leers, and like Picasso looks at the nose from both profiles. This is the closest thing that it can see—the nose. Meanwhile it defines the nose: a bilateral SOMETHING that rises into the space dividing the visible world in two, the right and the left. But the Look is looking for the head, it looks for the solution of the puzzle, for the answer to this night, to this dream—a decapitating one. The look is searching for itself, itself in person, it wants to see itself. It wants to like itself, narcissistically, foolishly, nearsightedly, blind for all that is not It, what isn't a STRIKING LOOK, a Pure Look, an eighteen carat look.

It would like to look at itself. The look *en face* and the look from the profile. It would like to study its wideness, its sharpness, to discover its face from a new, still unknown perspective. It would like to penetrate into itself, dive into its past, into its ancient, protozoic descent, when it was still carefully touching the world with pseudopods and tentacles.

The Look had a fearless desire to see itself.

But you became frightened by this audacity. Who knows what is hiding in it? This is perhaps the entrance into a completely new, yet undiscovered hell from which there is no return? Disappearance in one's own eyes and endless torment?

You are afraid of yourself lying on the bed. (They say that one has nightmares if one sleeps with shoes on one's feet.)

But who has turned the light on? He could swear that, this morning, when he climbed into the room, he took off his wet clothes and muddy shoes, put on his pajamas, crept under the covers and turned the light off! And in the bed you were still thinking: Love?—how all this is still unexplained! Is it the Song of Songs, Cleopatra, Beatrice, Laura, Romeo, Phaedra, Don Juan, Werther, Stendhal or Casanova? What is love?

He remembers well: first he threw himself on the sofa drenched from the rain and tired, then scanned Stendahl's book About Love. Later, with closed eyes he thought about the many insoluble questions concerning love and suffering in love. "How beautiful and how amiable you are, o sweet love! Your stature resembles a palm tree and your breasts are like bunches of grapes. Beautiful you are, my dear, as Tersa, splendid as Jerusalem, terrible as an army with banners. Solomon had a vineyard in Balamon. . . ." "*Minus dormit it edit quem amoris cogitatio vexat,*" is written in Codex Amoris by Andre le Chapelain from Avignon. How many sad, empty days, how any sleepless nights, how much fear, anxiety, longing, misery, madness! How much suffering. How much blood was spilled because of "Sweet Love"! How many hearts have palpitated! How many heads have rolled!

"*La douce pensee*

Qu'amour souvent me donne!" wrote the ill-fated page Guillaume du Cabstaigne from Provence in the twelfth century, a moment before his master, Monseigneur Raymond de Rousillon cut off his head, tore his heart from the chest, roasted it and served it to his wife, the page's mistress. Then he asked her if the heart she ate was good—and he showed her Guillaume's head. She replied that it was so good and tasty that no other food or drink would ever eradicate the taste Guillaume's heart had left. After that she jumped out of the window killing herself, the unfortunate madame Marguerite.

He gets up and opens a window. Below him is a dark, wet, three-story high abyss. Well? Should I jump? How do they jump with the parachute?—and he imagines a perilous aeronautic super slalom. The parachute did not open. . . .

But this: You lie on the bed dressed and in the room the light is burning! And in the light you dream that you decapitated yourself! This is the worst of all—in the light!

No, it was I who last night tried to perform some kind of surgery on myself. Perhaps I did get up, turned on the light, dressed and even went out? The streetcar? No, the streetcar came before that. All is so blurred, disconnected. Say something, o you blind things! And you, shining servant!—he addresses the light bulb. Under the ceiling, the bulb burns indifferently, mute, deaf. It glares and remains silent. It's the only witness who looks from above, who has eyes.

Maybe I really did try to kill myself?

He remembers the paper knife and begins to shudder. Where is the knife? A lot depends on that. It should be over there, on the table. And in the evening they say to you: "Rest well!"

The knife is on the table, thrust up to its handle in a thick, half cut book. The book lies on its hip, powerless, slaughtered. This alarms him even more. Slaughtered! Who has thrust the dagger so deceitfully into its belly? (This was Wells's *Short History of the World*. The poor short one!)

Carefully he takes the knife out of the *History's* belly.

I must have done something with this knife after all!—This thought won't let go of him. It's Enka's silver gift for his last year's birthday.

He went to the mirror and was frightened by *the one* in there who looked at him so strangely. O my, how persistently! He would like to scare him off. . . . But he noticed that *that one* was also scared, that he looked with distrust. . . . No, a man doesn't believe another man, not even in the mirror!

But what is it, my friend? How would we look without heads? He grabbed his head by the hair with the left hand, and with the right one he made a very careful move with the knife across the gullet. Glub . . . went the gullet, slaughtered. Then he took the head between his palms and started to turn it as if it was really cut off. How strange this is—to hold a human head in one's hands!

And perhaps it even went like this. Some important, urgent thoughts had rushed to the vestibule of your dream. They pound, awaken, alarm, demand that they be received and heard immediately. And the kindhearted Dream, in order to protect you from a messenger with bad news, simply took your head and whispered to your body. "You have nothing to think with, you don't have a head. Just sleep."

Sleep . . . and over there, two meters from the dream a dagger is thrust into the belly of History!

DAGGER! In this word the "r" is the most fearful thing. It contains the element predestined for slaughtering. In other languages this is an instrument for sharpening pens, for cutting apples . . . but a *dagger* means slaughtering, murder, crime, massacre. A dagger without the "r" is a crazy joker. It pricks out of mischief, as a thorn, as a needle hidden under the chair. *Barking, rattle, fire*—all the terrible nocturnal phenomena which make man afraid to lie down and fall asleep.

You think: What should I do with it? Indeed, you are afraid to fall alseep beside it. Hence, you speculate: Wrap it well in a whole newspaper, tie it tightly with a rope and lock it in a drawer. Lock the drawer key in the closet, take the closet key over to the kitchen and lock it in . . . in something there, then return to the room, lock yourself in, and throw the key of the room out the window. It is too complicated. Stupid too. It can all be put back again.

What should he do? He sits on the bed with a paper knife in his hand. It's night. All smart people sleep, but he is afraid to fall alseep for fear that in the sleep he might slaughter himself with the dagger. He thinks embittered: One puts muzzles on dogs, one puts bars on windows, everywhere there are fences, pillars, locks, red lights, light houses, signals, warnings: BEWARE, DANGEROUS DOG! WATCH FOR THE TRAIN! IT IS DANGEROUS TO BEND FORWARD! HIGH VOLTAGE! (And the Maestro laughs) POISON! To protect you even better, they scare you with a dead man's skull; experts on trains, seas and in the air, experts in police stations guard you and your two shoes from burglars and collectivists. In each capital an expert protects you from an unexpected attack with pacts, alliances, friendships and, in general, he guards your interests abroad. Pastors guard your soul, statesmen guard your body. Moreover, they compete, even fight over who will protect you better. So they perfume you with incense and sprinkle you with holy water. They insure you with sacraments and blessings—that's for the soul, and for the body—they surround you with powerful safety devices: The People's Union, Non-Aggression and Mutual Assistance Pact, Maginot Line, Siegfried Line, with cannons, tanks, U-boats, airplanes, guns, mines, bayonets, pistols, in one word—with an impenetrable circle of fire and steel. They tell you: "Here you are safe now and don't be foolish to despair. We are here, you can sleep peacefully."

Sleep . . . But, no, gentlemen, you misunderstood me. I, of course, I feel safe with you, I mean with your clever and powerful protection. And I am not afraid of anyone while you are here. But when I fall asleep, then you are gone, then I am alone and dumb like some kind of an idiot. Do you see what I dream? How can I sleep? I am afraid of the dagger. Of this paper knife. In your circle, safe from fire, pacts and bayonets—don't be surprised—I am very poorly protected from myself! I am panic-stricken like a scorpion. What can I do, I am a scorpion. And if you don't let me out, I am afraid that I shall inject myself with the deadly injection, just like a scorpion, out of despair!

It occurs to him that he ought to lie down after all. But why, when Van der Liebe will appear immediately frantic on account of his terrible death and mumble insanely: "Give me back my head, thieves, give me back my head, head, head. . . ."

Melchior leaned against the window. The barracks still sleep. Like a dog the guard crept into the watch-box and there he dozes tormented by military dreams. Here, in the neighboring house lives a young woman in the last stages of pregnancy. What will she give birth to? A daughter. When she grows up a little but she will teach her that a woman holds three corners of the house and that the husband holds only the fourth corner. (Who will hold the corners when the bomb falls?) If she gives birth to a son, the father will provide for his FUTURE which could last even longer than three months. He will buy him a rifle with a spring and tin soldiers. Let the boy play. The boy will stand guard the whole day long in front of *their house,* as that soldier across the street in front of the barracks. He will shoot at the unarmed children— the enemies from neighboring streets. And when in the evening the father comes home, he will shoot at the father: "Bang! Daddy, I killed you. You are dead, daddy, lie down." Daddy is worried and serious, he doesn't pay attention to the child's play. He carries a newspaper in his hands, a special edition. The boy is mad that daddy won't lie down when he is dead and with a killer's fury he shoots again: Bang! But daddy isn't falling. In despair the boy throws himself on the floor pounding with his fists and crying because one doesn't respect the rules of his game. "Why won't you satisfy the child?," the mother interferes. "What? Should I die in order to satisfy him?" Father doesn't feel like joking. "Well, for the sake of the game . . . O, you are impossible." "Soon we shall indeed play a game," says the father anxiously. The boy listens slyly to the conversation, and, when he realizes the futility of mother's intervention, he screams even louder. In the end father spanks him and chases him to bed. In bed, hurt, he sobs in the dark. Later he hears in his sleep father and mother talking in bed in a low voice. Mother cries and father tosses sighing: "If only the child were not here!" And the boy thinks: "Father says of me that it would be better if I did not exist. All right, tomorrow morning I shall kill myself with the rifle in the woodshed," and he thinks about how he will put a little stone in the barrel and discharge it into his eye.

Leaning against the window, thinking about this little drama, he didn't even notice that day was dawning. A grey cloud in the middle of the sky started to turn slightly red. From its height it spotted the sun below the horizon.

Far away the trains are humming, the early trains depart.

Melchior greets the morning from the window: "Good morning, Morning! Welcome! Ho, I . . . I live!" But this was only a moment of welcome. "O, I live . . . so what?" A dull and desperate anxiety seized him again. In his whole body he felt a strange and repulsive fear.

The landlady got up. One can hear her reel and tread in the twilight, still drunk from the sleep. Intentionally, she bumped his door with the elbow and mumbled: "He is awake all night. . . ."

Melchior felt the cold metal of the knife in his hand and shuddered from strange repulsion. Hastily he went out to the staircase and entered the landlady's apartment. He caught her before the bathroom door, dishevelled, flabby and squashed from the sleep.

"Again you did not sleep?" She gathered the robe on her bosum hiding her girllike and still ambitious breasts.

Please, take this knife m'am.

He is dressed, pale, with deep blue circles under his eyes. She looks at him almost with fear.

"What's the matter with you, Mr. Melchior? Why do you give me the knife?"

"Beside it I have nightmares."

"O, I also dream about those damned knives! And about snakes."

But she grabbed the knife with a certain passion. Melchior noticed that.

"Take a husband again, m'am. You are still in your prime."

"And why don't you take a wife?"—she replied with fresh morning coquetry.

Returning to his room, Melchior thought about Vivian. About Enka too. Her knife. In her dreams they don't thrust knives into her belly as they do to the poor landlady. Her dreams are like the cat's, about night mouse hunting.

From the nearby park a bird announces itself: Chi-chi-ko, chi-chi-ko. . . .

"Chichikov . . . Chichikov . . ." replied Melchior to her with literary sarcasm. "Dead souls. Now let's lie down with a dead soul"—he barely succeeded to utter, falling on the bed dead from sleepless nights and exhaustion.

Maria Malby

Vjekoslav Kaleb

(1905–   )

Vjekoslav Kaleb is a short story writer and novelist. Born in Tijesno, near Ši-benik, he graduated from a teacher's college and taught in many Croatian towns. Apart from the collection of novelettes which appeared during the Second World War, *Na kamenju* (*On the Rocks*, 1940) and *Izvan stvari* (*Outside of Things*, 1942), Kaleb has also published two other groups of novelettes *Brigada* (*The Brigade*, 1947) and *Hronike dana* (*Chronicles of the Day*, 1947), and the novels *Ponižene ulice* (*Humiliated Streets* 1950); *Divota prašine* (*The Beauty of Dust* 1954), and *Bijeli kamen* (*The White Stone* 1955).

His novels usually draw on the last war for their setting. *The Beauty of Dust* is the odyssey of two partisans who have lost their unit and make their way through territory in which friends are few and unarmed, while foes are numerous and powerful. *The White Stone* depicts the area behind the battle lines, a small island village of thirty-one houses at the beginning of the war.

Kaleb's story "The Guest" is typical of some of his writings in which he "observes separate details with the reciprocity of naive man, or a child, and subsequently, by association makes them meaningful with the lucidness of an irrationalist."[1]

THE GUEST

Three of them sat in the dark house under the ceiling of sooty beams: Frane on the log near the fire, Mara at the low table, mixing thick hominy for supper, their half-witted daughter squatting on the chest near the wall, preying like a wild cat.

The day had not been interesting; the boredom of a holiday had worn them out and made them quiet, so they rolled into the evening

---

[1]Svetozar Koljević, ed. *Yugoslav Short Stories* (London: Oxford University Press, 1966), p. 377.

as if into lukewarm water; nesting in the evening, feeling about its palace with their antennae, seeking pleasure like crabs on a rock.

"Praised be Thy Name . . .," Mara murmured, glancing through door at the glow sinking in the west behind the hill and through the leaves of almond and vine, sending only a little of its light into the house; the woman seemed to be afraid of the approaching night, of the uncertain journey through sleep, of vanishing until the morrow.

"With God's help . . .," she sighed.

The anxiety thawed from Frane's face . . . he obeyed: the bell from the church flung thin peals of sound which, like night swallows, prodded the darkness in ecstasy and sweetly vanished in the distance. An out stretched hand made the sign of the cross, a prayer was murmured, the whole soul, sleepy, carried on the waves of the tolling, was lost in the solemn calm of the evening as if in a more beautiful tomorrow.

When the last sound and vibration of the bells had died away slowly, the air was empty again, the pattern of silence fell on all things and pressed them to the earth like a dead body; everything—the whitewashed wall, the earth floor, the old furniture, the bed, the low table in the middle, the chest next to the wall, the hearth, the cask—was frightened into silence. The neighborhood must also have vanished, not a voice came from it.

At last Mara crossed herself again, and seeing that the weak fire was gaining over the light from outside, she lit the little oil-lamp hanging from a beam in the middle of the house.

"There is a little more fuel left in it, let it burn," she said.

Under her dishevelled hair the daughter's eyes flickered with the reflections of the light, kindling a cobweb of reddish-yellow sparks; she stared without a thought through the door into the yard.

"Hem!" She spoke up suddenly, her voice tart, her look focused on the entrance.

Mara looked at her, then at the door.

She started and frowned.

From the door two gentle, intelligent eyes were watching, calm and lonely as two candles at the altar. There was a big spaniel standing at the door, with long grey hair, his thin brown ears hanging, plastered to his cheeks like two pieces of velvet. He was strangely quiet, solemn, and his color matched the darkness; only his eyes stood out. He looked at the people intensely but acceptingly, expecting a sign of good will. Their looks were also fixed for a time upon his intelligent eyes, anticipation, trying to find out what he was up to.

They thought he was going to speak.

So they looked at each other for a while like three people and a dog, in expectation, and then the guest realized that nobody was saying a word, and so he stepped over the threshold and entered the house.

"Jesus Christ!" said the young woman quietly, her eyes wide with suspicion.

The beautiful, distinguished-looking beast stopped at the table and looked at the woman again.

His look seemed to her inquisitive, somehow full of wisdom and furtive knowledge. She looked aside.

She turned to her husband.

"H'm, it seems he has got something to tell us!"

"H'm?" His face was more serious now; there was suspicion in it, a shade of fear and respect.

"Yes, yes . . . that one. . . ."

Dawning hope was perhaps awakening in him like an old memory: a strange, trifling occurrence sometimes brings the desired change to a home. When the light hid like this behind the hill, disappearing, and the darkness covered everything like an old witch, like a clucking hen hatching under her feathers a new tomorrow, then hopes and fears swarmed in silence, by the fire, in the light of the oil-lamp, strangely shaped hopes and fears, like the castles in clouds created by the embers and the bluish flames playing on them. This is a different entertainment every day.

Frane wiped the strange thought from his brow and said, sobered against his will: "Let's have supper."

The woman moved towards the table.

She put a yellow lump of hard hominy into a small bowl and passed it to her daughter on the chest, and she and her husband began to eat together from the big bowl.

The dog came to Frane and looked eagerly at the spoonfuls of food, following them with his eyes from bowl to mouth.

The two old people glanced at him with caution, evading his look;

their nostrils sniffed the refined scents emanating from the dog, as if a doctor had entered the house.

"Where is His Grace from?" Mara asked vaguely of her husband or the dog, expecting the answer rather from the dog.

And Frane looked inquisitively at the guest.

And he, instead of saying something, just raised his front leg and his front paw dropped on Frane's knee.

Frane was worried. He cut a piece of hominy with his spoon and threw it on the floor.

The dog just looked at the yellow lump on the black floor without budging.

"He must have it on a plate," said the woman. She reached for the wooden plate cautiously, put several lumps of food on it, and took it to a corner of the house.

"Here it is . . . this . . . if you please. . . ."

The dog understood. He took his paw down from Frane's knee, approached the plate, and slowly, beginning with the smaller lumps, ate the hominy.

After this he was not interested in their supper any more, but he sat as before on his hind legs in the middle of the house and began to watch his hosts again, first one, then the other.

It became quite dark, an early autumn evening. The fire in the hearth was dying, the house lit only with the flame of the oil-lamp. Mara, respectful of the guest, raised the wick and improved the flame. A merry grin appeared on the daughter's face, her eyes flickering with curiosity. Frane looked from below his reddish eyebrows, new thoughts cropping up. Suddenly his eyes began to blink, as if he were thinking hard, and then he got up, straightened his back, and stood very solemnly in the middle of the house.

"Pour a little wine," he said significantly.

There were steps in the yard.

Neighbor Spirkan came in.

"Good evening. . . ." He stopped. "And whose dog is this?"

"I don't know," answered Frane.

The neighbor's little son Jerko peeped from the door, with a look of surprise, questioning the dog and the inmates.

"A distinguished-looking animal. Looks like a human being."

"He has said: 'Good evening,' " the daughter remarked.

"H'm?" Spirkan looked at each of them in turn; then at the dog, his eyebrows raised.

The women started, as if stung.

"Has he?... I haven't heard!"

Spirkan examined the dog again, more carefully, then he questioned them with his eyes, suspiciously: why were they hiding the truth from him?

But he did not say a word.

Little Jerko ran away from the door.

Frane, as if wanting more light in the room, went to the hearth and put some wood on the fire. He moved with solemnity, taking no notice of Spirkan.

They sat around the fire on the old logs, as if retiring to take counsel. The flashes from the flames began to dance on their faces, and the shadows danced on the wall.

The dog also stepped towards the hearth, but stopped humbly a little away from it. His head and eyes, lit by fire, stood out against the dark background.

They could see him well. But they shut themselves in this square of the hearth, in its light and warmth, as if protected by a real fence. Somewhere far away they felt the strange animal, with its illuminated face peeping through the wall of darkness into their corner. Who could tell whether these eyes were bringing good or evil.?

They worded carefully the thoughts which occurred to them.

"You see, winter's coming. . . ."

"It's a hard lot, brother, hard . . . life's bad for a farmer."

"And Heaven knows if . . ."

Then some inquisitive people began to drop in from the village: "Frane's got a strange dog!"

The old bell-ringer Markutina turned up, too, hoarse and asthmatic, with bushy mustache, one eye rolled out, its lids inside out, red like a living wound.

"Oho-ho—who is this guest?" He was a little pleased, as he was always pleased with every change and any news, even if it was not good.

He noticed the calm, intelligent eyes, almost like a human's watching from below.

"You see . . . he looks like a person. . . ."

"He has said: 'Good evening'," said the daughter.

"Has he?" Markutina looked round, asking everybody in turn.

"Shut up, you fool!" The mother lost her temper, then glanced cautiously at the dog.

Markutina and Spirkan rolled their eyes doubtfully:

"H'm—who knows where he's come from!" whispered Spirkan.

"A strange dog!" said Kazo.

"Eeeee . . ."

"Who knows what he is . . ." said Spirkan and added more loudly, looking at him askance: "Perhaps he understands. . . ."

Saka, a young, hot-tempered farmer, tall and red in the face, interrupted them harshly:

"Whose is he?"

"God knows," sighed the woman, but the trembling of her upper lip betrayed her pride—she and her husband were obviously most important here. "We were just sitting here, here, when he appeared at the door. . . ."

"And says he: 'Good evening' . . . ha, ha, ha. . . ." The daughter gave a short peal of laughter and her face contracted as if shivering with cold.

They all fixed their eyes first upon the daughter and then upon the guest sitting quietly in the middle of the house blinking as if he had nothing to do with what was going on. They meant to enrich time with their expectations, but the dog suddenly got up, approached the bed, sniffed it carefully, and jumped on to it. From the bed, above them he looked at all the audience, as if asking permission, sniffed the middle of the bed, kneaded it with his paws, turned three times, in an ordinary doglike way, curled up—and lay down with his snout under his tail.

At once he began to breathe wearily and murmur, closing his eyes.

The audience moved little by little towards the bed, and went on with their business in a circle.

"Look how beautifully he has lain down...like a real gentleman," a woman warbled kindly.

"He has taken his place, as they say . . .," said Nikac.

"Intruded into another man's house. . . . And who's to pay for the expenses?" said Frane's sister loudly, so that the guest should hear.

"Ah, you can't help it, the animal is tired. . . . Who knows how far he's come?" Nikac resumed his flattery.

"Or if the devil himself is in him. . . ." Markutina stopped in fear.

"Of course . . . what else? . . ." added Kazo with a breath of malice, eager to spoil Frane's hopes. He turned and moved away a little, as if the guest might jump up in self-defense.

"Whoever he is," Frane flared up like straw on fire, "he's come to my house. There's no need for your quibbling! I shall . . ." The words were extinguished in doubt.

"This is what I'm going to do." Saka grasped the handle of the axe in the corner.

"No, no . . . don't!" Mara was afraid.

The dog looked at her, gentle and sleepy, and blinked innocently. It was obvious that he was not trying to follow the conversation.
It was abvious that he was not trying to follow the conversation.

"Leave him alone, leave him alone. . . ." Frane frowned, pretending boredom.

"Brothers," Spirkan spoke up solemnly, "our village, for instance. . . . Ah, who wants to come to our desert. . . . What was I going to say? . . . This must have been an act of grace. . . . Our village which has been abandoned by God and men . . . that is to say. . . ." He looked at the dog and stopped, then looked at the others as if asking: Is this how one should put it?—and inviting them to help him.

"What village? Damn the village. I protest . . . this has nothing to do with the village, this is my house, and I want to have this clearly established . . .," Frane shouted resolutely and glanced at the dog.

Everybody was silent.

"Eh, my God," Nikac began wisely. "Eh, my God, who knows if we live by what God gives us. . . . Who knows what brings luck, what brings misfortune. . . ."

Frane looked around the audience expecting approval. They all stood thinking, eager with curiosity, full of their own zest, silent, refusing to deserve the merit for the good or take responsibilitly for the evil; looking at the fine, distinguished animal with its silky hair and intelligent eyes.

"Let's say the rosary to the glory of Holy Mary," said Spirkan's sister, old spinster Kata.

"H'm?" Everybody stared at her, but the interest was soon exhausted.

Kata's round eyes and her pedantically sharpened mouth showed that she expected her suggestion to become significant.

"I tell you he hasn't come to the house just like that. . . ." Nikac agreed with what he had said before.

Then Spirkan began in a flattering voice, glancing kindly at the dog, unwilling to give offense, even going so far as to praise it:

"Dogs can be very, very intelligent animals . . . very intelligent. . . . A major had a dog, and the dog always bought his newspapers for him. . . ."

Markutina understood the policy behind the argument at once, and in order to make a correction, not letting other people overtake him, he said:

"The dog is man's friend. . . . They say that a dog—and I've heard it with my own ears—has died on his master's grave. . . . The dog's heart broke with grief . . . like a human being's would, my God, there you are."

"And I've heard," Kazo imposed himself again speaking softly, covering his mouth so that the dog would not see it, and trying to make Mara hear him, "that once a master's soul entered the body of his dog, and the dog wandered about the world while the master was lying in bed as though dead, until the dog met a man who was willing to carry him over the nine mountains to the fasting waters. . . ."

"What 'fasting waters'?" Saka asked contemptuously.

"Fasting, fasting, yes. . . ." It was Kazo's turn to show contempt for the question now because he did not know how to answer it. "Over the nine mountains he had to carry the dog."

"For Christ's sake!" exlaimed Mara softly and looked at the dog with fear.

The women's eyes were sparkling.

"Then," Kazo went on, "and then. . . ."

"Ouuuuuuummmmuumm . . .," murmured the dog in its sleep and Kazo stopped agape.

The silence was intense and watchful.

The hosts were very worried.

Markutina, who was the bell-ringer and the beadle, approached Frane, his face conscious of his professional qualifications, and whispered:

"I would send for the parson," and he looked carefully at the dog.

"Yes," said Frane, "we could, to hear what he would have to say."

"Well, Saka could go."

Frane took Saka aside.

"Come, let Luka lend you his horse, and go and bring the parson. . . . You will be back by nine."

Saka scratched his head.

"H'm?" And he looked at the dog, sleeping quietly now, very solemn.

Frane managed with difficulty to persuade Saka to go to the village with another man and bring the parson.

When Saka was gone, Spirkan spoke up very seriously:

"I wouldn't have sent for the parson . . . nnno. . . . You see that the beast . . . I mean this one . . . is lying quietly like a lamb. . . . Who knows what a parson's wisdom may bring on us. . . ."

Frane was worried again.

Mara waved her arms.

"Brothers, what's this? . . . Why has he come to our house?"

"I would kill him, and have done with it!" someone said behind another's back.

"Wait, wait. . . ." Kazo pushed the others aside. "I'll be nice to him and just ask him what he wants. . . ."

"Ah, you, why should you ask him, why should you? . . . What right do you have to claim wisdom?" Markutina pushed him angrily, afraid that this might come to an end without the parson.

"Well, I, I, I . . . ." Kazo brought his finger close to Markutina's eyes.

"Mmmmm." Markutina turned to him sideways and challenged him with his elbow.

"Nothing, it's nothing. . . ." Frane raised his arms solemnly. "Nothing. . . ." It seemed that he was going to say something very significant.

At this moment the dog got up. He looked absent-mindedly at the audience: he was not surprised that they were so many. He stretched himself very competently, yawned, and shook in a doglike way from head to tail. Then suddenly he became matter-of-fact: he jumped to the floor and walked in his most ordinary way to the door, without looking at anybody, not even at Frane, who was standing nearest to him with his arms folded on his breast as if he were in front of his own shop.

Everybody retreated quickly and made way for the dog.

They turned their heads after him, they stretched their necks a little, but their feet remained in the same place.

The dog could be seen in the moonlight outside, stopping at the gate of the yard, raising his leg, like a quite ordinary dog, wetting the threshold, and disappearing into the night.

Svetozar Koljević

Ivan Dončević

(1909–   )

Ivan Dončević was born in a farming family in the village of Moslavina. After having attended a college of writing and journalism, he devoted himself to writing. Dončević belongs to the circle of distinguished contemporary Croatian writers. In his writing up to the Second World War, he wrote mainly about the life and people in his village, Moslavina. After the war, he published some of his best collections of short stories: *Bezimeni* (Nameless, 1945); *Četiri priče* (Four Stories, 1948), and *Mirotvorci* (The Peacemakers, 1953). These stories are noted for his inclination to write about "the small man," describing his moral and physical courage. *The Insect Collector*, written in 1953, describes life in Croatia's capital, Zagreb.

THE INSECT COLLECTOR

My name is Marjan Lesnjak, but even while I was still in high school they gave me the nickname of Suleiman and today they still call me that although I've never had anything to do with the religion of the Turks. I don't mind the nickname, it's not an insulting one. What's more, when they call me Suleiman, they usually add "the Great," and this, it must be admitted, is not insulting at all. Apart from that, the Turks have always appealed to me, regardless of the "Turkish heel" and all the other things the blind bards sing about (but then I expose myself to the danger of having my patriotism questioned). Despite everthing, I still say the religion of the Turks is the best, most beautiful, and most reasonable of all the religions I know. So I don't get at all angry about my nickname! But what does make me angry is my not being able to remember how I got it and what it was all about. So that I'm really only angry at myself, and that's allowed because I don't do anyone else any harm.

I'm angry because that's what my nature is like, a nature that is not simple. Anyway, who in this world is simple? It's quite clear to me that I'm not simple, but rather complicated—even very complicated; but for that very reason interesting and unusual, although the people around me don't think so. On the contrary, they think that I'm a sleepyhead, a mouse, a quiet simpleton who doesn't even know how to count to five, or something of the sort, and I let them think so and go on repeating to myself: "Just go on being silly, my friends, I know what I know and some day you'll have to reckon with me. . . ." I do know how to console myself, that's a fact. But alone with myself, in my room among my insects, I let my anger get the best of me; and a boundless anger it is, too. I look at myself in the mirror and see a terrible gloomy face with buring eyes—sometimes the look in those eyes frightens me. And that's when my insects take over. Bravo, insects! I have a wonderful collection of insects. I am no expert, no entomologist, but I've had this hobby of collecting insects as an amateur since I was a boy. My collection is neatly divided up into cardboard boxes of equal size with plastic covers that I make myself and the insects, stuck on their pins, can be seen through them. I am proud of this collection although there is no rare specimens in it like, for instance, the ones that live in underground caves and haven't even been given name a yet. No, my collection is made up of ordinary, or should I say, domestic insects, from butterflies and houseflies of all sorts and sizes to wasps, hornets, grasshoppers, bumblebees, stag beetles, praying mantes, darning needles, cockroaches, ladybugs, horn bugs, spiders, stinkbugs, May bugs, cicadas, dung beetles, scarabs, and hundreds of others. But no matter how ordinary it is, to me it is a wonderful collection. What would I do without it? I spend all my free time with it, since I have no wife, no children, no sweetheart or friend. So I am committed to loneliness and to them, my insects. And when I get angry, when people insult and humiliate me, then the insects are the ones I vent my anger on and that makes it easier for me. For instance, the director of our company is a rude, hot-tempered man. He comes into the room where we're working, rolls his bulging, spectacled eyes around the room, and stops right behind me. "And you," he rasps right in my ear, "turn the page for a change, draw a line, add something, subtract something, make a mark on the page, do anything—but just do it, don't just sit there sleeping! What the devil were you doing last night?" He leaves. Actually, I was adding up figures in the ledger very industriously, I had become completely absorbed in my work, but am I to blame if my face always looks sleepy? What a beast that director is! But I'll get even with him. My time will come, and then he'll sing a different tune. Just you wait, brother, just you wait. But I have to go slowly and not do anything silly that would spoil everything ahead of time. At home I go to my collection and find the box with the hornets. The hornet is just like our director, sleek and yellow. Then I take an awl and say with the greatest pleasure that can be imagined: "Take this awl in the neck— and again in the neck—and again—and that's for saying I was sleeping when I was not sleeping, because I hate you, take this. . . ." After I finish, I quiet down. That's the way I lose my temper (and my temper is terrible) and that's the way my insects help me overcome my rage. I have every one of the people who ever insulted me, or made fun of me, or did anything bad to me, stuck on a pin an preserved in one of those boxes of mine. For instance, the janitor, a replusive and malicious old crone, is the horsefly, and the lazy waiter in the restaurant where I eat is the dung beetle, and the head bookkeeper in our company is the scarab, while the chief of accounting is a stinkbug (he smokes the foulest tobacco imaginable). And so on down the line. Every one of them has felt the awl in his neck at least once.

How wrong people can be! They think I'm a quiet and timid fellow who bears all insults with resignation like the early Christians. They think I have no brains or strength and that I was born for them to make a monkey out of me. How wrong they are, how wrong they are! I have more brains and strength than all of them put together and enough passion to roast anything touching me if I'd only unleash it, but I go on smiling shyly, I withdraw; deliberately, intentionally I hold back, and because I hold back, people take it the wrong way. But the devil with them! It's better that way than if they saw through me and realized my intentions, which are really horrible, which. . . . But it's better not to say anything about that. That is my secret—a gruesome secret.

Not long ago I celebrated my fortieth birthday. I'm not superstitious, I don't believe in fortunetelling—that's all a lot of nonsense, as foreign to me as it is to any reasonable man who has seen for himself that only science can uncover life's secrets. But I am just as convinced, in contrast to most reasonable people, that the stars have an effect on man's character, and therefore on his destiny, and that this influence is not bunk, or mysticism, or superstition, but a scientific fact. Because astrology is a science like any other. What is more, in my opinion it is more exact than philosophy or political economy. I have consulted two astrologers in my life. One of them was a woman, even a very attractive woman, blond, plump, middle-aged. She had very intelligent, moist gray eyes and fine hands, and I fell a little in love with her. The second was an old man of dignified bearing with a beautiful gray beard, curly and cut off straight like those of the Assyrian kings. They drew up my horoscope on the basis of information they asked me for, and they did so independently of each other. They discovered strange things, quiet identical. Not only did they describe my character with astonishing accuracy and explain certain things unknown even to me, but they described all the important events in my life that no one but I could have known about. I learned, for instance, that I was born under the sign of Cancer, that I was susceptible to rheumatism, circulatory diseases, and disorders of the liver, that I was timid in affairs of the heart, that my lucky number was seven, and my lucky day Monday. I also learned that I had chosen the wrong profession and should have been a pharmacist, male nurse, sailor, musician, or historian, and in no case a bookkeeper: this stupid occupation was probably the source of all my misfortunes. Then I learned—and this was the most important of all—that there would be a great turning point in my life after I had passed forty, a turning point that would be of decisive importance for me and for those around me. Forty years of age! Fearfully I waited for my fortieth birthday to come and finally, two weeks ago, on June 30th, to be exact, it came. What now? I was excited. What was going to happen in my life, what would happen to shake it to its very foundations and would it now take a turn for the better? I hardly slept or ate for fear of the unknown, for unfortunately human knowledge is limited knowledge and even the wisdom of the astrologers sometimes cannot lay bare secrets. . . .

But the secret laid itself bare and very soon, too. One morning, just as I was leaving the house, it began to rain. It was still raining at about ten o'clock when I looked out the window. It was a cold, gray, drizzling rain, more like autumn than July. I had no umbrella and only canvas shoes on. The director came in and as usual stood next to my desk. I nervously turned a few pages of the ledger and dipped the pen squeakily into the inkwell. But he didn't say a word: just coughed and went on. A little later he called me to him. "A discharge," flashed through my mind; the doorknob to the director's office was wet with perspiration from my hand, I quaked in my trousers, and because of this I blushed like a schoolboy.

"Sit down," said the director, smiling and offering me a cigarette.

"Thank you, I don't smoke," I stammered, while he went on smiling and looking at me over his eyeglasses. Then he lit a cigarette and blew the smoke diagonally over my head.

"And, I," said the director a bit later, blowing the smoke over my head a second time, "I have the idea of putting you up for our Management Board. What do you say to that?"

At first I didn't understand. Probably I just gaped. He then went on to explain his idea at length, but I no longer remember all the details he sketched out for me. But I do remember his saying that he had very strong reasons for choosing me. Since danger no longer threatened me, I began to pull myself together. Aha! He thought I wouldn't be a nuisance to him on the Management Board, that I would simply nod in agreement to all his proposals—those were the real reasons he had for suggesting me! His strong will was well known, lots of people in our company were already openly and loudly complaining about it! But we shall see! He's another one who will get a big shock about me when the time comes.

"Well?" he asked, raising his eyes over the spectacles.

I agreed, of course—why shouldn't I? The secretary hiccoughed two or three times and grew pale when she saw how he escorted me to the door, slapped me on the shoulder, and extended his hand to me. Something like that had never happened before.

It is unbelievable how fast and how thoroughly many of my men and women colleagues changed their attitude toward me after this—precisely those who had been the worst, who had never stopped teasing me and insulting me by saying, for instance, that I had the nicest bald spot of all the baldies, that I was really a dangerous ladies' man but clever to hide it so well, that it was better to be born without a nose than without luck and that I had both to spare, that I was almost certainly very wealthy but keeping my money in a sock for a rainy day, and so on. The dogs never let up, not one opportunity did they pass up to take a stab at me, to humiliate me, and to make a laughing stock out of me. Now they kept quiet, putting their tails between their legs, the rats. Rats and cowards. Now all of a sudden they all behaved so nicely. Mr. Suleiman, they would say, said so-and-so! Did you see, they'd ask, how Mr. Suleiman frowned when they took his eraser from his desk without asking permission? He'd never do that to anyone! How strange it was, they'd say, how you could live with somebody for years, desk to desk, breathe the same air, and all at once you see what a fine and wonderful person he is, a whale of a fellow, and before that you never saw it at all! . . . That's the way they behave with me now, but I know why. I became a member of the Management Board at a critical moment. Our company, as everyone knows, turns out pencil boxes, pens of various kinds, and writing tablets. It is not a big company but it is a solid one, and moreover, it has a monopoly in the state and literally dictates the prices of its products. The buyers kick, but their kicking doesn't bother us one bit; our business dealings are fair and in keeping with sound economy. And since the company does business on these principles, we are often able to distribute bonuses— awards and such; but because of this, naturally we sometimes have arguments and dissatisfaction, which are quite typical of ordinary small men when it comes to handing out money. And it's because of this money, and only because of the money, that everyone is interested in being on good terms with members of the Management Board. And it was because of that cursed money that everyone's attitude toward me changed from the bottom up. But I'm not naive, I can see through their hypocritical intentions and don't fall for that stuff at all; I only scorn them even more—actually they are repulsive to me, I hate them. And I'll get even with them, I'll bet anything that I'll get even with them, because my time has finally come. . . .

Crazy weather, it's raining again. Just a few minutes ago the sun was shining, but then a huge black cloud came, followed by a cloud-burst. Again I had no umbrella and my canvas shoes on. I watched the rain pouring from the window, a muddy stream flowed down the street, people were taking cover in lobbies, and others who were in a hurry jumped funny little jumps over the puddles in the downpour; soaked to the skin, their clothes stuck to them; it was very interesting looking at the women. . . . But the rain stopped soon and the deceitful sun came out from behind the clouds again. I was the last out of the office.

Down in the lobby I found a fellow employee, Irena, from the commercial department, studying the sky and getting ready to go. But when I appeared she smiled, showing all her fine teeth in a face as shiny and freckled as a turkey's egg.

"I was just about to leave," she said, showing her teeth even more.

I nodded to indicate I understood.

"I didn't want to ruin my pumps," she continued, putting out a leg with a dark red shoe, too heavy-looking for my taste. But the leg was very nice, strong and thickly grown with curly chestnut hair, but that did not detract from its looks. Funny I had never noticed before what pretty legs Irena had.

"It's stopped," I said, stepping outside and raising my palm upward. The sun shone brightly from a space between the clouds.

"Actually, I don't usually go in this direction," said Irena as soon as we had started off, "but today I have something to do this way so I hope you don't mind if I go along with you?"

Of course I didn't mind. "What the devil," I thought, and stole a glance at her sideways. She caught the glance and this embarrassed me, but she got very chummy and grabbed my arm. And so we went arm in arm along the wet sidewalk. She was chatting about this and that and smiling while I tried to break in with something witty but didn't succeed. All at once she stopped and asked, squinting: "Where are you going tomorrow?"

"Tomorrow is Sunday," I said, swallowing hard. "I'm going to a soccer game."

"Fine," she said, pressing my arm. "I've got something to do in the Maksimir Park district and I'll be finished at about the same time the soccer game is over. Let's take a walk through Maksimir Park— we can do that without people thinking anything, can't we? After all, we are co-workers."

Again I swallowed hard and of course I had nothing against our taking a little walk through the park after the game.

Afterwards, I felt very good during lunch in the restaurant I eat in and which I otherwise hate. The waiter-dung beetle, a disgusting character, always unshaven, unwashed, with dirty hands and finger-nails, a lazybones and spiteful creature who had in it for me and tortured me in the most underhanded way, making every mouthful I ate there bitter—even that waiter-dung beetle did not seem as impossible and unbearable as usual that day. I even smiled and said something pleasant to him when he pushed the plate of dishwater that is supposed to be soup under my nose while moistening his repulsive fingers in it. And I paid the cashier-wasp a compliment, telling her she had a lovely necklace. It was really a cheap thing from the bazaar, made of green glass beads and in very poor taste. With her long thin neck and the necklace, she really looked frightful, but I paid the woman a compliment anyway because of my own good disposition. She blushed and then paled with vanity and gave me such a sweet look that my conscience pricked me for the outright lie I had told. I even got scared that the lie might have some unpleasant consequences. But inside me, I sent the cashier and the consequences to the devil. At home I took out my boxes right away, pondered a long time selecting the one I wanted, and at long last chose the ladybug, or, as she is sometimes called, God's lambkin. That day Irena had been wearing a red dress with white polka dots so that the ladybug with its polka dots bore the closest resemblance to her. Sweet little ladybug! Tenderly I touched the round wings of the enchanting insect and as I did so I felt an unknown rapture fill my heart, while shivers of pleasure went up and down my spine as though from a wave of low voltage current. . . . And still there are people who say that astrologers are swindlers! And here my time was coming, coming with mathematical precision, all the signs said it was so. . . .

I felt wonderful at the soccer game, too. My club was not playing so that I wasn't too excited; the game was poorly played and uninteresting, but I felt wonderful nevertheless. Some bumpkin in a yellow outfit tripped up an opponent in a green outfit who fell and writhed in pain on the grass. I have a great feeling of fair play and yelled, "Dammit, that's the way butchers play. Damn!" A thick neck in front of me began to turn around. "If I show you how butchers play," he rasped from a pimply and unshaved snout that he stuck under my chin, "If I show you. . . ." His dull eyes squinted in the fat face, crawling over me as though looking for something. "Goal! Bravo, yellow! Get going, yellow!" the enthusiastic fans around me started yelling at just the right moment. Hats were thrown in the air, the snout in front of me disappeared, and I sighed with relief. But a little later, the greens got a goal, the thick neck began to turn around again, again the dull swinish eyes studied the lines of my face. "The damned butcher," I thought, sensing danger, "he's obviously looking for a fight," So I turned a little to the right as though speaking to the fellow next to me and said, "That goal the greens got is no goal at all. It's a crime! They got it from an offside position! And what kind of referee is that? Into the drink with him! It's a scandal!" That's the way I spoke, as though talking to my neighbor, and this, it seemed, softened up the butcher: his piggish eyes squinted and teared and I thought how his eyes would squint and tear in the same way if someone tickled their owner a little on the soles of his feet. The neck began to turn again it turned for a long time, then went back again and finally stayed in its normal position. I felt wonderful because I had gotten the better of that devil. I felt wonderful because the greens won in the end anyway; the butcher was pale and downcast and mumbled something unintelligible to himself. I was feeling wonderful for other reasons, too.

Irena was already waiting for me. Some young men, muscular and sun-tanned, were rowing on the lake, showing off their skill and their biceps, which they strained more than was necessary (I hate those addle-brained adolescents who ruffle their feathers in front of any skirt). Irena was standing under a tree, swinging her purse and probably stealing glances at the biceps. Although she had become attractive (or even dear) to me overnight, still I wasn't crazy enough to forget the real truth about women as the Bible describes them—that is, that woman is a deceitful creature, faithless and unclean, that she is capable of betraying her husband, friend, or lover at the first opportunity she gets. . . . But maybe I was being unjust to Irena? As soon as she noticed me coming, she looked so sincerely happy that she almost fell on my neck when I reached her, she did not even look at the young snots any more! I still say that women are what the Bible says they are, but I also say that there are honorable exceptions. And why shouldn't Irena be just such an honorable exception?

Well, the devil take me if she wasn't the cutest girl I knew! Where could my eyes have been that I hadn't noticed it before? She had the prettiest and most desirable body I had ever seen (with a dress on, naturally) and she was so slender and well built and lively and flexible, her luxuriant chestnut hair falling to her shoulders in a sort of old-fashioned style (but even that was nice), the skin of her bare hands the healthiest, softest, most velvety and cool skin I had ever touched. I had touched her unintentionally when we met, but she didn't get angry, just squinted a little and burst into laughter. I also noticed then that she had strange yellowish eyes (which probably shone in the dark) and that the freckles on her face were not at all a shortcoming but an advantage. They made her face resemble—if I may use a poetic expression—a fresh, dewy, reddish-yellow peach. "What the devil," I thought, greatly excited, "how nice that is: like a peach!"

We walked along the path between the oaks. Here and there on the benches couples sat, embracing. Evening falls in this park much earlier than it does on the street so that during their silly but nevertheless attractive love play the couples in the dusk were protected from the eyes of curiosity seekers and the malicious glances of promenaders.

"I love nature," chatted Irena ceaselessly, "I love nature, nature is my big weakness. Can you feel the smells coming out of the earth? Oh, that smell of decaying leaves and mushrooms! I don't like the decaying leaves, but I love mushrooms. Listen to the frogs." She pressed my arm firmly, we stopped, she leaned her head on my shoulder, and for a while we listened to the frogs croaking in the pond under the water lilies, "I like frogs too." she whispered softly as we left. "Are you sorry," she suddenly asked seriously, "are you sorry to be walking outdoors like this with me? No? Be honest, tell me what you think, because I only like honest people." Then she moved away from me a little. "I'm probably boring you. . . no, no! Don't deny it, I'm sure that I'm boring you to death with my blabbing. But what can I do?"

I assured her at length that I didn't find her boring—on the contrary, whatever she said was terribly interesting.

"All right, then, let's sit down on this bench," she said, and drew me down on a nice bench, half hidden by the bushes, "and let's turn the record on the other side. Have you ever been very much in love?" And she lit a cigarette.

"No, I haven't," I answered quick as a shot. "No, I've never been in love."

"That's interesting," she said.

"But maybe I will be," I continued, blushing as red as a beet, but she couldn't see that in the dark.

"Really interesting. Just go on."

"As I said, maybe I will be. All of us are bound to fall in love once in our lives."

"That's true. Just go on, I'm terribly curious."

"That's all there is," I burst out, and saw immediately that what I had just said wouldn't do, that I must seem awfully funny to her, and stupid as well. I felt ashamed but there was no help for it. That's the way I am, "timid in affairs of the heart"—that was it and still there were idiots who dared say astrology was a swindle.

A stupid silence ensued. Irena tapped her foot nervously, inhaled quickly two or three times, then threw the cigarette away gloomily. The red tip of the cigarette described an arc in the dark and sizzled out. I didn't know what to do. I was clumsy, there it was; I stretched out my legs and clasped my hands behind my head; I was bathed in perspiration but I didn't know what to do. It's a funny thing with me. I notice everything around me. I can feel things that are not so obvious at first glance, I can tell precisely what people's intentions are no matter how they try to hide them, I see everything, I know everything, I guess everything, but I do everything wrong, completely wrong. There is no doubt, for instance, that this girl was offering herself to me, that she was after me openly; I can see that and it panders to my vanity that a young and pretty girl is after me and offers herself to me. So? So nothing. Instead of grasping the gift that offers itself to me, I perspire like an idiot, stretch my legs, clench my fists, and don't know what to do with myself or with her. Stupid, really stupid.

But fortunately Irena was not stupid. She was quiet for a time. probably offended, tapped her foot nervously, again lit a cigarette and again threw it away, and even sighed audibly two or three times. Then all at once she moved up very close to me—as though nothing had happened. She's wonderful. I adore her. Now she was talking about the ordinary things at the office.

"I don't like that office," she said simply and quietly, as though we had just been talking about it. "The people there aren't nice, they play all sorts of underhanded tricks on each other whenever they get a chance, they're all mad at one another, egotistic, envious, no character, but what can I do? You have to earn your living somehow. But I'd be happy if I were out of that place, any place, just not in that office."

"I don't like the people in our office either." I grabbed wildly at a subject in which I felt quite at home. And immediately I felt easier.

"I don't like politics, and today politics is all that counts," continued Irena. "I hear some bonuses are going to be given out, but I know that when they are, I'll get nothing at all."

"How can you be sure?" I wanted to console her.

"Like that," she replied, "I'm just sure of it. Because they don't look at the person, they look at his politics."

"That's true, "but maybe it won't be like that."

"What do you mean?"

"Simply that. Maybe something has changed."

"I don't understand. Why should things have changed? And how have they changed? I'm sorry, but I really don't understand you."

"Leave that to me," I said finally.

"Oh!" she exclaimed.

We didn't talk about the office any longer. I felt exceptionally fine. I felt like a man who had become conscious of his power to do this or that, as he chose; the power was there, it was only necessary to exercise it. I'll eat my hat if I don't put up such a fuss in that Management Board tomorrow that those gentlemen will lose all desire to go on with their tricks. Enough of that business! Are we in the jungle? What had this poor girl done wrong? They were envious of her, that was it! She was young and pretty, and if she'd go to bed with them, then they'd sing a different tune. . . . I know them; I know them, those office bigwigs! But this is the death knell for their arrogance, I'll eat my hat if it isn't the end, and never again will this dear creature have to complain of their injustice. That's the way it is and that's the way it's going to be, I can tell you! It would have been better if they had drafted the most poisonous scorpion into that Management Board rather than me. . . . I felt wonderful; an invisible power and self-confidence and determination had flowed into me. And that poor girl drew even closer to me, she was so close that I felt the warmth of her breast at my left shoulder and the warmth made me dizzy, so dizzy I had to squint. Then she put her hand on my knee and . . . and what was I supposed to do? To grab that hand, to draw her near, to nestle my head in her breast that was rising and falling rapidly, to . . . Damn it? Time passed and I did nothing. The hand rested on my knee for a while and then trembled nervously, the fingers spreading and contracting (I heard her nails scratching dryly on the trouser material), then the hand slipped and withdrew. Finally the girl said in an unnaturally deep, hoarse voice: "It's already late, let's go."

I stood up and we left. The whole way to the streetcar stop we didn't say a word. I was ashamed. But at the streetcar stop she put her sweet little face next to mine, her smiling, freckled, dear little face, a little paler than usual (probably from the night dampness), and said:

"I have time tomorrow, too. If you want to, we can see each other again in the afternoon. . . ." The streetcar moved, she jumped up on the running board. "All right?" she yelled.

"Yes, yes, tomorrow. . . ." I waved. Then I waited for the next streetcar.

I was ashamed, it's true, but I consoled myself. Who says I'm a wax saint? That simply is not true. I'm not a wax saint, or a bungler, or a coward. I just don't have enough experience with women. And I am a bit too shy. But we'll see tomorrow, tomorrow. . . .

The next day the Management Board met in the afternoon. We were to discuss the bonuses; there had been gossip about it for some time. In a sleepy voice the director read out the names and after each name, the sum that was being proposed. For this one, so much, and so on. All right. Accepted. For that one, so much. All right. "It is a cinch," I thought to myself, "sitting on the Management Board and just nodding your head." My name came up too. "All right," the rest of the board said unanimously. "The money will come in handy," I thought. "I'll buy some summer slacks." The bookkeeper's name came next, followed by the accounting head, and then many others. Accepted! Then Irena's name came up. The director said that she did not deserve to get anything because she was neither industrious, nor disciplined, nor did she do her work specially well. He was sorry, personally, continued the director, because she was the only employee not on the bonus list, but taking all the aforementioned facts into consideration, it was only just that she receive nothing. But that was only his proposal, let the others say what they thought! The chief bookkeeper-scarab gave his opinion right away: "I agree with the director's proposal. The woman in question is lazy and indifferent. Apart from that, her private life leaves much to be desired. For the sake of the company's reputation, we ought to go into the matter of her personal life sometime. Perhaps the fact that she will not receive a bonus will have a salutary effect on her." Then the chief accountant-stinkbug took the floor and said: "If certain other things were in question,"—he put special emphasis on the "other things" and winked—" "if certain other things were in question, then this young lady would surely get first prize. But let the young men hanging around on Zrinjevac street and in front of the Dubrovnik Cafe have their say about that. We here are making decisions about specific jobs, isn't that so? Therefore, concluded the chief accountant, lighting a pipe that had gone out while he was talking, "I agree entirely with the director's proposal. Though," he added, "as far as any salutary effect is concerned, I really doubt it." Others then spoke up in the same vein. It was necessary for me to say what I thought. First I blushed profusely and then grew pale (something is wrong with my circulation, I've noticed for a long time), then I stammered something and nodded my head. "I must take care of myself," flashed through my mind, "I must avoid all excitement because, by nature, I am inclined toward diseases of the liver and circulation. Apart from that, it would not be a good thing to cause a scandal at my very first meeting. There's time for that! As a matter of fact, it would even be very stupid to create a scene at the very first meeting. . . ." Those present accepted my nod of approval and no one noticed anything. The meeting was soon over. But how surprised all these good-for-nothings would be some day! I was happy in advance at the thought of how I would fool them.

Irena was washing her hands in the hall sink and smiled at me from afar. Poor Irena! We hardly had time to make the appointment for the afternoon. . . . After that I sat at my desk, did nothing, and boiled with anger. The good-for-nothings! But they'll see who's boss some day when I get hold of them!

Again that afternoon she was at the appointed place ahead of time; I liked that particularly. Again she almost fell on my neck when she saw me, and I liked that too. We followed a stream through the woods and then another one over fields where women were harvesting wheat and tying it up into bundles. All the women down to the very last one one had red bandanas on their heads and looked at us mockingly as we passed. Then we came to another stream and after that to the edge of a pine wood that stretched out along the plateau as far as the eye could see. In the twinkling of an eye Irena had found a half-hidden path through the undergrowth. For a time we went along with bent heads and then came breathless to a clearing. It was a beautiful clearing, shady and carpeted with grass as smooth as silk. Irena threw her bag on the ground and sat down.

"Isn't it beautiful here?" she asked, wiping the perspiration from her shiny, freckled face.

"It is beautiful," I replied.

"You might think I knew every bush, mightn't you?" she continued when she noticed my questioning glance stop at a suspicious-looking box (its color washed away by the rain), a crumpled bit of paper, a ribbon, and all sorts of other things people usually leave behind them. "But I've never been here before," she said, raising her voice. "I only love nature and that's why I find my way around in the woods so well. And this is the first time I've ever been here, my word of honor!"

If she said so, why shouldn't I believe her? Otherwise I really might get the idea that she had already stretched herself out in this nest before. . . .

She watched me from below: her mocking, bold glance seemed to say: here's the chance of a lifetime, and now let's see you do your stuff, brother, let's see what you're worth. . . . That's what women are like! The Bible has already had its say about them, but despite that my heart beats faster when I'm alone with her, with this very Irena, and I'm inclined to believe that she isn't one of the women the Bible is referring to.

"Sit down," she said, continuing to watch me from below with her mocking, bold glance.

I sat politely to one side.

"Sit over here," she said, pointing to the space next to her. "And talk to me. Yesterday you were in poor form."

She didn't have to make fun of me. And she didn't have to plant me so close to her. I tried to talk, but it just didn't work. I spoke disconnectedly about astrology, but I quickly perceived that the subject didn't interest her. Then I spoke about insects, about different kinds, about my insects. She opened her eyes wide, then drew her knees together and rested her chin on them, again squinting at me mockingly and boldly. A little later she stretched out on her back and dug her fingers into her hair. What should I do? My head was spinning. "But why?" I thought with my last bit of consciousness, "why did she plant me so close to her?" But my head was whirling around.

"Ah, bravo," exclaimed Irena suddenly, gently stopping my hand, which had at long last gotten a little courage and dropped to her knee. "Today was the meeting, wasn't it? And I completely forgot about it. Did I or didn't I get anything?"

"Those good-for-nothings," I mumbled casually, because I didn't want anything to obstruct me now that I had started.

"So I got nothing, eh?" she asked stubbornly, pushing away the hand that was getting more and more daring. "Tell me, Did I get anything?"

"Those swine, who . . ."

"So that's it!" she yelled, and sat up.

When I completely lost my head, when I tried to embrace her and sought her lips, mumbling words I'll never be able to repeat again, she pushed me away with all her might and jumped to her feet. I was taken aback. I was hurt. I was like a little dog that gets a kick for no reason at all.

"So, that's it!" she rasped, furiously shaking off bits of grass that clung to her skirt. "So that's it! So the gentlemen have done me in, have they! Lovely!" She seemed to be burning, to be smoking with rage. "They've done me in, by God!" Under her furious blows, her skirt whirled wildly above her head and without embarrassment she showed her legs all the way up to her stomach. (My God, she had lovely legs!)

A stupid situation. But maybe all was not lost.

"Irena," I whined, and licked the spittle from my lips, "Irena, I . . . of course . . . but . . ."

"What do you want?" She stood over me, her arms akimbo. "Look at the liberties you're allowing yourself! Is that the way to behave, eh? Look at him, will you, and he's supposed to be a fellow employee! He couldn't give me support when I needed it, and here . . ." It was only then she remembered to lower her skirt and tuck it between her knees. "Phooey. Shame on you."

Again I whined in a small voice: "Irena . . ."

"Shut up!" she shouted, and continued with revulsion, "You're bald and moldy. Look at the old devil, will you? Look at him, will you! I could be his daughter and he's acting like a hot old goat. Shame on you. Phooey!"

I looked at her wildly.

"And what more would you like to know? Such a handsome fellow, such strength, such a legendary hero! Suleiman the Great! Bah! And actually and insectologist, stinking and good-for-nothing! Go on, get out of here, you old monster, before I . . ." She wanted to say something very vulgar but thought better of it and added, "before I kick you out!"

That, then, was the way it ended. I collected myself slowly, the way a child collects his spilled marbles. I finally came to the conclusion that this dame was the worst bitch I'd ever met, that she had insulted me and humiliated me and mocked me more than anyone else had ever done. Horrible! But what did I do, what in God's name had I done to her that she had to mock me in such a rotten way? Nothing. Nothing at all. Despite all my efforts I couldn't remember a thing I had ever done wrong to her. That was a woman for you: a creature unclean, faithless, and underhanded. . . .

I came home and there was a ringing and roaring in my head. I took out my insects, the whole collection, and laid them out neatly on the table; but even my insects couldn't make me happy this time. I took the disgusting ladybug and pricked her to bits, cutting her up like a butcher: "There, take that in the back—and again in the back—and again—that that for playing around with me so shamelessly, take that for saying I'm bald and old and a monster, take that, you insatiable streetwalker, take that. . . ." I pricked her hard, tearing her to bits and pieces. Then I cleaned the pin and threw the pieces into the fire. But still I had no real peace. My anger was terrible, insatiable, my soul thirsted for revenge. How was it that I found no peace? "Is something wrong with my health?" I thought in panic. "Really, there must be something wrong because nothing like this has ever happened before. My circulation! My liver!" Before I fell asleep I decided that the next day I would go to see a doctor and let him examine that damned blood and liver once and for all so that I knew what was wrong with me.

I could not fall asleep. Damned liver! I thought and I thought and got sick of thinking; I threw up everything I had eaten that evening. What an unlucky fellow I was! I looked around at other men and women: they lived and had their troubles, perhaps worse than mine, and they bent under the blows of fate, struggled, fell back, and groaned, but nevertheless it seemed to me that these men and women had an easier time going through life than I did. How was that? I didn't know. Except that like this, in the night, when I am alone with myself, it is hard for me, terribly hard. . . . I'm tired, and I can't fall asleep. Through the window I see a piece of the clear sky between the dark walls of the apartment houses and on that sky a handful of wise, motionless, and ice-cold stars. Ah, stars! My only hope! Would the time ever come that would draw a sharp line between yesterday and today? . . . I'm tired, I'm terribly tired, and I can't fall asleep. Then I finally fell asleep, a sickly and broken sleep. I dreamed I sat in a big, cold and severely furnished office turning the dial on the telephone, but turning the wrong numbers so that I had to begin all over again. Finally I succeeded in getting the number I wanted. "Hello," I yelled into the mute hollow of the receiver. "Hello! Hello!"

From far off a voice as ghastly as a whisp said, "Who's calling?"

"Mama, it's me, Marjan, your son! Do you hear me?"

"I can hear you, son. What do you want?"

"Mama, I feel bad, I feel awfully bad. They've insulted me so much. They've humiliated me and mocked me mercilessly. What should I do?"

"Bear it" said the voice like a whisper.

"I know, but I can't bear it any more."

"Bear it, when I tell you to. Therein lies your salvation." (My mother hasn't changed a bit. She's telling me the same things she said when she was alive, when at least they made some sense.)

"But, Mama, I can't stand it anymore. Are you listening? I can't. I've come to the end of my rope. I must hit back. I must hit, scratch, choke, and if need be, kill. Do you understand, Mama? And kill."

"You're crazy," whispered the voice, slightly angry. "I didn't give birth to you so that you should be crazy."

"Quiet, Mama. Enough of your impossible advice! I want them to respect me, to fear me, to tremble before me. Do you hear? I want power."

"Power is damnation, I've told you that so many times."

"Damnation! And isn't this damnation, what they're doing to me now? There's a dame there, an ordinary tramp, and if you only knew what a bloody fool she made out of me!"

"Take care with women, son! They also bring damnation, I told you about that, too."

"Damnation, damnation, damnation! What do I care about damnation? I want to live. I want to live at all costs . . . are you listening? . . .

I want to live, even at the cost of killing."

"Watch your tongue, you idiot, and pray to God to help you in your madness. Women and power are the worst whips in His all-powerful hand. In the name of the Father, the Son, and the Holy Ghost. Amen."

I wanted to shout that what she was saying was stupid and that I didn't give a damn for that whip or that all-powerful hand, but the old lady probably was tired. I heard a yawn on the other end of the wire and then the click of the receiver being put on its hook. What was it she said? Power and women? Power and women? Ah ... I must have struck myself on the forehead with my fist (as people do when they remember something all of a sudden) and I woke up from the blow. . . .

I woke up. A piece of bright sky shone through the window—gray-green sky with stars growing pale before the dawn. Power and women! Of course! How could I ever have forgotten?

"Write down on this card what you want most in life!" Mama had said. I wrote: power and women. Everybody in the room—Mama, the postman's three daughters and their boy friends, the old fortune-teller, and some other people from the neighborhood—all gave one another knowing glances and laughed. "Look at the little devil, look what he's thinking of! Look at Suleiman the Great! He'll do great things in life!" They all laughed and they all called me Suleiman. And from then on, everybody called me Suleiman.

Suleiman! How had I forgotten? True, that was long ago—thirty-two years!

Something made me want to go out, out of the room. I dressed quickly. Outside, the dawn was coming up, on the street the milkman's cans were toppling and banging against one another, the first streetcars could be heard. I went down the stairs easily and lightly, whistling. At the bottom of the stairs stood the janitor-horsefly, a disgusting crone who couldn't stand me and whom I couldn't stand.

"Good morning, Granny," I shouted in passing, and she seemed to turn to stone at the sound of my voice. "How did we sleep, Granny, and what did we dream? Something nice, thank God. Me, too. At your service, Granny."

I felt wonderful. I didn't walk but danced, pirouetting, leaping, smiling blissfully to myself. "There, you see," I thought aloud, "I knew something would happen after all. Something extremely important. Something that would change my life from the bottom up, turn it in a more favorable direction! Life begins today! And from today onward, let those lice, those robbers and good-for-nothings, those whores and ne'er-do-wells watch out, because my time has finally come! Let them watch out! And people thought astrology was a swindle! Idiots, now they'll see. . . ." So I walked, dancing and leaping along the streets, the passers-by looking after me in panic.

In front of the office I met Irena.

"Maybe you think I'm afraid of you, eh?" Her eyes widened. "You think you got me down, don't you? Go on, you, you've done nothing at all to me, nothing, do you hear, nothing. . . ." She ran wildly upstairs.

And I stood downstairs, laughing as loudly as I could.

Cordia Kveder

Petar Šegedin

(1909–   )

Novelist, essayist, story teller and writer, Petar Šegedin was born in Zrnovo, on the island of Korčula. He has published two novels: *Djeca božja* (God's Children, 1946) and *Osamljenci* (The Lonely Ones, 1947), followed by *Na putu* (On the Road, 1953), a collection of travel pieces; a volume of essays *Eseji* (Essays, 1955); and a volume of short stories, *Mrtvo more* (Dead Sea, 1953).

As a short story writer, Šegedin is a writer whose world is very specific and clearly limited. He usually writes about his native country, painting it in powerful but sometimes gloomy colors.

Šegedin's prose is psychological or analytical. One of its main features is an intellectual view of human destiny and man's problems.

THE MARRIAGE OF FIGARO

I'd been crouching in the darkness for quite some time, my dear G., until I remembered you. Then I lit the oil lamp left to me my by landlords, very simple peasants of this island, and now I'm sitting here at this crude, unfinished table writing you with a small pencil. I'm writing you, I confess, to save myself. I think less and less about my singularity among the multitude around me, and so often it seems to me that I'm some kind of insect. Really, in the lamp's light, I'm sitting and with a small pencil writing down some symbols which could also be made by some insect. And yet, you see, this is supposed to be a picture of my thoughts and my condition. What is this? I'm afraid to think about that question, and for this reason, I remain among the insects. This isolation and simplicity have taught me many things.

Writing you at this hour, it seems, I'm at the bottom of a deep ocean, and you are somewhere above, on the surface in an entirely different world, in that world to which I once belonged, where everything I have learned here would look, I wouldn't say funny, but at any rate, distorted. And so I sit and write you. Words, all just small, tiny words, as if some insect in front of the oil lamp were actually stringing them out. Common sense is somewhat lost here, but that's exactly why I'm writing you. And I've already come so close to all the living things around me, that sometimes it seems—ah, but forgive me, forgive me! How much better it would be if I stopped talking altogether. . . . And don't be surprised at that. You are so far from me, up above, on the surface. How many days has that lasted already? A month, two, a year even? I don't know anymore, I've been so lost. Nor do I pay any attention to my illness now. I've forgotten it. And the man and woman from whom I rented this stone hut, when they appear before me, it's as if some strange fish were appearing. They don't understand why I stay here so long and why I behave so strangely. eating only what they bring me, not asking for anything in particular.

But I'm not writing you this to explain where and how I live; that's the last thing I want to do. Reverting to the most simple, almost animalistic living pleases me. I chuckle at everything that happens to me, often sing some childhood song, or talk with my long lost relatives and friends. And so, this letter, too, is but one aspect of this life of mine, and I'm not ashamed to tell you that now and then I also cry, but all in a simple way, and somehow aware that all this is for no real reason. . . . Therefore, don't take all I write to you too much to heart, if this letter ever reaches you. After a while, maybe the time will come when I will again laugh or get angry. I decided on this letter for some reason unknown to me, or, better yet, I don't know whether it's of exceptional importance or whether it belongs to those reasons which happen simply and unnoticed every day. And even if it were so serious, even then it wouldn't be important, and yet. . . . You are the only person I know who takes a direct and lively interest in me, as if I were one of your closest relatives, and I thought: well, it wouldn't be so bad if I let him know about this also. Let everything be brought out in the open: the thought occurred to me that any one of these beings among whom I live could simply swallow me. That's not important my friend, I know, and I have said that to you already, but if I should disappear, then you'll know where I disappeared to. Don't weigh my lack of concern by the scales of your environment above, on the surface. Things are different here.

And you see, now and then, it seems that all this has happened because of some newspaper which appeared here two days ago in the yard in front of the stone hut where I live. Torako brought it and covered his head with it during his midday nap, protecting himself from the flies that annoy us here. And I did the same thing the next day. I covered my face with that old newspaper and fell asleep sweeter than usual. But waking up, entirely unexpectedly I remembered him, Mr. Arkadijevič, the lawyer from Petrograd, born 1867. . . . Arkadijevič, huh! And you know nothing about him, but from htis letter you learn a lot. A lot? An, everything is relative, and I am so subjective.

It disturbed me so much that I folded up the newspaper, and I don't have to tell you that I didn't even read it, that I immediately put it behind the hut and placed a rock on it. Why? Probably so that the wind would not carry it away. But why shouldn't the wind carry it away?

I crouched alone in the darkness filled with these confused thoughts which I know will be incomprehensible to you, up there, but indeed, that's the way it should be. That Tarako and his newspaper on his face, and later on my face, and then right away that Arkadijevič, born 1867 in Petrograd, his fate which I identified with mine, and not only with my own at that. All this overpowered me in some inexplicable way, so that I jumped out of the darkness, lit the oil lamp, and decided to describe it all to you, even if I appear like some insect.

Now, you see, I'm writing before the lamp and really am an insect. An insect. . . . But I must tell you about that Arkadijevič, so that you will understand properly the insect also. From here, it seems, that's the best way to explain these moments of mine. He is, as you will see, the cause of this darkness. How strange all that is here: I see so clearly picture after picture, so clearly that it seems those pictures no longer even reflect what has happened, and that is what I fear most of all. . . . Because sometimes it seems that it didn't happen at all, but that it was imposed on me together with the wretched thought that I could even disappear here in this desert. And today, when my landlord walked by, it seemed as if he could have been that Arkadijevič from Petrograd, born 1867. Because why else would Tarako have brought that newspaper here, here in this desert in the middle of the sea? And he even slept under it! Well, that's what happens to a man's memory when he's left more and more to himself. And that desire to fall completely silent. . . . And the one who leased the stone hut to me is called Sanduk in the village. Imagine that! His wife told me that. Sanduk and Tarako! What names! Of course that too began to plague me.

But you're so high up there, on the surface! Don't I envy you at this moment. But how I crave this isolation. And writing you all this, it seems that I am surfacing, because in the end Arkadijevič is the man who I met in my former life, while I was still up there. This memory is taking such a hold on me that it seems like all that is here now, in this darkness with which this small oil lamp is struggling. Actually, it's as if all this is taking place now, and yet it began in the Gare de Lyon. . . . Paris, here in the flickering of the oil lamp. . . . I was traveling on some business, but today I no longer remember what it was, so much did that meeting with Arkadijevič overwhelm me. And now, right over there in the semidarkness, I see clearly many people, masks on that blackened Parisian station. All the faces which you have never seen, and again, as if you've met them every day. And so it happened that I even began to wonder about all those faces that appear and disappear, all filled with themselves! You see, this "filled with themselves" means filled with their own fate. See how I have already begun to speak in your manner, but that's because such a manner was rather similar to this one, except here, instead of people, animals surround me. Night has cast its darkness here; there's only this small oil lamp. And there's no telling how many of them are lurking in the darkness as I write this to you. But let them lurk with their faces and souls. It's nothing new! It was the same way up there too. Even then, at that Paris train station, I wanted to choose one of those faces, to get to know it better, to see if it would say or mean something to me. That's it, you see. To look for someone, to search for someone else, and that hasn't left me either. I fled from up there, it seems, only because the search deceived me. But, you see, this happens here too. But let's forget that. I began to peer into those faces at the Paris station, but one face kept erasing the next and I could not choose one. That won't happen here, I thought, but it happened differently. Here, among the insects, butterflies and fish, only Sanduk and his wife appear. How I fear that! And this small lamp of mine glows so peacefully, and bathes me so softly in its light that I sometimes think the lamp was the one I should meet. But let's forget that. From this light of mine to that crowd at the Lyon station . . . and entirely by chance, but that's how it happens so often. A stout little man in an old bowler, out of fashion now, approached me, and as if in passing asked me about the platform for the Basel train. I didn't know where the platform was and told him so, and thanking me, he left. I was traveling to Dijon and it wasn't more than two or three minutes later when the old man returned and began to explain to me that there was no train to Basel now, but that he would ride the Orient-Express, and from Lausanne change for Basel. He would still get there two or three hours earlier than by waiting for the direct train. And all this, as if we had known each other a long time and he were obliged to give me an explanation. He spoke French very well, yet with a foreign accent. I listened to him, and his already withered face with a small nose and narrow little eyes, his lips that had entirely receedd into his sallow skin, everything seemed larger and imposed itself more brazenly. Even then I had thought: see, if you search for something, it will come to you by itself. The face, that's what I mean, the face. But I didn't answer him, and he too got lost, apologizing completely unnecessarily that he had to go for his baggage. He left me alone. How strange: at that moment, I again felt alone in the true sense of the word. . . . Ah, how I'd like to show you, really show you this loneliness. It is the abyss that pulls me, that has pulled me even to this place. . . . I hover among the people, that's right, hover. . . . Hovering, I reached the coach, and when the train had set out, he too, the one with the bowler, opened the door. . . . My entire life that word pursued me, like the one of those curs and pests that we avoid with loathing: bowler-cockroach, blower-bedbug. And closing the door, he sat opposite me, so naturally, even with some show of superiority, as if we had already agreed upon it, and this allowed him to behave with almost patronizing freedom. I sat in silence. We were alone. The train was already hurrying through the suburbs when he introduced himself.

"I am Arkadijevič, a lawyer and retired financial advisor. But I work because I do not like to be without work. But you don't look French?"

"No, I'm not French," I answered quickly, afraid that he would think that I wanted to pass as a Frenchman. "I'm a Croat, but I'm temporarily in Paris. I'm traveling to Dijon on business. . . ." I spoke as if confessing, even apologizing to him, but right away he became aware of that, and I became angry with myself. But that did't help me reestablish my independence from him.

That's how the conversation began. While he spoke, I noticed his fine silk shirt, his small well-groomed hands, and his calm, casual demeanor: he seemed to be an experienced gentleman from high society. And in no way could I understand how easily he crossed the bounds of social convention. Probably he sensed my thoughts, because he immediatly began to explain himself to me freely, in such a superior manner that he grew still more in my esteem. His mouth opened, each time as if cutting anew into the skin.

"Are you surprised at my behavior?"

"No, no. . . ."

"With good reason. . . ."

I looked at him in confusion, awaiting further surprises. That man was capable of doing anything. And, with his narrow eyes, he stared at me as if checking whether or not he had made a mistake, and being convinced, it seemed, that he could possess me and that I did not threaten him, he continued in a free, almost insulting manner.

"But you see, that is a trait of people without a homeland, of people who are always adapting themselves. . . ." With that, his small eyes closed and opened, creating in me the mood required for listening to this sincere and wise man.

"Hm, hm, hm. . . ." I emitted unintelligible nasal sounds, trying to save myself.

"Everywhere we are searching for support, a connection. . . . We are always in peril, that's why things are as they are. And there are more and more such people, and it is getting harder and harder to be like that, because a style has been created. . . . Ah, when I remember I was a young lawyer in Petrograd! The beginning of a career. So many plans and hopes! Because in essence, I was not a gambler. . . ."

And the more he talked, the closer he became to me, and I began to open up more selfconsciously.

"Ah, Petrograd, Petrograd, 'White Nights'. . . ."

"And are you interested in literature?"

"No, no. I'm interested in only one great name of yours. It's trite, I know. I said 'White Night's' . . ."

" 'White Nights,' I know, I know, that's what everyone thinks, but I'm a financial expert."

" 'White Nights,' 'White Nights,' " I repeated, ashamed of all that literary interest before this financial expert.

He fell silent, and my 'White Nights' hung alone in the air, making no impression whatsoever. How I would like to show you, my dear G . . . , this kind of loneliness, almost despair. It seems this loneliness is my fate. . . . And, you see, I am again writing about something I didn't want to. The silence lasted quite a while, and it disclosed between us the naked roar of the train which was flying through the yellow fields and small groves, by the knolls, the rivers, noisy and loud, as if we were crashing down a precipice. . . . But we had already been forced on each other, so we had to talk. And again he began to speak, cutting the withered skin of his face. But the conversation became banal, as if Arkadijevič had closed off some areas where I could not find my way, but opened those in which I could share.

"Where do you eat in Paris?" And not waiting for an answer, he took upon himself the role of drawing me out, beginning to talk so much that I didn't need to take part in the conversation. "I usually eat at 'Chez Fouquet,' near the Rond point des Champs Elysées, and if you want, we could meet there. I'm returning in a few days. . . . One can always be of help to someone. You are alone in Paris?"

"Alone. . . . Yes I am, I'm alone in Paris. . . . Why not, we could get together. . . ."

"I am an agent for many companies. . . ."

I did not want to tell him which business I was in, and got up, excused myself for a moment, then went out of the compartment. It seemed he was following me, and I actually glanced back several times to make sure he wasn't. Since he didn't appear behind me, I remained in the aisle looking at the countryside already covered by the stretching shadows of the setting sun. I love such moments. Everything then seemed to be ripening like fruit, ripening and fading away. And when I felt dusk deepening, I returned to the compartment where I found Arkadijevič exactly as I had left him, resting his head on the white cover of the headrest. He looked at me fleetingly like a relative, but now he seemed somewhat smaller, paler. Again we were sitting opposite each other, as if assigned by fate. Then it dawned on me that I was not the only one burdened by old age, and right away, it became clear that he needed me also, that he, too, was afraid of loneliness. My leaving the compartment was taken as a threat. Looking at him, it occurred to me: now he'll tell me all that, maybe even with my own words: "It seems this loneliness is my fate. . . ." But he did not speak—the silence remained between us for quite a while.

And so, my dear G . . . , how many of the tiny symbols have I jotted down for you in this yellow-green light? Insect. . . . And I see all that clearly in the twilight. Really, will you understand all this? I am writing about Arkadijevič so that I can explain to you something that I myself don't even understand, something sticking in my throat and choking me. I crouched in the darkness for such a long time and jumped up remembering you, and now I'm getting more and more afraid of these tiny symbols which have to signify something. A message? ! . . . But I'll return to the noise of that train flying in the late evening dusk. How clearly I see him there in the twilight. And only when the lamp had been lit above our heads did Arkadijcvič speak again:

"Are you married?"

"No, no," I said, defending myself with a sly tone of voice.

"So, anyway, you are married. That's good, good," he said, and for the first time I felt that he wanted to tell me his troubles.

"I, unfortunately, am not. And I'm old. You wouldn't believe how old I am. Eighty. And now I am traveling to visit a woman. She lives in Basal. I must be in Basal tomorrow morning. It's her birthday. But, if I don't get there . . . ," he spoke as if he wanted to show how completely he was confiding in me.

He drew so close to me that I seriously began to fear that nearness, and it became clear that he, too, feared that loneliness, that very same feeling that I feel now and then and immerses me into such a state as I find myself in now, I looked at him, drenched with that fear, and thought how good it would be to approach him out of solidarity. And I even wanted to tell him something about this feeling of mine, but such terror began to seize me that I had to get up, and not finding anything to do standing, I again sat down, still more embarrassed. But he didn't pay any attention to me or to my thoughts; he was so taken by what he had already told me. And already the darkness was gathering in the train windows. I looked at him in the corner opposite me, indeed, like some marvel, like some ancient town abandoned somewhere by the seashore, like some strange being which, arrested in its form, performs its mission, and then again, like some lonely, deserted old man. . . . And then his long life began to reveal itself to me: where and when he was born, and to whom he was traveling. But that question didn't require any ordinary mathematical answer: Petrograd, 1867, but rather that live certainly that has been lost and is no more. Why should I be the one to look for it, to find it? Because of this, here, now, this light of mine, my scribbling to you, to you my dear G. . . . Is it really something, or not? If it is something, what is it? And will you ever to able to decipher ˈthis' from these symbols? This . . . I'm afraid. And that moment on the train was like this moment, with the light of the lamp bathing him, and I even wanted to ask for some explanation from Arkadijevič: where is the 18 % of yours? Where is that that was, and . . . And I began to look more carefully at his small withered hands, his fashionable clothes, shabby and frayed here and there around the sleeves, on the soiled lapels, and finally at that head with all its experience in the course of eighty years. . . . In fact, like a city where all sorts of things happened and still do. Some insect which carries out its mission. . . . And so I looked at him at that great distance and I felt less and less at ease because of him, his dejection, his isolation. Eighty years from Petrograd to Tokyo, from Tokyo to Shanghai, New York, and there he is now, traveling from Paris to Basel to some woman, and telling stories, looking for a relative, but since he doesn't exist, he adopts everyone who happens to be near him. He talks and everything he says magnifies that isolation and dejection. His narrow lips open and string out words like some yet unknown, unfamiliar being.

"No, no, no. I would like for us to get together in Paris. As soon as you have time, come to the Fouquet. There one can eat well and meet interesting people. I know Paris like the back of my hand. We could arrange something with the publishers. I know them well. She writes too, that one in Basel. You should see what a beautiful house she has. Clever woman, clever woman. You wouldn't believe how a woman, becomes, yes becomes, clever. That's for sure. And I'm afraid of her. She's harsh, very harsh. She doesn't forget easily. So, this time too, I'll tap on the little window, because her little house is a one story frame house. For that reason she's called Snow White. . . ." He spoke, stopping from time to time, as if choking, but in the process he also smiled, glancing at me as if wondering if he could tell me something else in confidence.

"And what is she to you? An aunt?" I asked showing more and more openly an interest in his story.

"Hm. . . . An aunt, aunt. . . . My dear sir, life is vast, and one is but a fly, nothing but a fly, a fly, or if it pleases you more, let's say a swallow. You fly through life and set out on many trips, but you wouldn't believe how in that vastness, that infinity, you finally have no place to go, but again . . . yes again, you return to the very same place. I am saying you are a fly, a swallow, and even if you were an eagle, so what? It's all the same. I say 'you,' but I don't mean you in particular. I know from my own experience! I was alone and I remain alone in that vast space, and as you can see, I'm still flying, flying. . . . I've been cheated on a grand scale, and on a small scale. I've had illusions. And so, now I am fraud incarnate. I know my own face. Pure egotism. . . . She explained all that to me. And tomorrow when we meet at her house on her sixtieth birthday, it will be the same again. Ah, ah, but already I have such a weak heart. The same topic of conversation for years. Do you know what that is? How old age dries up and deforms things."

No one came to our compartment and that man began to seem assigned to me by someone to explain something to me that I myself have been searching and waiting for in that space of his, huge and yet so small that we must return to the same places, encounter past situations and faces. And the train kept hurrying through the night and yet still had more than two full hours to go. He had already devoted himself entirely to his giving, his lecturing, and I felt so obligated to him that I got up, helped him remove his overcoat, and hung it for him right behind the compartment door. He thanked me, but somehow in a familiar, fatherly fashion, trusting me so much that he told me to get from the inside pocket of his coat a cigarette case from which he took some snuff. Having become somewhat more at ease around him, in a well meaning way, I again evoked the 'White Nights,' and he, sniffing the tobacco, answered calmly, as if he wanted to put everything in its place:

"Nothing, nothing. . . . I was a young lawyer. A large city, sir, a large city. But for us young lawyers that was not such a great name, after all. . . . Fetjukovič! . . . Literature! Yes, I remember only the death, the funeral. . . . Nothing, nothing. . . . All that is so far away, so terribly distant, and the fly had not yet recognized that the trips passed. You see, I feel so good now. And is it hot here? Isn't it? I don't know when I change trains from Lausanne to Basel. Hm, if I knock on her window too early, Snow White might even fly into a rage. A hard shelled swindler, a turtle, a turtle. All that, she could throw at me, and even shout it. And you should see how energetic she is. But she doesn't want any trouble, no trouble. Perhaps she would even cry. I am to blame. Yes, I admit it and do not deny it, but that's how it is: It happened and can no longer be changed. What a stain! And so many of these stains, and all because of what? Because of selfishness, I say to myself. And yet I still live selfishly. . . . Life is long. Who says it's short?" From Petrograd to Tokyo, from Tokyo to Shanghai, you crouch inside yourself and don't get up. Like a beast of prey you're ready to grab from ambush what seems possible, but you don't let yourself be caught at any price; you only devise your masks, change them, now this, now that, this one with a smile, that one cold as stone. . . . And so you work up to this conversation, to this road to her! And I need her so much! . . . Believe me. I've waited for her birthday all year. I stay two or three days at her house, tell her everything, look her straight in the eye, but Snow White doesn't want me to stay with her. . . . Hm. . . . And this time I intend to persuade her to let me stay, but I know she won't let me. . . . She has no one, she's alone, all alone, and she still won't let me. . . . I am to blame, and all because of the isolation, that selfishness."

"And you're to blame?!" I interjected, absorbed in his story, listening to the roar of the train and looking at the darkness out the window.

"Would you mind taking my suitcase from the rack? I'd like to lie down for awhile. It always fits so nicely, under my head. . . . You don't mind, do you? O, years, years. . . ."

As if reminded of something important, he began to recite in a somewhat weak and trembling voice:

> "But there, alas, where the firmaments of the sky,
> Shine in the pale blue brilliance,
> Where the shade of the olive lay in the water,
> You fell asleep with the last dream,
> Your beauty, your sufferings,

Disappeared in a funeral urn,
And with them, the kiss of reunion . . .
But I wait for it; it is behind you . . ."

I took down that old-fashioned little suitcase, my dear G . . ., and gave him the overcoat too. He began to smile and make himself comfortable, reciting for the second, third, and fourth time his verses, and the last line "But I wait for it; it is behind you . . .," he repeated several times. Shaking like an old man, he arranged all his things cautiously, so that all that had happened to now, and what he had said, seemed pitiful, lost. All those small gestures, touching his things several times. And when he had arranged things the way he wanted them, he took out a small box, drew out from it a vial, poured two or three little pills onto his palm, popped them into his mouth and, mumbling I don't know how many times "But I wait for it; it is behind you . . .," he stretched out on the seat. I realized just how lost this old man was. Neither the food that he eats at the Fouquet, nor his acquaintance with the publishers, nor the fact that he has such a mouth and always finds his way, helped him hold onto that esteem with which he presented himself in those first moments. The empty loneliness of the man began to show, that lonely man from Petrograd, Tokyo, Shanghai, Paris, and of this moment, the man. . . . But having settled down, he began to speak:

"Yes, yes. . . . There, you see. Now I feel fine. My heart, my heart is giving out on me. And to tell the truth, I am afraid of her. Am I to blame? You are a small man, she tells me. A small man. . . . He, he, he, my young man. You travel all over the world, experience good and evil, but nevertheless, you are still a small man. 1 . . And she looks at me and smiles, and I begin to say that it is high time that we behaved like human beings. . . . But then she gets furious. 'A man,' she says, 'when he begins to speak about being human, beware of him: the beast has evil on his mind!' I am to blame, I am guilty."

"But how did you offend her so?"

"All that is of little importance now, but then, it was. . . . Ah, not even then it wasn't anything. . . . And you see, she never even mentioned a word about it to me, never reproached me, never even a word, but everything about her speaks only of that. I hear it in her voice as soon as I enter and greet her. . . . But do you want to hear what happened? . . ." he said reclining, as if soothed by his words. I looked at him, round, small, his clothes sagging on him and his mouth receding, so that one could not tell where that weak, mellow, overpoweringly, sweet little voice was coming from.

"Yes, if you don't mind, I am interested. . . . You've created a picture of that woman in my mind, and we met for the first time right here in the train, and since I already know about you, true it's not much, but still. . . . You are an emigrant. . . . To live an entire life alone, without a home, without a country. . . . That has always disturbed me. . . . The feeling of loneliness is a terrible abyss which swallows the entire person. . . . And I am. . . "

"Right, right, my son. A man lives within himself and lies in wait for prey, not secure from either side, and cheats his fellow man with various tricks. . . . In an empty space. . . . Is the home perhaps an illusion, and yet. . . ." He fell silent and I felt that he regretted that he had been too open. Then followed a long silence and again the roar of the train, and the eerie emptiness was revealed, and then almost unexpectedly, when I had already become accustomed to the noise of the train, he spoke again: "I will have a hard time falling asleep, and it would be so nice to take a little nap because. . . " and again he fell silent and I myself thought how it would be best to let him fall asleep and be alone. The darkness and the moaning of the wind began to flow, and I, too, began to search within myself, but I couldn't tear myself away from that woman, somewhere in Basel, to whom this old man was traveling. All this was supposed to be some fateful love, or still more likely, some banal old age liason about which this old man was dreaming. So I thought and looked at him, small, stout, stretched out on the seat, and various thoughts came to mind: how that mound of flesh harbors a great life which was opened to me by chance, and how I will never again forget him, but I would still like to meet that woman in Basel. I would have to see her in order to know him better, and not only the two of them at that. . . . And I myself am having trouble with my life. Ah, these thoughts, one following the other, intertwining, and in the end, revealing my own self. It went on like that until he spoke again:

"And you would be interested in knowing how I offended her so? I know, I know. . . . But that's not especially interesting. . . . I had returned from New York to Paris and tried to settle down permanently in that city. When I remember that, I always feel ashamed. . . . Hm, it's stupid! One lives as best he can and thinks about it only if he's able. To judge one's self and to repent. . . . Who until now has been able to seize his true moment, the one immediately following the present? . . . And she too was in Paris then, a ballerina in a chorus." And again he began to recite the verses:

> "Your beauty, your suffering,
> They disappeared in a funeral urn,
> And with them, the kiss of reunion . . .
> But I wait for it; it is behind you

"I met her while helping a manager of Russian origin in his international affairs. She too was an emigrant. After her morning practice, we used to meet in a small restaurant on the Boulevard des Italiens. At that time, I was already close to fifty years old, and she, thirty. Everything was already over with her career, and I too had given up hope. . . . She confided in me and I skillfully tried to take advantage of her confidence, pretending I was confiding in her also. . . . A game, just a game. . . . I am guilty. . . . How wonderful were those cups of coffee, that absinth, that beaujolais between us on the table. And she had such beautiful hands and those blue eyes that always sparkle. . . ." He spoke naturally, but still it seemed to me that he knew the story by heart, that even now he was pretending, arranging. And when he suddenly became silent, I left him to himself. But he got up, drew from the pocket of his overcoat a small black box, opened it, and showing me its contents which I could barely make out, said "Please, if I have a heart attack, inject me with this. I will leave it beside you. . . ." I was confused, but he again lay down, and everything was as before: the noise of the train that sped through the darkness and the darkness itself. And again he spoke: "Yes, I wanted to tell you everything to the end. . . . We bared our souls completely to each other in our confessions: we appeared alone, abandoned, stripped, and the thought of a common journey which we were to make, hand in hand, to the end suggested itself. So one idea led logically to another: to pull together, to work together to the end of our lives, to swindle the people together, but remain loyal to each other. On the roadlessness of this icy expanse, that becomes the only value, and consequently the only reason for existing on this earth. But I was a scoundrel and betrayed her. How I deceived both her and myself. All that coffee, the absinth, the beaujolais, the light and her hands. . . . That's it! All the coffee, absinth and beaujolais turned to tears. I had found another woman whose wealth promised to deliver me from my perennial poverty. . . . And she would have understood that, if I hadn't renounced her at that particular moment. . . . In the cafe L'Opera, when she needed me so much, and I no longer recognized her. . . . Yes, and for that reason, she will never recognize me again. . . . And so I've been coming to her on each birthday, and you see how I go to her, to discover again that idea of walking down that roadlessness together, but she doesn't want to understand. . . . There, that's what it is. . . ."

He stopped, and again I allowed the silence and the roar of the train to swallow up that somewhat still make-believe tale.

"Human loneliness must not be betrayed," he uttered.

"No, it mustn't," I answered in a voice strange even to myself.

"So you see, I will arrive tonight, rap at the door, the window, and again she will say: 'Here he comes. . . . How persistent that old man is.' But that light is bothering me. May I have your newspaper?"

I gave it to him, not even thinking what he would do with it, and when he opened it and covered himself with it so that a paper roof rose above his head, everything in this life of ours seemed so wrinkled. No order whatsoever. . . . And the newspaper was *Figaro*. The boldface title of the paper stood out so much on the side facing me, that for the first time I began to take an interest in that word. Fi-ga-ro. What does that mean? I became so absorbed that I even forgot to offer to turn off the light. "The Marriage of Figaro" came to my mind, Figaro qua, Figaro la and things like that, until the old man under the newspaper began to look like some strange kind of Figaro. "Of course," I thought, "this time the offended old woman will finally take pity on him and they will meet in their loneliness. And that will be their marriage—'The Marriage of Figaro'; they will offer each other their hands, and nothing from the outside world will be able to prevent them from believing in each other any longer. The loneliness will be bridged and they will stand hand in hand against the world." I thought, rather I dreamed their own dreams, and he already seemed asleep to me. If I'd listened more closely, I would have heard his breathing. But the paper cover was trembling so, above his head, that I was more and more afraid that it would slide off if the train shook just a little more. And he jerked twice, but *Figaro* by some miracle remained over his face as if it knew: he is entitled not only to this roof above his head, but also to its name; as if it knew that it was going with him to that old woman. . . . Since he hadn't made a sound for some time, I could also lean back and doze off. It was still a whole hour to Dijon. I leaned against my overcoat and closed my eyes. I must have slept for quite a while. Opening my eyes and coming to my senses, I saw that he no longer had the newspaper on his head, and his right hand had dropped down off the seat and was touching the floor where *Figaro* was lying. I got up, picked up the paper, folded it like a roof and put it on his head, then sat down again. The hand touching the floor disturbed me and I again got up, took hold of it gently and put it on his chest, but it slid off again. I smiled at that and once more lifted it up and now intended to place it between his coat and shirt, but it seemed to me that it gave some resistance, a strange resistance. Then I noticed that the entire body behaved strangely, and not thinking about anything in particular, I took the paper roof from his face and moved my face closer to his. What? ! . . . No, he was no longer breathing. I became feverish. I began to shake him, but it was useless. He no longer moved. I opened the door of the compartment and began running down the aisle, calling the conductor, and only then it occurred to me that he had given me his black little box and asked me to give him an injection if he had a heart attack. I rushed back to the compartment but the train was already entering Dijon station. I gave him the injection, into the same arm that hung touching the floor, but it was all in vain. He never regained consciousness.

I won't tell you about all the inconvenience I encountered in Dijon because of that incident. Of course, I gave the police all the information that I knew about him. In his papers we found her address. They called her, and she actually came. Both she and I were at his funeral together with some other faces which most likely were not connected with him in any way. That's how I met her. Completely gray, thin, and lively in speech and movement. I remembered her sharp profile: there was something oriental about it. And if I'd known French as well as I do my own language, perhaps my dear G. . . , I wouldn't be writing this letter to you, but to her, that old woman. But she, after all, is already dead. We talked a little. We barely had the chance to do that.

Yet, I suceeded in telling her this, and probably her story, but she didn't want to go into it. . . . She listened to it, smiling, not saying anything to the stranger who accidently found himself there, unexpectedly woven into the fibre of their lives. But in parting, she gave me her address: to write or visit her.

How many years have already passed since then? Not many, but not few either. Driven by my loneliness, I came to this small island and this stone hut in the middle of a dying vineyard. A quiet cove. . . . The winds on the open sea. . . . But nowhere is there real intimacy. Ah, that intimacy! That is exactly what drove me to this isolation. But you see, it's strange. More and more it seems to me that it's better that there is no intimacy. Here it seems that if I really come to face it, I would find the very terror. . . the terror that lurks for me. . . . Listen and understand—it is lurking.

The lamp is slowly dimming. Again the darkness will come and everything will become an ear, full of danger. I'm at the bottom of the sea and from the distance creatures keep approaching, creatures which have no other intention than to devour me. And there are so many of them! But what a tsar I am in this loneliness of mine. I defend myself easily from the creatures. Only, to tell the truth, one day, when my landlord fell asleep under the newspaper, I was seized by the fear of myself and the fear that I might die hear alone, sleeping under that newspaper. . . .

There is still some light; the flame of the lamp sometimes flickers violently, giving me signs. All right, but why do I keep writing all this to you? At the beginning I had an idea, but you see, his story swallowed me. . . . Yes, yes, through that story I am sending you the message about the absurdity of my life that I discovered on that lonely road.

The lamp has gone out. Darkness. I am cowering alone. Time and listening. . . . An insect! . . . But I no longer see or know. . . . But something keeps urging me to start swimming through the space and time, to search for him, Arkadijevič and his time. . . . I know, I know, I realize, I listen to the depths, I sail, I boil in the sounds, but it's just the same: nothing, nothing, nothing. . . .

Donald Davenport

Jure Kaštelan

(1919–   )

Kaštelan was born in the village of Zakučac; he had his first poems published while still a secondary school student in 1936 and 1937. His first collection *Crveni konj* (Red Horse, 1940), was seized by the police because of the author's revolutionary convictions and activities.

His poetic creations center around three collections: *Pijetao na krovu* (Rooster on the Roof, 1950); *Biti ili ne* (To Be or Not to Be, 1955); and *Malo kamena i puno snova* (A Few Stones and Many Dreams, 1957).

Kaštelan has introduced modern trends into Croatian poetic expression, from surrealism to a lyricism resembling the folk poetry of García Lorca. His cycle *Tifusari* (Typhus Victims), is one of the most dramatic sagas of suffering and death.

A FORTRESS WHICH SURRENDERS NOT

I am a fortress with only one flag—the heart.
Invisible walls built out of wounds.
I resist invasions
With a lullaby
I am transformed in an armor of dreams.
Vanguards wake on all towers, and on the shore
reeds and tamarisk hide the little boats.
Weathercocks look upon the distant iron troupes
as they sharpen their arrows,
grease their muscles and thighs and prance
on wicked tin and fiery steeds.
The bridges have been lifted. Irresistible torrents
    guard the gates.

The moon disappears at dawn and out emerges
bright sun.
I am a fortress with only one flag—the heart.
I am a fortress which surrenders not.
The dead, freed of their senses, do not surrender.
Lightnings, in their swift flight, do not surrender.
The living, with gem-like eyes, do not surrender.
Strongholds surrender, but not these made of dreams.
These give up and defend themselves alone.
I am a fortress with only one flag—the heart.

Maria Malby

Vladan Desnica

(1905–   )

Vladan Desnica was born at Zadar and received his law degree from the University of Zagreb. Up to the end of the Second World War he wrote much, but published very little. He translated lyrics, prose and philosophical works, particularly in esthetic philosophy, from Italian and French. Since the Second World War he has published a number of short stories: a collection *Olupine na suncu* (Derelicts in the Sun, 1952); *Proljeće u Badrovcu* (Springtime at Badrovac, 1955); *Tu, odmah pored nas* (Here Just Beside Us, 1956); and a novel, *Proljeća Ivana Galeba* (The Springtime of Ivan Galeb, 1960).

JUSTICE

One Sunday afternoon some years ago, as I was returning from a long walk into town, I happened in the middle of the road on the disgusting scene of a man mercilessly beating a woman. His face had a furious, quite bestial expression. He had grabbed the poor woman by the hair, dragging her back and forth over the road until she fell to her knees, and then began hitting her across the eyes and mouth without regard for where the blows fell.

Burning with rage I wanted to rush the man in an attack that would be the fiercer, since that sense of pure charity motivating it was the greater; a feeling of charity so considerable that I would certainly have been furious in my attack, striking out ruthlessly about the mouth and eyes, heedless of where the blows landed. Very likely my face would have taken on an enraged quite bestial expression, judging by which truly no one would be able to recognize the nobility of my motives.

However, I recalled several occasions when I had rushed in precipitously and gotten carried away, whereupon a wavering checked my rage, stopping my readiness for philanthropical intercession instantly. Perhaps this turn my recation took was affected by the presence of another onlooker, a vaguely smiling, shortish man in middle years, plump-cheeked with light yellowish hair, who looked on tranquilly. I can recall that his easygoing indifference at first prompted my loathing. But almost immediately I struck the same attitude as he, shoving my hands into my pockets to watch.

The effect of example is irresistible, such that though we often consider the people about us as stupid, in effect we redeem that sin by following its example. Thus, I took my bearings and calmed down, whereupon that familiar "other half" which brings judgment spoke to me.

I have long been profoundly convinced that the main prerequisite for justice is fantasy. To be fair judges we have to know the backgound, motives, causes, relationships and dependencies of the matters which we judge so as not to go by the external aspect of things. Our obligation before we pronounce judgment is to question the hidden motivations, the exigent conditions, the long chain of offenders; to stand in the shoes of the person under indictment; to search out the thread's end of the tangled skein. But since all these factors are never adequately known to us, we must endeavor to reconstruct them through the exercise of fantasy which soon shows that, with a minimal effort, circumstances could be imagined which would cast a very different light on the entire matter.

Moreover, there is no situation which a fair measure of fantasy could not present under circumstances which would completely justify the scrutinized act—whatever it was— for though we set the guilty party on one side of the proverbial scale, if we weigh out the possibilities for justification upon the other end of the balance, the moment must arrive when the latter will tip the scale.

So I pondered. Who knows what guilt, what evil, this woman had brought upon the man? Who knows what he may have done for her, sacrificed? How much he has put up with, forgiven, or kept quiet over? What shamelessness, what cynicism might she not have arrived at in her downfall? Perhaps she is some kind of a monster-mother who abandoned her child, in paroxysms of croup, to rendez-vous with a lecherous goat. In that case wouldn't she be the guilty one for bringing her husband to this ugly falling out, this bestial display? Isn't his outburst, however ugly, nevertheless ultimately, humanly understandable? And might he not feel our intercession on the woman's behalf the final injustice? Yes, it's just as well I stayed out of it.

While I stood in thought as the shower of blows continued, a third passer-by carrying a tennis racket under his arm happened along. He was a tall, blue-sweatered young man with long wavy hair who appraised the situation in a flash, cast a scornful glance at us, the two passive onlookers, and without more ado flung himself on the man—exactly as I had wanted to do only a while before—and began to thrash him, thoroughly and not caring where he hit. Startled, the man let the woman go and turned to defend himself while she crawled out from under, getting up from her knees in a return to life much faster than could have been expected after that buffeting. She brushed the dust from her elbows and knees, arranged her disordered hair (an attention which immediately made her seem rather less a victim), then disappeared unobserved.

On the opposite side of the road an elderly man appeared leading his little son by the hand on a walk. Attending to him with a grandfather like patience, he was pointing out something in the crown of one of the poplar trees bordering the road, most likely a bird or a nest. Catching sight of the fight, he halted but quickly got his bearings: before him a young blockhead was mercilessly beating his fellow man and an older one at that. It was an obviously unjust beating (since to the weaker we instinctively accord the righteous role). The elderly man also saw two selfish, worthless characters looking on indifferently and this prompted his speedy decision. He jerked back, set the child to one side, and launched himself on the attacker (since we instinctively equate the stronger with the attacker) thrashing him with all he had.

Watching this new complication, I reasoned that had I not restrained myself a little while before, those blows would be showering on me; furthermore, I would now be dealing out punches, bitterly and full of conviction, to a person who had interceded from exactly the motives as mine and who would thus be a man of the rationale, my comrade-in arms.

There it is, entirely out of charity and on behalf of humanity, three human beings are knocking the daylights out of each other for someone else, while, slightly removed, two worthless egotists aren't lifting a finger. Two egotists, three attackers, four people beaten black and blue. From a mere handful of men emerge sinners of every description: culprits for taking part in a fight, culprits for lackadaisical nonparticipation, culprits for interfering in another's private matter or for not interfering, weaklings and philanthropists, offenders for arbitrarily dictating justice and offenders for thwarting it. When I had first come on the scene I felt scorn for the plump-cheeked man, yet immediately assumed exactly the stance he had taken. I first approved and argued for each of the participants, only to condemn them the following moment, by acclaiming the next person to join the fray. The incident developed and interruptions occurred just as I had wished—quite as though I were invisibly directing them. Yet after all that ruckus, even now, it is still not clear to me who was in the right and which outcome I truly hoped for! I knew that I wished defeat on each assaulter and victory to each one under attack; success to the weaker and failure to the stronger. The difficulty was that each of the participants passed from the role of attacker into attacked, of stronger to weaker! Who could figure the just stand in such a situation? If right is on the side of the weak, is fault then identical with strength? Must the term "righteous man" be paid for with defeat?

At the end of the row of poplars, still quite far off, the dark frame of a policeman hove into sight. The mere appearance of official justice had an uncommonly abrupt effect. Combativeness gave way at once and the fighting stopped. The elderly man, remembering, hurried to his child. The husband reshaped his crumpled hat. The young man shook back his curly hair and pressed a handkerchief to the bruise above his eye.

The surplus of accumulated energy was spent, volatized in the tepid Sunday afternoon after justice had been given satisfaction.

Jan Dekker

THE TALE OF THE FRIAR WITH THE GREEN BEARD

This is quite a simple story; something like it could happen to anyone. It all depends on whether we set out in that direction; and then —the rest takes care of itself.

Let us imagine a man, quite an ordinary man, an average human like a million others, dreaming one night—and what may one not dream about, how many and varied are the things that come to man's mind in dreams! But is that reason enough to draw conclusions from them? Dreams are, after all, pure fantasy, there are no logical rules or laws about them. For example, a man dreams one night about a monk with a green beard. Or, if you will, a monk with a squint in his left eye. Or anything else—it doesn't matter. Anything at all! Because, in his dreams, a man sees such things as would take him more than a hundred years to envision in a waking state. He may dream, for instance, of a "man wthout buttons," that is, of a man who doesn't have a single button on his clothes. Not that his buttons have fallen off, and the bits of thread can still be seen where they were once sewn. This man just has no buttons, as though he had lived his whole life without them; he doesn't even have buttonholes. A thing, as one can see, not particularly unusual or fantastic and, while awake, not really awe-inspiring. But in dreams, such a buttonless man can acquire a certain similarity, a certain vague relationship with that aquatic animal which is usually called a "manfish."

But let us not digress. Let us not lose the logical thread of our story. Let us remain with the "friar with the green beard," as long as we have chosen that example. Well, as we were saying, a man one night dreamed of a monk with a green beard. Very well. Throughout the whole of the following day he didn't give this a thought. But that night, just as he was peeling off his right sock before going to bed, it suddenly occurred to him that he might dream of the friar again. But the night went by without his dreaming of him. And the next morning, while going to the office, he thought: just imagine, I didn't dream of the friar with the green beard after all.

But matters need not take such a course. The opposite can happen: the man may not think of the friar during the day and yet dream of him that very night. These two cases are in fact identical; both the alternatives lead to the same result. But let us rather remain with the first possibility, since we have already set out in that direction. Well, then, that evening he thinks about the friar but fails to dream of him. And so on the next evening, and the third and the fourth. And every morning, while washing his face and shaving, he thinks: Well, last night I didn't dream of him again. He thinks of him familiarly. And such a thought gives him a quick little sense of pleasure. As though he were putting a saved up-coin into a small cashbox every morning. And then there came the morning when he did not think of the friar. But that was why on the following night he dreamed of him again. Then, for some time, every day he either dreamed of the friar or thought about him; and sometimes it was both.

And then a scandal broke in the office. Quite understandably, in such a situation anyone would forget a score of things more important than a mere friar! A huge embezzlement had been discovered in his department and all the employees, including himself, were subjected to questioning. That was the law. He, however, was completely calm. From the tone of his questioners, he realized from the very first moment that he was under no suspicion. Still, such things were always unpleasant. But that also passed. And a week later (it was a fine, sunny day, and after lunch he went for a walk in the zoo) he recalled with pleasure that during the whole of the investigation at the office he had neither thought of the friar nor dreamed of him. Even now he would not have thought of him, had not a priest passed by him along the way. True, this was a priest and not a friar; and the priest did not have a beard, much less a green one. But that's what our memories are like; sometimes we remember things by association through similarity and sometimes through contrast. More frequently through contrast. If, for example, we have a small dog whose right eye has been knocked out, and somewhere we see another small dog whose left eye is missing, we might cry out: Well, now, this one is missing an eye too! Only mine is missing a right eye and this dog, a left one. And I firmly believe that this small dog withtout a left eye will remind us no less of the one we own without his right eye, than if this one, too, were deprived of a right eye like our own dog. And, by this same logic, when we see a cat without a left eye, we'll say; see, this one is missing an eye, like my Tootsie, except that the cat has no left eye and my doggie no right eye, and this is a cat, while Tootsie is a dog. Also, if we see a dog that has no eyes missing at all, we might say: See, just like poor Tootsie, except that he has both eyes! And as all things are of necessity mutually similar or dissimilar, the conclusion might be drawn that every object can remind us of every other object. All this brings me to the idea that those things which remind us of something else need not depend on similarity or dissimilarity, but on something quite different. On what, I don't know! But I'm sure it's something that, regardless of similarities and dissimilarities, lies deep under the ocean, like a cable.

Of course, that evening, while undressing, he again thought of the friar. And in the morning, while shaving, he said to himself: How strange, yesterday I thought so much about him, and yet I didn't dream of him! I might almost say that when I keep thinking of him all day long and expect surely to dream about him, I don't dream of him at all; but if, while I am awake, I don't even give him a thought, then, sure enough, he appears in my dreams! Very strange! Looks as though I must think about him .quite intensely in the daytime so as not to dream of him at night!

"Nonsense," he said finally, with a wave of his hand. And when he arrived at the office he looked at his desk calendar, grasped a few random pages, turned over a fat sheaf of them onto a date in the distant future, and wrote the words "the Friar," in blue pencil. He did this because he recalled how in his childhood, after having recovered from an attack of influenza, a low, persistent fever had continued. Only a few degrees above normal, but still, there it was. His mother was beside herself with anxiety. "How long will this last, doctor? . . . What shall we do, doctor? . . ."were the words she adressed to the family physician, whereas he, an elderly and experienced man, thick-set and short of breath, was not in the least perturbed. "Simply stop taking the child's temperature," he had advised phlegmatically. "Let the child go to school and let him play with the others.. And then, when you take his temperature a few days later, you'll see how it will all be gone." And indeed, that's the way it was. So now he thought: That's how it's going to be. I'll stop taking the temperature!

And this really helped. At first he thought about the friar less and less frequently, until he finally dropped him entirely from his thoughts. Almost two months went by without his ever thinking of the friar, either asleep or awake. And then one morning, all unwittingly, he turned a page of his calendar—and there was the friar. From then on he kept recurring to him with growing frequency—if not all the time, at least whenever he glanced at the calendar. Everything the calender stood for now seemed to be closely bound up with the friar: the former stuck to the latter like two caramels in a paper bag inside a warm pocket. Everything connected with the calendar now reminded him of the friar, and whatever had associations with the friar—such things as church, an altar, and the like—would remind him of the calendar and the friar. If he met a funeral procession, immediately the friar came to his mind! If he saw an agricultural calendar in a shop window of the Farmers' Co-operative—again the friar came to mind. If, while waiting in his bosses' reception room to get his signature, his eyes chanced to fall on the calendar, or only on the wall clock, or even the barometer, his mind would immediately run to the friar. True, in his dreams the friar appeared less frequently, but somehow at more regular, almost fixed intervals of time. And it seemed to him that now he could correctly foretell those nightly visits, that he knew exactly which was the "friar's day," just as one knows the charwoman's day or the day the rent collector is to call.

For some time all went well. But then logic came into play, that devilish logic which comes at the end to spoil all that which illogicality cannot undo: now in the mornings he no longer asked himself whether he had dreamed of the friar or not, nor did this give him the slightest pleasure any longer; it was, in fact, inconsequential. He realized that between the words "I dreamed of the friar" and "I did not dream of the friar" the whole difference lay in the "did" and "did not," but that in both cases the friar" remained unchanging and permanent. He remembered how every morning while shaving he had naively enjoyed the thought: "Well, I didn't dream about him last night," or, "Well, I wasn't thinking of him today," and he smiled bitterly to himself, saying, "What a fool I was!" Did not thinking about how he didn't think of the friar really amount to thinking of him? And this critical thought at once demolished all others: it was only some kind of metastasis of the friar. So that, whichever way it was, alseep or awake, as a daytime visitor or nightly guest—the frair was there! And at once it struck him that during all that time, from the very beginning—during the investigation at the office, and all the while up to the fateful turning of the calendar's pages—the friar, invisible, had been there all the time, right behind the curtain. And one morning, while shaving, he stopped and groaned in the middle of the empty white bathroom: "Oh, if only I could forget . . . only forget. . . ." He drew the razor down his cheek several times and again stopped short: "But what is forgetfulness? And can one ever be completely calm? Even if it settles upon you, how can one know if that is the real, final genuine forgetfulness or only temporary oblivion? On what grounds could one reckon with certainty that one day some chance encounter, some small trifle, anything at all, would not unexpectedly, and thereby powerfully, reawaken the idea of the friar?" He lay the razor on the cold white porcelain shelf above the sink, looked at his haggard face and shadowed eyes in the mirror, and said aloud: "There is no salvation for me." His voice sent shivers down his spine.

But man is strong. Man is a resistant creature; a stubborn, wiry being. Man does not give in so easily. And he began trying to defend himself with the same weapon, that same "logical thought" that had ruined everything before. He began rationalizing: Actually, "to think of the friar" was not the same as "to think of one's thoughts about the friar"; although at first glance it did seem the same thing, it really wasn't! There was a small shade of difference here. In the first case, the friar is something that stands above me, something that tyrannizes me, something that governs and controls me; in this case he is the master, and I his slave; in the latter case, it is he who is subservient to me, he is my object: the object of my thoughts. In this, then, I am still the master. "Yes, I am the master," he said aloud in front of the mirror.

There, that was a possibility, another way out of the whole dilemma. Perhaps the only way. And this time the man really calmed down. Once again he found the will to live. On sunny afternoons he sometimes went for walks in the zoological gardens. He even gained a few pounds. This was obviously a good sign. From then on, he weighed himself regularly. Now he thought of the friar without anxiety, without any particular repercussions, almost nonchalantly. "In time, he'll completely disappear," he reassured himself. And the very fact that the friar became unimportant to him resulted in his thinking of him less and less frequently. It was like being in love: as soon as you got the first signs that she returned your love, you became cockier; you could afford the luxury of diverting your thoughts from her from time to time for the sake of a little change. It was like that in everything, the question always being, who is stronger, who is the master: you or she, you or the friar?

One Saturday, while he was sharpening his razor, he caught himself whistling. "It's been ages since I've whistled!" he said to himself. And then he went to the movies. It turned out to be stuff and nonsense. A silly, improbable love story fit only for teaship waitresses or young hairdressers. That evening, while undressing, something fell out of his pocket onto the small rug near his bed. He bent down to pick it up: it was the card that showed his latest weight. He reread the figures printed on it and once again rubbed his hands with satisfaction over the fact that he had gained. He smiled: "Looks as if I'm really rid of him at last."

But that very night he dreamed of the friar again. He seemed a bit thinner. He smiled sourly, winking his left eye and shaking his forefinger: "You are mistaken, my friend, sadly mistaken. Come what may I'm inside you for good. Remember—you will never be able to drive me away."

And then—then, there was really no more hope for him.

Olga Humo

Slavko Mihalić

(1928–   )

Making a comparatively late appearance in the postwar generation of Croatian poets, Slavko Mihalić, born in Karlovac, has published a number of books of verse: *Komorna muzika* (Chamber Music, 1954); *Put u nepostojanje* (Journey Into Non-Existence, 1956); *Početak zaborava* (Beginning of Oblivion, 1957); *Godišnja doba* (The Seasons, 1961); *Ljubav za stvarnu zemlju* (Love for Real Earth, 1964); and *Prognana balada* (The Banished Ballad, 1965).

Mihalić's poetry is modern intellectualistic lyricism with an abstract lexicon expressing concrete states of anxiety and fear in the contemporary world.

A BANISHED BALLAD

To my mother, my father

It happened unexpectedly
The south wind was in the air
Autumn resembled spring
It happened with the sun's smile
on the lips

That man, otherwise with a back huge
As a mountain
Otherwise, with a whirl of wisdom in his eyes
Otherwise, with hands as heavy as thunder
One could hear the blow of his fist a long time

That man, on that strange day
I say: a girl unbuttoned
Her shirt
(She stared through the window
Instead of into the mirror)
I say: on the shore a pussy willow
Had opened up

He resounded from his innermost being
But he dispersed all the clouds.

He started to sing in such harmonious voice
The street was stunned (as if it had lost
Its dress)

First out of shame
Then out of enormous joy

An orange vendor opened wide
The door of his shop

And still he was not satisfied
And still he was not satisfied
He had not had enough
And he wrote above the door
Take what belongs to you

But after the night that followed
After minutes in dark evening suits
After seconds with cylinders and bamboo
Sticks

The accursed northwind blew
The girl buttoned up her shirt
Catkins fell off the willow trees
The merchant went to serve his customers

Starting with the suburbs

And that man who had sung
Reduced to a microbe
And slavishly immobilized

Was banned

Well, someone had to pay

Maria Malby

Vlado Gotovac

(1930–   )

Gotovac, born in Imotsko, is a poet of marked introspective dialogues. He is a pure and spontaneous lyricist with an obvious inclination towards the emotional and philosophical. This is particularly noticeable in his short stories and essays.

His best poems are direct, communicative, lyrical miniatures of exceptional value. His published works of poetry are: *Pjesme od uvijek* (Poems Since Ever, 1956); *Jeka* (Echo, 1961); *Opasni prostor* (Dangerous Space, 1961); *I biti opravdan* (To Be Justified, 1963) and *Čujem oblake* (I Can Hear Clouds, 1965).

A FLOWERY MANUSCRIPT

You are tempting my tenderness while the wind blows
    through the tulips
Carrying their color toward my window
And through many more flowers the colors come to the
    window
That opens like greedy nostrils over the perfume
Of a dear woman

This melancholy is my tenderness that brings you this
    manuscript
And begs you to correct mistakes
This multicolored wind is the only one
That knows the worth of guarding flowers
It springs from my garden
It flies without notice by.the Moon
It is starry until the morning
When it comes to flowers wet and wounded

Steeped in blood
It grows in my garden like a sunflower
Until the first crickets

That is the manuscript of my tender playing
Timid like soft rabbits and as harmless
And I surrender it to you as much as I love you

Vasa D. Mihailovich and Ronald Moran

Introduction
Slovenian Literature

The Slovenes, occupying the extreme northwestern corner of Yugoslavia, have been considered a historical curiosity. Despite many years of foreign occupation, they have succeeded in preserving their native language and developing a rich literature. All of this has been done in the face of tremendous odds by a people numbering less than two million.

Slovenian literature could be divided into the following periods. (For the purpose of this essay, only the last two periods will be analyzed.)

1. The epoch of the religions and didactic writings, whether Protestant or Catholic (during the counterreformation), and of the first glimmers of national consciousness (1550–1768).

2. The epoch of the gradual awakening of national consciousness and the birth of autonomous secular poetry (1768–1830).

3. The epoch of true literary creations (1830–1941).

4. The period after World War II.

The first representative of Slovenian romanticism and the founder of Slovenian *"belles lettres,"* France Prešeren (1800–1849), had a scant literary tradition preceding him. There were two kinds of literary traditions—the oral heritage and the clerical didactic literature. The former was restricted to the peasants who were largely illiterate, and the latter was limited by its narrow religious theme. There was no encouragement or help for the Slovenian language from the governing circles, who favored German language and culture. It is indeed a mystery that the greatest Slovenian poet and literary innovator emerged under such circumstances, and that he accomplished all of this despite the misfortune which followed him throughout his life. Prešeren's knowledge of European literature and European languages as well as his familiarity with Slovenian folk poetic tradition can solve this puzzle to some extent.

Prešeren began publishing in an annual collection of poetry, *The Bee of Carniola,* in 1830, a journal dedicated to the cultivation of the Slovenian language and literature. Following Petrarch, for whom he had great admiration, Prešeren chose as a medium of his inspiration the most difficult poetic form—the sonnet. His *Soneti nesreče* (Sonnets of Unhappiness) summed up in a perfect outward way the tragic destiny of his life. His own unhappiness was translated into a feeling of resignation and tolerance. Prešeren's unfortunate love for Julia Primic was only a part of his misfortune. There was also the one which befell the Slovenian people during the long years of foreign occupation. His personal and national frustration merged with uncanny effect in *Sonetni venac* (A Wreath of Sonnets), his collection of fifteen sonnets. He fully deserves to be called "a great poet of a small nation."

The central figure of the Slovenian cultural and political life after Prešeren's death was Fran Levstik (1831–1887). His importance in the development of the Slovenian prose parallels Prešeren's in poetry. Levstik is considered to be the initiator of the Slovenian short story, of Slovenian literary realism and literary criticism. He knew the peasant life in Slovenia well, as he himself was from the countryside, and he strove to present it objectively and honestly.

The expression "Moderna" in the history of Slovenian literature signifies the period between 1899 and 1918. The year 1899 was the year of the publication of Cankar's poetical collection *Erotika* (Erotica) and Župančič's *Čaša opojnosti,* (The Cup of Intoxication) and the year 1918 was the end of World War I and the incorporation of Slovenia into the newly created Yugoslav state. "Moderna" is a complex literary phenomenon which does not stand for a single term of reference. It is often used in connection with different literary currents: symbolism, decadence, new romanticism, and impressionism, all prevalent in the beginning of the eighteen nineties.

"Moderna," as a literary movement, grew as a reaction to realism and naturalism and the acceptance of modern Western literary currents of the time. It was a search for a more sincere and personal form of expression. Although vacillating in its allegiance to different literary schools, "Moderna" emphasized the value of art as an end in itself. This view was not popular with those intellectual circles in Slovenia who saw in literature an instrument for the propagation of nationalism. The differences of opinion between Cankar's and Aškerc's generations also extended to foreign literary influences. The new literary generation to which Cankar and Župančič belonged welcomed cultural and literary exchange with the West. Aškerc and the so-called young Slovenians favored indigenous sources of literary inspiration.

The important components of Slovenian modernists were social concern, the search for social Utopia, and the conviction that the most sacred duty of an artist was to embody in his work the ideas of freedom and justice. The most important representatives of "Moderna" in the Slovenian literature were Ivan Cankar, Oton Župančič, Dragotin Kete, and Josip Murn-Aleksandrov.

Cankar started his literary career with a scandal. The collection of lyric poems *Erotika* was banned by the church as immoral and dangerous. The Ljubljana clerics bought all of the copies of Cankar's book and ordered them burned. During his stormy life and conflict-ridden literary career, he often changed positions from symbolism and decadence to neo-romanticism and utilitarian art. His ideological and social position, nevertheless, remained the same. He was a poet of human longing and of the human heart. His sympathy was with his sensitive heroes who aspired to better, almost unattainable ideals but who could not adapt themselves to everyday life and who suffered when they had to compete in life with other people who cared only for their own petty interests. Cankar's heroes are individuals who have failed in life: eternal students, servants, and artists. From the bourgeois point of view, these are worthless people, although all of them have visions and dreams of a better life to come. Their antipodes are characterized in Cankar's description of the Philistines with their greed, calculation, and disregard for others. Cankar was at heart a lyric poet, although he wrote dramas and novels. He always approached the issues raised in his works subjectively, with strong feelings of sympathy or hatred and contempt. His favorite and most successful genre was the vignette, a short, often autobiographical, narrative. The images of his mother, his childhood, and his youth are often subjects of his prosaic narratives.

Cankar is considered the greatest prose writer in Slovenian literature.

His style is simple, colorful, and precise, and the Slovenian literary language was enriched and brought to new levels of creative possibilities by his writing.

Of all of the Slovenian modernists, Oton Župančič (1878–1949) was the only one who lived long enough to develop his literary career fully. He appeared on the Slovenian literary scene with his collection *Čaša opojnosti* (The Cup of Intoxication) in which he paid his tribute to modernism. His poems from that period were erotic, decadent, and individual. Župančič's success in overcoming the fashionable pessimistic influences might be due to his close touch with the Slovenian people and soil as well as to his poetical talent. His *Duma* (Meditation) is a succinct expression of patriotic feelings. Župančič's influence on the postwar development of Slovenian poetry has been crucial. His poetry ranges from introspective and philosophical poems to nature lyrics and children's poems. The form is unsurpassed in Slovenian poetry in its melodious quality.

The time span between the years 1918 and 1941 could be divided into two periods: (1) the period of expressionism from 1918 to 1930; and (2) the period between 1930 and 1941 known as the period of social realism.

The last years of World War I were a turning point in Slovenian history, as the Slovenian people were then severing their links with Austria-Hungary and making the decision to join the South Slavic community. Slovenian literature was full of optimism for a better future as is shown by Cankar's *Podobe iz sanj* (Images from the Dreams) in which he proclaimed the rising of a man and humanity from selfishness and enmity and their mutual destruction by the light of brotherhood and love. Oton Župančič wrote hymns dedicated to the mother language and to the belief in a national rebirth in *V zarje vidove* (In the Light of the Dawn), 1920; while Alojz Gradnik in the book of poems *Padajoče zvezde* (The Falling Stars, 1916) expressed the same sentiments.

The postwar years were a disappointment. Many Slovenes remained behind the Slovenian borders. The relationships between the peoples in the new Yugoslavia were not as good as had been expected; the young generation came to literature terribly disillusioned after World War I. A new short-lived period of expressionism appeared. Its representatives were the brothers Kralj and Veno Pilon in plastic arts,

Marij Kogoj in music, and Srečko Kosovel and Josip Murn-Aleksandrov, among others, in literature. The human personality, was at the center of interest in this new literary movement regardless of social or national proclivities. This was a reaction against the preceding "Moderna." It was based on a violent antirealism and on the refusal to imitate, repeat, or reproduce anything which already existed. The old ideological division in Slovenian literature between the idealistic clerical and the realistic liberal orientations gave way to a multitude of literary and political programs. The truth about the human condition was expressed differently among different expressionists: for the writers who were conservatively inclined, the ideal man was a religious man; for the representatives of Slovenian liberalism, he was a psychophysical man trying to satisfy his instincts.

The style of expressionistic writers could not compete with the elaborateness and technical perfection of Cankar and Župančič. There was indeed more concern among impressionists for different states of the human soul than for an emphasis on the formal aspects of literature. Most of the Slovenian writers in the period between 1918 and 1930 are expressionistic to some degree, showing the literary characteristics of expression presented above. Since it is impossible to find a common denominator for all of the qualities generally supposed to be typical of expressionism, the Slovenian writers are usually divided into two groups: (1) the generation of relatively pure adherents of expressionism; and (2) the generation of direct predecessors of expressionism. To the former group belong the expressionistic-religious poetry of Anton Vodnik, the social poetry of Tone Seliškar (Vodnik in *Žalostne roke* [Sad Hands], Seliškar in *Trbovlje*), and Božo Vodušek's collection *Odčarani svet* (The Magic World, 1939). To the latter group belongs Župančič, who in literary creativity bridged the gap between "Moderna" and expressionism. Župančič's book of verse, *V zarje vidove,* represented not only expressionistic work *per se* but also a high point in his poetical creation.

Alojz Gradnik, an outstanding Slovenian poet between the two world wars, was Župančič's disciple and the most typical adherent of pure expressionism. The main subject of Gradnik's poetry is love in all of its different aspects. Although an admirer of Schopenhauer's pessimistic philosophy, Gradnik formed a pantheistic philosophy of his own in which an individual is just a link in an invisible chain of life. With the death of an individual, this chain does not break, as the death is not an end but a new birth. Nothing is lost in nature; everything grows in order to die and be born again. He was a lyricist who, according to his own confession, had not written a single epic poem or piece of original prose.

Srečko Kosovel occupies a unique place in Slovenian poetry of the nineteen twenties. Some critics (e. g., A. Slodnjak) deny his association with expressionism on the grounds that in his poetry he portrayed not abstract human beings but real Slovenian people. He has often been described as the poet of the rugged mountain region, revolution and death. His early death at twenty-two prevented his talent from maturing. Kosovel widened the horizons of Slovenian literature with his refreshing metaphors, the exactness of his rhymes, and the melodiousness of his verse. The first collection of his verse appeared after his death under the title *Zlatni čoln,* (The Golden Boat, 1949).

The period between 1930 and 1941 is described as social or new realism. The new literary movement differed from the expressionism preceding it by a shift in thematic emphasis. The universality of the spiritual life of human beings was abandoned in favor of a much narrower theme—that of the social and economic situation of the Slovenian people. The new interest in social themes was due to the unsolved social problems of Slovenia in the thirties. New realism found support and inspiration in the traditions of Slovenian literature, e.g., the novels of Janko Kersnik and Cankar's critical attitude toward life and society.

The first literary manifestation of the new trend was the anthology *Seven Young Slovenian Writers* (1930). These writers were under the direct or indirect influence of socialism, and they paid particular attention to the description of life in small social units, especially villages in the eastern part of Slovenia. The main respresentatives of new realism were Prežihov Voranc, Ciril Kosmač, Miško Kranjec, Anton Ingolič, and Ivan Potrč.

Prežihov Voranc (pen name of Lovro Kuhar) was the most typical and representative writer in the neorealistic literary movement. His preoccupation with social problems stemmed from his experiences in life and not from abstractly conceived ethical or religious beliefs. Born in a peasant family of manual laborers, he faced the social questions of his days in a most direct fashion. His literary career started in 1925 at the peak of the impressionistic period with the publication of his realistic *Pripovedke* (Stories). The appearance of this book was against popular literary taste and the work remained unnoticed. Ten years later, in 1935, his stories about the village proletariat of his native province Koruška attracted attention. The literary taste at that time was more receptive to the social themes which Voranc so skillfully treated. The book *Dobredob* (The Natives), published in 1940, is a collection of stories which were described as "the peak of contemporary Slovenian and Yugoslav prose."

Ciril Kosmač first appeared in the periodical *Ljubljanski zvon* (The Bell of Ljubljana) in 1933. He was a representative of the psychological trend in Slovenian neorealism. *Gosenica* (The Caterpillar) describes the fate of the prisoners in the Italian fascist jail; *Človek na zemlji* (The Man on the Earth) describes the struggle of peasants for their land. Like Voranc, Kosmač has been involved in the political and social issues of the day. Most of his writing has an autobiographical character. Kosmač, like the hero of his story *Gosenica* "The Caterpillar," was an inmate of an Italian fascist jail. The immediacy of his experiences and their transformation into literary form has given to Kosmač's art an actuality and pertinence to social and political commentary of the times in which he lived.

Contemporary Slovenian literature is characterized by literary pluralism and variety. It is difficult and almost impossible to define and outline different literary currents. This is due partly to our closeness in time to the period under observation. A time perspective is necessary for the evaluation of a literary period and of its place in the development of a national literature. In the territory of Slovenia with only a million and a half inhabitants, there is a vigorous national literature which ranges all the way from the most conservative realism to the hermetically closed poetry and poetical abstraction and from the positions of programmed constructiveness to the nihilistic positions and the dominance of absurdity. Major Western literary and social movements have their dilemmas fully discussed and possible answers given within the framework of contemporary Slovenian literature. As in the past, Slovenian literature is under the influence of the most diverse influences and trends from both the West and the East.

A dominant feature which is characteristic of Slovenian literature as a whole, in the period under consideration, is undoubtedly the element of social criticism. It appears in poetry as a revolt against conventionality and as an attempt to recognize individuality, while in prose it is expressed as critically tinged social and political themes of liberalism. The literary tone is moral in the majority of cases.

The period between 1945 and 1948 was in many ways abnormal in the context of Slovenian literary and political history. Slovenia had been exposed for centuries to Western influence. Catholicism, the Latin alphabet, and types of Slovenian social organization originated in the West. In the period between 1945 and 1948, Slovenian cultural and literary life was suddenly exposed to influence from the East, and what was even more ominous, cultural contacts with the West were completely severed. Stalinist literary precepts ran havoc in Slovenian literary life. Blind conformity and the denial of free cultural inquiry were foreign to the Slovenian liberal spirit which for a thousand years had enjoyed the benefits of the major Western cultural and literary ideas. The situation changed radically after 1948, the year of Yugoslavia's emancipation form the Eastern bloc. The Eastern cultural influence was replaced almost overnight by the profusion of literary and philosophical ideas from the West. The result was a disorientation and imbalance in Slovenian literary and cultural life. The enthusiasm for and the interest in the contemporary Western culture have not always been discriminating and critical. The profound thinking in Western existentialist philosophy was imported along with superficial products of popular entertainment. Many aspects of literary themes and cultural dilemmas pertinent to the West had no bearing on Slovenian social or literary life. The unassimilated cultural influence from the West coexisted with the already established Eastern influence.

The most distinguishing characteristic of Slovenian literature in the period immediately after 1948 was its complexity. This characteristic becomes even more prominent in comparison with preceding periods in Slovenian literature. The period of war for independence (1941–44) and the immediate postwar period belonged entirely to poetry; prose was abandoned during the war years. This poetry was permeated with idealism, affirmation of life, and belief in the promising future. It was optimistic, positive, and actively engaged in life. The poets were members of the resistance movement, and their poetical activity was an extension of their social and nationalistic preoccupations. The postwar years, better known as the period of economic reconstruction in economics or as the "cult of the shovel" in literature, failed to measure up artistically to the preceding literary period. The reason for this might have been the tendency of the writers to dwell on only one side of human nature, its socio-economic relevance to society, while the writers of the war years portrayed the totality of the human being, a man facing death and annihilation.

The complexity of the situation after 1948 and especially after 1950 signified a new era in the history of Slovenian literature. Esthetic pluralism was created, the strong forms of art were disintegrating, and absolute values were giving way to the relative. Existentialism brought with it the spirit of negation and doubt. The meaning of man's existence, his relation to reality and to society, became the primary concern of writers. A new generation of nonconformist poets appeared. After the reestablishment of the traditional ties with the West and also after several years with the East, a synthesis and normalization of the cultural life took place. A significant new trend occurred; the new literary forms and tendencies became thematically and historically connected to the prewar literary movement of expressionism and new realism, and in that way, the cultural continuity of Slovenian literature was born. The degradation of feelings, an attempt to come to a new understanding of reality by intellect, is characteristic of such writers as Kajetan Kovič, Janez Menart, Ciril Zlobec, and Cene Vipotnik. They manifested in their literary creations the new changes which were realized in the Slovenian literature of the fifties. Other writers who were formerly characterized as war writers, such as Matej Bor, have evolved with the new concept in writing. The real world has been replaced by their own private world with its own laws, its own scale of feelings, and its own mode of expression.

The sixties are witnessing a new polarization of literary life in Slovenia. On one side there is a reaction against the Western influence; on the other, there is a tendency to integrate the Slovenian contemporary literature even closer with developments and currents of contemporary Western literature. The literary controversy has political and economic implications as the participants tend to base their ideological positions beyond the purely literary issues. The journal *Revue Perspective* gathers the nonconformist writers whose rallying points are the criticism of society and the hierarchical conditions in Slovenian cultural life. The most prominent poets belonging to this

518 INTRODUCTION TO YUGOSLAV LITERATURE

journal are Dane Zajc and Gregor Strniša. Their poetry, typical of
this group of writers, consists of the utter disillusionment and complete disregard for all social aspects. Along with this young generation
of poets around *Revue Perspective,* the older generation, represented
by Matej Bor, appears with a newly found literary voice in *Šel je
popotnik skozi atomski vek* (The Traveller Went Through the Atomic
Age).

The period from 1960 on is to a great extent the period of poetry.
Slovenian literature is being exposed to the most diverse philosophical,
speculative, and international literary movements. The generation of
Matej Bor and Cene Vipotnik is often characterized as belonging to
the traditional literary area among new romanticism, late expressionism, and new realism. The difficulty of ascertaining precisely the
respective influences of these literary schools of this generation of
Slovenian writers shows clearly in the complex character of their
literary output.

The year 1965 was very significant for the resurgence of Slovenian
prose. The novels appearing in that year, *St. Pavel* (St. Paul) by P.
Zidar, *Pot ne pelje v dolino* (The Road Does Not Lead into the Valley) by I. Koprivec, and others, were marked by merciless criticism
of society. This young generation of novelists became creative only
after World War II. Social and political vicissitudes in the postwar
period destroyed their faith in the future of Utopian socialism. Their
attitude of doubt and negation is in all probability the result of their
intense disappointment.

The contemporary Slovenian literature in the late sixties is a gloomy
and foreboding socio-critical commentary of the times. The extent
to which this literature is a true reflection of socialist society or a
private vision of the authors is difficult to say. The final resolution
of this question will go beyond the field of literature itself and will
involve the complex question of the relationship between an artist and
his society.

France Prešeren

(1800–1949)

France Prešeren was born in Vrba near Bled in 1800 and died in Kranj in 1849. He studied law in Vienna from 1822–28 and practiced law in Kranj.

He was the author of poems and collections of poems entitled *Soneti nesreče* (Sonnets of Unhappiness, 1832), *Sonetni venac* (A Wreath of Sonnets, 1833–34), and *Krst pri Savici* (Cross at the Savica, 1836).

A WREATH OF SONNETS

I

A Slovene wreath your poet has entwined,
Of fifteen sonnets is the chaplet bound,
And in it thrice the Master Theme must sound:
Thus are the other harmonies combined.

Now from this source like streams in order wind
The sonnets, and the head of each is found
By the last line of the last sonnet crowned;
This is a semblance of your poet's mind.

From one love all my thoughts arise, and lo!
Whene'er I sleep at night they cease to flow,
But stir when darkness flees before dawn's rays.

You are the Master Theme of my whole life,
Which will be heard when I have ceased my strife—
A record of my pain and of your praise.

II

A record of my pain and of your praise
Will this be to Slovenes as yet unborn,
When moss shall grow upon my tomb forlorn,
And over all that grieves me and dismays;

And haughty maids with beauty to amaze
Like yours, on hearing these my strains, will scorn
To lock their hearts in armor: they'll adorn
Their love with faithful thoughts and faithful ways.

For all Slovenes will dawn then brighter days
And kindlier stars upon their land will gaze,
More brilliant songs will come with better times.

Yet my songs, too, with sweetly flowing rhymes
May still survive the future's changing phase,
Since from my heart's deep roots have sprung these lays.

III

Since from my heart's deep roots have sprung these lays,
A heart which can't be silenced any more;
Now I am like to Tasso who of yore
Would sing his Leonora's fame and praise.

He could not plead his love whose tortuous maze
Bemused his years of youth, and fiercely tore
His life beyond all hope; and yet he bore
The burden he revealed in secret phrase.

My passion is aflame, although I find
Your glance gives me no hope when you are near;
Lest I offend, my lips are sealed by fear.

My poor heart's fate, so bitter and unkind,
My secret burden—all this they make clear,
These tear-stained flowers of a poet's mind,

IV

These tear-stained flowers of a poet's mind,
Culled from my bosom, lay it wholly bare;
My heart's a garden: Love is sowing there
Sad elegies each with my longing signed.

You are their sun whose radiance, purblind,
I seek in vain at home and everywhere,
In theater, on promenade and square,
Midst revels where the chains of dancer's wind.

How often through the town with watchful eyes
I wander, praying for a fate more kind,
Yet catch no glimpse of that elusive prize.

I shed my tears to loneliness confined:
Hence all these songs which from my love arise;
They come from where no man can sunshine find.

V

They come from where no man can sunshine find—
Not from those regions by your glance caressed,
Where all the cares of this world are at rest,
And sweet oblivion follows close behind;

Where joy reigns with a fullness scarce divined,
And vanished are the conflicts that distressed;
Where song springs from an overflowing breast,
With sweetest harmonies of every kind;

Where nursed by pure love, grow the fairest flowers,
Luxuriant in beauty and in grace,
As though kissed by the breath of vernal hours.

My songs that praise you come from no such place;
They grew untouched by any friendly powers,
Unblest by soothing winds of warmer days.

VI

Unblest by soothing winds of warmer days,
My songs remain, since from you, haughty maid,
They never won the word that might be said—
The word that neither saddens nor dismays.

As you were bred upon the German phrase,
Like many a Slovene girl, they were afraid
That from such flowers on our Parnassus laid
With cold disdain you would avert your gaze.

Our muses were not loved in our own land:
They were but spinsters doomed to lonely ways,
While foreign beauties won both heart and hand.

Like flowers that bud within the glacier's maze,
Our songs are sparse, as though by nature banned,
Above them savage peaks the mountains raise.

VII

Above them savage peaks the mountains raise,
Like those which once were charmed by the refrain
Of Orpheus, when his lyre stirred hill and plain,
And Haemus' crags and the wild folk of Thrace.

Ah, would, to cure the dearth of these our days,
An Orpheus dowered with song of native strain

Were sent to us that all Slovenes might gain
Fresh fire to set their frozen hearts ablaze.

His words might kindle thoughts that would remind
Us of lost pride of race; discord would cease;
Our people in one nation then combined

Would see that feuds no longer did increase.
His strains would bring the rule of joy and peace,
Where tempests roar and nature is unkind.

VIII

Where tempests roar and nature is unkind:
Such was our land since Samo's rule had passed
With Samo's spirit—now an icy blast
Sweeps o'er his grave reft from the nation's mind.

Our fathers' bickerings let Pepin bind
His yoke upon us, then came thick and fast
Bloodstained revolts and wars, the Turk at last—
With woes our history is deeply lined.

Our age of glory had to disappear
When deeds of valor ceased in our past state
And triumphs that our songs could celebrate.

The flowers on our Parnassus shyly rear
Their heads—the flowers that have been spared by fate:
They were all fed on many a sigh and tear.

IX

They were all fed on many a sigh and tear—
The humble blooms on my Parnassus grown;
My tears of love flowed not for you alone,
But also for the land I hold so dear.

My soul was filled with bitterness and fear
At love so scant to a trusting Mother shown;
The thought that no more love from you I've known
Is throbbing in me like a wound severe.

All the reward I wished for was that you
And I together deathless fame might share,
That native songs our poignant tale might bear;

That all Slovenes should waken and that true
Content and joy might come. Despite my care,
Frail growth these blossoms had, so sad and few.

X

Frail growth these blossoms had, so sad and few:
As when on some warm February day
An early rose unfolds her petals gay,
Enjoying for a space the sun anew,

But bends her stricken head as soon as due
Storm-driven mists come, and with icy spray
The hoar-frost falls from skies grown cold and grey,
While hill and dale are decked in snowy hue.

Thus did your beauty's sun upon me smile—
A radiance I would search for and pursue
To warm the petals of my love awhile.

But false that sunshine proved. They had to rue
Their error in a frost naught could beguile,
While over them malignant storm clouds flew.

XI

While over them malignant storm clouds flew,
Your poet's days were but disgust, despair;

By all the furies harried, he nowhere
Could find release nor any rest he knew.

As in Diana's shrine Orestes, too,
Had eased his weary soul from all its care,
So I from my love's shrine once hoped to bear
Away a heart and mind appeased by you.

Such fleeting dreams were quick to disappear,
No sooner on my eyes had flashed the light
Of every hope than blacker was the night.

Since then my heart has been both dark and drear;
How could the verses sprung from it be bright?
Behold how weak and faded they appear!

XII

Behold how weak and faded they appear!
They have no strength or beauty. Thus the pale
Untended roses in some lonely vale
Midst ruins their sparse heads with sadness rear.

Weeds stifle them, rank nettles interfere,
All kinds of pests their fragile roots assail;
Transplanted to a garden, although frail,
They would revive in blossoms gay and clear.

If my poetic flowers in sunlight grew,
They's live again and freshly thrive ere long
For you, their queen—these blossoms of my song.

To make them more resplendent then, imbue
Their jaded forms with life both fresh and strong!
Send but your rays their glory to renew!

XIII

Send but your rays their glory to renew
And let me look for dawn's light not in vain
In your dear face, to hold back night's domain
And calm the wildest storms that ever blew.

Fall will the load of heavy cares I knew,
Their fetters will be loosened, chain by chain,
And all the wounds they caused that still remain
With gentle soothing will be healed by you.

The cloud then from my frowning brow shall clear,
Within me hope will shine and thrive once more,
And from my lips sweet words again shall pour.

My heart no longer shall remain austere,
And from the inspiration in its store
Then will fresh flowers spread fragrance far and near.

XIV

Then will fresh flowers spread fragrance far and near,
Like roses when the winter's passed away,
And spring displays its marvelous array,
While through the trees white scattered blossoms peer.

The bees hum in the air sun-drenched and clear,
The shepherd's up by golden break of day,
Loud trills the nightingale on every spray—
All nature is aglow with joyful cheer.

I know I scarce deserve such bliss; my mind
Is full of dread that you may still disdain
These poems or be vexed by them again.

Let them at least some little favor find
With you; to ease by it his bitter pain,
A slovene wreath your poet has entwined.

THE MASTER THEME

A Slovene wreath your poet has entwined;
A record of my pain and of your praise,
Since from my heart's deep roots have sprung these lays,
These tear-stained flowers of a poet's mind.

They come from where no man can sunshine find,
Unblest by soothing winds of warmer days;
Above them savage peaks the mountains raise,
Where tempests roar and nature is unkind.

They were all fed on many a sigh and tear;
Frail growth these blossoms had, so sad and few,
While over them malignant storm-clouds flew.

Behold how weak and faded they appear!
Send but your rays their glory to renew—
Then will fresh flowers spread fragrance far and near.

V. de S. Pinto

Fran Levstik

(1831–1887)

Fran Levstik was born in Spodnje Retje in 1831 and died in Ljubljana in 1887. A Slovenian linguist and poet, he was the first representative of realism in Slovenian prose. As a lyricist, he continued in Prešeren's tradition. He authored short stories, linguistic treatises, satires, and translations: *Ježa na Parnas* (The Ride on the Parnassus, 1854), *Ubežni kralj* (The Fleeing King, 1858), *Napake slovenskega pisanja* (Mistakes in Slovenian Writing, 1858).

MARTIN KERPAN OF VERKH

Mocilar would sometimes tell me how people long ago used to live and carry on their occupations. One Sunday afternoon as we were sitting on a bench under the shade of a linden tree, he told me the following story:

In Inner Carniola there stands a village, Verkh by name. In the olden days an enormous man, called Kerpan, lived in this little village. He was so tall that never again will the world see such a man. Though he was an indolent person, yet he carried English salt from the sea on his little mare. Carrying salt in that remote period was already forbidden, and the frontier guards were continually on the alert to catch him in an unguarded moment, for they were afraid to fight openly with him just as later on they were afraid of Stempihar.: Kerpan, however, always managed to keep out of their way and took care that they never succeeded in outwitting him.

---

[1]Joze Stempihar (1739–1796), an extraordinarily strong peasant contrabandist.

But one winter things began to happen. Snow was lying around for miles. Only a single narrow snow-path, available to the inhabitants, led to the other villages for, contrary to conditions at the present time, there were then no roads in that vicinity. In our day the situation is entirely different for there is now, thank God, a path to every kitchen garden.

At that time Kerpan was carrying a few hundredweights of salt down the narrow snow-path on his little mare when suddenly a beautiful carriage came clattering up to him. Its occupant was the Emperor John who was then on his way to Trieste. Kerpan was a simple fellow and did not recognize him; besides there was little time for him to scrutinize the features of the monarch. He did not even have time to take off his hat, but quickly picked up the little mare with her burden and carried her to one side of the road so that the carriage would not run her over.

Do you think this hardened Kerpan's arteries in any way? No! It was no more of an effort for him to accomplish this act than for another man to carry a chair.

The Emperor, seeing this feat, ordered the coachman to stop the horses. When the coach came to a standstill, he asked the giant, "Who are you?"

"They call me Kerpan," the giant answered. "My home is in Verkh at the Holy Trinity, a two hours' walk from here."

"What are you carrying in that pack?" the Emperor asked.

Kerpan was quick to reply, "What am I carrying? Some German tinder and grindstones, Sir!"

The Emperor, wondering at that statement, said, "If those are grindstones, why then are they in sacks?"

It did not take Kerpan long to think of another answer: "I was afraid they would break because of the cold and so I wrapped them up in straw and packed them in sacks."

The Emperor, pleased by the giant, continued: "And you know how to handle such things? Of course you do since you moved your little mare so easily. In truth, it hasn't much flesh on its body, but at least it has bones."

Kerpan grinned and said, "I know your horses have more flesh on them than mine, but I wouldn't trade my little mare for all four of yours that you have harnessed there. As far as moving my mare is concerned, sir, I can carry two mares like that and walk two hours with them. Or even longer, if necessary."

"This is worth remembering—and bidding," mused the Emperor.

A year passed and Kerpan continued to carry his freight over hill and dale.

Now it so happened that a terrible giant named Berdavs came to Vienna. The giant challenged all the heroes of our kingdom to battle, just as Pegam[2] had done in the old days. It may be said for the Emperor that he did not have any cowards among his people who would have forced him to say, "Nobody dares to challenge the giant,"—but any one who tried to fight the giant was sure to go down in defeat. The giant was not a man with a merciful heart, for he killed everyone he overcame.

This began to worry the Emperor and caused him to think: "See here! What's going to happen to us? What's going to happen if Berdavs cannot be overcome? He has already killed my highest ranking nobles! Confound it anyway, nobody is a match for him!"

The Emperor continued to complain in this manner. His coachman, overhearing him, approached him with great humility as he stepped before the great lords, and said: "Don't you remember, Your Majesty, what happened two winters ago near Trieste?"

"What happened?" the Emperor asked him somewhat ill-humoredly. "Whom are you talking about?"

"Kerpan who carried German tinder and grindstones on his little mare," the coachman replied. "Don't you remember how he moved the little mare in the snow, as if putting a dish on the table? If Kerpan can't beat Berdavs, no man can. That's all I have to say."

"Yes, of course," said the Emperor, "we will send for him at once."

They, of course, sent a big beautiful coach for Kerpan. At the moment Kerpan was in front of his cabin, loading salt on his little mare. The frontier guards had in the meantime discovered that he was setting out on his business again. They came upon him and attacked him. There were fifteen of them, but Kerpan had no fear. He scowled at his assailants, grabbed one and thrashed the others with him. As a result of this thrashing they all took to their heels.

---

[2]Pegam (Czech), in Slovene folk songs, a reference to the Czech Vitovec who in the service of the Celje counts fought against Emperor Frederick III.

Just as this was going on, a beautiful coach drawn by four horses, drew up. The Emperor's messenger, who had been a witness of this encounter, stepped out of the coach and quickly said to Kerpan, "Now I know I've hit it right. You're Kerpan of Verkh at the Holy Trinity, aren't you?"

"Yes, I am Kerpan of Verkh at the Holy Trinity," he said. "But what do you want? If you want me for the salt, I advise you to be quiet. There were fifteen of my assailants and still I wasn't afraid, thank the Lord, and I'm not afraid of any one of you. That's certain!"

To this caustic reply the messenger, who did not know exactly why Kerpan talked about salt, said, "Lock up your mare quickly in the stable and put on your Sunday clothes. We'vre going to Vienna to see the Emperor."

Kerpan looked at him doubtfully and replied, "Whoever goes to Vienna had better leave his belly home. . . . That's what I've heard old people say. But I intend to carry my belly with me wherever I carry my freight, until I die carrying my salt."

"Don't think I'm joking," the Emperor's servant said to him.

"Certainly not, and it wouldn't be healthy, either," said Kerpan.

"Everything I've told you is true," the messenger replied. "Don't you remember how you moved your little mare for a coach two winters ago? The gentleman in the carriage was the Emperor, and it was nobody else but he! Understand?"

Kerpan wondered at this and said: "The Emperor?—you mean the Emperor?"

"The Emperor! The Emperor! Listen! A terrible giant called Berdavs has come to Vienna. He is so strong that nobody is a match for him. He has already killed enough warriors and lords to fill a graveyard. So we decided if any living Christian can overcome him, Kerpan can do so. You are the last hope of the Emperor and the city of Vienna."

These words greatly consoled Kerpan. Everything he had heard pleased him very much and now he said: "If there's nothing else but that confounded Berdavs, listen to what I have to say! Fifteen Berdavses for a small meal is for me what pushing a stone through a puddle of water, over which a seven-year-old child can jump, is for you. Only make sure that you aren't leading me by the nose!"

Saying this, Kerpan quickly unloaded the salt from the mare, put it in the stable, went into the cabin and put on his Sunday clothes so that he would not be ashamed to be presented to the Emperor. When he had changed his clothes, he ran out and got into the coach. Then the two men started quickly for Vienna.

When they arrived in Vienna, the whole city was in mourning. People crawled about, looking as downcast as ants whose ant hill has been set afire.

"What's the matter with you people?" Kerpan asked. "You're all so sad.

"O, Berdavs! Berdavs!" cried the great and small, men and women alike. "He has just killed the Emperor's son who was heartbroken with mortification because the Crown had no hero brave enough to fight the giant. He went to try his luck with Berdavs, but what's the use? Like the others, he too fell. Up to this moment nobody has come back alive from the fight."

Kerpan told the coachman to drive quickly. They finally arrived at the Emperor's court which, they say, is very large and beautiful. A guard always stands by the gates, night and day, summer and winter, even in extremely cold weather. The guard quickly announced Kerpan's arrival as is the custom when anyone of royal birth arrives.

The order had been given day after day for the past fortnight that nobody be announced and that everything remain quiet until the time when such and such a man should arrive. So the Court was anxiously looking forward to Kerpan's arrival in Vienna. Why shouldn't it have done so? The members of the Court were at their wit's end to know what to do in such a desperate and, in fact, seemingly hopeless situation.

The Emperor, hearing the shouting, knew at once who had arrived and he rushed out to meet the giant whom he escorted into the upper chambers of the palace. It was wonderfully beautiful in those rooms, even more beautiful than in church. Kerpan just gaped about in wonder at so much regal magnificence.

Presently the Emperor asked him: "Kerpan of Verkh! Do you still remember me?"

"Why shouldn't I?" Kerpan replied, "It's about two years since we saw each other. Well, you look nice and healthy, as one can see by your face."

"What good is one's dear health," the Emperor replied, "when everything else goes wrong! Perhaps, you've already heard of the giant? What will be the outcome if events don't take a more favorable turn? See, he's even killed my son!"

"What else could happen! We'll take his head, of course!" Kerpan said.

"If we only could! But I don't think there is a hero under the sun who could take off Berdav's head!" the Emperor replied sadly.

"Why not? I've heard it said that all people know everything. Everything can be found in the world, and we can't find a hero to fight Berdavs! Weak as I am I'll thrash him, if God grants it, so soundly that he'll never come back again to terrorize Vienna."

Nothing could have pleased the Emperor more than this! Something, however, still worried him. So he said, "you have convinced me that you are strong, but consider the fact that he used weapons since his youth, while you until the present time have only grindstones and German tinder about Carniola. Perhaps you have never seen a spear or a sword other that those in the pictures of the Way of the Cross in your village church. How do you mean to fight him?"

"Don't worry," Kerpan said, "about how and what I'll fight him with. That's my business. I'm not afraid of sword or spear or any other of the giant's weapons whose names I don't even know, granting that he had any of these in his possession. . . ."

All this appealed to the Emperor, and he quickly ordered a pot of wine and some bread to be brought to Kerpan, saying: "Here, Kerpan, eat and drink! Then we'll go to pick out your weapons."

This seemed to Kerpan a very slight reward. A pot of wine for such a hero! He kept quiet, nevertheless, because he was filled with wonder. What more did he want? He had, of course, heard that the lords all had dainty appetites because they ate the very best food whenever they felt so inclined. But a simple man, such as Kerpan, always had other things up his sleeve! He, therefore, drank the wine in one gulp and quickly got up. The Emperor noticed all this and, because he was a shrewd man, he also saw at once that a larger portion should have been allotted to one with such a strong body. That is why they gave him daily, for the remainder of his stay in Vienna: two hams; half a ram, three capons, and, since he did not eat crumbs, the crusts of four loaves of bread made of white flour, butter and eggs. Furthermore, he was supplied with as much wine as he could drink.

When the Emperor and Kerpan came to the armory, that is, the place where such weapons as sabres, swords, breastplates, helmets and other war paraphernalia are kept, Kerpan made several attempts to choose a weapon, but he crushed everything he took in his hands, for he was indeed an extraordinarily strong man. The Emperor almost shuddered from terror when he saw this but he summoned up enough courage to ask, "Well, will you pick out something soon?"

"What can I pick from?" Kerpan replied. "These things are mere toys. They wouldn't do for the giant you call Berdavs, and they won't do for me, Kerpan. Where do have anything better?"

The Emperor began to wonder and said, "If these things won't do for you, I don't know what else will be suitable. We haven't anything bigger and better."

"I have an idea," said Kerpan. "Show me where the smithy is."

The Emperor quickly took him to the smithy which was also in the court, for monarchs have all sorts of things, even a smithy, so that they can always have a hammer and anvil available in case a horse gets unshod or there is something to be forged or repaired. Kerpan selected a piece of iron and the heaviest hammer in the place. The blacksmith always had to swing this hammer with both hands but in Kerpan's hand it sang as if he were sharpening a scythe.

"That bronze rascal!" all who saw him said. It now even seemed a distinction to the Emperor to have such a strong, strapping man about the palace.

Kerpan forged and forged. He worked the bellows with all his might and finally made something so large that it resembled no particular weapon but it was more similar to a cleaver than to anything else. When he had finished, he went into the Emperor's courtyard and chopped down a young, bushy linden tree which stood spreading its branches over a stone table where in summer the lords and ladies assembled as the tree was a refuge from the rays of the sun. The Emperor who was always at his heels, quickly ran up to him and cried, "Kerpan! What are you up to now? May the devil let you burn! Don't you know that the Empress would rather part with all our horses than have this linden tree chopped down? And you've cut it down! What *shall* we do now?"

But Kerpan of Verkh answered him fearlessly, "What is done is done. Why didn't you show me another tree, since you're so particular about this one? What shall we do? A tree is a tree! I must have wood especially for my own use—the kind I'll need for the fight."

The Emperor remained silent because he saw that there was no use crying over spilt milk. Still, he worried about his future excuses to the Empress.

Kerpan first made a handle for his cleaver. He then cut a pole half a fathom long and made a very large club from it. Thereupon he went to the Emperor and said, "I have my weapons now, but I don't have a horse. Surely we won't have to fight on foot."

The Emperor, still somewhat uneasy about the linden tree, said, "Come and take whatever horse you wish. I know you are only boasting. When shall I be Pope in Rome?—When you will kill the giant. If you mean to do anything, take him and chop off his head, if you are really any good, so that my country will have peace and you will have great renown!"

Kerpan was rather angry now, but he swallowed his anger and said: "As far as Berdavs is concerned, I know he isn't a plaything. It won't be like chasing a sparrow who is afraid of every stick and stone out of the bush. How many heroes have you on whom you can depend? Remember, Your Majesty, I'll do what I promised, even if all the backbiters, intriguing against me, burst from anger. If people only always kept their promises as I mean to keep mine, provided God does not strike me dead, no one on earth would know the meaning of a lie. But the world is wicked and does not know that God is great and man is small. Let's go now. Let's go pick out the horse. Still, I do not want one that will squat on all fours under my weight, before the giant, to your humiliation and to my annoyance. The Viennese would laugh and you would say: 'Look at him. He's even ruined my horse!' "

The Emperor became motionless from terror. He listened to this wisdom coming from the lips of Kerpan and followed him. When they reached the stable, the monarch asked him, "How will you be able to tell whether the horse is good or not?"

"By the simple fact that he won't, if he's any good, let me pull him by the tail over the threshold," Kerpan replied.

"Just try it!" the Emperor said. "You've already made trouble enough for me with the Empress, you sly old rascal. I'm warning you; take care that they don't kill you. Theses horse are somewhat spirited."

Martin Kerpan, nevertheless, pulled the first one, then the second one, and all the others, over the threshold, including the horse that the Emperor himself rode only twice a year, that is, on Easter and on All Saint's Day. This especially must have irked the Emperor.

"You haven't any horse I like," Kerpan said.

"If these don't satisfy you, you will have to fight on foot. You aren't an ordinary man! I know there isn't a horse in the Empire you couldn't pull out of the stable, you clown!" said the Emperor sullenly.

"That's not so!" Kerpan said, "I have a little mare at home that none of your heroes can pull over the threshold. I'll bet my head on that, if necessary, so that the Viennese and Berdavs won't say I'm lying."

"Not that mare you *danced* with in the snow."

"Yes, that's the one, that's the one!" Kerpan retorted.

The Emperor became angry and said, "It is perfectly clear to me now that you are either a fool or are trying to make one of me! Take care, Kerpan! My arm is long!"

"Even if it is as long as you say, still it can't reach the giant's belt, much less pluck his beard," Kerpan replied with a laugh. "But let's leave such joking to idle people who have no other work except to annoy their neighbors with their jokes. Let's talk rather about Berdavs who still has his head on his shoulders. Send someone quickly to get my mare, or let me go myself. But then I don't know whether I shall come back again?—For God, however, everything is possible!"

Having heard Kerpan's wish, the Emperor quickly sent to Verkh for the little mare. When they brought her to Vienna, Kerpan said to him, "Get all the heroes of Vienna together now, if there are any more of them left! As weak as my little mare may seem, there isn't one among them who can pull her even to the threshold, much less drag her over it!"

Riders and hostlers and all who knew the effect of fear in handling a horse, whether he is spirited or gentle, made attempts without success, for nobody could even move the little animal. She threw everyone who touched her on a dung heap.

"Hang it!" they said. "Small mare, great strength!"

The day came for Kerpan's fight with the giant. It so happened that it was also St. Erasmus' Day.[3] Kerpan took his club and cleaver, mounted his little mare, and rode out of town to the meadow where Berdavs fought his challengers. Riding on his little mare, his long feet dragging on the ground, Martin Kerpan was certainly a strange sight. He was wearing an old, broad-brimmed hat and a thick homespun coat. It is needless to add that he was afraid of no one. In fact, the Emperor himself liked to listen to him when he was saying something very audacious.

When Berdavs saw the rider, his foe, he began to roar with laughter. "Is this that Kerpan—the man from the distant village of Verkh at the Holy Trinity—whom they sent for to fight me? It would have been better for you to have stayed at home by the stove, so that you wouldn't grieve your old mother, if you still have one, or your wife, if Allah has blessed you with one. Get out of my sight, and be quick about it, while I still have some pity in my heart for you. If I get angry, you'll soon lie covered with blood on the ground like the Emperor's son and a hundred others like him!"

"If you haven't yet made your peace with God, do so at once," Kerpan replied. "I don't intend to wait too long. I'm in a hurry to get back home to my stove. Your words have awakened in my heart a burning desire for my cabin and my stove, but I won't go until I cut off your head. I beg your pardon! My Lord, the Emperor, gave me this task. Previously I had neither heard of you nor of your greatness, nor of all this bloody fighting. Come nearer so that we can shake hands. We have never met before this time and probably will never shake hands again. They say that God does not like to have anyone come before the Judgment Seat with anger in his heart."

The giant was, of course, greatly surprised by these words. Thereupon he quickly rode up to Kerpan and gave him his enormous hand. Kerpan squeezed it so hard that blood began to gush from the giant's finger nails.

Berdavs gave a low groan and still said nothing, but he thought to himself, "This fellow is big and strong. Well, what of that—a peasant is a peasant. At least he doesn't know how to fight like the heroes."

The two combatants turned their horses about and rode away swiftly in opposite directions. Berdavs raised his sword high in the

---

[3]June 2.

air as a preparation for chopping off his foe's head in one stroke. Kerpan, however, quickly covered himself with his club and let the giant thrust his sword deep into the soft linden wood. Before the giant could unhorse him, Kerpan jerked Berdavs off his horse to the ground, laid him flat on his back as though he were putting a baby in a cradle, stepped on his neck, saying, "Well, hurry up now and say a little Our Father or two and repent for your sins. You can't go to confession any more now and I can't wait very long. I'm in a hurry to get back to my stove. You see, I can hardly wait to hear the bell in Verkh at the Holy Trinity ring again."

Having said this, Kerpan slowly raised his cleaver and cut off the giant's head. He then returned to the city.

The Viennese, who until now had watched the fight only from afar, went to meet him. The Emperor himself came to greet him and embraced him in the presence of all the people who were shouting at the top of their lungs: "Kerpan has saved us! Thanks to Kerpan as long as Vienna shall stand!"

It made Kerpan feel very gratified to think he had won so much fame. He carried himself on his little mare as though he were about to invite friends to dine with him. Indeed, he could well afford to do so for even here in Carniola, if anyone kills a worm or a snake, he does not know on which bush to hang it so that it may be seen by more people.

When all the princes, generals and lords of the land had assembled with Kerpan in the palace, the Emperor himself was the first to speak, "You just choose anything you want! I'll give you whatever you want for conquering so great a foe and saving the country and the city from such a great scourge and disaster. There isn't a thing in the Empire I wouldn't give you for the asking. You may even have Jerica, my only daughter,—if you're not already married."

"I was married, but I'm not now," Kerpan replied. "My wife is dead and I never looked about for another. I don't know how it is to be badly off and to be displeasing in the sight of God and honest people. I have already seen your daughter. Perhaps she is as sensible as she is beautiful but she belongs to a rich family, she's used to luxuries that I can't afford to give her. We, however, are not quite such beggars in Verkh at the Holy Trinity. We, too, have smoked meat hanging off spits all the year round. But I don't know how it'll be now.

"Once Marjeta and I carried grapes in back-baskets to Trieste. On our way back, she was taken suddenly ill. This annoyed me so much that I can't describe it. I'd sooner have both of my shoulder straps break in church as I'm about to light the candles for Mass. But there was no way out. I had to put her in one of the baskets, put the basket on my shoulders and march off with her.

"I managed well, for Marjeta was as small as a girl of thirteen years —although she was really thirty when we were married. She was, therefore, not heavy. Wherever I came, they asked me what kind of goods I was selling. It's a beastly business to carry a woman around the world in a basket! Just suppose something like that should happen to your daughter and me on the road? The road from here to Verkh drags on like chicken gut. Being a poor man, I have no basket and my little mare has only one saddle! It wouldn't be strange if your daughter became ill, for we all know that soft women like her aren't used to the plop-plop, plop-plop of horses' hoofs from five o'clock in the morning till eight in the evening. If one thinks this matter over carefully, he'll soon see that it is better for the princess to stay with you and for me to remain a widower even if I am not exactly reconciled. But man should not refuse whatever burdens God may inflict upon him."

The Empress never forgot the incident of the bushy linden tree, spreading its branches over the stone table in the garden. This was really the reason for her absence, but she listened behind doors as is the habit of women who want to know everything. When she heard the Emperor offering their daughter in marriage to Kerpan, she burst into the room and shouted to the latter: "You won't have her! No, you won't! You chopped down my linden tree and I won't give you my daughter! My dear husband, you must have water on your brain —I can't say anything better for you—to say such things when you yourself know they are nonsense. And you, too, gentlemen, ought to be ashamed of yourselves. It isn't decent to have a peasant fight for you! My linden tree would still be standing there today and the giant would have lost his head too, if you amounted to anything. But I know! Since men have become so effeminate, every woman who marries is mad!

"It's true, Kerpan, you saved the Empire. It's also true that you have saved Vienna. For that reason you are going to get a barrel of wine containing fifty small *veders*,[4] a hundred and five loaves of bread and twelve rams. We'll also give you forty-eight hams. Now listen closely! All these things you may take home to Carniola, if you wish, but you must not sell them here or on your way back home. When you return to Verkh at the Holy Trinity, you may do whatever you please with them.

"And now as there is no longer any Berdavs to annoy us, it wouldn't be a bad idea for you to saddle that famous little goat you call a mare and go back nicely to Verkh. Give my regards to all the people of Verkh, especially the burgomaster's wife!"

Having said this, the Empress went back at once to her room. All the lords were very much ashamed. Why shouldn't they have been? She had given them such a severe scolding, just as they deserved! Kerpan made such fierce grimaces that he resembled a thunderstorm. His eyes flashed underneath his angry brows as though the sky were flashing beyond the little town of Mokrice. His brows bristled up like two brooms. Good God, how strange they all felt around him! Even the Emperor seemed timid as he looked sidewise at him. Imagine, the Emperor! However, because they had been such friends, he slowly ventured to say to him, "My dear Kerpan, just be quiet. We'll make everything right!"

Kerpan paid no attention to these remarks. Putting his club on his right shoulder and his cleaver on his left, he went to the door, saying, "May God guard you! And no offense!"

With these words, he raised the latch and started to leave.

Thereupon, the Emperor ran after him and called to him, "Wait a minute! Let me explain! God forbid! Surely you aren't a jellyfish!"

"What is it?" Kerpan replied. "Don't you think I've heard enough of this already? My beard would reach to my belt, or even to my toes, if I didn't shave myself twice a week. But then who would sweep the floor after me if I didn't do so myself? Who sent for the coach and four? You or I? I didn't need Vienna but Vienna needed me! Why do you treat me like this now? Must I swallow your complaints about the meat and bread I ate? I have already eaten the bread, black and white, of many a mother and drank the wine of many a father, but I'll never get such service, even here, as I get in Razderto at Klincar's

---

[4]An old Slovene measure of 10 pots containing 14.5 liters.

place. There isn't anything worse in this world than giving something and then begrudging it! Whoever does not wish to give anything, let him keep it for himself! But who'd have thought that there are still laws about linden trees! Was that little tree your God, or what? That kind of wood grows behind every bush in Carniola, but Kerpan isn't to be found on every corner—not even in every court, thank the Lord! Then again you give such gifts that one can't even get to them. It's just as though you'd tie a mouse to a cat's tail in order to make the cat turn around without being able to catch the little animal. Fifty small *veders* of wine, a hundred and five loaves of bread, twelve rams, and forty-eight hams! Such provisions aren't really bad, but what's the use? I can't sell them, and it doesn't pay to carry them from Vienna to Verkh! But I'll do something that nobody has ever dreamed of! I'll bring all the planks in Vienna together in the courtyard and if these are not enough, I'll begin on the trees. I'll cut down everything that comes under my hatchet, whether it be a full-grown or a small-leafed linden, a dogberry or a snow-ball tree, underneath a stone table or underneath a wooden one. I'll then build a cabin in the middle of the courtyard and lie in bed until the barrel is empty and I have eaten everything. But let another Berdavs come to Vienna again and then you can just send your coach and servant, or even your daughter, for whom I have little or no use, to fetch me and see what you will bring back from Verkh at the Holy Trinity! If that person be Kerpan, he certainly won't eat meat and bones but you will have to stuff him with oak straw. Then even the sparrows won't be afraid of him, much less the giant! I meant to go without a word of parting but since you stopped me, please don't be angry if I said anything bitter to you. Surely you remember what the late Jernejko of Gole said: 'Must I feed one with a loaf of bread whenever I quarrel with him? Whatever makes a person angrier, that's what I snap back at him.' And now good-bye!"

Upon hearing this, the Emperor said, "Be patient, Martin! At least, don't be so impatient. You won't go from this house. Believe me, you won't! I'm master here, understand!"

"Every man is as God made him," Kerpan replied. "Every man has a burden of his own. If one hasn't a hunched back, he has a snout! My behavior doesn't suit you; I can see it doesn't. Let's not talk about my staying here. Even my little mare, which they call a goat, is not used to dry fodder. At home she can graze in the forest, on the cowpaths, along the roads!"

At this moment, the Minister Gregor, who held the keys to the imperial coffers,—for they have a separate servant for everything in royal courts—joined them.

"Do you know, Your Majesty," said the Minister, "that your jester Stefan is dead? Yesterday we had an eighth-day Mass said for him. May God grant him celestial light! Stefan and Kerpan! In many ways there is a striking resemblance between them. What do you say? Perhaps this man can take his place. You never can tell. He's a slyboots. He's aft and ridiculous too and just as glib. There isn't a fellow like him in all Christendom!"

"Do you know this, Master Gregor?" Kerpan replied, "I was your fool once but I won't be again. The small and great would laugh at me and my homespun humor, if I'd accept your offer!—It's all right now that I remember! I almost forgot what I have had on the tip of my tongue for a long time. Your Majesty, remember you once met me with my little mare?"

"Quite right, quite right!"

"And what was I carrying?"

"Grindstones and German tinder."

"That's not the truth! I was going to Trieste. I know as much about Jerusalem as I do about the appointed hour of my death."

"And I know just as much about grindstones and German tinder. You know, I wasn't telling you the truth at that time, for which I am very sorry. I was carrying English salt. I wasn't exactly afraid of you or your coachman, but so it goes when a man turns from the right path. Let him be ever so strong, still he may be frightened at the mere rustling of branches."

"Don't you know it's forbidden to do that?" the Minister Gregor said. "This is a dangerous man. He is a menace to the country. Seize him and lock him up!"   :

"Who'll do that?" Kerpan asked. "Perhaps you will, you longlegged beanpole! You who are as dry as a spit! You, who with all the authorities to help you, hardly make half a handful! I can throw you with one hand over the roof of St. Stephen's church standing in the middle of the town! Don't waste your breath!"

"You just tell me, if you want anything else," the Emperor said.

"You and I won't be enemies, not if God grants it. And you, Minister Gregor, let him alone. I know how it is!"

"Listen to me then," Kerpan went on to explain. "I know my fight with Berdavs has made me famous. Who knows? Perhaps some of the loafers in Vienna will write stories and poems about this fight. Perhaps even such stories and poems might be recited at some future time when neigher our bones nor our dust remain, provided Master Gregor does not have something else written in the books. But let him do as he likes. Now, if you please, give me a letter that will hold good for every lord in the kingdom. You must also stamp it with your seal, so that I'll be able to carry my English salt freely all over the world. If you grant me that, and if I ever bother you about anything else as long as I carry my freight, you may call me the worst scamp you ever saw!"

The Emperor was ready at once to do what Kerpan wished but the Minister Gregor could not be made to agree with him. The Emperor, however, did not listen to him but said, "Gregor, take your pen and write down what Martin said!"

Though the Minister Gregor looked surly, he did what the Emperor commanded him to do, for everyone is somewhat afraid of an Emperor. When the letter was written and sealed, the Emperor said to Kerpan: "Martin, will you sell me your bread, wine and all those other things? It'll be easier this way. I'll speak to the Empress about it, so that it will be all right. I'll give you a bag of ducats and you will leave the goods here. Who would lug this around from Vienna to the Holy Trinity?"

"I know a bag and a half with an additional crown-piece would be a fair price, if I were selling it to my brother; but let it go at your price. I don't mind since it's you and as long as I won't have any trouble with the Empress because of this. I don't like to crawl on my belly before lords! At least I have witnesses that assumed responsibility from all the trouble that might result from this sooner or later," Kerpan replied.

"Don't be afraid," the Emperor assured him, "I'll smooth this matter out myself, without your help. Here's the bag and here's the letter too. But aren't you going from this castle tonight, if you really intend to go at all. The day is already far spent and night is falling."

"Many thanks," Kerpan said, "most of all for this little letter which

I shall throw into the teeth of anyone who will try to stop me on the road. I won't refuse the bag, either. Who knows what may hit one in the unknown darkness of the night? Perhaps it might come in handy yet. People always say: 'A bird in the hand is worth two in the bush!' But I won't stay here over night, if you don't mind. I feel a strong urge to be in Verkh at the Holy Trinity again. I'd like to ask you for something else. That is, if you'd send someone with me to take me to the road. The city is big. There are so many houses. I have never seen so many before in all the time I have been carrying my salt, although I have already been to Reka, Kopre, Verkhnika, and Ljubljana. But in those places there were never so many streets. The coachman and I drove fast and I know as much about the road I came on as I should if had my eyes blindfolded, although I looked right and left. But it isn't given to every man to know always where he is."

The Emperor promised him his servant, gave him his hand, and told Gregor to do likewise. The Minister made no objections, but his face was yellow with rage because of the letter.

Kerpan swung his club and cleaver over his shoulder and these were his last words to the Emperor:" If any Berdavs or anybody else should ever come to Vienna, you know where the place is that they call Verkh at the Holy Trinity. I'll give your regards to the burgomaster's mother and the people of Verkh. Good-bye!"

"Pleasant journey," the Emperor said, but the Minister Gregor said nothing.

Anthony J. Klančar

Ivan Cankar

(1876–1918)

Ivan Cankar was born in Vrhnika in 1876 and died in Ljubljana in 1918. He was the author of long and short novels, critical essays, and poems, *Hlapec Jernej* in *njegova pravica* (Servant Jernej and his Justice, 1907), *Kralj na Betajnovi* (The King of Betajnova, 1902), *Hiša Marije pomočnice* (The Home of Marija, the Maid Servant, 1904), *Za narodov blagor* (For the Good of the People, 1901).

A SIN

It was warm and the snow was melting on the roofs; the water was dropping from them, and the drops were glittering in the sun. The well-dressed city people were walking in the streets.

Mother arrived in front of the school too early. On the large square it was still quiet; the windows of the big school gleamed, and I could hear from time to time the voice of a teacher, who spoke in the school with a sharp and strident voice.

Mother had come from far away; she had come from a village which was some four hours' walk from town. Her boots—male boots, which reached her knees—were completely covered with mud. Even her skirt was splashed with mud—a wide peasant skirt, with green flowers. Mother had in her right hand an umbrella and a big bundle with shirts and a new pair of boots for Joze; and in her left hand she carried a big kerchief in whose knot there were ten dinars, tied up, which she had brought to Joze.

Mother was tired and hungry; that morning she had not bought bread in order not to break the ten dinar bill. Her legs ached and she coughed; her face was thin, and there were deep hollows in her cheeks. She walked slowly up and down in the square, looking at the windows which glitterred as if covered with gold.

The bell rang in the school; it kept ringing for a long time, followed by noise and commotion. A crowd of pupils pressed forward to the big door; first the little ones from the lower classes came out—screaming and running down the square. Behind them came the older pupils—they walked more seriously and with more self-confidence. Joze came too, in a crowd of merry friends. He caught sight of his mother—her peasant skirt with green flowers, her high muddy boots, a red blouse, a mottled scarf on her head bound from the back, her big bundle and the clumsy umbrella.

"Is this your mother?" a friend asked him.

"This is not my mother!" Joze answered. He was ashamed of the peasant skirt with green flowers, the high boots, red blouse, the kerchief, the umbrella, and the big bundle. In that big bundle were his new shirts which mother had been sewing at night, while tears were dropping on them.

He hid himself in the crowd and passed her by.

Mother stood and kept looking with her worried eyes.

Soon the noise stopped, and only an occasional pupil would come out of the school; then the bell rang and everything became quiet again.

Mother was about to go to Joze's apartment and wait for him. After a few steps, it occurred to her that perhaps he had to stay longer at school; so she returned and continued waiting.

Her legs ached; she leaned against the wall and looked up at the windows glittering in the sun. She waited until noon. A bell rang again at noon, and outside it also started to ring, one could hear from all sides the noon bells. Again there was noise and thick crowds pressed forward out of the school. Mother came closer to the big gate—quite close—looking for Joze.

He was not there. Everything became quiet again; only teachers were coming out now. Bearded, serious, they looked back at her.

She became worried, scared, and it occurred to her that perhaps he was very ill at home, waiting for her, calling his mother. She rushed to the apartment and her legs trembled.

Joze was at home; he sat at the table and held a book in front of him. When she opened the door, he stood up at once and started coming toward her.

"Well, when did you come?"

"At eleven."

"Didn't you see me waiting for you?"

"I didn't see you!" answered Joze.

In the afternoon they went walking downtown. They walked on a nice street. On the right side all the houses sparkled as if it were a holiday. Sparkling drops of water were falling, dropping down the drains, gaily hitting the stone sidewalk. Joze was accompanying his mother on her way home. He walked close to her and held her hand. He felt as if he wanted to hide himself and to start weeping aloud. He kept meeting his school friends; he also met the friend who asked him in front of the school: "Isn't that your mother?" Joze was not ashamed any longer; he felt like shouting: "Look, this is my mother!"

He walked next to his mother, but a sin lay on his soul, which oppressed him, so that his legs were tired and heavy. He walked beside his mother like Judas beside Christ.

They parted outside the city, and Joze felt like kneeling before her and hiding his head in her lap: "Mother, I have renounced you!" But he did not kneel. When mother was far away, he shouted after her.

"Mother."

Mother turned around.

"Good-bye, mother," he exclaimed; and so they parted. From the distance, he could see his mother walking slowly on the muddy road; her body was bent, as if she carried a heavy burden on her shoulders.

Joze went home and sat in the corner on the big bundle which his mother had brought, hid his face with his hands and started to cry.

A sin lay on his soul and no tears could wash it out. They slipped from him, as from hard stone.

This was long ago, but the sin is lying on his soul, as heavy and as big as the first day, and so his life is now full of sorrow and suffering.

Dragan Milivojević

VIENNA EVENINGS

In elegant carriages there parade
Crooks, bankers and thieves on high levels
Past blossoming chestnuts in the evening light
And past our row of poor devils.

But I know all those faces with indolent eyes,
So cunningly winking, so sated.
Who could delete the swindler's brand
With which their brows are decorated?

Long fingers in those *glacè*; kid-gloves,
Adroit in acquiring of treasure,
Have, plundered, debauched, and raped and killed—
All for profit and pleasure.

And the answer to this from our righteous Lord?
In wealth they now swill and wallow.
Of gold, and honours, of majesty's pomp
Much more they have than they can swallow.

In carriages crooks and thieves parade,
But I'm still the same poor devil:
Weary and hungry, with stumbling steps,
A prey to disease and all evil.

Janko Lavrin

Dragotin Kete

(1876–1899)

Dragotin Kete was born in Prem in 1876 and died in Ljubljana in 1899. He was the author of the cycles of poems entitled *Izprehod* (The Stroll, 1898) and *Na molu San Carlo* (On the Pier of San Carlo, 1899) as well as the collection *Novi akordi* (New Accords, 1899). In five short years he created his poetical opus from the imitation of folk ballads to mature individual poetical creation.

HOW GREAT MY LOVE

How great my love, you ask me, I should try
To tell you, dear. Am I a bell whose tone
Is wonderous clear? Nor am I Solomon.
I stutter like a sage grown old and shy.

But wait! When under Doomsday's rending sky
The trumpet calls mankind unto God's throne,
And all alike—all differences gone—
Shall stand before Jehovah's judging eye:

"Ye poets," angrily at us He'll roar,
"Five loves hads't thou, thou six and thou a score.
Not unto Purgatory shall ye go.

But straight to hell, incorrigible race!"
I then approach with you—joy in my face . . .
"A constant lover here? No wonder, though."

A. Lenarčič and J. Lavrin

RECOLLECTION

What have I done to Thee, righteous Lord?
Did I not doubt Thy existence?
Did I not break all commandments of Thine?
Of penitence there's not an instance.

I too was a thief, a débauchee,
And a killer—worse than a bandit.
Count those who once loved me and whom I yet spurned
And murdered their souls pure and candid.

My own soul I murdered when I defiled
It in all its innocent raiment.
It is a big and heavy bill
For which I now demand payment.

Here is the bill! But where's the reward?
Like them I claim compensation.
I knock on Thy door: Where's my award?
Come, honor Thy obligation.

J. Lavrin

Oton Župančič

(1878–1949)

Oton Župančič was born in Vinica in 1878 and died in Ljubljana in 1949. He is the most important Slovenian poet after Prešeren. He studied history in Vienna from 1896–1901 and lived in Western Europe (Germany, France, England) from 1905 to 1910.

He published collections of poems entitled *Čaša opojnosti* (The Cup of Intoxication, 1899), *Čez plan* (Over the Country, 1904), *Samogovori* (Monologues, 1908), *V zarje vidove* (In the Light of the Dawn, 1920), and *Zimzelen pod snegom* (Evergreens Under Snow, 1945). He was a translator and an author of poems for children.

MEDITATION

(A Fragment from "Duma")

Their backs and shoulders are as strong as cliffs;
their necks (a load, O tyrant, you can place thereon)
will carry all and will not bend.
Their hearts love peace and they are stout;
their pride needs no vain words:
as if they were not born of mothers
but from mountain crags.
Into the world they go, and foreign countries boast
of their hands' work and skill.
There—in America, there—in Westphalia,
they're lost to us beyond the reach
of sight.

Where are you, native land? Here in these fields
beneath Triglav? Among the Karavanks?
Or 'midst the furnaces and in the mines
beyond the Ocean—you who have no bounds?

There was a time I wished you'd broaden forth,
expand and broaden o'er the world,
and now 'tis plain that boundless you have grown:
like seeds you scatter into distance all your brood.

Will you, like swallows, tempt them home again?
Will you, like doves, unite them 'neath your roof?
Or will they, once beguiled by might and glory
in foreign lands, no more return to you?

Where are you, native land? Here in these fields.
beneath Triglav? Among the Karavanks?
Or midst' the furnaces and in the mines
beyond the Ocean—you, who have no bounds?

I apprehend and feel you. Ah, the poet's dream
for many a year has hovered over you,
watching, listening, weeping, hoping
your secret to disclose.

The oyster, deep within the sea, its pain intense
into a gem has gathered.
Oh poet's heart what gathers within you?
Oh poet's heart—it is your pain.

I. Zorman

OUR BODIES

Our bodies are like vessels made of gold,
containing all our ancient heritage,
in us their sap keeps throbbing as of old
in passions, joys and pains of every age.

In our blood countless lives unborn pulsate,
the coming lives of our entire race;
each germ, each cell fights for its destined state,
and in this way the future molds its face.

Its will is stronger than the will of man,
it lashes us together: husband—wife.
Accursed be he who puts on it a ban—
he banishes himself from world and life.

J. Lavrin

Prežihov Voranc

(1893–1950)

Prežihov Voranc (pseudonym for Lovro Kuhar) was born in Kotle in 1893 and died in Maribor in 1950. He was a representative of social realism and one of the most prominent novelists between the two World Wars. He emigrated from Yugoslavia in 1929, traveled in Europe, and returned to Yugoslavia where he participated in the guerrilla movement from 1941–42.

He published *Pripovedke* (Stories, 1925), *Dobredob* (The Natives, 1940), *Borba na tujih tleh* (The struggle on foreign Soil, 1946), and *Solzice* (Lilies of the Valley, 1949).

THE BIRDMAN

The old birdman pushed open the door to the porch and slowly, with a great effort, crossed the high doorstep. When he was finally outside, he stooped, tightened his worn-out overcoat, and glanced fearfully at the space in front of the hovel where the first pale gleams of the March sun were shining. His body shivered as if suspended in the wind, and his knees shook, so he leaned on a knotty walking stick that he grasped convulsively in the long, dirty fingers of his right hand. For some time he shuffled his feet as if he could not make up his mind, and then he began to move along the path that slanted off to the little town whose roofs were visible from the narrow valley below the hill.

The birdman was a strange creature. Nobody knew his real name and nobody cared. He was single, and for decades he had lived in a hovel overlooking the little town, drawing an insignificant pension from somewhere. He was well-known primarily because his face resembled that of certain hook-billed birds. At the end of an unusually long neck, in the middle of which was a large Adam's apple, perched a birdlike head. His narrow face consisted of a low, receding forehead from which, starting from the hairline, there jutted a powerful bone that curved to a pointed extension at its end. This extension, similar to the beak of a hawk, was the birdman's nose. Its expression definitely made his head look like that of a bird, although the other parts of his face contributed—such features as protruding lips, a thin, hardly visible beard, shallow eyes almost stuck to the nose, and ears sticking out like those of a bat.

It was known that the birdman's room was full of birds that screeched all day long, and that it looked just like an aviary—everything covered with a thick layer of birds' droppings and an unbearable smell. The birds flew freely about his room and nested wherever it suited them. The whole of his slender income was spent on their food. It was said that sometimes he was possessed by a strange passion and let his birds go to the point of starvation. The birds would scream despairingly while he sat motionless in a corner savoring the dying birds' screams. Some people were horrified at this and threatened to destroy the aviary and to bring the birds' torments to an end. But this never happend.

On this particular day the birdman had been driven out of his hovel by hunger. For two months he had languished in his aviary amidst a flock of birds including canaries, bullfinches, goldfinches, ortolans, wrens, jays, magpies, tomtits, sparrows, turtledoves, owls, thrushes, and hens. Since Christmas, thick snow had covered the ground so that he had been unable to find any kind of food for them outside. In autumn he had picked up roots, turnips, and potatoes in the fields, and plucked some grain from the wheat sheaves. But all that had already been used up and for the last ten days the aviary had lived on refuse and garbage.

The hungry rabble could hardly be kept under control now. Day after day they screeched more and more desperately, attacked him, and made such horrible sounds that even he, who was used to them, could not get a wink of sleep for several nights. The more delicate birds even collapsed and were devoured, bones and all, by the others. Only the night before, the kite buzzard had been so overcome by hunger that he had gulped down a pedigree canary to the last feather. That was why he had to be put in the cage under the bench, where he looked as if he, too, were about to expire at any moment.

Three hens were huddled under the stove. One black, one white, and one speckled. Only a feeble flapping and cackling could still be heard from the dark corner. With wings spread and necks outstretched, the hens lay on the floor and watched their master with bloody, desperate eyes.

The birdman put his hand on his skinny knee and looked at them with eyes full of compassion. After a while he said in a hoarse voice:

"Little hens! Chickies! Don't be afraid! You're thin, so now you must pick up your strength . . . that's it . . . pick up your strength. . . . You over there, you black one. . . ."

As soon as his eyes were satisfied, he got up, caught the larger birds that might gobble up the others in his absence, and locked them in their cages. The birds submitted, offering no resistance. When he had finished, he put on his overcoat, which was completely covered with birds' droppings, put a basket on his arm, picked up his stick, stood in the middle of the room, and said aloud:

"Quiet! Today you are going to get something to eat!"

From all sides, from the walls, from under the bench and the table, from underneath the cupboard, some ten feeble voices began to croak and to squawk, as if the birds wished to show they had understood. Only from under the stove were no voices heard at all.

The birdman noticed this; his birdlike face twisted a little and then he walked out of the hovel.

The birdman approached the houses of the little town with a feeble step. As soon as he reached the first house, he met a crowd of children sliding along a frozen shady path which was like a deep gutter. The birdman was always an interesting sight for the children and they surrounded him immediately.

"Here's the birdman, here's the birdman!" shouted the children on the slippery path.

The old man, who seemed hardly able to stand, appeared to pluck up courage. He suddenly strengthened himself and stared at the children, who made faces of unutterable hatred at him. They withdrew a little and began to shout from a distance, "The birdman, the birdman!"

Then the old man raised his stick as if he were going to chase the toddlers nearest him. But they skipped off in time. A few of the boldest burst into malicious laughter and began to shout: "A duck, a duck! The birdman, the duck, the duck!"

These words seemed to strike the birdman like a thunderbolt. He stumbled, and it seemed that he would fall full length to the ground. But he still had enough strength to keep on his feet. He crouched like a hedgehog; his eyes, which had been watching the children with a hostile look, withdrew behind the red swollen lids and grew fearful and puzzled. As though through a distant mist he discerned the contours of the first house of the town before him. Full of fright and confusion, he dashed toward it.

"Duck, duck!" shouted the children after the fleeing old man.

In a flash the birdman succeeded in reaching the entrance of the house. He leaned against the door with his whole weight and pushed it open, so that he almost fell across the threshold; then he slammed it behind him with such violence that the whole house trembled. He was shaking all over. Thus frightened, and in a cold sweat, he dropped on a chest just behind the door and almost fainted.

Then the door to the kitchen opened and two women dashed out.

"What's the matter?" cried the first of the two. But as soon as she spoke hse noticed the old man sitting on the chest and leaning against the wall.

"Oh, it's the birdman!" They both recovered at the same time.

"And what are you doing here?" asked the first woman.

The old man gave a little start, but he was so frightened that he could not utter a single word. He only directed his vague, lost look toward the front door. Outside, the voices of those arrogant children could still be heard shouting: "Duck, duck!"

Then the women looked at each other, blushed a little, and smiled. The older one soothed the old man, "Those are only children's jokes, you old birdman! That's nothing! Now, then, you had better come over here where it is warm."

The old man looked at her gratefully, gathered his strength, and, tottering slowly, followed the women into the kitchen where they indicated that he should sit down on a low stool near the coalbox. He twisted about, put his palms between his thin, trembling knees, lowered his head on his hands, and remained silent.

The women left him in peace so that he might warm himself. In the meantime they looked at each other suspiciously and wrinkled their noses at the unpleasant smell that soon pervaded the whole kitchen. Despite this discomfort, they could not hide the smile that fluttered across their faces.

To tell the truth, the birdman had the reputation throughout the district of being not only queer, but even mad. Besides, everybody knew that in spite of his passion for birds, he despised all birds with large beaks, such as ducks. Never had any bird that had the slightest kinship with a duck entered his aviary—neither a duck, nor a goose, nor a woodcock, nor a heron. His entire birds' paradise consisted of crooked-beaked and pointed-beaked kinds. Whenever he caught sight of a wide-beaked monster, he almost had an epileptic fit. Malicious grown-ups and children, knowing this weakness, made him angry by calling "duck," while the peasants chased him from their sheaves when the wheat was drying and he tried to pick off a few ears for his birds as he passed by.

For a while the two women watched the shivering old man silently and with a strange, uncomfortable feeling. They looked in disgust at his sharp, birdlike features, his bloodshot, red-rimmed eyes, his dried-up body. They were particularly horrified at the sight of his hands, with their long fingers like claws and sickeningly long nails. Then they remembered that the birdman had never cared for women; people said he adored birds instead, particularly hens. . . . In recalling this, everybody, both old and young, shuddered.

As they watched the birdman, the women forgot for a time that they had a hungry man in the house. Then they made a pot of tea and added a good dollop of rum. The younger one cut a big slice of bread.

"Here, have a bite and something to drink!" they invited him.

By now the birdman was quiet. He was still shivering from exhaustion, since he had not eaten anything hot for a week. He finished his tea before the women even noticed it, but he did not touch the bread.

"Why don't you take some bread?" asked the older woman almost reproachfully.

The birdman kept silent; he only raised his eyes imploringly. The woman understood.

"Oh, I see!" she said, and then added in a good-natured voice:

"You just eat that bread. And as for the birds, I shall give you something else to take to them."

She poured him more tea, and only then did the old man snatch up his bread and eat it.

The women took his basket, which he had placed near his feet, and prepared some food for the birds—a mixture of potatoes, beets, and grain.

"Have you got hens too?" asked the younger one meaningfully.

'Yes, I have," the birdman replied in a low voice.

The woman put some extra grain for the hens in his basket.

"That's for your hens!"

The birdman thanked the women and slowly walked out of the house. The older woman saw him to the door, warned the children to leave the old man in peace, and quickly returned to the kitchen, where she promptly washed her hands to clean them of contact with the old man's basket. The younger did the same.

The old man did not start directly for home, but waddled to the little town. He went to the merchant where he had left the last few pence of his pension, and where he could still buy some trifles on credit. From the merchant he went to the butcher, who sometimes gave him refuse for the carnivorous birds. He did not go there in vain. The butcher put in some stinking, yellowish offal. When the birdman had stuffed it all in his basket on top of the other things and was about to leave, the buther asked him to wait a bit. He disappeared, and quickly returned with a big mousetrap in which was a live young rat.

"This might do for the hawks and the fowls," he said, pointing to the mousetrap. "Our cat has so many, it is already sick, of them."

The old man blushed. The animal was rushing about excitedly in the narrow space. When the old man looked at it, it stopped immediately and remained motionless. The animal did not move even when the old man put his long fingers into the mousetrap, but yielded without resistance and let itself be pushed into a separate compartment of the basket.

From the butcher's the birdman went to the baker's, where he bought some bread and where something more found its way into the basket for his birds to drink. It was already dark when he disappeared past the last houses, on his way back to his hovel.

When he entered the room, he was welcomed by an earsplitting, hellish screeching released from desperate starved throats and beaks. All the croaking, whistling, cooing, and crowing was drowned by the cawing of two crows, accompanied by and mingled with a feverish rattling and fluttering of wings. The birds dashed themselves against the walls and ceiling, fell on the floor and dragged themselves into the corners, while those that were in cages hit themselves against the wire netting.

This was the usual scene whenever the old man returned home with a full basket. The carnivores had smelled the offal, and the granivorous birds, the grain.

It was almost dark in the room: the two little windows, which were blocked with rags, pots, and bottles, let the last feeble rays of daylight into the narrow aviary. But soon they disappeared, and the hovel was wrapped in darkness.

The birdman sat on the bed, put the basket on the table, and remained motionless, sitting in the dark. Although there was no fire, the room was not too cold, warmed as it was by a whole flock of winged creatures. For a common villager, perhaps, it might have been cold, but the birdman was warmed by his own nature, which was akin to that of the birds. He felt happiest in that atmosphere, in that cauldron of smells and stinks.

Then it began. . . .

Perfectly still, he listened to the sick screaming and desperate fluttering of the starved birds, reminding him of death, which excited him and provoked a mysterious, morbid passion. The stronger and louder the birds' shrilling, the more intense his passion grew.

Half an hour or more passed. The old man sat on the bed motionless, with his legs crossed, as if he were afraid of something distant and strange; listening to his own wild blood. Had the room not been so dark, one could have seen how his birdlike face glowed with a secret self-satisfaction, how his lips trembled.

He tried to distinguish the separate sounds. That feeble sipping . . . oh, that was the canary. He is angry not only because he is hungry, but because he has lost his little mate, eaten up by the vile kite. Now there was another voice that squeaked tensely, as if the narrow bird's chest were letting out its last breath . . . the finch. She was already exhausted, but she could drag herself on for another day or two. . . .

Yes, she could. But the Hartzer would certainly die. The devil would likewise have taken the bullfinch and goldfinches. Those tiny birds have no resistance. . . . Behind the cupboard a titmouse twittered . . . tsvr . . . tsvr, so feebly that it was hardly audible. Its tiny eyes already had in them the true glitter of death. Two magpies screeched on the wardrobe.There was only one owl in the house, but she screamed as much as five other beaks together. She was still fairly strong. In the cage above the bed small wings fluttered constantly. A baby bird had got entangled in the net and one could hear the tiny body hopping up, falling back to the bottom of the cage, resuming its flight, and flapping down once more. . . . That was the bullfinch; his mate, however, was quiet. Next to him the thin voice of a goldfinch was twittering, hardly audible, at its last gasp. Two buzzards, shut up under the bench, croaked restlessly; but the most annoying of all was the kite, which in fact was less hungry, having swallowed the canary; but that bite had very likely only quickened his appetite. Everything was in motion, shrieking, screaming. . . . The owl alone crouched motionless in her corner. She had started squawking once, quite feebly, as if in panic, but now she was quiet; just two bright eyes glittered from the small corner. . . .

The birdman listened to the sobbing in the aviary.

Suddenly his body jerked; he shook his head, rose, and shouted, "oh, you've been suffering, haven't you, my little birds? I've also been tormented, they tortured me so much that they drove me mad. . ."

At first his voice brought complete silence, but afterward such a cawing and croaking broke out that the hovel's foundations trembled. There was a harrowing shriek of dying creatures. One could hear the straining of the muscles of the wide-open beaks, narrow chests inflating wings spread with the last scrap of strength, flapping with hope.

The birdman laughed with satisfaction. He was less excited now, and the strength that had abandoned him earlier gradually returned to his exhausted muscles.

The squalling did not abate. The birds suspected that the end of their suffering was now approaching, and that surmise elated them.

The birdman put his right hand into a drawer, took out a match, and lit the lamp on which there was no glass because it long ago had been broken by the birds. The reddish flame soon illuminated the place faintly. The magpie sat on the old man's head, the crow on one shoulder, the owl on the other, while other birds hung down his sleeves, chest and back. The birdman did not drive them off; but looking thus ridiculous, he began to fuss about the room, talking to the birds in a mild, plaintive voice, "chickies, birdies . . . now you're going to get something to eat; just in a minute—now you'll get something."

Then he bent over the basket and began with the utmost care and gentleness to feed the birds. Every kind of bird had its own small trough in one of the corners into which he poured seeds, grain, or crumbs. Now he could release the birds of prey from the cages because they were no longer dangerous. The owl stood on his wrist, perching determinedly. Not until she had grabbed a half-rotten beef rib did she relax her grip and fly to her corner.

The basket was well filled and the birdman poured the drink and cut the food generously. The hungry beaks devoured and gulped, the wings fluttered greedily, and the sharp claws scratched enviously.

The birdman waddled from one corner to the other, pouring more maize. That was for the hens. But whereas the other birds swallowed their food with savage fury, the hens did not appear at all.

The old man's dried lips twisted, distorting his face into a grimace.

"Now, now!" he said in a loathsome voice. "You are on strike, little hens, aren't you?"

He crouched in front of the stove and started to stir a heap of wheat with his clawlike fingers, pretending to peck.

"Little hens, little hens, my chickies! Don't be afraid, just come, come on," he murmured, continually stirring the small heap of grain.

Some time passed before the hens moved from under the stove. The black hen was the first to crawl up to him. Peeping sideways at the heap of wheat, she began to approach, as if distrusting the masters' invitation. Finally she drew near the heap with the utmost caution. The birdman knew he must withdraw if the hen was to begin pecking, so he got up and moved away. But the black hen did not start eating at once, but continued to watch to see what was going to happen. Finally she went up to the food and slowly began to peck at the grain.

Only then did the other two come out from under the stove and peck at the supper with the same hesitation and lack of enthusiasm as the first. Their appetite, however, gradually increased, and soon they were swallowing their food greedily.

At the sight, the birdman's face lit up. With the tip of his tongue he licked his thin, almost invisible lips, and murmured in a sleepy tone: "I knew it, my chicks. I knew it. . .''

All the birds were eating except the kite under the bench, who was the last to take his turn. Although his cage had already been opened, he did not obtrude himself, but remained crouching on the earth, swaying his body forward as if he wanted to start flying in a certain direction. In the meantime his gullet kept him warm by its noises.

The birdman turned his eyes toward him. The kite considered the old man's look calmly. They kept on like this for some time, like two adversaries estimating each other, both reluctant to be the first to give way. The kite, however, was the first to yield. He bent his neck and waddled forward as if his legs were about to collapse.

The birdman was moved; aware of his superiority, he addressed him generously, "you, glutton, you are going to get something too!"

The kite nodded with satisfaction; the old man returned to the basket, put his long fingers into the separate compartment, and produced the rat. Holding it by its long tail, he swung it high in the air above the head of the kite, who now slowly hopped toward him. He stopped in the middle of the room and raised his head toward the prey.

The animal was quite stiff and swung in the air with his legs stuck together. Crouching on his claws, the kite swung to and fro with the movement of the animal.

Finally the old man let go the rat's tail. What followed could rather be guessed than seen: the buzzard caught the body as it fell and his claws sank into it. One could hear the bird's feathers cracking as they rose, the squeak of the prey before death, the brief struggle, the immediate devouring of the rat, and finally the fluttering of wings.

"Have you eaten it up already?" asked the birdman in an almost compassionate voice. For another moment he watched the feeble efforts of the greedy little bird, then he sat down on the bed.

The old man slowly bent toward the lamp and extinguished the wick with two fingers. The room was wrapped in darkness. The birds were quiet; they had eaten and drunk, so they all went to their resting places. Only now and then was heard a thin voice or a light fluttering of wings, but there was an atmosphere of satiety and drowsiness that overcame the bird inhabitants.

Amidst this peace the birdman remained sitting silent and motionless for almost an hour. He gazed at the darkness without wishing to see anything through it. His whole body and soul derived pleasure from the impenetrable silence and looked forward to the occasion when something heavy, sweet, and inevitable would emerge in his callous limbs.

Gradually, the old man was pervaded by a pleasant warmth. He rose to his feet and cautiously, as if afraid that some of the birds might hear him, stood by the bed. And in fact nothing moved—every creature was fed, calm, and at rest. He made one step, then another, and listened again, feeling his blood pulsating, every single nerve tingling.

He was by the stove.

He stood there for at least five minutes and, holding his breath, listened for any possible sounds. Then he bent down, quick as lightning, put his hand under the stove, and grabbed the first hen he could feel.

"Gra, gra!" cackled the frightened bird wildly. She stretched her neck as if she would die at that very moment.

Her cackle woke all the inhabitants of the aviary and was immediately answered by countless cacklings, cawings, screechings, cooings, and squawkings. As if bewitched, the old man remained standing, rooted to the spot. It seemed as if he felt ashamed at the awakened bird world. He stood there motionless for a time, until the birds slowly calmed down. With the utmost caution he then grasped the hen with the other hand. Although it was pitch dark in the room, he immediately recognized which hen he was holding in his hands. He immediately fell into a rage.

"You get back under the stove, you white one!" he said, and chased the fowl back to its place. The hen's body fell heavily to the earthen floor and lay there as it had fallen. He bent again slowly and grabbed another hen. Just like the rejected white one, this one burst into a desperate screeching—the room again resounded with its dreadful, frightened squawks.

But by now the birdman was a little bolder; his icy body was imbued with warmth. He did not wait for the screeches to abate, but promptly grasped the hen in both hands. But, again, it was the wrong one.

"I don't want you either!" he said impatiently, and put it back under the stove.

He bent down for the third time and finally dragged out the black hen. This one screeched even more loudly than the first two, and her cries were accompanied by the violent squawking of the rest of the birds.

The old man pressed the hen closely to his breast and began talking to her, "my little pullet, my tiny black one, don't screech, don't!"

The warmth of the hen's body, which he could feel, excited his stomach. So he pressed her even more closely to him, then took two hasty steps up to the edge of his bed and sat down on the straw.

When, after a long time, the hen fell to the floor and blindly flew under the stove, the birdman remained sitting there motionless. The cold began to creep through his veins. His hand lay on his knees devoid of any strength, but his eyes, as if blinded, blinked at the corner behind the door.

A few uneasy moments passed.

All of a sudden the birdman's body went down, his eyes protruded like those of a madman; he gaped, and an inhuman shriek resounded, "a duck!"

The old man's eyes sought the corner and stared at a yellow phantom, with a gaping beak and unutterably disgusting appearance—they fell on the apparition of a real, genuine duck. . . .

The shriek was so hideous that instantly all the birds went mad. They abandoned their corners and perches where, until now, they had been asleep. There was a frightful, pathetic screeching; the fowls kept flying at one another, hid themselves behind the furniture, clung to the walls with fluttering wings, and then fell to the floor.

The birdman jumped to his feet, and his legs began to tremble with horror. He stretched out his arms and covered his eyes to ward off the specter, which laughed sardonically. But the more he defended himself and tried to hide, the more visible the specter grew, emerging more and more horrifying from the corner.

"Oh . . . a duck, a duck . . ." The old man groaned helplessly, and stretched out his hands in despair.

"Oh!" echoed the frightened dark room, full of confusion and the fluttering of wings; around him the big burning eyes of the birds glittered from the darkness, and the fluttering wings touched him fearfully.

But the old man was completely deaf and blind to all the commotion.

In his despair he began to defend himself furiously. He snatched an old shoe and flung it at the phantom.

"There you are, damn you—you filth!"

The shoe was thrown into the corner and it fell on the floor with a loud bang.

But the phantom remained untouched. Moreover, its beak jutted out even more persistently than before from its duck-yellow throat . . . .

Now the old man took the lamp from the table and threw it at the yellow apparition. The lamp broke and the birds flew off in every direction.

But the duck still crouched in the corner. The birdman was ready to faint. Whatever he could get hold of in the dark, he flung at it: bottles, clothes, the basket, straw. A hellish screeching filled the hovel. The birdman foamed at the mouth.

"Aren't you ever going away?" he groaned, and began to retreat slowly to the opposite corner. His eyes desperately sought a way out, but they could not find one—behind the door was the grinning phantom and the windows were barred.

He shuffled toward the bench where the hawk usually crouched by the moor buzzard. But the birdman's trembling fingers groped in the dark in vain: there was no hawk there. The awareness of a deadly struggle for existence had sobered him for the moment. He whistled, knowing that the bird would answer this invtiation. The next moment the hawk replied with a moribund but greedy screech and sat on his shoulder, so that he could feel the thin feathers against his cheek.

"You've come!" wheezed the old man gratefully.

He removed the bird from his shoulder, took it around the breast in both hands, and began to push it like a shield in the direction of the phantom.

"Here, jump . . . catch hold of it . . . gobble it up!" he panted.

And feeling confident that he was holding a safe weapon in his hands, he drew near the apparition.

But the buzzard, frightened to death and strangling the old man's fingers, did not jump the duck, since its eyes could not discern it; and as soon as the old man's grip relaxed, it flung itself on the old man's chest and clung to him desperately, gripping him with its claws.

The old man was so startled by the hawk's abrupt movement that he almost fell on his back: he was only halted by the edge of the bed.

Suddenly a voice full of hatred came from his chest, "go away!" he shouted, and began to tear the buzzard away from his chest. But the bird refused to leave him. Finally the old man succeeded in tearing it off, not knowing that the bird's merciless claws had torn away bits of his clothing and flesh.

Relieved of his burden, the birdman took an exhausted and panting breath and leaned against the bed, gazing into the darkness. He was obsessed by a dreadful awareness; he grew stiff and, in spite of his excitement he was in a cold sweat.

"I've lost the battle!" His voice grew silent, calm, sorrowful. He toppled down on the bed and burst into bitter tears.

The hens started to cry with him so bitterly that even the fainting birdman was almost aware of it.

"You, my dear birds, you are crying too, my little creatures, you are crying because of me, because of my miserable, bitter life."

And the birds actually cried.

"The duck, the duck!" he yelled with a last effort, and fell down on his back.

At that moment the duck's apparition disappeared before his eyes. The room resounded with the last srceeching of his faithful bird-companions, but he could no longer hear their greeting.

A fortnight later the people from the little town broke into the hovel. The lonely old man had not made his appearance all that time, nor was there any smoke coming out of the chimney. Nobody was worried about this, as there was nothing unusual about it. But it seemed strange to passers-by that none of the birds' voices could be heard from the hovel, and that was why they finally forced the door.

They saw a dreadful sight: all the furniture was broken into pieces and scattered about the floor, while the floor itself was thickly covered with various kinds of birds' feathers and gnawed white bones. Of all the birds that had for so many years shared that narrow, stinking place with the birdman, all that was left were the two hawks, the owl, and the two crows.

At the foot of the bed, on the bare boards, was the dead birdman, lying on his back. The two hawks were standing, calmly pecking, one from each of the eye sockets. The owl was perched on his chest, deepening an open wound with its beak. The two crows strutted at his sides.

After the birdman's death, the birds were left alone, silently watching their master, who could not move. When they grew ravenous, the hawks began to strangle the other birds, and soon they finished their work. They first attacked the small singing birds, then the forest birds, and finally the hens. When the last scrap was devoured, the carnivorous birds turned to the dead birdman and demolished him, bit by bit.

Zora Depolo

Srečko Kosovel

(1904–1926)

Srečko Kosovel was born in Sežana in 1904 and died in Tomaj in 1926. He was the editor of the journal *Mladina* (The Youth) and the author of impressionistic poetry.

ECCE HOMO

To Thee I speak, but Thou art far.
My shadow into a thousand shadows grown.
I'm lost in them, I blunder all around.
How can I ask Thee: "Whither bound?"

O'er the shadows are cold ashes strewn.
Nerves tortured by abstract shapes
in the ego's innermost place.
God? I do not know his face.
The thing that burns: the thirst for Truth, Redemption.
The sacred thing: all that's sincere and simple.
And around me
the melancholy dull-grey pavements
of the dead who cannot die.

P.S.   You won't grasp this, I'm sure, but you may try.

J. Lavrin

Ciril Kosmač

(1910–   )

Ciril Kosmač was born in 1910 in West Slovenia. His novels belong to the social realistic movement in Slovenian literature. He is the author of the collection of short stories entitled *Sreča in kruh* (Happiness and Bread, 1946) and of the novel *Pomladni dan* (A Spring Day, 1950). The combination of epic and lyric elements was presented in *Balada o trobenti in oblaku* (The Ballad about the Trumpet and the Cloud, 1956–57).

THE CATERPILLAR

In my primary school I was taught that scientists had divided life on earth into three classes: men, animals, and plants. Animals were assigned the middle place, and as there is a saying that the middle way is the best way, animals are in the best way. They have body and, apparently, reason and free will too. They have no soul, for if they had a soul, they would not be—animals. And all their life is, perhaps, so purposeful and natural because there is no one to stuff their heads with the catechism of nothingness and the sublimity of submission. The big ones devour the little ones; this is a natural law with them. The same happens with men—in spite of the human and the divine laws which positively forbid it.

I do not know an awful lot about animals. I am a farmer and I know only the ones which I have met on our farm, in the fields, and in the wood. All these animals, according to a tacit agreement handed down from one gereneration to the next, were divided into five groups: useful, tiresome, harmful, poisonous, and indifferent. In the first group we put, first of all, cows, pigs, and hens. We had little to do with horses, oxen, and bulls; our farm was small and we did not keep those animals. The tiresome animals were mice, rats, flies, spiders, moths, fleas, and crickets. All these breeds have inhabited our house from time immemorial—and we have never been very much annoyed on their account. The oral tradition has preserved to this day the custom of setting traps, mead, tobacco, poison, various deadly and soporific powders, and similar things for these animals so that they should not multiply too quickly. But they were never openly refused shelter in our house. Admittedly, bugs and lice were also in this group and we had no patience with these two species: we had lice during the war and fought them with lye and water poisoned with herbs; whereas the bugs had their republic in grandfather's bed—and this was why we burned the bed after grandfather's death. The harmful animals lived in the freedom of nature: we set traps for hares because they gnawed the bark on the young trees, we pursued foxes because they stole hens, and we burned old rags all around the corn fields to drive badgers out. The poisonous animals were all snakes except for the slow-worm. The indifferent ones were birds, butterflies, bumblebees, hornets, bats, frogs, and so forth. We did not have much interest in them. We used them in everyday conversation without thinking of them: lives like a bird, flies like a butterfly, buzzes like a bumblebee, stares like a hornet, drinks like a frog, and so forth. We knew of fish too, but we did not think of fish as animals: they were fish.

The caterpillar is also an animal. I do not know when I saw one for the first time. So far as I can remember, I knew three kinds of caterpillars: the hairy ones, dark grey and reddish in color, coiling into a spiral as soon as I touched them with a blade of grass; the bare, green ones which looked very dirty to me, and the ones which had a hairy wart on every ring. The last seemed to me the funniest and the most interesting of all; they reminded me of my aunt who had the same kind of warts on her chin. Caterpillars were harmful: mother complained that they had nibbled away her cabbages, and in spring father complained that they damaged his seedlings. I also learned at school that from every caterpillar a butterfly was born. And I suppose that the young lady-teacher who explained it to us must have had excellent marks in pedagogy: she brought out the beautiful and useful moral of the fact in the following story:

"Look, my little ones, as a beautiful butterfly hides in the apparently ugly caterpillar, so a good heart hides in an ugly man. Little butterflies are really wonderful, aren't they, my little ones?" she said, and clapped her hands.

We all agreed with this.

"Yes, yes," we cried. "All the butterflies are beautiful except the night ones."

This was all I knew about caterpillars at the time. Later on, my life took such a turn that I came to know them better.

In April 1930 I was taken from the gaol in Koper to the Roman prison Regina Coeli. I felt weak after a three days' ride without bread, water, sleep, or cigarettes. And the worst of it was that my hands were numb; my fingers swollen and blue. When I was unharnessed, that is to say when the carabineer took off my handcuffs, purulent blood gushed from my wrists. I could not move my fingers for many days. I held the rough wooden spoon between my palms and could feel it scratching my mouth. I crumbled bread with my knees, which were sharp enough for the purpose.

Still, all the weariness and the pain did not prevent me from examining my new abode carefully. For a prisoner a change of cell is what a journey to an unknown part of the country is for a traveler. Everything is new: the windows, the floor, the shelf, the door, the bed—and it can take him at least a week to count all the squares in the net and interpret all the inscriptions which his predecessors have incised with iron nails, needles, or their fingernails in the walls and the window-frame.

The cell in the Roman prison was literally a wardrobe compared with the one in Koper: three yards long, two wide, two and half high. Its interior was not interesting, but no cell is interesting at first glance, and I have seen many: the vaulted ceiling, the cement floor which a trowel in a mason's clumsy hand had divided into fairly irregular squares, the whitewashed walls. There was a small shelf in a corner, and a chipped water jug on the shelf. Two lines of an old poem were carved on one side of the shelf: "How brightly shines the star/ Yon behind the mountain bar!"

Below the two lines, in righteous wrath manifesting itself in a large scrawl, someone had added acidly: "BALLS! NOTHING SHINES!"

The traces of various inscriptions and drawings could still be discerned through the whitewash. The inscriptions were of the kind usualy found in cells at that time: "W LA LIBERTA," "WE WANT

FREEDOM," "W LENIN," "SLOVENE BE A MAN," "A MORTE IL RE," and so forth. There were no excessively telling drawings. Only a sketch of a naked, big-breasted woman, with her legs apart, could be seen. At this moment a flat, starved bug crept across the drawing in search of blood.

I gave up the careful examination of my cell. There would be more than enough time, I told myself, and walked to the window. The window was relatively big, with crossbars and a net, screened from the outside with stair-shaped ground glass. Such screens are called wolves' gorges in Italy and they are put in front of the windows so that prisoners can see only narrow strips of sky. When I stood on tiptoe, stretched my neck, and looked to the left as far as I could, I caught sight of the hill Gianicolo with Garibaldi's monument. This was the whole of my wide view. It really was a wide view compared with the window at Koper which offered me only a piece of grey wall.

But it was something more than that. There was a little piece of life nearby. A wild chestnut tree grew below the window. It must have been fairly thick, old, and high, its branches reaching the second floor. In its striving for the sun from the darkness of the prison yards one of the shoots reached my window. The shoot was alive, fresh with May. There were twenty-four opened leaves on it, and four were still closed—in dark-brown resinous buds. In a few days they would suck enough sap from the sun to break the dark-brown casing, like chickens break their shells, and open out. And they did open out. They were small, light green, like half-opened babies' fists. They turned towards the sun like a child to its mother. Every morning there were several dewy pearls on them. At sunrise, before I could see the sun, in each of the pearls a tiny little sun was lit up. On the first of May I counted the little suns: there were fifty-seven of them.

The small leaves grew incredibly quickly. Every morning they were wider, their green darker. I watched them every day, I knew each of them individually. If they were to be torn off and put in my straw-mattress I could tell in which order they grew on the shoot. I came to relive my spring with them: the old pear tree in front of our house at Tolminsko, the lime tree behind the shed, and my father who, when spring came, poured hot water over his old wooden plough so that there should be no play between the colter and the share. And

I discussed my future with them too. I was sure that their lives would be spent and that they would fall off before I came out of prison.

On the fifteenth of May, as every morning, I jumped secretly out of bed at sunrise and went to watch the little suns in the pearls of my leaves. It was a golden morning, as the saying is. And on that golden morning I noticed at once that the little tip of the leaf which peeped from behind the ground glass was shaking, gently and unevenly. All the other leaves were quiet in the sun. I was upset. If it had been the wind, they would all have been shaking, I decided. What was the reason? The question was born in me. I quite forgot that I had risen from bed too early. I stood on tiptoe and stretched my neck as much as I could in order to see the whole leaf and discover the cause of its restlessness. I was so absorbed in it that I did not notice that the door had opened. Gaoler Cesare came in, put his hand on my shoulder, and almost implored me to lie down.

Cesare and I had our own arrangements. We lived "as buddies," as we said in prison. When they had sent me a large piece of cheese from home I asked Cesare to cut it for me. Cesare smiled and took the cheese away. It was a good hour before he came back. He had cut the whole piece into small cubes. I was somehow glad of it. I sat on the bed immediately and began to kill the endless boredom of my time by trying to put all the cubes together again into one piece. I was hard at it all the afternoon—and when at twilight I succeeded in putting every cube in its place, almost half of the cheese was missing from the middle.

While I was busy with this Cesare looked in often through the small window. When I had finished and a large hole gaped in the cheese in the middle of my bed, he opened the small door and asked me what I was doing.

"Oh, nothing," I said, "just wondering, because I've never noticed before that cheese seems to have the properties of camphor in your hands: as soon as it comes in contact with air, it evaporates."

Cesare was silent for a time, and then asked:

"Will you report me?"

"I don't know," I shrugged my shoulders.

"I'll tell you quite frankly that it's not in your interest," he said. "It won't do you any good. They'll put you in an underground cell because you dared impute theft to a civil servant. And I will be a witness, of course, that is to say I shall have to give evidence against you. When they close the door behind you, I shall be asked to report to the main office and they'll take away half my salary. That is what they do in such cases."

We were both silent.

"I'll buy you some cheese." Cesare interrupted the uneasy silence. "You know, I have three children and a wife. Imagine. They'll be grateful to you."

I did not report him, I never meant to. I knew that we were both poor. Since then had we lived "as buddies."

So on the fifteenth of May Cesare only warned me. He shook his head and went away, and I stretched my bones on the straw mattress again. I stared at the window and waited impatiently for the cracked, brittle ringing of the prison bell to interrupt the morning silence, and °or the drawl of pigeons cooing, with its sickly suggestion, ever since the prison days at Koper, of the moaning of tortured prisoners.

When seven o'clock rang I jumped to my feet at once and went to the window. The leaf was still shaking, but I still could not discover why. I started on my daily journey, that is to say I began to walk about the cell: four paces from the window to the door, four paces from the door to the window. Almost every time I stopped at the window and looked at the leaf. So I walked all the day. I looked particularly sharply during the examination of the cell, when a gaoler tapped an iron rod against the crossbars of the window. I did not see anything.

Day was giving way to night and at twilight I saw what the matter was. From behind the ground glass appeared the head of a caterpillar. First the proboscis, then two rings forming its strong nape, and three pairs of sharp legs. I pressed my head to the net and I know to this day that my heart beat loudly. The caterpillar moved its proboscis round and round, nibbled at the leaf and swallowed, swallowed. The leaf was literally disappearing. When it grew dark the whole body of the caterpillar appeared. With its thicker hind legs it stuck to the stem from which the leaf had been nibbled off.

There was more life now before my window. But with life had come struggles. The caterpillar was certainly more alive than the tree: it had its proboscis, legs; in short—it lived, as we say. I watched it for two days. I came to know it quite well.

When it had finished with the first leaf, it retreated to the branch and, using the shoot as a bridge, started for the second one. It seemed to me that the leaf shook before its approaching destiny. It shrank into itself. Everything showed that it wanted to be small and invisible.

The evening was approaching. The sky was red, I did not know where the sun was setting. How insecure and utterly lost one is when all one's ties with nature are broken.

I stood on tiptoe and stared at the caterpillar. And as it sometimes happens when you hold a pencil in front of your eyes and look at a hill in the distance that the pencil moves away and grows into an enormous pillar on the distant hill, so the shoot of the chestnut tree moved away from me. It became a thick trunk lying across Gari-baldi's monument on the top of Gianicolo, with its twelve leaves like twelve green sheets. A huge antediluvian animal crept about on the tree devouring the enormous leaves. Then I saw the greatness of small, insignificant struggles. I felt the question nudging me: the cater-pillar would devour all the leaves; what would happen then? Where would life be at the end of a life? No life lives by itself. Now there was still time. The decision has to be made: the caterpillar or the tree. Both could not live—for in this case life devoured life.

And I chose the tree. Why—God knows. I asked myself this question and could find no answer in my mind. However, it seemed that the heart knew the answer, but it did not know how to shape it into words.

I plucked out of the straw mattress several blades of sea-grass and plaited them into a small whip. And I began to poke at the caterpillar with the whip. I did not manage to move it, for it was too far away and stuck fast to the tree. It clutched firmly at the nibbled stem.

While I busied myself with this, the door opened. But this time it was not Cesare. It was the departmental inspector, short and fat, a real beast.

"Aha!" he cried with indescribable pleasure and every hair of his bushy, black mustaches stood on end, threatening me. "Who have you been talking to?"

"Talking? I haven't been talking to anyone." I made my answer sound as hard as I could. "I've been trying to drive a caterpillar away. It's eating leaves. It's eating the tree!"

He moved his legs apart so that his nailed boots squeaked on the cement floor, his spadelike hands firmly planted into his hefty sides.

He leaned so near to me that I could feel his breath saturated with the smell of garlic.

"You're cheeky, boy," he observed and put out his chin in Mussolini fashion. "And you're too young to lead old men by the nose. A caterpillar! Ha! You're a caterpillar, gnawing and nibbling at the tree of state!" he shouted. The very fact that such a clever observation had occurred to him was so thrilling that he had to repeat it twice and he kept prodding me with his fat forefinger as if driving the idea into my head. "Yes!" he concluded, shut the door, and went away.

I went back to the window and watched the caterpillar. It seemed to me so like the stout departmental inspector who had just left my cell. I came to hate it so much that I wanted to crush it. I stood on tiptoe, held fast by the crossbars at the window, and began to blow with all the force of my wretched lungs.

Then the door opened again—and the inspector made a report on my transgression. Of course, he did not forget to quote in the report his clever observation about a caterpillar nibbling at the tree of state.

That very afternoon I was examined by the assistant superintendent, a stout man with thick, sooty whiskers which looked like tar-coated irons preventing his blood and fat from bursting his swollen head. When I mentioned the caterpillar to him he flared up, incredibly enraged. All his blood rushed to his head, he rolled his eyes and sucked in his breath, stamped his short legs, hardly able to show me the door and utter:

"Get out, villain!"

On the second day I was taken to the superintendent of the prison. The superintendent was apparently a very gentle man. He looked like Pirandello: short, grey bearded, bald headed, with small grey mustaches, bowed. He sat at a wide writing desk, sunk in an armchair, turning over the leaves of the long report on my transgression, supplied with proper signatures and stampings. After a long silence he coughed and asked without looking at me:

"Well, boy, what's the matter with you?"

I shrugged my shoulders and was silent. I had decided not to mention the caterpillar any more.

"Here's a charge against you. You've broken the rules."

"Yes," I affirmed.

"You confess? It's a good thing, and useful too. Come and tell me now why you were hanging on the crossbars of the window? That is, of course, against the rules. And after all, you aren't new here. How long have you been in prison?"

"Eight months."

"Eight months. Enough time to get to know the house-rules. Have you got a copy in your cell?"

"Yes, I have."

"And what does it say there?" he said in a drawling voice and slightly raised his eyebrows, still without looking up at me.

"It says: Paragraph 7. Prisoners are forbidden to stand by the window and hang on the window crossbars. Offenders will be punished according to paragraph 46. . . ."

"Hush," whispered the superintendent and raised his hand. "Whom did you call? Whom did you talk to?" His voice was a little louder. "I hope you realize that you're here as a political prisoner and that we have to be more severe with you. First of all you mustn't get in touch with other prisoners."

"I know," I said.

"Tell me then . . .," and he did not finish his question. His head moved on his neck; he looked around the office, got up suddenly, crossed his arms on his chest, and sadly shook his head. He took the bell and rang it. The departmental inspector came in and stood at the door. The superintendent stared at him, looked around the room and again at the inspector, shook his head, raised his hands, clicked his tongue. The inspector also looked around the room and waited. His black whiskers almost stood on end with fear. This went on for a minute. Then the superintendent grasped the edge of the table, leaned very far forward, and shouted in a desperate, quivering voice:

"Where are the carnations, man? Did I give orders that there must be a bunch of red carnations in every office, or didn't I? How long have you been here? Have you got my circular? And what does it saaaay? . . ." His voice drawled again.

"On the way, sir, on the way." The inspector was put in a flutter and disappeared. His nailed boots squeaked in the corridor so mercilessly that the superintendent stopped his ears and wailed: "Villain!"

After a few minutes the inspector came back and put a bunch of red carnations on the table.

"Are these the biggest and freshest ones?" the superintendent asked, looking desperately at the flowers with his watery eyes.

"Yes, the biggest and the freshest," the inspector affirmed hesitantly.

"Liar!" screeched the superintendent.

The inspector touched his swollen cheek as if he had been slapped on the face.

The superintendent reached into the pocket of his white waistcoat, drew out a small violet phial, opened it slowly, and sprayed the carnations. An ancient, heady scent swam about the room. The superintendent breathed it in loudly through his nostrils, sat down, and thrust his nose into the report again. After a short silence he said, drawling:

"Perhaps you were talking to a caterpillar?"

I felt that his look had sharpened. A barely discernible acid smile was outlined at the corners of his thin old lips.

"Yes, I watched a caterpillar. It devoured leaves. Life devours life. And man is. . . ,"

"Hush!" He raised his hand. "You're too young for philosophizing. And for teaching others. And . . ." Then he raised his head and looked at me. The expression on his face was changed. As if puzzled he murmured in a loathsome, sweet voice: "Eh, eh, stand there . . ."

I stepped back from the table.

"Stand by the window, yes, yes, a little father away." he wriggled, quivering in his armchair and sizing me up from top to toe.

"How old are you, boy?"

"Nineteen."

"Nineteen. Come here," he added, indicating with his eyes that I was to stand by his side.

I approached. His arm, moving slowly, rose towards me. I heard the click of his elbow-joint. His arm did not stretch out, it did not touch me. He moved to the edge of the armchair and, hissing, whispered, "Bend your head."

I made another step towards him. He pinched my left cheek. His hand was smooth and cold—repulsively humid. I jumped two steps away. The superintendent's hand remained for a moment in the air, and then he drew it back to himself, like a snail drawing in its horns.

"You can explain to yourself the philosophy and the ethics of this. You need it," he said in his previous tone of voice, rummaging in the report. "And to spare you the trouble with the caterpillar," he added after a short silence, "I'll have you moved underground for three days."

"Yes, sir," I said and turned to the door.

"Hush, wait," he said slowly. He held the lapel of his dress-coat with his dry hand, on which the veins were visible: he shrank into himself, twisted his head like a young bird, and buried his beaky nose in the red carnation in his bottonhole. He spread his nostrils and breathed loudly—and in this position, between two deep sighs, he whispered, scarcely audibly, "Six days."

When I came from underground back to my cell, after six days spent in darkness, on bread and water—it was the twenty-third of May—I rushed to the window at once. The shoot was still there with two leaves on it. The caterpillar had eaten all the others; now it was busy with the last but one. Everything would be finished soon, I thought. Two more leaves, two more days, and there would be no more life in front of my window.

The twenty-third of May was a sultry day. The sun, somewhere above the town, was certainly dim. Just before noon the air became thick. The sky darkened slowly. I expected a storm. About five o'clock the wind began to blow. It whirled up the dust from the yard and blew it to the second floor.. The shoot quivered.

At half past five the May religious services were held in the prison.

Political prisoners never went to chapel, so that they should not meet each other. All the services intended for us were performed at the intersection of the corridors. There was a staircase there, and at the top of the staircase there were an altar and a pulpit. At half past five the chaplin came to the pulpit, and they opened our doors a little, about a span, so that we could hear his squeaky voice. I had never seen the chaplain, but I still knew him well. Prison chaplains and doctors are usually a strange mixture of good and evil, cunning and deep drinking.

That afternoon the chaplain spoke of the Virgin, of innocence, of lilies, of St. Joseph and St. Aloysius, of passion and similar troubles gnawing the souls and bodies of the prisoners who had not taken the Virgin and St. Aloysius as their examples. When he came to the end of his wisdom, his voice rose to something that should have been singing. The voices of the prisoners could be heard in the cells. Each cell sang its own song: Slovene, Italian, lay, pious, or rebellious.

Outside, the storm blew more and more fiercely. I stood by the window and looked at the shoot disappearing with every gust of wind, taking a long time to come back. The caterpillar would fall off; I sensed it like the beating of my pulse, and waited impatiently. The shoot came back and the caterpillar was still on it, although the shoot had realized that the wind was a good ally, had exerted its own strength to the utmost, and had shaken violently. The caterpillar also struggled for survival. It lay down, took cover, and stuck to the stalk as fast as it could. It felt its end approaching: it would fall before giving birth to the multi-coloured butterfly for which it had eaten, for which it had climbed so high.

The storm grew more violent, the first drops of rain fell. I could see two of them splashing on the last whole leaf. The first pellet of hail. The shoot moved away, did not come back for a long time, and then came back with the caterpillar again. This happened several times. Then the lightning cut across the sky, it thundered, a fierce gust of wind grasped the shoot. I waited a whole eternity. The branch came back without the caterpillar.

The prisoners' song still resounded in the corridors, with the chaplain's squeaky voice floating above it.

When evening approached I stood on tiptoe again, clutching at the crossbars to count, in the setting sun, the pearls and their little suns on the last leaf. The air was cool and pleasant, prisoners talked in the yard, pigeons cooed from the roofs. I looked at the shoot, which had moved away slowly and was now lying across Garibaldi's monument on the top of Gianicolo. A bare, thick branch, with a wide green leaf at its end fluttering like a fiag in the wind. Then I remembered the old cook who, when I was a boy of eighteen in a prison in Gorica, advised me every evening to dream of something green, preferably of a horse in a meadow, for it meant freedom.

I don't know how long I went on watching. I was startled by a hand on my shoulder. I started back and jumped to the floor. Cesare was standing in front of me, smiling benevolently and almost imploring me:

"Please don't stand at the crossbars. You'll be punished again. You'll get twelve days this time. You're too young and too weak for such a punishment. You may fall ill. You've grown thin during the last few days. One can see it!" He put his hand into his pocket and took out a piece of cheese. I did not say a word. When he left, I was quite alone. I looked around the cell. It was only then that I saw that he had brought me two golden oranges which looked very strange on the grey straw mattress of a prison cell.

It was quiet outside. Only the last leaf—the green flag—fluttered in the wind after the storm.

Every year when the countryside begins to turn green I open the window of my room and go out. merrily, to the parks to see the budding trees.

Spring always comes so suddenly. All of us wait for it, all the time, and we are still surprised when it comes. Until recently it was winter: cold, the room full of tobacco smoke, a lonely raven in the sky, a bare branch in the wind. And a warm southern wind had come overnight, the raven had flown off, the branch was freed from the wind—and from the little eyes on the twigs dark-brown, resinous, shining buds had emerged. For two days the buds warmed themselves in the sun and strength gathered in them: they broke through their dark membranes and little light-green leaves came to see the sun, like so many thousands of hands stretched out to life.

I walk out of town and turn to the hills. I go from bush to bush, from one apple tree to another and look for—caterpillars. There are no caterpillars. It's too early for them.

I look for a glade in the wood and lie down. I wriggle from one place to another until I find myself lying right in the middle; the tops of the trees have to make a circle above my head. Then I go on lying like this: the first swallow in the air, the first bee on a flower, the first ant on a blade of grass.

I look at the sky and think of the caterpillar.

A shoot grows nearby; leaves have already come out on it and pearls of dew have gathered on them. I look at the shoot and the branch moves away to one side and outlines itself against a distant hill and across the white church on the hill. I look at it: everything is large, the branch, the leaves, and if a caterpillar were there, it would be an antediluvian animal. And I do not know even now which I would choose: the caterpillar or the leaf.

Everything has remained the same as it was in the Roman gaol when I thought of life and its forces. Life devours life; animals devour plants, men animals, and each other into the bargain. So what? A knot has been made out of this—and to live probably means to be in the knot.

I rise and return home, walking along the brook. I stop and see my own figure in the water. We nod our heads to each other and smile.

At the crossroads I meet a gipsy who has just come out of her bud.

"Do you want a *dinar* or a cigarette?" I ask.

"A *dinar* and a cigarette," she answers.

"That is frankly and honestly said," I affirm merrily.

The gipsy straightens her back, and her thin, dirty blouse is stretched tight across her young breasts. She takes her multi-colored scarf off her head; her damp, shiny black hair is scattered over her shoulders.

"Shall I tell your fortune?" she asks, bowing her small head and wetting her full lips.

I walk on, striding along the road. In the furrows made by the cartwheels there is water, and I have forgotten that my soles are torn.

Now I think of the caterpillar no more. I smell violets along the way, I think of a girl with dewy eyes, a brisk step, shyly telling lies; my gown flutters in the spring breeze, I straighten my back, show my healthy teeth, black with tobacco smoke, and laugh at life, harsh as it is, right in its face.

"Ha!" I say, "six days . . . pooh . . . and then? If nothing else happens, at least the wind will come and blow the caterpillar away, or a butterfly will be born."

So every year I celebrate my caterpillar jubliee.

Svetozar Koljević

Cene Vipotnik

(1914–   )

Cene Vipotnik was born in 1914. His first collection of poems, *Drevo na samem* (A Lonely Tree) appeared in 1956. This collection includes prewar and postwar poems which were scattered in different periodicals.

AN UNDERGROUND RIVER

The charitable sun quits his nocturnal stable,
morning spreads o'er the stony world,
I sink into the dusk, upon my earth-given bed.

Insidious time has battered me to the ground,
dark hosts of humiliation keep crushing me in
the spell of vagrant dreams, made putrid long ago.

Through green hollows to the silent bottom
the earthy water bubbles drearily,
with melting heart immerse I into it.

Robbed of the sunlight that the rosebuds drink,
the softly moving breezes of the spring,
both numb and still rest I in my deep grave.

In storms of Eternity once formed
from sky and mud, I'm now besieged
by never appeased gloom.

The changing years may yet restore my soul
locked in a stalactite; into the gloomy jail
of my abode the bright day then his beams will radiate.

The charitable sun quits his nocturnal stable,
morning spreads o'er the stony world,
I sink into the dusk, upon my earth-given bed.

J. Gradišek and J. Lavrin

A VISIT

A Woman sits on my prison bed tonight,
ominously silent like the grass on graves,
her figure darker than the darkness,
her heavy shadow strays over me.

Where eyes should be two beetles,
two brilliant beetles sleep on the eyelids,
and often, as if their sleep were light,
they sprinkle iridescent silver from their wings.

Where heart should be, there a dark first
opens its fingers in greedy ambush—
he who is faithful to life and light
will not easily escape its dreadful weight.

As if a roller squashed the heated limbs,
the walls pant wildly in compassion.
Oh, would their cry not die! Oh, would it reach
the space where people live, where forests burst into leaf!

Reverberating, distant, cherished stars
throw through the bars invulnerable wings,
the poisonous weariness that struck me down,
fades from my veins, my torpid sinews.

A wave of moonlight splashes
over the dark stature of my silent guest;
the night will pass, the tender throb of morning
promises the sun, the day that will endure.

J. Gradišek

Matej Bor

(1913–   )

Matej Bor (pseudonym for Vladimir Pavšič was born in 1913. Before 1941 his literary activity was limited to literary criticism. His first collection of poems *Previharimo viharje* (Let Us Overcome the Storms) appeared illegally in 1942. *Pesni* (Poems) appeared in 1944, also illegally. His postwar collection of poems are: *Bršljan nad jezom* (The Ivy above the Dike, 1951), *Sled naših senc* (The Trace of our Shadows, 1958).

A WANDERER WENT THROUGH THE ATOM AGE

II

A wanderer went through the atom age
and from a height
looked down—
where the atom age lay—
all around,
as far as the eye could reach
concrete and iron,—
iron and concrete,
all possible shapes
throwing long, immovable shadows
from neon lights across time.
The wanderer looked,
and at the thought
of how superfluous his heart was
amidst all this,
he shed a tear.

The tear fell upon the ground,
and a little bird that stood there drank it,
and having drunk it, said: "Your tear is bitter."
"I know."
"Why is it so bitter?"
But even before the wanderer could say
his usual "don't know"—
the bird was dead.
He picked him up
and took him down to where the atom age lay
to bury him.
But in vain:
all around concrete and iron,
iron and concrete,
and not enough earth bearing birds and flowers,
for even a bird's grave,
with a flower planted upon it.

IX

A wanderer went through the atom age
and met a fellow wanderer
who asked: "Where are you going?"
"I don't know."
"Nor do I."
"Then come with me. We'll land up somewhere."
And they went together;
a third joined them
without asking where they were going,
glad to find what seemed to be the way.
And so it was with the fourth, the sixth, the tenth,
the thousandth and the hundred thousandth.

Then the first wanderer said to the second:
"Where are all these people off to?"
"They are following us."
"Don't they know we've no idea where we are going?"

"No, they don't"
"But we ought to tell them."
"On no account, they would kill us if we did."
"Then we had better part and go our own ways."
And they parted.
But behind them arose such a pandemonium
that it shook the whole atom age.
All of them were quarrelling
as to which of the roads
taken by those two was right.
And before our wanderer could get far enough away
to escape the bloodshed,
blood began to flow.
Bespattered with it
he stood on the outskirts of time
and stared down at the atom age.
And he was sad, so sad,
that even sadness shied away from him.

XII

A wanderer went through the atom age
and had a vision:
he was rocking far up
in a silver gondola
and saw below him
the roundness of the earth

like a landscaper in the moon:
ashes covered
the last dome of hope
and with it
the last memory of what had been.
Among the ashes waded
a crowd of loathsome ghouls,
and having reached the crater
into which the clouds had squeezed some rain

which was not rain,
and drank;
and when they had quenched their thirst
they wiped their mouths which were not mouths,
with hands which were not hands,
and with eyes which were not eyes
they stared aloft at his gondola.
"Who are you?" he asked.
"Your grandsons.
The atom breed."

J. Lavrin

Ciril Zlobec

(1924–   )

Ciril Zlobec was born in 1925. He published a short psychological novel, *Moška leta našega otroštva* (The Manly Years of our Childhood, 1962), whose theme is war.

A CHILD'S EYES

No, these I could not have.
But now children
all have the eyes of a child again,
spring is reflected in them all year;
. . . then
blood was reflected in mine.

No, these I could not love.
But now children
love the meadows again,
pick flowers again, weave them into their laughter;
. . . then
flowers blossomed into lead,
we secretly covered the dead with them
in the open graves.

No, these I could not believe.
But now children
all believe in good people again:
. . . then

I saw the beast in them
and I walked the lonely roads,
alone,
so alone,
so terribly alone.

I was merely a child,
and I thought I had to live.

Rudolf Zrimc

Pavle Zidar

(1932-   )

Pavle Zidar was born in 1932. His first novel, *Soha z oltarja domovine* (Statue from Fatherland's Altar, 1962), is of an autobiographical nature. His second book, *S konji in sam* (With the Horses Alone, 1963), goes back to the theme of the war.

MAY GOD GRANT US HAPPINESS

This summer, I am at home for the last time. I am a teacher now. I am in the garden reminiscing about father's death. His carnations are still here, glowing like coals, and the elder tree is still fragrant. Snatches of vivid memories keep calling me to his last moments. Tomorrow I will leave and never again return to his carnations. Perhaps I will look at them once again, but I will never see them in such a way as I see and sense them today.

Death was so clearly drawn on his face, like a map of an unfamiliar continent. We became accustomed to it, to death, as we did to the aunt, too, who day by day sat outside his door, clinking her rosary.

Father was still cursing and thus filled us with hope that he would stay with us through the winter.

"As long as Joza curses," the people said, "there's nothing to worry about."

He swore sharply like the chopping of wood, without the least bit of penitence. Manfully he pulled God by his damned, entangled beard.

He, Father, already knew what that damned God had cooked up for him, because he could no longer stand, eat, or smoke.

With the Devil, it was much better. He called him when he couldn't change position or when he didn't dare clear his throat. And strangely enough, the Devil was always on hand. Then he could turn over, and clear his throat.

Mother had already become deaf to his cursing God and Hell. Only, in her heart she was worried about his last hours. For his eternal peace. Already she had persuaded several people to remind him of his Christian duty. When the hour comes, silent and powerful, when his soul departs. Mother only knew that he would not last the winter. And she alone was not disturbed by his robust and convulsive curses. The louder and more frequently he cursed, the more anxious she became about him.

Sometimes she scolded him, with understanding, for what he was doing.

"It's nothing," he shouted. "I'm pulling down that holy ox from the pulpit. I spit on him. Spit! If he knew how much I suffer, that God of your priests would heal my ass so that at least I could sit on it once more before I die. But he doesn't exist, and he never will. For that reason don't drag the priest into my house. Anyone but him."

Father really suffered terribly. He was decomposing alive and he stank like a manure pit. And he was not able to breathe his last. Death squatted in his eye sockets, on his nose and forehead, and jeered into his thin, deathly blue ears.

From the courtyard he heard the seasonal workers, the children, the women, healthy as cornel trees. And us too: me, mother, sister— as we ate, walked about, snored. And from night to night, he was more alert than during the day. The pain became still stronger at night, boring deeper like a cutting river.

"Night is my Lucifer," he complained through parched lips. "Night, Nac! At night everything opens up and I must endure every pain one by one, and there are one hundred thousand of them. All are alike. Every one of them howls until it's drowned out by another.

"Oh, Nac, listen to that boy sleeping. I tell you, he snores so much that it shakes the bed. And me, not a minute. If there's justice anywhere, it's not up there. God is flogging me, but shouldn't he be ashamed, the old devil, to lash my living flesh, my wounds? Why didn't He try that when I was healthy?

"That, Nac, that's not God.

"Look, there's work to be done. Look at the garden. The carnations are all drying up, they don't water them. Look. Only the old women come here, they just nod and stink like the plague.

"Not long ago Neza came. She's already deaf as a post, and she shouts: 'Joza, it's time to make peace with the Lord.' 'Me,' I said, 'but I'm a man. Mary should come to me . . . .' You should have seen how that deaf devil heard me. She muttered into that hairy chin of hers and disappeared without a trace.

"Nac, I tell you, that swine does not exist."

He looked at his old friend, Ignac, with wet, blinking eyes. He knew that Nac would carry him, change his clothes, and bless him with holy water.

Nac offered him a cigarette, but Father didn't like it.

"No," he said, "from now on I'll smoke another kind. The wavy ones. See to it, Nac, that they light the candle from my christening day. You light it. Let my smoking in this world end with that candle."

Slouching, he looked into the distance in front of him. He spoke more quietly, he spoke for the last time in his life.

"How will my orphans live," he thought of us. "They don't know anything. The boy is only half grown, and the little girl is still in a crib. If it weren't for them I would have gone long ago. This way I cannot, because of them. At least now they'll get something from welfare. But what will happen later?"

Nac nodded his head (he was always nodding). And blew thick smoke toward the ceiling.

"What you say is true," Nac began, "you've already suffered enough on their account. But they'll make it somehow. Do you remember the Revcots? They were even smaller when they were orphaned, and you do recall that they took care of themselves. You just die, Joza."

Father calmed down for awhile, gratefully looked Nac in the eye and didn't say another word. His pains eased, like the halyards on a mast. He no longer heard either me, the laborers, or the women. He didn't hear anyone. From his face, death stepped in front of him like a mirror. "Yes," he told it. Now he will no longer decompose. "Yes, you are the right one! All white, you murmur like the Sava River. So, so, you only blow softly. Someone should help me in my last hour."

He looked at the Sava River, and listened. It grew like in the time of the flood, broad and glistening. It hurried through the valley, between the pines and the houses, where all things human had fallen silent. From time to time it brushed his feet with a wave and pulled him toward itself. He ran along the spurting stream. His heavy head sank into the frothing path of the great river.

"Oh river," he shouted, "carry me on," and he lowered his ear deeper and deeper there, where the sand could already be heard.

His face shone, a paleness reflected unevenly on his sharp bones. His eyes were sticky like snails. Shyly he breathed.

"Nac, he is dying," mother shouted like in a dream. She bent over his dehydrated body, over the ribs which were sharply bulging in an arc, and she attentively listened whether anything was still stirring in that emaciated body.

"Nac," she said, "it's flowing . . . something's flowing."

Father partially opened one of his eyes, but it again stuck together. Perhaps he had time to see how mother was listening to his river. The river which carried him free from pain.

"Yes," Nac said, when he, too, bent over his friend. "Something really is flowing."

For a moment, mother drew her face out of her apron. It was like a bird's head, red, black, and full of birds' fury, rather than sadness.

Nac went out in the courtyard, quickly called the women, and sent for the priest.

I had to leave the room.

The women, most of them old, were sprouting as if from the earth in their long holiday dresses, with tufts of grey hair under their kerchiefs, toothless, with bristly chins, childlike lips, and heavy rosaries on their arms, and with trembling gnarled hands. They reeked of mustiness and dark chests. They were moving their lips quickly like children when they want to spit out a mouthful.

In the kitchen a candle flickered and a droning prayer was saving Father from perdition. They prayed loudly. For his last hours. The first to speak out was Neza, who in a long and cunning voice begged the Lord's mercy. And then the others repeated in a bass boice. Each one had his own prayer, full of the negation of a sinful and irreverent life.

"Pray to God!" a screechy and prolonged voice shouted:

> "We yield to him,
> When the hour comes,
> When the day comes,

When the sinner of the flesh
Again returns to dust.
Forgive, sweet Jesus,
His trespasses,
And redeem his soul,
Before he goes to the grave."

The old women sang repeatedly:

"And redeem his soul,
Before he goes to the grave."

I was standing on a bench: all the old women were kneeling, placed about the room like coffins. Mother leaned against father, held his hand in hers. Nac was sitting on a coal box and father was radiant like God. The flame of the baptismal candle glided across his face, like a snake chased by a hunter. The old women were completely intoxicated by the prayers, and their old legs no longer felt the affliction of walking.

When the priest and the sacristan came with the incense burner, the old women began to coo like doves. The priest and sacristan began to sing and compliment each other as if they were quarrelling in front of Father.

"He'll pay us. . . ."
"He won't. . . ."
"He will. . . ."
"He won't. . . ."

With complete understanding the priest took mother by the hand. While chewing with his mouth, the old sacristan untied a small white bundle. And then they left very abruptly. Likewise, the old women gathered in the courtyard in a black heap.

"At least he could have accepted the holy oil," they said, paying no attention to me.

"We prayed nicely," they bragged to each other. The rosaries disappeared into their laps, deepened by old age, and they no longer clanked. Two by two, they silently crawled away through the courtyard, stumbling over their heavy dresses. They left to warm up supper.

Father finally fell into a sleep. The river was no longer heard. His ear did not catch the sound of the sand which just a short while ago had so pleasantly called to him. His chest was rising like a tent, swayed by a light breeze. Beneath his nose appeared beads of sweat. His closed eyes had already escaped their heavy black rings. And on his face a single blemish was no longer visible. He was white, and if one were to touch him, he would certainly have rustled like paper. And yet this world was still reflected on his face, although his protruding hands were peaceful and already dead.

Father slept a long time. His restless dream lasted until morning. True luxury before death. Who wouldn't desire it after that ordeal?

When he looked for us in the morning, we stood at his bed like before the communion rail. His voice was resonant and troubled. He was no longer pleading. Healthy, as if after all this he would get up and go out to work.

He said that he would die and that we must go on, each to make his own life. He said that life is a sow and that he would rest a little only after death.

"You just wait and see!"

Indeed, he said nothing more, no good-bye before such a parting.

Cheerfully he showed us the road into the future, the road back to life, and firmly shut the door behind him. Immediately after that, Mother cried out, and I ran with that news from door to door and delivered it like milk. Only, the neighbors didn't thank me, but were most often surprised, and patted me on the shoulder as if they wanted to say how hard life would be from now on and . . . but already I was running to the others.

No, death did not crush me. I was even joyous, because it was really news, and I even magnified it. Certainly I must have wanted to play my role in some tasteless Serbian comedy. The actors were somewhat inhibited.

"What is it?" I assured them. "My father wanted to die!"

"Everything is all right," the stage manager said with memorized sorrow. But the people didn't understand that. People, my boy!

From then on, I was indeed afraid of people.

But father didn't want me to cry for him. He wanted me to leave him in peace.

Isn't it honest of me to say this?

Well, no: remember how I suffered for your sake, and no one will love you any more. . . .

My father hated that and I do, too.

If you're going to die, do it in a respectable manner.

My grandfather fell on St. Martin's Day, and he burned like an oiled rag.

"The devil is melting," he shouted. "Make room."

Burnt, but still alive, he was pulled out. Twelve children were trembling in front of the hospital, but he did not want to see them.

"No," he said to grandma. "They would have a terrible memory of me. And I could not die. If you wish me well, Mommy, give me a half liter of brandy."

And when he got it, he poured it down his parched throat in the same breath. He died just as quickly.

"Thank God," grandma said. "Now rest in peace."

In the garden it had already become dark while I was reminiscing about father's death.

The shadows awoke and slid over the carnations and lettuce.

"Oh, father," I sighed. Tears were burning my face and I was distractedly plucking leaves from the elder tree.

You will be no more.

I closed the gate and visited his old paths.

Everywhere I still felt his presence!

Is it because I am leaving?

"That's why, that's why!" I heard him say.

Good-bye!

You just go on, son.

Donald Davenport

Dane Zajc

(1929-   )

Dane Zajc was born in 1929. He published some of his poems in the journal *Mladinska revija* (Youth Review, 1948–51). His first collection of poems entitled *Požgana trava* (Scorched Grass) appeared in 1958. He is the author of the collection of poems entitled *Jezik iz zemlje* (The Language of the Land, 1961) and the poetical philosophical drama *Otroka reke* (Child's Rivers, 1963).

BLACK BOY

You stand on the yellow desert sand—
There you stand, black, boy,
Around you—the walls of the sky.
They saunter through you
with trailing sadness.

At dawn you notice night-tracks in the sand:
thin serpentine lines.
You are seized by a yellow terror of the sand.
But you can not run away.
Your arms are full of birds.

At noon old men arrive.
They lean on their staffs lake grey birds of prey.
They watch you in silence.
You speak to them.
But as soon as you say a word,
your mouth dries up.

Rudolf Zrimc

600

A DYING TREE

I

The forest flame in scarlet fire.
Autumn fire,
fire of destruction.
The tree beyond bore no fruit.
Sad is the tree.
The tree is dying.
God knows what's in its memory.
The Spring?
The Summer?
Unhappy tree.
There is autumn beauty.
Perish shalt thou in scarlet fire.

II

The tree was dying,
lonely between earth and heaven.
No helping voice, no rescue.
Its leaves hung silent.
Hushed were the paths around.
The birds had flown.
The tree was dying.
Red leaves dripped to the ground
like drops of blood.
Beautiful in death,
it stretched its arms to heaven
like a man sucked down into a marsh.

J. Lavrin

Introduction
Macedonian Literature

In contrast to the other South Slavic literatures in Yugoslavia Macedonian literature presents a paradox. It is at the same time the oldest and the youngest Slavic literature, oldest in the sense that it goes back to Old Church Slavonic literature which began on Macedonian soil and flourished in the so-called Ohrid literary school in the tenth century, youngest because its full development uninterrupted by political persecution took place only after the end of World War II.

It is difficult under these circumstances to attempt a periodization of different literary movements as is usually done in the textbooks and manuals of literature. Historical events have conspired to continue annihilating modest literary achievements and to prevent cultural and literary continuity. The Turkish occupation from the end of the fourteenth century to 1912 isolated Macedonia from the cultural influence of the West. The Western cultural movements of humanism and the Renaissance which helped to shape Western culture never had any impact on the Southeastern part of Europe occupied by the Turks. The cultural decline which resulted from the Turkish occupation was not alleviated by the newly created conditions in the aftermath of World War I. Macedonia was the focal point where most diverse national aspirations clashed. The intense nationalism of Macedonia's neighbors, the Serbs, Bulgarians and Greeks, allowed neither the expression of Macedonian national feelings nor the use of the Macedonian language. The result was the continuation of the twilight of Macedonian literature in the period after 1918 in the Kingdom of the Serbs, Croats and Slovenes.

Only in the period after World War II with the recognition of the Macedonian language as an independent language within Yugoslavia were the conditions fulfilled for a regular and uninterrupted development of the Macedonian national literature. The periods of Macedonian literature parallel the division into historical periods.

1. The period of Old Church Slavonic literature, expressed in the activities of the Ohrid school, corresponds to the historical period of Slavic colonization of the Balkans.

2. The Turkish occupation coincides with the scant remains of Macedonian medieval literature and continues into the nineteenth century when the literary activity showed signs of improvement.

3. The period from 1918 to 1945 which coincides with prewar Yugoslavia witnessed the appearance of Kočo Racin and the birth of Macedonian contemporary literature.

4. The period after 1945 is marked by the recognition of the Macedonian nationality and language and the beginning of an uninterrupted development of the Macedonian national literature. This periodization does not include Macedonian poetical folklore tradition. That tradition has continued to exist throughout the entire history of the Macedonian people regardless of wars and foreign occupations and prior to its disappearance provided the support for the final resurgence of Macedonian national literature.

It is appropriate to start here with the middle of the nineteenth century as the Old Church Slavonic period is sufficiently removed in time and the medieval era is only of marginal importance for the development of Macedonian literature.

The middle of the nineteenth century witnessed the gradual emancipation of subjugated nationalities in the Turkish empire. The young Macedonian middle class, the merchants and the tradesmen, were actively engaged in the creation of a new national Macedonian culture in opposition to the Turkish occupation and Greek cultural and clerical dominance. These new cultural trends were expressed in poetry which had already been used as a medium of literary expression in poetical folklore. The common denominator of this poetry was the spirit of national romanticism and the hope for a national awakening of Macedonian people.

Konstantin Miladinov (1830–1862) published only fifteen poems of which the most outstanding one was the autobiographical *T'ga za jug* (Sorrow for the South). In that work, a young poet (in exile in the north) is longing for his homeland far away. The poem is typical of this generation of Macedonian poets who had to live abroad in exile

INTRODUCTION TO YUGOSLAV LITERATURE

because of the repressive conditions in their country. Miladinov's versification and the motifs of his poetry are borrowed from the oral tradition.

Rajko Žinzifov was born in Titov Veles-Macedonia, but he spent his entire life in exile in Russia where he taught Old Church Slavonic. His poetry, almost forty poems, is characterized by its intense concern for the Macedonian people living under a foreign yoke and by the poet's feeling of helplessness in view of his insignificant role in the national struggle. Žinzifov, under the influence of the Moscow Slavophile group, idealized the history of Macedonia and considered the national spirit embodied in their customs and folklore. The theme of *T' ga za jug* is also dominant in his poems *Ohrid* and *Velikden*.

Gligor Prličev (1818–1882) was born in Ohrid and studied at the University of Athens in Greece. His epic poem, *Serdar*, written in Greek[1] won a prize in a literary competition. The hero of Prličev's poem is Kuzman Kapidan, an outlaw and rebel against Turkish tyranny. The appearance of *Serdar* coincided with the Macedonian nationalist resistance against an intense Hellenic cultural influence. Prličev was caught in a dilemma either to continue "singing in Greek like a swan" or "to start singing in Slovene (Macedonian) like an owl." His inadequate Macedonian prevented him from choosing the latter course.

The lack of a national Macedonian literary language was felt to be a tremendous disadvantage by the poets in the 1850's. Each of the three poets mentioned above wrote in a language variant of his own: Miladinov used the Macedonian folk idiom; Žinzifov used a "middle Bulgarian-Macedonian" literary language; and Prličev wrote in Greek, although advocating a new literary language based on the Old Church Slavonic.

Krste Misirkov (1874–1926), the author of the book *Za makedonskite raboti* (About the Macedonian Question, 1903), faced the issue of the Macedonian literary language in the most constructive way by selecting the contemporary spoken Macedonian as the basis for a literary language. His outline of morphology and phonetics to a great

---

[1]This poem is considered by Greek literary historians as a part of Greek literary tradition.

extent conforms to the norms of the current Macedonian literary language.

The period between the two World Wars is inevitably connected with the name of Kočo Racin and his collection of poems *Beli mugri* (White Dawns) published illegally in Zagreb in 1939.

Kočo Racin (1908–1943) was born in Veles and died in World War II as a guerilla fighter. The most characteristic feature of his slender literary output is the social and national concern for the fate of nationally and socially exploited Macedonians. The heroes of his poems are the people who suffer and are ruined in the process of earning their pitiful livelihood. For example, Lenka, a worker in the tobacco factory, dies of tuberculosis before she can put on her wedding gown.

Racin's poetical activity is also significant for the development of the Macedonian literary language. Although a native of Veles (central Macedonia), he succeeded in overcoming the dialectic influence of his own region. His conscious and industrious cultivation of the language resulted in the introduction of morphological and lexical features of other Macedonian dialects and in making his literary output more representative of the whole Macedonian population. From this point of view Racin has embodied Misirkov's theoretical ideas on the Macedonian literary language.

June 7, 1945, was undoubtedly the most significant event in the history of Macedonian literature because on that day the recognition of the Macedonian literary language took place. Since then, Macedonian literature has been a medium of expression which transcends any particular dialect since the norms of the Macedonian language consist of a combination of phonetic and morphological features taken from different dialects. The first postwar years witnessed the emergence of Macedonian prose as well as the development of drama and comedy. It is difficult to separate different tendencies of Macedonian postwar literature, and it is impossible to separate clearly defined literary movements. Social realism had an ephemeral existence and was quickly replaced by different modern trends. One has to keep in mind that the development of Macedonian literature was far from being continuous in the sense of literary traditions with the exception of the poetical folklore. After 1945 when Macedonian literature finally began to exist, it was exposed to a mixture of the most diverse influences from the East and the West. Macedonian writers had to make up for the time lost. In twenty-five years they had to create what other literatures created in hundreds of years.

After an uneven, highly emotional prose of the postwar years, Blaže Koneski's (born 1921) calm and objective narrative prose provided a significant landmark in Macedonian literature. The subject of Koneski's collection of short stories *Lozje* (The Vineyard), published in 1955, is the everyday world of average people. The method of his short stories is a subtle psychological analysis of characters which penetrates into the most hidden recesses of the soul. The characters who at the beginning of Koneski's narrations appear to be simple and one-sided individuals gain in complexity as the stories proceed and appear finally at the end of the stories as spiritually complex personalities. Koneski has also been active as a poet and as the author of a Macedonian *Grammar,* published for the first time in 1953 and republished several times.

Slavko Janevski is probably the most prolific Macedonian writer and the founder of the Macedonian full-length novel. The evolution of his literary activity is typical for the Macedonian literature as a whole. His long novel, *Selo zad sedumte jaseni* (The Village Behind the Seven Aspens, 1952), describing the corruption in prewar Yugoslavia is definitely realistic while the long novel, *Mesečar* (The Moonwalker, 1958), is impressionistic. The change of literary direction within such a short time span is characteristic of Macedonian literature as a whole.

Aco Šopov born in 1923 is primarily a poet who started writing immediately after World War II. His first collection, *Pesni* (The Poems), appeared in 1944. The evolution of his poetry from social to intimate and lyrical parallels the evolution of Janevski's prose from realism to impressionism. This shift of emphasis from the objective to the subjective was characteristic of the postwar development of Macedonian poetry and could also be observed in the poetry of Srbo Ivanovski, Gane Todorovski, Gogo Ivanovski, and Blaže Koneski. Šopov's collection, *Stihovi za makata i radosta* (Verses About Torment and Happiness), published in 1952, was hotly debated in Macedonian literary circles because of its subjectivity.[2]

---

[2]Social realistic literary criticism opposed subjective literary themes.

Macedonian literature is in the process of creation. Literary traditions are still being formed. New novelistic genres are being created: the historical novel (Popov, Abadžiev); the satirical humoristic novel (Leov); and the psychological novel (Janevski). Contemporary Macedonian drama is being developed satirically and realistically also (Kole Čašule, T. Arsovski, S. Drakul). The existentialist and surrealist concepts in literature are pursued in the novels *Dve Marii* (Two Marys) by S. Janevski; *Belata dolina* (White Valley) by S. Drakul; and T. Georgievski's *Sidovi* (Walls) which appeared in the 1950s and 1960s.

Macedonian literature has advanced rapidly since 1945. One of the main factors in this development was the final solution of the Macedonian national question within the framework of postwar Yugoslavia as well as the final recognition of Macedonian as a national literary language.

Kočo Racin

(1909–1943)

Kočo Racin (Kočo Solev) was born in Veles in 1909 and died in 1943 in the hills of Macedonia. He published a collection of poems entitled *Beli mugri* (White Dawns, 1939), a novel entitled *Afion* (Opium), in fragments, and the treatise *Bogomilite* (The Dissenters).

ELEGIES FOR YOU

Yesterday I took a stroll
Down the green hill,—
Tall beech-trees overhead,
Wide shadows weaving carpet-thread.

I walked like one in a trance,
Head bent and void of sense,
My heart an overloaded nest
And a black stone in my breast.

Oh grief—green, gorgeous hill!
Oh grief—cold running rill!
Birds sing—you sit in tears.
You mock the sunbeams with dark fears.

You hide the untimely bones
Of warriors in your loins,
Young men lying here and there
Deep in the woodland lair;
But why do you hide your song?

And why do all your trees,
With their boughs that hang
Down budding in full leaf,
Rustle such a secret grief?

D. Cooke

Slavko Janevski

(1920–   )

Slavko Janevski was born in Skopje in 1920. He has published the following collections of poetry: *Krvava niza* (A Bloody String, 1945), *Pruga na mladosta* (The Youth Railway, 1946) (with Šopov), *Egejska barutna bajka* (An Aegean Gunpowder Fairy Tale, 1950), *Pesni* (Poems, 1944–48), *Lirika* (Lyric Poetry, 1951), and *Leb i kamen* (Bread and Stone, 1957). His prose publications include *Ulica* (The Street, 1950), *Klovnovi i luge* (Clowns and People, 1955), *Selo zad sedumte jaseni* (The Village behind the Seven Aspens, 1953), *Dve Marii* (Two Marys, 1956), *Mesečar* (The Moonwalker, 1959), *I bol i bes* (The Pain and the Fury, 1966).

AN AFTERNOON

A squeal of the complaint quivered from behind the iron bars of the dogcatcher's cart. Every sound in that summer heat, every voice, every shout was born with a definite purpose: in order to die, to float around, and to lose itself forever, being neither an event nor a novelty.

And that which was neither interesting nor new appeared in this way: a long, narrow street on the outskirts, with old, monotonous houses on both sides, divided by a rough cobbled pavement. A lumbering, blind, little horse pulling its own fate indifferently along the streets. An old cart, ghostly and unpleasant like a jail.

A dreadful rhythm of four worn-out hooves and the rattling of four rickety wheels. The horse, meek and subdued, pulling in its yoke another fate: a white, yellowish-eyed dog, a street urchin, harmless behind the bars as well as in freedom.

And something more—the third fate walking behind the cart: a thin-faced child with dry lips and moist cheeks, holding with both hands the bars and sobbing quietly and hardly audibly through his extended nostrils. His sight never left the dog. The child should have thought and understood that the dog was crying with some of his own tears, dog tears, but just the same, he was crying as people do.

And still the fourth fate was swaying behind the horse, the master of the other three fates: a middle-aged man with a big stick in his hand, a steel wire strap attached to the end of the stick.

Nothing more than that.

The wheels were scraping the cobbled pavement, the cobbled pavement was rattling the wheels, and all of this was combining and melting in that eerie monotonous sound held tightly between rough old walls. The yellow-eyed fate began to whine from the cart. The worried child raised his head and pressed his dry lips together, gripping the bars more tightly with his skinny hands and stiffening his legs. The bars were strong, he was weak, and the cart kept moving. The child did not fall. The cart pulled him slightly. He kept remembering, it is better to walk than to keep his legs stiff.

"Belčo! . . ."

The child believed to have uttered the dog's name, but he did not utter it, he remained silent. His lips were so tight that only a knife could part them. And still the dog heard him; he retreated, fidgeted, and returned to the bars. The child felt the opening, the wet muzzle on his fist, and became more upset. Those were, certainly, dog's tears, just as warm as his own. The man was swaying behind the horse. Once in a while he would turn, stooping in order to see the bare legs behind the cart and to sigh. He did not sigh because of sorrow but because of fatigue and the extreme heat. He continued thinking, should he take away his wife's shoes? He kept pondering, should he take his own shoes to be repaired and then go barefoot for some time, or should he go on like this until he wore them out? The child was bothering him, and he did not have enough willpower to go back and chase him away.

The houses were all the same—worn out, unsteady—and the street appeared to be endless. There was the end, everything had an end; it was only the horse who was lumbering and slowly pulling the cart to the end. Even if he were to pull it to the end, he would then again have to enter a new street, as a man with a dog trap in his hands enters one day after the other.

"Sir, let him go, the dog is mine," the child kept begging behind him.

The man, without moving, was about to sigh, but instead of that he sniffed only. The hot air was burning his nostrils without satisfying him, and he went on breathing with his mouth open. Should he give the dog back?

"Come, come, young fellow, for heaven's sake! Why is there a law that dogs will be hunted and destroyed? Why. . . ?" No, really, it would be better to walk barefoot for some time. That is more economical, and the shoes will last longer. . . . "Hell, young fellow, why do dogs exist in this world? If there were no good purpose in it, they would not have invented a law against them, here. . . ." No, no, he must go barefoot for a while. That is economical. That's it. Yes, that's it. "The dogs certainly are of no good in this world."

"Sir. If you wish, I will bring you a turtle. I can catch a crab for you."

"Go away, I tell you. Don't bother me."

"I have something else at home. Colors and a little bell.'"

"You picked them up in the garbage."

"No. I haven't picked them up in the garbage."

"You stole them."

"No. I haven't stolen them. They are mine."

"Go away, young fellow. Don't make me angry."

"Let Belčo go. If you want, I will catch you a lark."

The man was not listening to him any longer. The horse was not listening either. The dog was not whining any more; perhaps it should be that way, that the dog should be driven and that the child should walk beside it.

"Sir. . ."

Four strange, connected fates were passing by. The man was first, swaying; after him the horse was pulling the dog and the cart; behind walked the child with his face glued to the bars.

"Belčo."

The child was not saying anything, only sobbing, and the dog was listening to his name, wagging his tail, and licking the dry hands pressed to the bars. If all should be this way, then it was a new and unknown game. The child let loose of the bars and approached the man carefully. Two fates were pleading from his moist eyes—his and the dog's. If he were to prove to the man that Belčo was quiet and that he did not bite and that he played with children, the man would let him go. Of what use Belčo to him? Let him catch some other dog, any other dog, only let Belčo go. Everybody liked his dog; not a single child threw at stone a him.

"Sir. . ."

"What's the matter?"

"Sir . . . here—look!"

The man turned his eyes only. The child was begging, but now his face was dry, and it was shining with some inner flame. The more the child resembled an adult, the more the man became childishly suspicious.

"What is that?"

Several objects were lying on two little skinny hands: a grasshopper attached with a needle to a little stick, a silken ribbon, a little key.

"You found it in a garbage can."

"No, I didn't find it in a garbage can. These are new. I caught the grasshopper in the field."

"You are lying. You probably stole it."

"No, I did not steal it. It is mine. Belčo is mine, too. . . ."

The man continued to stare. In front of his eyes were two transparent palms. Everything was transparent on them—the yellow transparence of the grasshopper, the red transparence of the ribbon, the colorless transparence of the key. Wherever he looked, the man saw those palms—under the horse's hooves, on the rough walls, in front of his old shoes. The palms stood in the way of his thoughts—whether to walk barefoot or not.

The child was looking at his bent back. He was discouraged but still hoping.

"Sir. . ."

"Sir. . ."

"What is it?"

"Let Belčo go."

The man turned his eyes only. His face was peaceful and saintly gentle. The child was crying. Well, let him cry; all children cry for some reason, simply in order to cry. They grow because of it, and when they grow up, there will not be any more crying. They will be angry then when children cry.

"Sir. . ."

"I should lock you up, you, you rascal. Beat it."

The child fell behind a little. He would have liked to run up to the horse's bridle to pull himself up and to throw himself in front of the cart, but he did not do it. He was thirsty. He would like to have returned home for some water, yet he did not return. He walked, licking his salty tears, and begging.

Everything has an end, even a long, narrow street with two rows of old, monotonous houses. The cart turned behind the last house. The dull rattle of the wheels and the hooves were left behind, ebbing away slowly and leaving behind it a dull emptiness in the desolate street.

The dead grasshopper lay on the street, stuck with the needle to the little stick. A child would find it and discover a new world there, and he would be happy. If he was not to find it, the little bug would stick to somebody's shoe.

Dragan Milivojević

SILENCE

When the poppies pull themselves up from their roots
and start out
one after the other
towards the sunset
do not follow them.

There are no weddings any more
and at each step stands autumn
ridiculous, white and bare.

When the poppies leave behind them devastation
shut up the rain inside you.
Let it ring in the gutter of your veins
beneath a familiar ceiling.

And be quiet.

When the wind falls upon your window
with three thin cries
and the weeping of a half-grown crane
again be quiet.
The poppies hate speaking.

B. Djuzel and H. Erskine-Hill

THE SONG OF THE ETERNAL SAILOR

I left along the distant roads, my apple-tree, and now
    you bloom alone,
my heart is my helmsman, blind yet seeking blue bays,
if I hear the wind in the evening, I forbode your ruin. . . .
Has someone's hunger pulled you out by the roots
as I roamed alone?

When the blackbird whistles shrilly three times at dawn,
do not wait for the sun. Listen, I am still digging roads,
on a mast I carry a black flag from tavern to tavern
and hide the pain under my skull.
Oh does the blue lightning bring you a blue downfall
and do the rains lash you?

I have no more strength to come calm and tall
and to lean my forehead against the sleepy water.
from the blows to rest my hands on the rye until dawn,
and then to go nowhere. . . .
My apple-tree, the autumn is already here, there is no
    shore to sail to.
And so I dream of a secluded, small, and deserted harbor.

Vasa D. Mihailovich

Blaže Koneski

(1921–   )

Blaže Koneski was born in Nebregovo near Prilep in 1921. A Macedonian poet, historian of literature, and linguist, he was actively engaged in the development of the Macedonian language. His publications include the following collections of poems: *Mostot* (The Bridge, 1945), *Zemjata i ljubovta* (The Land and the Love, 1948), *Pesni* (Poems, 1953) *Vezilka* (Woman Embroiderer, 1955). His prose works include the collection of short stories entitled *Lozje* (The Vineyard, 1955).

He has translated from English (Shakespeare), from German (Heine), and from Serbo-Croatian (Njegoš).

THE RYE

The willy-nilly tranquil mood of women, old and bent
resigned to fate.
A somewhat silent speech, monotonous and stunted
in words of common everyday
by dry lips whispered.
Yet when the wind begins to blow,
a shaking to and fro of heads,
a waving of countless agitated hands,
a song profound and full of supplication,
melancholy like music
on a hot day—at a country station.

A. Lenarčič and J. Lavrin

THE TREE TRUNK

The fallen leaves are calling
those few leaves which still,
afraid of the uncertainty of falling,
tremble upon the tree:
"Come down and die with us,
escape from the high winds
into silence, close to the ground.
Strip bare this burnt-out skeleton,
make him stretch his black arms into space;
let his body sink to the bed of the river,
below the waters of the autumn rain.
And we shall crowd thickly around him
so he can never step out
from the circle of his yellow souvenirs."

B. Djuzel and H. Erskine-Hill

THE EXHIBITION

The well-lit exhibition hall faces the street where the marketplace is already becoming alive in the evening. The cashier leaning on the register is waiting for another hour to pass so she can leave. The drawings by the children seem to be sleepy and annoyed at meeting curious visitors. Well, the time is coming when all good children go to bed.

The visitors to the exhibition were smiling in a kindhearted way. They had a warm understanding of the childish imagination and were happily appreciative as they were only when looking at the works of a great man, who was of course already dead and recognized as a genius. They were trying to give meaning and to justify. And there were the dilettante painters; they thought it was their duty to make more or less acid remark. But the painters themselves found at the children's exhibitions the need, clear and strong, to approach the art simply and sincerely.

Here now are two students in their last year at the art academy, lively and enthusiastically following from one painting to another the steps and the words of an older artist, a well-known expert in arranging exhibitions. Their enthusiasm carried over to the girl accompanying them, one of those girls who neither studied nor read about the plastic art but because of her association with artists had an envious knowledge of the terminology. This girl was outgoing and vivacious in the typical way. She was deep in thought, and when addressed about some subtle point, she would seriously but mechanically nod her head. It would not be strange if some day she became the wife of one of the two young experts with the brush. This would depend on the extent of his conviction that he found her a being who could really understand and appreciate his talent.

"Look, please," the wide gesture of the old artist held their attention.

The drawing, "My Grandfather's House in the Village," one could say, fairly corresponded to its title. It shows with sufficient liveliness the atmosphere of a spring morning in the country. The grandfather is washing his face in front of a well. A winding path leads along the garden from the well out into the yard and upward through the meadow, and then all of a sudden aims into the blue sky. The painter's finger was indicating exactly the direction of the path, painted like a rope ladder used by ships. It seemed as if the next thing for the grandfather to do would be to climb up the path and visit some friends. The path looked like a rope ladder leading up to the attic. The symbolic path awakened different associations. In the other corner of the painting as an earthy counterbalance to this symbolism, the following scene was depicted: A cat from the neighborhood climbed up to the top of the fence with the intention of climbing over, but at the last moment noticed a mottled dog secretly watching and ready to jump, maybe to strangle her. That was the way they were presented. frozen, bristling one against the other. The child's hand introduced a particular charm into this scene by drawing the cat twice as large as the dog. Nothing could prevent her, logically speaking, from jumping and covering up the dog completely.

That detail did not escape the artist's eye.

"Only, here, look at this. How faithfully and sensitively the moment of sudden, instantaneous staring between the dog and cat is depicted. You can almost hear the hissing and snarling, can't you? Did this humourous exaggeration harm the drawing? No, the child embodied, in essence, a truth of life, its spiritual correspondence. The child approaches this directly, the way he plucks plums from the branch he reaches. Everything goes well until our schools impose ideas on the child that painting amounts to coloring tiny squares in which we catch the world as if in a net. Later, if a real talent appears, let him look for himself. How difficult it is then to look! This is what our school is doing, you know; this is interesting. We had quite a few arguments during our selection." The teachers were quite surprised when the artist indicated other works in front of which he kept stopping longer than by the others.

When the sale started, the young people said good-bye and left. The artist yawned, looked at his watch as if hesitating, trying to decide whether he should leave after them; he stayed nevertheless, standing a little bit aside in the middle of the hall, staring into nowhere. He was about fifty years old, with grizzled hair. He looked like a good-natured, somewhat tired lion.

A woman and a young girl entered the hall, probably the last visitors to the exhibition that day. They did not enter as passers-by who accidentally glance in the showcase and decide to come in. Their hurried look showed that they came there intentionally, that they were afraid they had not come on time, and that they were now happy that the exhibition had not closed yet.

The artist looked at them with interest. Although he specialized in landscapes and still life, in front of his penetrating eyes were outlined several rough lines of their life. Both had black aprons—mother swallow and baby swallow. The mother was weak, somewhat tall, and very slightly stooped. One could imagine her working on a sewing or weaving machine in a collective workshop, where she looked at the visitors from the corners of her eyes without straightening her head. She was still young, but her pale face looked somewhat widowish, resembling the pale faces of Catholic nuns. The young girl might have been ten years old, one of those children who grow fast and because of that are weak and tender. The artist guessed that the girl had one of her drawings at the exhibition and that she brought her mother so they could see it standing in this well-lit hall in the center of the city where there were many visitors. They must have agreed on the most convenient time to come, and the mother might have left her work an hour early, but still they came late and almost lost the money they paid for the bus. It was good that they arrived on time.

That was what the artist thought and, as it were, accidentally went wandering around the hall in the direction in which they went. Actually, he was interested in overhearing their conversation and in seeing their reaction to the exhibition, especially if the young girl turned out to be one of the participants.

Mother and daughter holding hands went first to the opposite wall as if compelled to complete their arrival from outside to the extreme point in space.

"How beautiful, Mother," the child said with wonder, looking searchingly as if trying to understand every detail.

The mother did not want to stay there long. It seemed to her that the cashier was not friendly and that they had to hurry as much as possible so that they could see the most important thing which brought them there.

"We shall look them over later, child," she said. "Let us first find your drawings. Tell me, which are they?"

"The teacher told me that they chose two. You know, the one with the shop opposite us, which I drew from our little window, and the one with the bronze goblet and the roses you brought me."

"Look well now," the mother told her, putting her hand across the child's shoulders and leading her slowly along the drawings.

The farther they closed the circle of the hall, the more their steps were hesitant and halting. Perhaps, it would have been better to leave at once with the hope that those two drawings were placed on that part of the wall, which for some reason they could not see. The circle was closing, nevertheless, and the mother held her young girl a little bit tighter. The mother was thinking it over.

"Go and see once more if we have not missed them accidentally," she said.

"We have not, mother."

"Look just the same, once more."

The young girl left, more to please her mother than in any real hope of her own. She wandered around absent-mindedly and returned shrugging her shoulders.

They were not there.

The mother looked up and fixed her eyes for an instant on the artist, as if asking for an explanation. This appeared so only accidentally. How did she dare ask for an explanation at all, let alone from the unknown man who had nothing to do with their case. She stopped close to the entrance and stood there for a long time as if looking at a drawing, afraid to leave at once, for fear of appearing to flee. They left suddenly, nevertheless, arm in arm.

The artist made a subconscious gesture to run after them and to make them return. He really owed them an explanation, and he was the man, although they did not know him, who could have corrected this situation. He was the one who took the two drawings from the wall in the morning before the opening of the exhibition; they were still standing on the desk of the exhibition office. He could have hung them up again and explained to the woman and the young girl that all this happened because of an accident—the drawings were not well displayed, he took them down that afternoon, and the next day he wanted to put them up in a better place which they deserved. Why didn't he make them return so that he could console and gladden them. This hesitation, as it often happens, ended up in an inaction and everything remained as before. No, something had changed, now the artist became sad and guilty. Why did he take down just those two drawings? Was it really necessary, was that justified after they had all already passed the selection committee? The artist thought; he remembered well: When all the arrangements about the exhibition were completed, he noticed all of a sudden that those two unfortunate drawings appeared dry and empty and that they really depressed the well-balanced corner of the hall. It was enough to cover them up with his hand to see that the corner without them became really more cheerful. He decided, then, to take them down, and he was certain of the correctness of his decision even now. Something though forced him to check and find out it he had exaggerated momentarily while deciding.

He hurriedly entered the exhibition office. The drawings were lying one on top of the other on the office desk. He took the top one and began to look it over carefully, putting it gradually away from himself as long as his arm could stretch. This was the drawing depicting the bronze goblet. The artist unwillingly smiled with pity. The goblet was placed on the kitchen table with two roses inside. One could see that the edges were drawn with a ruler. It was painted with blue color which became thinner with an exact symmetry from the edges to the center. The background was a painted wall whose lines were presented in the form of folk embroidery. The drawing of those lines required many hours of instruction. There was nothing left of that struggle of keen childish feeling against the commonplace pattern which threatened to restrain it. The basic idea behind the exhibition was the demonstration of the childish spontaneity about which the artist spoke. And yet the artist felt vaguely that something responded in that drawing to his compassionate smile. Yes, that piece which looks as if the plaster fell from the wall. There was something fragile, moist in it. That piece responded to his compassionate smile with a discreet, guilty smile of its own. Yes, but this was undoubtedly too little.

The artist came out to the hall feeling calmer. He was now fully convinced that he was not mistaken and that he could not have been wrong carrying out consistently a correct principle in his selection and attending to its purer expression. The expert criticism also emphasized his merit in this endeavor. Why, then, did he feel the necessity to take courage and justify himself? Maybe it was because of the way the woman looked at him, asking for an explanation; maybe the strength of that feeling was due to the smile about the fallen plaster which appeared more expressive to him because of the strong light in the hall. The smile carried over from the drawings to the wall, as if that were its place, as if this were not an exhibition hall but a little kitchen to which the woman and the child would sadly return in order to forget another small unhappiness. Would they forget it, the artist was asking himself with good reason. He knew himself that such small incidents remain in the soul for a long time, and now and then grate at it like little grains of sand. He was aware in this particular case that he would have preferred to have abandoned his just principle, no matter how unwillingly. He realized that fairness could sometimes give birth to cruelty. If he could find a mistake, it would originate in the fact that the drawings were not refused to begin with and that the teacher should not have told the children which works were accepted for the exhibition. Even afterward circumstances could combine themselves in such a way that the effect would not be the same.

It might have been that for some reason both of them would not have come to the exhibition or that they would have arrived while it was closed or that only the young girl would have passed by in which case the surprise would have been easier to bear. They would not in that case have looked at each other, sad and powerless, faced with another insult. It might have been, after all, that he would not have been there to observe this sad incident. He would not then have been in the position of one who determined the principles but one who applied them from afar.

Life, sometimes, avoids the easiest ways and creates intricate events as if to instruct us. The difficulty here was that his critical thought about a child depended too much on these vain enterprises about which the high and mighty were arguing. If there were a great artist in question, this would not have mattered; he had experienced that himself.

The time had come for the exhibition to be closed for the day. The cashier was locking the desk, doing her hair, and putting on lipstick. As they were going out, the artist could hardly see her straight legs disappearing among the passers-by. Lost in the crowd, he was moving away as if he had nothing to do with the exhibition.

Dragan Milivojević

Aco Šopov

(1923–   )

Aco Šopov was born in Štip in 1923. He has published the following poetry collections: *Pesni* (Poems, 1944), *So naši race* (With Our Hands, 1950), *Na Gramos* (On the Gramos), *Stihovi za makata i radosta* (Verses About Sorrow and Happiness, 1952), *Slej se so tišinata* (Merge with Silence, 1955), and *Veterot nosi ubavo vreme* (The Wind is Bringing Good Weather, 1957).

I SEARCH FOR MY VOICE

I search for my voice in the savage calm of the sea;
the sea turns to stone.
In the yellow desert of the Autumn I search;
and the Autumn grows green.
My arms are not my arms
(my arms with fingers of moonlight).
My eyes are not my eyes
(my eyes, eyes for a distant sight).
From the hard jaw of the time my word proceeds
and springs up in the fields with the teeth of seeds.

B. Djuzel and *H. Erskine-Hill*

THE PRAYER FOR A SIMPLE BUT NOT YET DISCOVERED WORD

My whole being begs you:
Discover a word that resembles a simple tree
and the palms of the hand, petrified and primevally naked,
that is like the innocence of each first prayer.
For such a word my being is begging you.

My whole being begs you:
Discover a word from which—as soon as uttered with a cry—
the blood begins to ache insanely,
blood that seeks a channel to flow.
For such a word my being is begging you.

Discover such a true word
resembling those peaceful prisoners
and that wind, that spring wind,
that wakes the deer in our eye-pupils.
Discover such a true word.

Discover a word about birth, about wailing,
discover such a word. And this temple,
enveloped in its antiquity and huge from waiting,
will open by itself obediently.
Discover a word about birth, about wailing.

Vasa D. Mihailovich

Srbo Ivanovski

(1928–   )

Srbo Ivanovski was born in Kočani in 1928. He has published the verse collections *Lirika*, (Lyrical Poetry, 1953), *Sredbi i razdelbi* (Meetings and Partings, 1953) and *Beli krikovi* (White Screams, 1956), the novel *Osameni* (The Lonely Ones, 1959), and the collection of short stories entitled *Žena na prozorecot* (A Woman on the Window, 1956).

THE BALLAD OF A FELLOW
WITHOUT HIS LOVE

He had his cloud above the sky,
his window on the street,
he had his cares to fill his thoughts
and for his daydreams peace.
All this was his by day and night,
in dark and light—
like books grown yellow with long use.
He also had an endless song,
persistent like a shadow
which followed all his steps.

It was but her he was without: his love.
And so he did not see the cloud,
nor looked beyond the window;
ignored the change 'twixt day and night;
and missed the echo of the song.
Had only she been there,
had only love been his,
he then would have had all.

A. Lenarčič

Živko Čingo

(1935–   )

Živko Čingo was born in the village Velgošte near Ohrid. He has published two collections of short stories, *Paskvelia* (Pelasgian, 1963) and *Nova Paskvelia* (New Pelasgian, 1965). Čingo is considered one of the most promising young Macedonian writers. His themes are those of life in the Macedonian countryside.

THE MEDAL

Paskvel is certainly the most beautiful village in our valley, but, to tell the truth, it's not the setting for a tale. It's so far away from the whole world. Even from the nearest highway, one must walk many kilometers in order to get to the village. But now it, too, no longer exists. Old man Noer Levkovski said, my dear cousin, that Paskvel has gone to the devil. Our Paskvel has cried, my dear little child. Poor Paskvel. And it used to give birth to such falcons. Both men and women, as only the good Lord could desire. Those were real people. For example, our neighbors the Devijevs, Uncle Nazer, Uncle Laster Trajčeski (may they rest in peace.) Ah! what giants! And if we want the truth, what a player Uncle From was. I bet you couldn't find such a marvelous bagpiper for miles around. Perhaps you will say, "So what! A player, and a bagpiper at that," but it's not quite so. Let the good saints punish me if Uncle From wasn't something like thunder. But as it is, even Uncle From has left.

Everyone! Everyone has left Paskvel. Now surely the woods have grown up all around it. Perhaps the birds came down from the mountain and moved into the warm nests of the people. Perhaps even the Paskvelian vineyards has withered up. And a vine is like a person. Abandoned, it quickly dries up. The small vineyard sheds up on the hill have surely grown desolate. And directly below was the valley. All green, of course, in the spring. This is precisely what I want to tell you about. It was spring then, and the whole valley was green. But maybe it was the end of spring and the valley was not green. No, maybe it wasn't really all like that, but you must believe me that the leaves touched the sky and it trembled in greenness. All the surroundings, too, attained that golden green color of the sun and foliage. Perhaps, really, it wasn't all like that, you understand, but, the devil take me, it all looked that way to me. I was in love. See, even during that time a man could fall in love. Yes, a man fell in love, not worrying about time. And I was devilishly, foolishly in love. I was done for, my dear comrades. Ah! That was love. . . . A devilish love. I fell in love with the constable's daughter, Itrina Isailovska. Lightning struck us down, both me and her. What a time for that to happen!

No, it seemed then that time didn't exist at all. It was reduced to trysts. So it passed quickly even that little moment stolen from the day. When we climbed to the vineyards, stealthily like rabbits, because it was still dusk and everyone could see us, as soon as we sat down on the ground—there it was, the appointed hour. All around us the boys and girls called to each other, singing some new shock workers' song. My little brother whistled incessantly and called me with a trembling voice. Ah, that voice, that whistle! I almost began to hate my younger brother. His damned whistling and that voice of Itrina Isailovska. A man lived as if on fire.

"Are you coming, my little angel?" Itrina whispered in a soft, muffled voice.

Oh, that voice, my dear people. I don't remember another voice like that. It was something like the river glistening below in the valley, all liquid and afire from the evening sun. Such was the voice of my good Itrina.

"Are you coming?" she whispered. "Are you coming, my gentle foal?" Itrina spoke panting, lying in the green vines. Oh! People, people! And the warm earth, so warm it almost burned. From that flame, a man couldn't open his eyes to look around. Everything was topsy-turvy. Only that voice of Itrina, so clear and insistent.

"Why are you leaving, my dear?" she asked. "Am I not good? God strike me."

"Let it be, Itrina," I muttered. "Let it be. Don't make it hard for me. You don't understand. I must go."

"My God," she said and took white flowers from her lips, and with the other hand slowly unbuttoned her blouse. "Oh, my God," she whispered. "I am such a slut. Argil Petronievski, I am a great curse. No one loves me. I am a devil. Everyone runs from me."

"No, no," I consoled her, bending over her high forehead, and, if a man bends over Itrina, he's a fool if he doesn't fall all the way. A man simply loses his head. He melts.

"Hey, Argil, the secretary is coming, Comrade Leunko," floated the frightened voice of my younger brother. "Hurry, fool, hurry. The secretary's already here."

"Oh that's all I need, the secretary," I thought, and large beads of sweat broke out over my entire body. Cold shivers ran through my veins. "Well, it's the secretary, comrade secretary," I recalled, and before my eyes appeared a mist and horrible images. Whatever a man thought, wherever he looked, comrade secretary was everywhere. Comrade Leunko, with his bloated and unshaven face. And his nose straight and serious. That, however, wasn't important. His eyes were sunken and dark. Comarde secretary certainly slept very little. That much must be admitted. A look sharp like a sabre. It would cut down everything before him. A look like a steel sword. And a voice so clear and loud. A merciless voice.

"Hm, let's examine ourselves, comrades. Let us give a report in sector one, five, eight, thirteen. . . . Let's analyze. Comrades! Item: the constable's donkey in the communal wheat—neglect. Now let's have a little self-criticism, let's have some self-criticism," comrade secretary repeated, and then fell silent as a rock. He turned from one person to another with a cold and piercing look from his small slanted eyes. It seemed as if he knew everything, as if nothing could be hidden from that devil.

"Let's have some self-criticism." The jaws moved, but the words weren't coming out.

I wanted to tell in detail about everything immediately, but when one met that look, that horrible look, my comrades, one couldn't think of anything intelligent. Everything became jumbled and incomprehensible. Let's see. . . . How did it happen?

. . . It was during the holiday. It was my duty to see who would come to church, to check how loyal we were to the party line. I observed everyone present and cursed them to myself furiously. Everyone hid his eyes from me; of course, the traitors didn't have a clear conscience.

It looked as if God himself was in a tight spot.

"If He wants to, let us discuss religion. Yes, let Him do that if He dares," I thought, turning my head proudly in every direction. But she, Itrina, the devil take her, as if she didn't want to know about all this—I looked toward her once, and she toward me three times. I frowned, and she smiled so gently and so warmly, and looked at me straight in the eye. Catastrophe! Moreover, she threatened me with her finger and slowly approached me. "And real catastrophe," I thought, retreating to a dark corner of the church. I forgot about the directives and prayed in the quietest voice to the saints to save me from that damned hussy. But she kept smiling so warmly and kindly with her sparkling eyes.

"No, Itrina, no, constable's daughter," I whispered. "Ours paths lead in different directions. They will never meet. Yours is finished, you scum, you murderer," I thought, and yet it was so pleasing to look into those radiant, green eyes. My hands clenched, now one, now the other. I saw that they wanted to touch her thick, bright hair, which had the scent of sunflower seeds. I even thought of chewing on her hair. Ah! Is it really possible? What should one do?

"And so, dear Argil," her voice interrupted me, "it means, you have begun to believe in God?"

"You know, comrade," I said and cleared my throat to correct myself, so that I could prove that it was a mistake, that she was not our comrade at all, and that she did not deserve all that. I conceitedly began to strain word after word:

"We, Itrina Isailovska, have nothing to talk about. And the fact that I am in the church is no concern of yours. A man can always change his mind in life."

"Ah, yes," she said. "A man sometimes changes his mind. Sometimes a man really does change his mind in life," she said and tried to hide the smile with her hand, a smile coming from the heart.

She was a fox, a real sly little fox. But I wasn't born yesterday either. Comrade secretary had filled my head with advice for just such an occasion. I knew by heart what to say to her, everything, word for word:

"God is a counterrevolutionary and a robber of the people. God is a kulak and a brigand. Down with private property, down with God!"

Ah! I knew all that so nicely, although I must confess, while I spoke these words, my heart was tightening up a bit.

"But why, dear Argil, don't you pray like other people?" said Itrina and winked at me, first with one, then the other eye.

"I do as I feel," I muttered, confused and surprised. It was evident that I wasn't prepared for such a question.

"I know what your'e like," said Itrina and, saying this, approached silently like a cat. "I know what you are looking for here."

Itrina was a strange girl and had such warm breath and fiery breasts. God, forgive me!

"I know, my angel," whispered Itrina in a burning voice. "I know all that."

"Ah, Itrina Isailovska," I mumbled, drawing into myself and calling out with a most pleading voice for all the saints to save me from that damned hussy.

"Most Precious God, Saint Petka, Dear Mother, Jesus Christ, Saint Peter, and you, good Saint Clement, save me from the constable's daughter. Amen." But, as if the saints had decided on revenge, not a single one blinked an eye. With no place to turn, a man had to fall on her firm breasts.

That's how it began, my good comrades, and immediately afterwards, I wished to be dead. I betrayed my comrades, I became a cur. A damned soul and a traitor to the Party! But how to say all this, how to keep one's head high, how to look comrade secretary in the eye.

"Let's have self-criticism. Only that voice alone, heavy as lead, fell from all sides. That voice struck about the forehead, the head. It hit everywhere and tore everything up by the roots.

That one day—I'll be a monkey's uncle if I didn't criticize myself thoroughly that day. Oh, that was some self-criticism. Our good female comrades began to cry sincerely, and the men encouraged me with fiery words, and everyone congratulated and embraced me.

"The victory is ours, the victory is ours!" the comrades shouted. Trajče Petlevski opened his mouth for the first time that day and, all excited, said:

"Comrades, I, Trajče Petlevski, from the bottom of my heart propose that comrade Argil be presented a medal."

"A medal, comrades!" a youth said and sobbed at the top of his voice. Oh, that was real happiness, that was life, those were real comrades.

"Are you satisfied now?" Itrina met me one day and asked. "Are you satisfied now, dear comrade Argil?"

"I am, I am," I said with my head held high and, without stopping, walked by, stamping my heels on the ground, my medal jingling convincingly on my chest.

"Wait!" Itrina said in a hoarse voice. "Did you confess everything?" She bit her lip. "Did you confess everything, dear Argil?"

"Yes, Itrina Isailovska," I replied, changing my voice. "I told them everything and now, I confess, I feel much better. Now I feel like a man. My soul sings. . . ."

"Feel much better," Itrina said, and drops of blood appeared on her lips. "Better, huh? Shame on you," she said and began scratching her face. "Shame on you, you damned devil." She wanted to tear at her breasts. "What a fool I was. My God!" she said and sobbed out loud. "How could I let you lay a finger on me. . . . I'll kill myself, so help me God."

And so Itrina spoke, and, as if out of her mind, ran down through the vineyards. She broke the young vines in gloom and beat her head on the ground. Then she got up laughing hysterically:

"Here, take it!" She lifted her dress, showing her beautiful, strong legs. "Here it is!" she said and pinched her thighs. "Now I'll go off to the soldiers and lie with them on their greatcoats. I'll lie with them. So help me, I will!"

As Itrina said this, she constantly moaned, then slowly and heavily walked toward the valley. She walked bent to the ground, as if wounded somewhere in the side. She looked as if she would collapse any moment. But she walked away and never again returned to our valley.

This happened in the twilight, and already people were calling to each other to go to the evening meeting. I walked stealthily, taking the most distant path so that I wouldn't meet the comrades. Perhaps I was afraid they would hear me crying. Suddenly comrade secretary appeared, spreading his dark, thin lips.

"What's all the noise about?"

"I . . . I . . . comrade secretary," I muttered, "I'm composing a song, a song about self-criticism. It comes from strong emotions," I said and quickly wiped away the tears.

"Ah, yes," replied the secretary, sincerely. "That's a good thing. A song about self-criticism," he repeated and scratched his head. "Yes, that would really be wonderful . . . a song about self-criticism."

Then he embraced me firmly, comradely, and, with heads held high, we set out for the evening meeting. The entire way, we sang some song about victory.

Donald Davenport

Kole Čašule

(1921–   )

Kole Čašule was born in Prilep in 1921. He has published the collection of short stories entitled *Prvite dni* (First Days, 1948) as well as the plays *Zadruga* (Village Commune, 1950) *Vejka na vetrot* (A Branch on the Wind,) *Brazda* (The Furrow) and *Crnila* (Unhappy Lives).

THE GAME

(Excerpt)

Act II

A room in a Macedonian Hotel. The place is modern, comfotrable and bright but without much taste. . . .

The curtain is raised on an empty room. The door opens slowly and the bellboy enters. He holds the door open admitting Mirko and then Irena. While they are finding a place to sit, the bellboy opens the curtains. The room becomes brighter, as it is a beautiful sunny day.

BELLBOY: We hope your stay is pleasant, Sir. Let me open the curtains. Is everything all right?

MIRKO: Thank you. Excellent!

IRENA: I would like to wash my hands.

BELLBOY: Of course! The first door in the corridor to the left.

MIRKO: Would you like to have a drink? Let him bring something, while we wash our hands.

IRENA: Yes, something cold.

BELLBOY: Lemonade?

IRENA: Yes, please, with a lot of sugar. (*Exits.*)

BELLBOY: And you?
MIRKO: A glass of wine with soda.
BELLBOY: A glass of wine with soda. We have excellent wine. Leave it to me. How about lunch?
MIRKO: What do you have?
BELLBOY: Everything.
MIRKO: Swell. We'll call you later. (*Exits.*)
Bellboy returns quickly with a vase of flowers. He puts the vase on the table near Mirko and Irena. Irena steps in as he is changing the sheets She looks clean and refreshed, wearing slacks, a pretty blouse, and has her hair tied up with a white silk scarf.)
IRENA: Do you always change the sheets?
BELLBOY: Every time we have newlyweds as our guests.
IRENA: How do you know that we are newlyweds?
BELLBOY: I know something else, too.
IRENA: For example.
BELLBOY: For example, that you just got married, that you are on your honeymoon and . . .
IRENA: And?
BELLBOY: . . . and that you are rushing to Ohrid and that you have a reservation in the Hotel Palace.
IRENA: How long have you known all this?
BELLBOY: Me? I am here to know all these things. No, I am only joking. They phoned us from Skopje before you arrived.
IRENA: They phoned?
BELLBOY: They notified us that you might be stopping at our hotel.
IRENA: Who?
BELLBOY: Yes, there was somebody. It seemed to me that there were at least half a dozen people speaking on the telephone! They sent a message to let you know that you should not worry about them, they are even happier since you left them, and they will not stop their party until you contact them from Ohrid.
IRENA: Thank you!
MIRKO: (*Comes in*): Water is still the most wonderful refreshment.
BELLBOY: I'll go get the wine. (*Leaves*).
IRENA: Your friends are still celebrating the wedding.
MIRKO: How do you know?
IRENA: They phoned. The bellboy told me.

BELLBOY: (*Comes in with the lemonade and the wine*) Here you are. It's just out of the refrigerator! (*Putting them down.*) Your boss sent a message; he said to tell you that you were a credit to your company.

MIRKO: Thank you.

BELLBOY: Are you going to order now or later?

IRENA: I am hungry. What do you have?

BELLBOY: Everything. Just imagine what you'd like and we will prepare it.

IRENA: That means that you only have a grill?

BELLBOY: What else did you expect here?

IRENA: I love grilled meat.

BELLBOY: Then leave it to me. Tell me, friend, where did you find her?

MIRKO: What?

BELLBOY: Take care! Somebody will take her away from you!

IRENA: Thank you!

BELLBOY: I'm going now. I'll try not to bother you again.

IRENA: Well, I am hungry.

BELLBOY: For grilled meat you have to be starving! (*Leaves.*)

MIRKO: Finally, this mess is over.

IRENA: It was fun. People were happy and they tried to make everything turn out well. And the presents! They were so much more than I expected! You really have wonderful friends!

MIRKO: You're not trying to gripe about my incorrect behavior towards them again, are you?

IRENA: Not at all! I just stated an undisputed fact. Your incorrect behavior does not matter to me any longer.

MIRKO: Does this mean that there is something wrong with your image as a communist?

IRENA: Maybe.

MIRKO: Now, please! (*Gives her a folder.*)

IRENA: This is surprising!

MIRKO: Because I kept my word?

IRENA: (*Taking the bank book out of the folder*) I never doubted you. What is this? Not three hundred thousand but four hundred thousand have been deposited.

MIRKO: It's for being a good little girl and studying hard.

IRENA: For that only?

MIRKO: For what else?

IRENA: Shall we say it is for my prompt agreement to the divorce?

MIRKO: You always seem to know the truth! Let's not talk about it today. Agreed?

IRENA: As you like it. And now something for you.

MIRKO: For me?

IRENA: Yes, for you!

MIRKO: From you???

IRENA: Shall we say—to a certain degree. (*Opening her handbag she takes out an envelope and gives it to Mirko.*) Here!

MIRKO: What is it?

IRENA: A small surprise.

MIRKO (*He opens the envelope, pulls out a piece of paper and begins to read. As he is reading, it becomes obvious that he is unpleasantly surprised*): What does this mean?

IRENA: Just what is written. A three-room apartment in a new building was awarded to you as a wedding present by your company. Wasn't that what you wanted?

MIRKO: Yes! But it is written here that this three-room apartment was assigned not to me but to you and in your maiden name.

IRENA: As far as I remember you didn't object when I told the clerk that I was going to keep my maiden name.

MIRKO: How could I have known that something like this was going to happen?

IRENA: I don't understand what is making you so excited.

MIRKO: You really are witty.

IRENA: I hope so.

MIRKO: Wonderful. It turns out according to this that I take up all the work so that you will receive a three-room apartment. I am curious how you managed that?

IRENA: Without much difficulty. I went to your boss, asked him, and he did this favor for me without hesitation.

MIRKO: How did you have the courage? Besides, what did you have to do for him, for him to give such a favor without hesitation?

IRENA: Apologize or else I am going to leave! I thought jealousy was completely irrelevant to our agreement.

MIRKO: I jealous? Ha, since when? Sit down, here, and don't pretend!

IRENA: I am not pretending!

MIRKO: We will return to Skopje and you will immediately change the decision about having the apartment assigned to you.

IRENA: Is that it?

MIRKO: What are you waiting for? Should I be enthusiastic about your deceit?

IRENA: You are using big words! And you're the last person in the world who should; besides, you're getting excited for no reason.

MIRKO: Interesting! What would you have done in my place?

IRENA: I would have behaved with more spirit!

MIRKO: How?

IRENA: The three-room apartment is yours, I never claimed it was mine.

MIRKO: Yes, and that is why you went to the boss to have it assigned in your name?

IRENA: Will you let me speak or will you continue interrupting me?

MIRKO: I'll be quiet!

IRENA: Thank you. Have you calmed down?

MIRKO: As never before.

IRENA: The way I remember it, according to our agreement—the three-room apartment after our divorce should belong to you? . . .

MIRKO: After all this I doubt it.

IRENA: . . . and the bachelor's flat will belong to me, won't it?

MIRKO: Well?

IRENA: And how am I to obtain the bachelor's flat (*a short pause.*) As you see. I've thought of everything? The only way for me not to lose the bachelor's flat is for you to assign the three-room apartment to me at the moment of the divorce! You are indispensable to the company, not I! If they want to keep you, it is cheaper for them to give me the bachelor's flat and you the three-room apartment, unless they want to get you another three-room apartment.

MIRKO: And you, you kept on giving me lectures in morality and saying that something was wrong with my image as a communist.

IRENA: Yes! I don't deny that even now.

MIRKO: Wonderful! I am interested only in the meaning of your action.

IRENA: I mean well.

MIRKO: I expected that!

IRENA: So this means that you are beginning to know me!

MIRKO: You've got the upper hand! You have gotten the better of me many times.

IRENA: That confession makes me particularly happy. And what did you expect of me? Should I have left myself to your mercy and ended up deceived by you? It seems to me that you have forgotten that we are partners in a game which . . . well, let us avoid big and rude words.

MIRKO: I am just interested: how did you wring all this from the boss?

IRENA: Your boss is a wonderful man and he has unlimited confidence in you. As they say in the business world, you are his pride.

MIRKO: You are being ironic.

IRENA: Unfortunately, not.

MIRKO: If you were my wife, I would have had more than a hundred thousand reasons to hate you now.

IRENA: How fortunate that I am not.

MIRKO: Thank goodness!

IRENA: Let's return to your boss. He would not have allowed it for anything in the world if he had known we had played such a trick on him and the company. He would not have permitted you to repay him in such a way. He was so good that he accepted without hesitation my explanation that it was a whim, which was intended to show you, by a joke, that women were not as inferior as you thought.

MIRKO: I have been looking at you and the thought won't leave me: what will you think of next?

IRENA: Anything which could occur to a young woman.

MIRKO: Good for you!

IRENA: What are you complaining about?

MIRKO: On the contrary! I am beside myself with happiness.

IRENA: I'm glad! (*A knock is heard at the door. Bellboy enters*).

IRENA: Come in!

BELLBOY: Would you mind a little snack while the main dish is coming!

IRENA: Wonderful! You are a magician!

BELLBOY: Fine. (*Leaves the snack on the table*).

IRENA: Do you always knock when you enter a room?

BELLBOY: Always when there are newlyweds. I know this business. You are fed up with people! What you need is to be alone at last.

IRENA: You are not a human being. You must be an apparition. There are no bellboys like you even in fairy tales.

BELLBOY: No, we are not all in seventh heaven are we?
IRENA: You deserve a kiss!
BELLBOY: Am I to include that in the bill, too?
IRENA: You may.
BELLBOY (*Brings over the cognac*): But this does not go with the lemonade.
IRENA: Oh, no! Not me, I am driving.
BELLBOY: And cognac only improves the eyesight.
IRENA: Are you sure?
BELLBOY: Just as sure as that you are the prettiest bride who has ever come to this hotel.
IRENA (*Threatening him with her finger*): Thank you!
BELLBOY: At your service! (*To Mirko*) Are you going to order anything else besides you wine with soda?
MIRKO: No.
(*Bellboy exits.*)
IRENA: This sullen behavior doesn't suit you. Don't forget we're on our wedding trip. Your face should be lit up with happiness and love!
MIRKO: You think so?
IRENA: You look like one of those people who has had his marriage arranged by his mother and father.
BELLBOY: (*First knocking and then entering, carrying a glass of cognac and a glass of wine with soda. Putting his tray on the table*): I am sorry to interrupt your conversation again.
IRENA: The snack was wonderful!
BELLBOY: It was for you, Madam. (*Exits.*)
MIRKO: Doesn't it bother you that a bellboy is flirting with you?
IRENA: What should I do when my own husband won't praise me? In that case even a polite compliment is pleasant! Something is missing. Oh, yes! Music (*taking out a transistor and turning it on*). How do you like this?
(*Mirko does not answer.*)
IRENA: What's the matter now? If anybody should be dissatisfied, it's me! Not you!
MIRKO: You???
IRENA: Yes, me (*reaching for her handbag and taking out a piece of paper*). Aha, here it is! The reservation for the hotel Palace in youᵣ name . . .

MIRKO: Finally, there is something in the world in my name!

IRENA: . . . The reservation is in your name for a room with double beds with a bathroom facing the lake!

MIRKO: They don't have better ones.

IRENA: I am asking you to change the reservation by telegram at the nearest post office to two single rooms. The balcony isn't obligatory.

MIRKO: You are forgetting that we are husband and wife and that we are on our wedding trip. Everyone knows that marriage partners don't sleep separately on their wedding night.

IRENA: Ah, is that it?

MIRKO: Yes, that's it!

IRENA: It seems to me that in our agreement about this fictitious marriage, there was to be nothing to which I would object. I was obliged to register but not to sleep with you! Isn't that true?

MIRKO: Is that so?

IRENA: Yes, it is.

MIRKO: Believe me, you won't be in any danger by sleeping in the same room with me.

IRENA: I don't doubt that!

MIRKO: You are doubting? Well, why then . . .?

IRENA: I need some quiet in order to make up for everything that I lost with this wedding of ours! If you don't change the reservation when we arrive to Ohrid, I will be forced to return to Skopje on the first bus.

MIRKO: You do have a sense of humor!

IRENA: I don't have any choice!

MIRKO: Well! So, let's say I change the reservation! Don't you remember that my boss told you that he, with his family and some friends, would be coming there tomorrow to be our guests for the weekend?

IRENA: Yes! So?

MIRKO: Tell me how we're going to meet them? In two rooms with single beds? What kind of explanation are we going to give?

for one apartment, or, perhaps, you are worried about the money?

IRENA: The Palace has apartments with two separate rooms! Ask for one apartment, or, perhaps, you are worried about the money? In that case, I'll pay the difference.

MIRKO: You will pay!

IRENA: Why not? I have money now!

MIRKO: You are quite the shrewd business woman, aren't you? I pity the man who marries you!

IRENA: But if I love him, it will be different.

MIRKO: Are you capable of love?

IRENA: Why not? I am already in love with a man! It stands to reason, then.

MIRKO: Good for him.

IRENA: Well, listen to that!

MIRKO: Good for him because he doesn't know the trouble waiting for him! If I believed in God I would have prayed tor him—never to have the opportunity to know!

IRENA: It could happen though . . . if I decide to do it he would never know!

MIRKO: What could happen to make you decide to do it?

IRENA: He would have to turn out to be more stupid than I thought.

MIRKO: More stupid? That means that you consider him to be stupid?

IRENA: Right! Sometimes, he seems to try very hard to convince me of it!

BELLBOY (*knocks at the door and enters*): Excuse me! Your friends are phoning. They are asking to talk to one of you.

IRENA: That means, they are still celebrating! Well, let's talk to them . . . they are darlings, aren't they? (*She stands up, puts her hand on Mirko's shoulder and leads him off stage.*)

BELLBOY: (*as soon as he is alone*): The young people sure know how to live! Without a doubt. (*he sets the table as the curtain falls*).

Dragan Milivojević

Gane Todorovski

(1929-   )

Gane Todorovski was born in Skopje in 1929. He has published the collections of poems entitled *Božilak* (The Rainbow, 1953), *Trevožni zvuci* (Disturbing Sounds, 1953) and *Spokoen čekor* (A Peaceful Step, 1956).

A PEACEFUL STEP

I.

Along grey crowded outskirts of the town
dusk is pouring its dark dust,
a messenger of the coming night,
stringing the evening sights
pressing on the senses with a fresh smell of darkness.

I believe: he thought night to be a small square
oppressing the lonesome without mercy
and that is why he went to her threshold
he went into the noisy dusk sunk deeply in himself.

I believe: the bottom of the night attracts the lonesome,
for them it is a haven hidden from all eyes.
Often in her the last prayers of the day are whispered,
often in her one discovers the absence of people

I believe: he thought night to be a quiet clearing
in which the weary long for rest

643

II.

In the morning we found him in the hospital chapel.
again alone on the concrete floor.
He was again lost to loneliness
away from which he prayed to be saved.

His eyes were open and clear
as the crystal washed sky on nights in May
They gazed at us with a greeting and proud-pure
and we wanted to find the answer
to the last step in his flight.
His eyes were like two openings.
from which we might unravel
what the October night hid from us.

Perhaps as Walt Whitman
we should have called a wreck
that corpse which the morgue
now brought out before our quivering legs,
this frail, this dear face
whom we knew not long ago as an eighth grade student
whom obituaries informed:
he died in an accident.

III.

Nobody ever knew why he fled from people
laying his body on the rails at the end of the town.
He left silent as steel in a cold embrace.
Hoping perhaps not to remain lost in lonesomeness.

Today his story is remembered
But the writing in stone will never tell
the silent desperation of this end
the peaceful step he made
on the night of October the eighth.

IV.

When reading Sandburg,
I stopped not without reason on that verse
in which the old man says:

"DEATH IS A PEACEFUL STEP
INTO SOFT, CLEAR MIDNIGHT"

Dragan Milivojević

Mateja Matevski

(1929–   )

Mateja Matevski was born in Istanbul (Turkey) in 1929. He has published a collection of poems entitled *Doždovi* (Rains, 1956).

BELLS

Somewhere bells are ringing. Somewhere far away bells
    are ringing.
The sounds are waves upon the wind whipped along the grass.

Somewhere bells are ringing. Sounding long, clear and tender.
But everywhere the land is still, only rhythmic splashing
against the shore of iron.

Somewhere bells are ringing. Swinging me above the high
    abyss
Running through the cage of sounds hollow and hopeless.

Somewhere bells are ringing. I am a child again ringing
and screaming.
All is closed. Bewitched
I hang myself upon the sounds.

Somewhere bells are ringing. Come strike me! Oh, how
    brave and tame am I
Time strike too, my memory, rudely without end.
Somewhere bells are ringing. Now and long ago.

Everything is painful, underneath the sky. On this grass of
familiar sounds lay me down.

Dragan Milivojević

Note on the Spelling and Pronunciation of Serbo-Croatian, Slovenian and Macedonian Words and Names

s — s as in sink
š — sh as in shift
c — ts as in mats
č — ch as in charge
ć — similar to, but lighter than, č—as in arch
ž — j as in French *jour*
z — z as in zodiac
j — y as in yell
nj — ni as in minion
g — g as in go
g — soft 'g' as in geese
k — soft 'k' as in key
s — dz
dž — g as in George
dj — soft 'g' 'j' as in jive
lj — li as in million